A GUIDE TO
RELIGIOUS MINISTRIES

For Catholic Men and Women

"There are many ministries but one Lord."
- Paul to the Corinthians

www.RELIGIOUSMINISTRIES.com

Catholic News Publishing Company
210 North Avenue, New Rochelle, NY 10801
914.632.1220, Fax: 914.632.3412, E-mail: info@religiousministries.com.

$10.00 per copy   Printed in the United States of America   ISBN 1-893275-57-4

Index of Postcard Sponsors

 Ways to Request Information

1 **Sponsored Return Postcard.**
Pre-addressed postcards may
be mailed directly to a
vocation office.

2 **Reader Service Card.**
(Postage paid) Complete and
mail one of these cards in order
to receive literature from several
religious communities active in
your area of interest. Located on
the last page of postcards.

3 **Direct Return Postcard**
(Please apply postage) These blank
cards are provided for you to complete
and mail to religious communities you
would like to learn more about. See
the index of advertisers listed on
pages A-4 and A-5.

REQUEST FOR VOCATION INFORMATION

Please send me information about
The Paulists

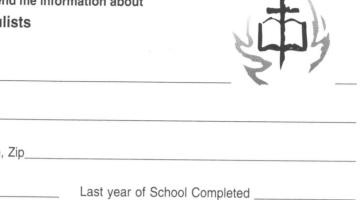

Name_____

Address_____

City, State, Zip_____

Age_____   Last year of School Completed _____

Telephone (   )_____

E-mail _____

Serving God as a priest, brother, sister or lay minister is a rewarding career.   3-A ↑
Vocation directors can help you discover if the religious life is for you.   3-B ↓

REQUEST FOR VOCATION INFORMATION

A Religious Community of Men in the...
HEALTH CARE MINISTRY

Ordinary Men, Extraordinary Lives.
in Hospitals, Nursing Homes, Retirement Homes, AIDS Houses. **SEND FOR INFORMATION** or call **1-800-556-0332**.

NAME ....

ADDRESS..

CITY..

STATE .... ZIP ....

AGE ....EDUCATION ....

Fr. Edward C. Nowak, C.S.P.
The Paulists
415 W. 59th Street
New York, NY 10019

Sending in these postcards to the vocation director does not obligate
you to anything, but it may be the first step towards your life's work.

ALEXIAN BROTHERS
Director of Vocations
3040 West Salt Creek Lane
Arlington Heights, IL 60005

BECOME A FRANCISCAN FRIAR OF THE ATONEMENT

**Please send me information about the Friars of the Atonement.
I am interested in becoming a ☐ Priest ☐ Brother.**

Name _____

Address _____

City _____ State _____ Zip _____

Last year of school completed _____ Age _____

Telephone (____) _____

Your e-mail address _____

"That they all may be one . . ." (JN 17:21)

Return this card today or visit us online at:
www.atonementfriarsvocations.org

This postcard is a service of A Guide to Religious Ministries.

Serving God as a priest, brother, sister or lay minister is a rewarding career. Vocation directors can help you discover if the religious life is for you.

5-A ↑

5-B ↓

REQUEST FOR VOCATION INFORMATION

"Prefer nothing whatever to Christ."

Rule of Saint Benedict

BENEDICTINE MONKS OF
SAINT JOHN'S **ABBEY**

NAME _____

STREET ADDRESS _____

CITY/STATE _____

TELEPHONE (____) _____ ZIP _____

E-MAIL _____ AGE _____

OCCUPATION _____

OR PRESENT SCHOOL AND YEAR _____

Phone 320.363.2548   www.saintjohnsabbey.org   vocations@osb.org

BUSINESS REPLY MAIL
FIRST-CLASS MAIL   PERMIT NO. 11   GARRISON, NY

POSTAGE WILL BE PAID BY ADDRESSEE

**Vocation Director
Franciscan Friars
of the Atonement**

PO Box 300

Garrison, NY 10524-0300

Sending in these postcards to the vocation director does not obligate
you to anything, but it may be the first step towards your life's work.

BUSINESS REPLY MAIL
FIRST-CLASS   PERMIT NO. 4   COLLEGEVILLE, MN 56321

POSTAGE WILL BE PAID BY

**Saint John's Abbey
Vocation Director
Box 2015
Collegeville, MN 56321-2015**

REQUEST FOR VOCATION INFORMATION

Benedictine Monks

Please send me additional information:

Name _____ Age _____

Address _____

City / State / Zip _____

Phone: ( ) _____ E-mail _____

Last Year of School Completed _____

Comments _____

_____

Serving God as a priest, brother, sister or lay minister is a rewarding career.   **7-A** ↑
Vocation directors can help you discover if the religious life is for you.   **7-B** ↓

SISTERS OF BON SECOURS
"Good Help to those in need"

Yes, I want to know about religious life.

I am requesting: ❏ **A phone call** ❏ **A visit** ❏ **Literature & DVD on Bon Secours**

_____ **Sisters** _____ **Associates** _____ **BS Ministry Volunteering**

Name _____

Address _____

City _____ State _____ Zip _____

Phone _____ Best time to call _____

E-mail _____ Occupation _____

Comments _____

1-877-742-0277 (Toll Free)

Visit www.bonsecoursvocations.org   cbsvocations@bshsi.org

Vocation Director
St. Mary's Abbey at Delbarton
230 Mendham Road
Morristown, NJ 07960

Place
Postage
Here

Sending in these postcards to the vocation director does not obligate
you to anything, but it may be the first step towards your life's work.

Place
Stamp
Here

Sisters of Bon Secours
Sr. Pat Dowling, CBS
Vocation Office
1525 Marriottsville Road
Marriottsville, Maryland 21104

REQUEST FOR VOCATION INFORMATION

Please send information about the

Sisters of Charity of Nazareth

Name ______________________________

Address ______________________________

City, State, Zip ______________________________

Last Year of School Completed ____________________ Age ________

Telephone (   ) ______________________________

Email: ______________________________

This postcard is a service of
A GUIDE TO RELIGIOUS MINISTRIES
210 North Avenue, New Rochelle, NY 10801

Serving God as a priest, brother, sister or lay minister is a rewarding career. Vocation directors can help you discover if the religious life is for you.

9-A ↑

9-B ↓

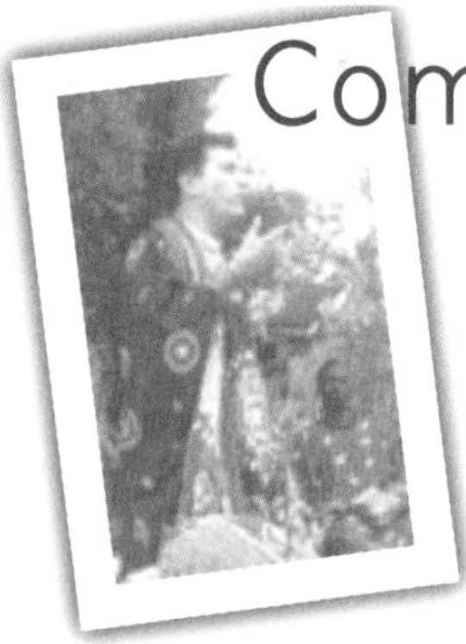

Comboni Missionaries

~ of the heart of Jesus

I would like more information about the:

Priesthood: ☐ Brotherhood: ☐
Lay Missionary: ☐

Name: ______________________________

Address: ______________________________

City State Zip ______________________________

Educational level/Age: ______________________________

☐ Me gustaría recibir información en español.

"You can be yourself"

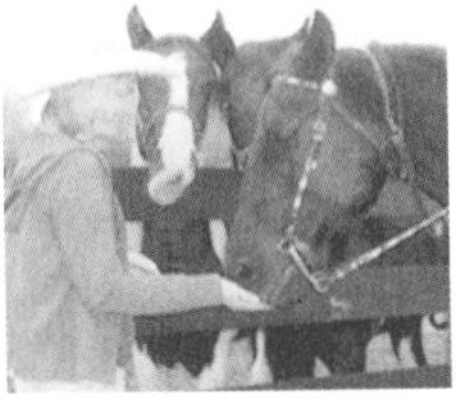

Sisters of Charity of Nazareth
P.O. Box 9
Nazareth, Kentucky 40048

Place
Stamp
Here

Sending in these postcards to the vocation director does not obligate you to anything, but it may be the first step towards your life's work.

NO POSTAGE
NECESSARY
IF MAILED
IN THE
UNITED STATES

BUSINESS REPLY MAIL
FIRST-CLASS MAIL PERMIT NO.78159 MONTCLAIR, NJ

POSTAGE WILL BE PAID BY ADDRESSEE

Fr. David Bohnsack mccj
Comboni Missionaries
88 High Street
PO Box 138
Montclair, NJ 07042-0138

REQUEST FOR VOCATION INFORMATION

I want to take a look at Glenmary. Please send me information about Glenmary priesthood and brotherhood.

Name_____

Address _____

City _____ State_____ Zip _____

Phone _____ Alternate Phone _____

E-mail _____

Birth Date _____

GLENMARY
HOME MISSIONERS

Serving God as a priest, brother, sister or lay minister is a rewarding career. Vocation directors can help you discover if the religious life is for you.

11-A ↑

11-B ↓

REQUEST FOR VOCATION INFORMATION

THE DOMINICAN SISTERS OF HAWTHORNE

With the grace and strength that comes from God the Father, through His Son in the Holy Spirit, we go forward in faith and confidence in Christ sharing His love with the poor through our particular charism and the inspiration of the Holy Spirit.

Please send me information about your community:

NAME _____

ADDRESS _____

CITY/STATE/ZIP _____

Call Sr. Alma Marie at 914.769.4794 or e-mail: SrAlmaMarie@aol.com.
www.hawthorne-dominicans.org

BUSINESS REPLY MAIL

FIRST-CLASS MAIL   PERMIT NO. 1   CINCINNATI, OH

POSTAGE WILL BE PAID BY ADDRESSEE

Vocation Department
Glenmary Home Missioners
P.O. Box 465618
Cincinnati, OH 45246-9897

Sending in these postcards to the vocation director does not obligate
you to anything, but it may be the first step towards your life's work.

DOMINICAN SISTERS OF HAWTHORNE
Rosary Hill Home (Motherhouse)
Hawthorne, New York

St. Rose's Home
New York, New York

Sacred Heart Home
Philadelphia, Pennsylvania

Our Lady of Good Counsel Home
St. Paul, Minnesota

Our Lady of Perpetual Help Home
Atlanta, Georgia

St. Catherine of Siena Home
Kisumu, Kenya

PLACE
STAMP
HERE

DOMINICAN SISTERS OF HAWTHORNE
Sr. Alma Marie Borja, O.P.
Vocation Director
600 Linda Avenue
Hawthorne, NY 10532

FRANCISCANS OF THE HOLY LAND

The Franciscan Friars of the Holy Land have been living and giving our lives for good, since 1209. For 800 years, we have been standing guard over this hallowed place, caring for the shrines of Christianity, supporting the schools and missions, and ministering to refugees and other needy people in the land of Jesus.

We need more good men to **help us keep Christianity alive in the Holy Land**. We need more good men to live and give, as He lived and gave. Can you live and give your life for good?

If you feel the call, then make a call to serve Him.

Phone: 202-526-6800   Email: vocations@myfranciscan.com

www.myfranciscan.com

Age

Zip

ST   E-mail address

Name   Address   City   Phone number

Sending in these postcards to the vocation director does not obligate you to anything, but it may be the first step towards your life's work.

REQUEST FOR VOCATION INFORMATION

What is the path through life that God is asking you to walk . . . to sow seeds . . . to bear fruit . . . ?
We invite you to explore the possibility of walking with:

The Franciscan Sisters of the Atonement

Name: _____

Address: _____

City / State / Zip: _____

Phone: (   ) _____

E-mail: _____

Director of Vocations

HOLY LAND FRANCISCANS
1400 Quincy Street, N.E.
Washington, DC 20017

Sending in these postcards to the vocation director does not obligate
you to anything, but it may be the first step towards your life's work.

FRANCISCAN SISTERS OF THE ATONEMENT
Vocation Ministry
41 Old Highland Turnpike
Graymoor, Garrison, NY 10524

REQUEST FOR VOCATION INFORMATION

Please send me more information about the:

Franciscan Sisters of the Poor

Name: _____

Address: _____

City: _____ State: _____ Zip: _____

Phone: (   ) _____

E-mail: _____

Best time to be in touch: _____

Present Occupation: _____

Date of Birth: _____

Serving God as a priest, brother, sister or lay minister is a rewarding career.   **15-A** ↑
Vocation directors can help you discover if the religious life is for you.   **15-B** ↓

REQUEST FOR VOCATION INFORMATION

The Josephites
Society of St. Joseph of the Sacred Heart

Exclusively committed to serving the African American Community

Please send me the information marked below about the Josephite Society.

❏ **Priest**   ❏ **Brother**   ❏ **Volunteer**

www.josephite.com • vocations@josephite.com

Name: _____

Address: _____

City: _____ **State:** _____ **Zip:** _____

Telephone: _____ **Date of Birth** _____

Your email address: _____

Education: _____ GRM 09 E

Sister Arlene McGowan, SFP
Franciscan Sisters of the Poor
60 Compton Road
Cincinnati, OH 45215-5105

Sending in these postcards to the vocation director does not obligate
you to anything, but it may be the first step towards your life's work.

BUSINESS REPLY MAIL
FIRST-CLASS MAIL   PERMIT NO. 16803   BALTIMORE, MD.

POSTAGE WILL BE PAID BY ADDRESSEE

Rev. Peter C. Weiss, SSJ
Vocation Director
St. Joseph's Society of the Sacred Heart
1200 Varnum St. NE
Washington, DC 20017

REQUEST FOR VOCATION INFORMATION

The Marianists
PROVINCE OF THE UNITED STATES

Please send me more information about the Marianists.

I am interested in:

_____ brotherhood _____ priesthood _____ sisterhood

Name: _____

Address: _____

City: _____ State: _____ Zip Code: _____

Age: _____ Telephone: (   ) _____

E-mail: _____

- -

Serving God as a priest, brother, sister or lay minister is a rewarding career.   **17-A** ↑
Vocation directors can help you discover if the religious life is for you.   **17-B** ↓

- -

Please send me more information about becoming a Maryknoll missioner.
I am interested in becoming a

❏ Priest   ❏ Brother   ❏ Sister

Name: _____

Address: _____

City _____ State _____ Zip _____

Phone: _____

e-mail: _____

Age: _____

Occupation: _____

Education Completed: _____

GRM09

BUSINESS REPLY MAIL

FIRST-CLASS MAIL   PERMIT NO. 2769   SAINT LOUIS, MO

POSTAGE WILL BE PAID BY ADDRESSEE

The Marianists
Bro. Charles Johnson, SM
National Vocation Director
4425 W. Pine Blvd.
St. Louis, MO 63108-9833

|.||....||....|||||...|..|.|.|.|..|.|..||...||.|.|..|

Sending in these postcards to the vocation director does not obligate
you to anything, but it may be the first step towards your life's work.

BUSINESS REPLY MAIL

FIRST-CLASS MAIL   PERMIT NO. 1   MARYKNOLL NY

POSTAGE WILL BE PAID BY ADDRESSEE

Fr. Dennis Moorman, M.M.
Vocation Ministries
Maryknoll Fathers and Brothers
P.O. Box 305
Maryknoll, NY 10545-0305

|..||||....|.|..|.|.|.|.||....||.||....|.|.|...||

REQUEST FOR VOCATION INFORMATION

Mercedarian Friars

Reason for request_____

_____

Name_____

Address_____

City_____ State_____ Zip_____

Email_____

Age_____ Last year of school completed_____

NOTE: We consider candidates 18-35 years of age.

Telephone_____Preferred time to call_____

I am presently: a student

                     working (occupation)_____

Serving God as a priest, brother, sister or lay minister is a rewarding career.   **19-A** ↑
Vocation directors can help you discover if the religious life is for you.   **19-B** ↓

REQUEST FOR VOCATION INFORMATION

Pontifical Institute for Foreign Missions

Yes, I would like to find out more about the
PIME Missionaries. Please send information to:

Name   _____

Address _____

City, State, Zip _____

Last year of school completed _____ Age _____

Phone   _____

Email_____

This postcard is a service of **A Guide to Religious Ministries**
210 North Avenue, New Rochelle, NY 10801

Mercedarian Friars
Vocation Director
6398 Drexel Road
Philadelphia, PA 19151-2510

Sending in these postcards to the vocation director does not obligate
you to anything, but it may be the first step towards your life's work.

Place
Stamp
Here

DIRECTOR OF VOCATIONS
PIME MISSIONARIES
17330 QUINCY ST
DETROIT MI 48221-9958

᠁᠁᠁᠁᠁᠁᠁᠁᠁᠁

REQUEST FOR VOCATION INFORMATION

The Passionists

Priesthood and Brotherhood

I would like to learn more about the Passionist Community.
Please send some literature to:

Name _____

Address _____

City/State _____ Zip _____

Telephone _____ E-mail _____

Last year of school completed _____ Age _____

Comments _____

_____

"May the Passion of our Lord Jesus Christ be ever in our hearts"

Serving God as a priest, brother, sister or lay minister is a rewarding career.   **21-A** ↑
Vocation directors can help you discover if the religious life is for you.   **21-B** ↓

REQUEST FOR VOCATION INFORMATION

Congregation of the Sacred Hearts of Jesus and Mary (SS.CC.)

Email: frlifrak@sscc.org • Phone: (508) 993-2442 ext. 309
I am interested in discerning my vocation as a
❑ Priest   ❑ Brother   ❑ Sister

Name _____ Date of Birth _____

Address _____

City_____ State _____ Zip Code _____

Telephone _____ E-mail _____

Educational Qualifications _____

Occupation _____

The
Passionists

Priesthood and Brotherhood

Fr. Bill Maguire, C.P.
St. Paul of the Cross Retreat Center
148 Monastery Avenue
Pittsburgh, PA 15203

Sending in these postcards to the vocation director does not obligate
you to anything, but it may be the first step towards your life's work.

Congregation of the Sacred Hearts of Jesus and Mary (SS.CC.)

Vocation Director
Post Office Box 111
Fairhaven, Massachusetts 02719 USA

REQUEST FOR VOCATION INFORMATION

I would appreciate more information about the Salvatorians:

☐ Sisters (www.sistersofthedivinesavior.org)
☐ Priests and Brothers (www.salvatorians.com)

Name: _____   PLEASE PRINT

Address: _____

City / State / Zip: _____

Phone: (Area code:)   –

E-mail address: _____

Birthdate: _____

Occupation: _____

Education level: _____

Please complete and return card or give us a call...
Women please call **(414) 466-0810, ext. 229**
Men please call **(414) 258-1735, ext. 104**

- -

Serving God as a priest, brother, sister or lay minister is a rewarding career.   **23-A** ↑
Vocation directors can help you discover if the religious life is for you.   **23-B** ↓

- -

REQUEST FOR VOCATION INFORMATION

Please send me your free vocations brochure.   **The Trinitarians**

Name _____

Address _____

City _____   State _____   Zip _____

Phone _____   E-mail _____

Age _____   Highest degree attained _____

MAIL TO:
Fr. Carl M. Frisch, O.Ss.T.
P. O. Box 5719, Baltimore, MD 21282-0719
410-484-2250 1-800-525-3554
E-mail: vocations@trinitarians.org

Proclaiming the Savior – Together in Mission

Salvatorians
1735 N. Hi-Mount Boulevard
Milwaukee, WI 53208-1720

|.|.|...||....|.|||...|..|....|||...|..|.|.|||....|.||

Sending in these postcards to the vocation director does not obligate
you to anything, but it may be the first step towards your life's work.

Fr. Carl M. Frisch, O.Ss.T.
Vocation Director
The Trinitarians
P.O. Box 5719
Baltimore, MD 21282-0719

REQUEST FOR VOCATION INFORMATION

Carmelite Sisters for the Aged & Infirm

"The Difference is Love"
SM

Please send me information about
the Carmelite Sisters

Name_____

Address_____

City_____ State _____ Zip _____

Phone_____

E-mail_____

Best time to contact me is _____

You may fax card to 518-537-5226 or call 518-537-5000
website: www.carmelitesisters.com

Serving God as a priest, brother, sister or lay minister is a rewarding career.   **25-A** ↑
Vocation directors can help you discover if the religious life is for you.   **25-B** ↓

Congregation of Sacred Stigmata
www.stigmatines.com 413-442-4458

Yes, I'd like to know more about C.S.S. community life as:

❏ Priest   ❏ Brother   ❏ Lay Affiliate

Name _____ D.O.B. _____

Address _____

City _____ State _____ Zip _____

Phone _____ e-mail _____

Education completed _____ Occupation _____

Vocation Office
Carmelite Sisters for the Aged & Infirm
St. Teresa's Motherhouse
600 Woods Road
Germantown, NY 12526

Sending in these postcards to the vocation director does not obligate
you to anything, but it may be the first step towards your life's work.

"Go Forth and Teach."

Father Geoffrey J. Deeker, C.S.S.
Vocation Minister
Congregation of Sacred Stigmata
554 Lexington St.
Waltham, MA 02452-3097

REQUEST FOR VOCATION INFORMATION

I am interested in a life of religious ministry. Please forward information about different religious communities. I am interested in being a:

❑ Priest ❑ Brother ❑ Sister ❑ Lay Minister

My particular interest for ministry in a religious life is in:

❑ Parish Work ❑ Education   Type of Community:
❑ Missions ❑ Health Care   Refer to front of A section for a description of each
❑ Undecided ❑ Social Service ❑ Apostolic/Active
❑ Other: _____ ❑ Contemplative/Cloistered
                           ❑ Monastic

Mr./Ms./Mrs._____

Address _____

City/State/Zip _____

Telephone _____

E-mail Address_____

Last Grade Completed _____Age_____

Comments _____

READER SERVICE CARD   To request information from several communities   **27-A** ↑

DIRECT RESPONSE CARD   To request information from one community   **27-B** ↓

REQUEST FOR VOCATION INFORMATION

I read your profile in *A Guide to Religious Ministries*.
Please send me additional information.

Mr./Ms./Mrs._____

Address _____

City/State/Zip _____

Telephone _____

E-mail Address_____

Last Grade Completed _____Age_____

Comments _____

_____

This postcard is a service of
A Guide to Religious Ministries
210 North Avenue, New Rochelle, NY 10801
914-632-1220 • info@religiousministries.com
www.religiousministries.com

Catholic News Publishing
A GUIDE TO
RELIGIOUS
MINISTRIES

BUSINESS REPLY MAIL

FIRST CLASS MAIL   PERMIT NO. 2121   NEW ROCHELLE, NY

POSTAGE WILL BE PAID BY ADDRESSEE

A GUIDE TO RELIGIOUS MINISTRIES
CATHOLIC NEWS PUBLISHING COMPANY
210 NORTH AVENUE
NEW ROCHELLE, NY 10801-9910

Sending in these postcards to the vocation director does not obligate
you to anything, but it may be the first step towards your life's work.

PLACE
POSTAGE
HERE

_____

COMMUNITY

_____

_____

ADDRESS

_____

CITY/STATE/ZIP

ATTN: VOCATION DIRECTOR

A GUIDE TO
RELIGIOUS
MINISTRIES

For Catholic Men and Women

WWW.RELIGIOUSMINISTRIES.COM

Published by The Catholic News Publishing Company

Table of Contents

Section A

Section B

A Benedictine Monk

is one who commits himself to live a life of prayer and work with a community of Catholic men under the *Rule* of Saint Benedict. His life's purpose is to seek God by living with his brothers in obedience to their spiritual father, the abbot, and to one another. Becoming a Benedictine monk is a life choice and a life journey ...

TAKEN ONE STEP AT A TIME.

Contact us for more information on becoming a member of our community.

✝ Saint John's Abbey

Call 320.363.2548 or email vocations@osb.org
Box 2015 Collegeville, MN 56321 • www.saintjohnsabbey.org

Use the Benedictine Monks-Saint John's Abbey postcard for more information

Send one of the postcards in this book for more information.

Index of Profiles

Index of Profiles

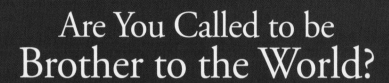

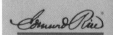

The MCCJ finds it's spirituality in the cross, as did **St. Daniel Comboni.**
" The works of God are born and grow at the foot of the Cross".

The life of the Comboni is not always easy, we go where there is no church ~ and build the Christian community from the grass roots ~ ultimately discovering the living God in new and surprising ways! We are an international, apostolic community of priests brothers and lay missionaries. Young men 18 – 30, open to the adventure and challenge of missionary life ~

Come, Dream and Build with us!

Contact: Fr. David Bohnsack
              88 High Street
              P.O. Box 138   (973) 685-6338
              Montclair, NJ 07042   revdavemccj@gmail.com

www.mccjvocation.com

Use the convenient Comboni Missioners postcard in this book for more information.

The Call to Religious Ministry

The decision to dedicate one's life to the service of God is a much different one than that of choosing a career.

Selecting a career field – in most instances, an occupation – involves decisions about education, personal skills, preferred job characteristics, desired income levels, and often geographic location. The decision impacts on family life, personal interests and long-range goals. A career decision answers the question, "What will I do with my life?"

The more important decision in life is, "What will I be?" Everyone is called to be with God, whether married, single, clergy or religious. Some people are called to be with God as a priest, brother or sister. It is not a calling to do anything, go anywhere, or become something. It is a call to a state of being.

Commitment

Commitment to a religious career often flows from one's whole being. This commitment is rooted in the core of inner being, and it affects and involves the totality of the person. If one is concerned only with external manifestations in a religious career, then that person is making more difficult the acquisition of a deep and inner sense of fulfillment and personal growth to be found in the pursuit of such a career. Religious careers enable persons to express adequately the being they are. External witness touches generally on the demonstrative; it manifests the character of a religious career, but this alone is not enough. When one attempts to justify the rationale and the validity of a religious career in today's society, there is a strong tendency to remain engrossed merely in its circumferential elements such as service to people in need, improvement of the qualitative aspects of human interaction, and the like. However, there is an important pivotal point from which all other elements spring and in which they are resolved. The act of feeding the poor or comforting the sorrowful is not in itself the living core of a religious career. When one makes an external manifestation the essence of a religious career, this essence is simply too shallow to subsist.

What then constitutes the being and validity of religious careers, and makes them relevant today? The same mystery that made religious careers relevant in the past and inspired men and women to dedicate their lives is present today.

At this point one may ask: "What then is the essence of a religious career? What constitutes the state of a religious career choice? What makes it what it is? What gives it its particular identity?" That by which the very being of a religious career as a state of life can be distinguished from another state is very simple; it is a very specific consecration, a consecration often contrary to popular belief. It is not a ritual of a self-gift to the Almighty, nor is it man-made. For it is ultimately the Almighty who consecrates and invests a person in a religious career.

The Need for Prayer

Individuals will be aided in a religious career choice through a life of prayer. The prayerful religious person is able to recognize in other persons their intrinsic worth and potential for good. The religious career person is seeking to make visible what is hidden, and touchable that which is unreachable. Prayer, the great power of grace, will help eliminate a behavior which is contradictory to the great principles upon which moral decisions are made. A person embarking upon his career choice must be

For 200 years, we have served as

Educators

Missionaries

Ecologists

Nurses & Social Workers

And more. Our ministries are as diverse as our Sisters.

We're noted for our work in education, health care and child care. We work with the young and the elderly, with men and women, with new immigrants and the homeless. We're spiritual directors, parish workers and artists. We work for social justice.

Join us in our ministries.

To learn more, call 718.543.4898
or email vocationsc@scny.org
and visit www.scny.org

SISTERS
of **CHARITY**
NEW YORK

Living Lives of Love

personally convinced that prayer and faith give purpose and meaning to this life. In this way, that individual can hope to instill the value of religion in others and manifest this value in him or herself.

The style of religious careers for the years ahead may be determined not so much by those who strive toward this ideal and this goal, as by those others who do not. The audience, the object of activity, the persons whom those in religious careers seek to serve, will determine the mode of relevant activity. The religious is, therefore, challenged to tailor the message to the audience, to communicate on terms which the target group can relate to.

Pursuing a religious career involves a great deal of work. The individual pursuing such a career should pray, seeking to know and gain direction in this regard. The individual should think. The power of the mind may be marshalled to think life through. Reading is important. Learn about the particular organization or denomination in which you anticipate pursuing a religious career. "Knowledge is power," said Socrates. The more one knows about a subject the better one can handle it. The more an individual knows about the particulars of the specific religious career of interest, the better that individual will be to handle the necessary decisions involved. Talking it over with persons whom we admire and trust, perhaps someone already living a religious career, can be most helpful. If an individual wants to pursue a religious career, then that individual should do the things early that will aid him or her in such a pursuit.

Personal Characteristics Needed

Those pursuing religious careers should possess self-confidence, the ability to make hard decisions, and a willingness to accept criticism and listen to people. They must be tactful, have personal drive and ambition, but yet be tolerant of other's shortcomings. An ability to work under pressure, to live up to moral standards, and ability to get along with others are the ideals to be striven for.

Whatever the denomination or the particular ministry within that denomination, certain predispositions are generally looked for. Good health is desirable as the religious career makes demands upon a person's physical constitution. A good and healthy body aids in the development of a good and healthy mind. A good mind is necessary, as one must be able to combine the spiritual and the intellectual. One must be able to relate meaningfully the theoretical dimensions of religion to the world of practical realities. The well-trained religious career person is thus aided in thinking – deeply – about important things that are necessary parts of the religious career. The supernatural rests upon the natural, and the religious career person must grow naturally and intellectually.

Choosing a life's career can be one of the most exciting, demanding and yet perplexing experiences one is likely to face. The choice made will determine to a large extent the focus of one's energy, attention, and efforts. That career choice offers the possibility of a genuine measure of satisfaction and fulfillment. That career choice will determine the nature of the role and the contribution the individual will make in today's complex and often impersonal world.

A person pursuing a religious career is also a servant, someone doing something, and doing this in a committed way. Giving oneself to the service of others makes that individual a symbol of concern not only in word and deed, but in all of that person's life as a totality of a human person.

Religious career persons are not supermen or wonder women. They are men and women living among men and women – sometimes wounded men and women whose mission is to heal. Often religious career persons are stammering men and

FRANCISCANS OF THE HOLY LAND

WALK AND WORK IN HIS VERY FOOTSTEPS

Think about it. What could be more honorable and more blessed than a Vocation of serving with the Franciscans of the Holy Land?

Protecting the Holy Shrines: walking and working, teaching and preaching in the very same places that Jesus did. That is the cause and the mission in the life of a Holy Land Franciscan priest.

The Franciscans of the Holy Land have been guarding this hallowed place - the most sacred of lands - and other shrines of Christianity for nearly 800 years. Our work in the Holy Land has also expanded to include support of the schools and missions, as well as caring for refugees and other needy people of the region.

Ours is a cause rooted deeply in the heritage and behavior of Jesus Christ. Walk with us, where He walked. Work with us, where He worked.

Think about it. It's a glorious thought. It's a wonderful vocation.

Become a Holy Land Franciscan prophet of peace and minister of reconciliation.

Contact: Franciscan Monastery of the Holy Land
Office of Vocations
1400 Quincy Street, NE, Washington, DC 20017
Phone: 202-526-6800 ext. 334
Email: vocation@myfranciscan.com
www.myfranciscan.com

Use the convenient Holy Land Franciscans postcard to request more information.

women whose mission is to preach; they are often weak persons whose mission is to conquer evil or console.

Surely the religious career offers the reward of full joy and peace for the individual aware of the call, honest in service, and giving freely for others. Incomparable happiness realized in deep personal fulfillment is often the reward for those individuals who have pursued a life's career in religion.

People caring about people can be manifested in the pursuit of a religious career. Religious careers offer opportunities, challenges, and lifestyles for a role of influence in molding the outlook and design of tomorrow's world.

Discerning a Vocation

What is a vocation? How does one discover it? Where does it lead? What has it to do with free will?

These are puzzling questions to anyone considering what to do with the rest of his or her life. Ordinarily they are questions facing a person in teen-age or early adult life but many reoccur at other times. Many women face such questions after their family is raised. A married man, his wife and family may very suddenly face the unexpected possibility of a vocation to the permanent diaconate.

Vocation, of course, does not refer exclusively to religious life or priesthood: these, however, are so unusual that frequently in Catholic circles they alone are called "vocations."

The word vocation means "a calling"; it is extremely important to keep this in mind. We are called by the providential arrangement of circumstances, by the realities of life, by our own limitations and potential, by the historical moment, and by our own emotional, intellectual and psychological needs. If one follows the teachings of the Fathers and Doctors of the Church in this regard, one comes to accept that a vocation is found in the providential arrangement of significant aspects of life and also by the grace which we receive to make the best of these situations.

The loss of awareness of this providential aspect of vocation is one of the things that leads to an immense insecurity in modern life. When people forget the divine and providential element in their lives, they try desperately to find a course through life like a man on a raft with neither rudder nor map.

It has been a consistent belief of Christians that the Lord gives each of us something to do, some work to perform that makes us an essential link in the chain of life. Parents pass on life to their children and, by good examples, instruction, encouragement and membership in the Church contribute to their growth in the life of grace.

Single people, including priests and religious, pass on life in a psychological and spiritual way by being a help to those around them. This passing on of life and grace is the ultimate vocation of the Christian. Cardinal Newman sums it up well when he says: "I am a link in a chain, a bond of connection between persons. God has not created me for nothing. I shall do good; I shall do His work; I shall be an angel of peace, a preacher of truth, in my own place, while not intending it, if I do but keep His commandments."

The idea of God's special purpose in our life is what gives the individual an awareness of his dignity and importance. Among great numbers of people we frequently feel like atoms, little and meaningless. As Newman says, "God has created me to do Him some definite service: He has committed some work to me which He has not committed to another. I have my mission. I may never know it in this life, but I shall be told it in the next."

If one is convinced of being singled out by the Lord for some work in this life, how

Be a Franciscan

Join the Franciscan Friars
of Holy Name Province

Become a priest or brother working together in parishes, urban ministry centers, and schools along the East Coast and in overseas missions, enriching the lives of others. Our sense of charity, solidarity, and purpose is shared by men who come from all backgrounds, including yours.

Are you being called to be a Franciscan friar?
If so, contact:

Franciscan Vocation Ministry
Holy Name Province
Fr. Brian Smail, OFM
129 West 31st Street, 2nd Floor
New York, NY 10001-3403

vocation@hnp.org
www.BeAFranciscan.org

1-800-677-7788

Send one of the postcards in this book for more information.

is that work discovered? First, we quietly discern or observe our potentials and needs and try to fit them into what we can do best. Often in such a process, God leads us by interior inspiration, by an attraction to do this or that work, to follow this person, or to marry that one. We will be attracted by a certain kind of work because it fits our capacity and because it opens to us possibilities of security or fulfillment.

The need for inspiration and divine guidance in any vocation cannot be overstressed. The Lord has led many people in mysterious ways. The only Trappist ever canonized, St. Benedict Joseph Labre, was led to his strange vocation not to be a monk but to be a hobo, by going from one monastery to another, vainly trying to fit in because of psychological difficulties.

St. Catherine of Genoa found herself married to the wrong man as a result of a political alliance of her family. Faced with such a situation, she relied on God and spent the rest of her life working with her husband in the service of the poor and sick.

From such experiences at least two rules emerge for discovering one's vocation. Both come from Holy Scripture: "If today you hear His voice, harden not your heart" (Psalm 95); and Our Lord's own admonition: "He who puts his hand to the plow and looks back is not worthy of the kingdom of heaven."

Apostolic Work

The apostolic works performed by priests, brothers and sisters – also called ministries – encompass a wide range of skills and services. Some religious communities specialize in one or a few types of ministries – health care or teaching, for example – while others have members engaged in many different ministries. The work itself does not constitute a religious "career" but is simply the expression of a religious person's dedication to God.

Some of the most common ministries are:

Parish Work
Home Missions
Child Care
Chaplaincies
 Prisons
 Hospitals
 Military
Education
 Administration
 Teaching
 Coaching

Social Work
Campus Ministry
Foreign Missions
Religious Education
Communications
 Film
 TV & Radio
 Newspapers
 Magazines
 Books

Health Care
 Hospitals
 Nursing Homes
 Visiting
 Nursing
Counseling
 Students
 Families
 Adults
Spiritual Direction
Retreats
Inner City Work

Cloistered, Contemplative and Monastic Orders

Although the terms "cloistered", "contemplative" and "monastic" may vary in meaning due to the founder's differing objectives and the interpretation by different communities in various parts of the world, a generally used and understood meaning of each is as follows:

Cloistered (*clausura*) refers to religious men and women who live in an enclosed space, not accessible to outsiders and who may not go outside the area without permission. Solemn vows are made by those in monasteries and convents where there is *clausura* and simple vows where there is no cloister.

Contemplation – the "loving gaze of the soul upon God" – is, in its widest sense, the goal of every Christian. Its highest earthly fulfillment is applied to those religious

Times Change. Needs Don't.

Glenmary Needs You!

GLENMARY
HOME MISSIONERS

P.O. Box 465618
Cincinnati, OH
45246-5618

800.935.0975
vocation@glenmary.org
www.glenmary.org

Send one of the postcards in this book for more information.

"Guanellian Priests & Brothers"

"Take in the most abandoned of all, have him sit at table with you
and make him one of your own, because this is Jesus Christ."

Blessed Louis Guanella, Founder

Proclaiming the Gospel of Life in service of charity, we share
- ✝ *a life in community*
- ✝ *daily worship and common prayer*
- ✝ *service to the poor and disadvantaged*
- ✝ *fidelity to the Pope & the Magisterium*

Our mission is a celebration of life as we serve
- ✝ *people with developmental disabilities*
- ✝ *troubled youth and the elderly in need*
- ✝ *parishes through pastoral ministry*
- ✝ *migrants and refugees through outreach*

**Consider joining our mission in answering Pope Benedict XVI's call
"to live no longer for ourselves but for God, and with God for others."
(*Deus Caritas Est no. 33*)**

Father Dennis M. Weber, SdC	**Father David Stawasz, SdC**
1799 S. Sproul Rd.	**St. Louis Center**
Springfield, PA 19064	**16195 U.S. 12**
(610) 543-3380	**Chelsea, MI 48118**
e-mail: fr.dweber@chs-adphila.org	**(734) 475-8430**
	frdave@stlouiscenter.org

www.servantsofcharity.org

Send one of the postcards in this book for more information.

Compassion has a human face.

T**he Sisters of the Good Shepherd** approach each person with the same care of Jesus the Good Shepherd. We are guided by the principle that *"One person is of more value than a world."*

Through Action and Contemplation our mission of *reconciliation* impels us to promote justice and peace. Our vow of *zeal*, the heart of the Good Shepherd vocation, leads us to search out the wounded and those left behind by the world. We minister in all areas of human service, with a particular focus on the needs of women and children.

There are two ways that a Sister of the Good Shepherd can express her zeal for God's people–*apostolic* and *contemplative*.

Is God calling you to love with the heart of a shepherd?

CONTACT: **Christine Alvarez**
Vocation Department
(732) 946-0515
gsvocny@optonline.net

www.goodshepherdsisters.org

Send one of the postcards in this book for more information.

men and women who do not engage in active ministries; who live in seclusion, apart from the world; and whose lives are taken up in prayer and meditation. In order to sustain themselves, communities perform such tasks as keeping bees/bottling honey, farming, translation, artistic work, vestment design and production, baking, computer typesetting and Web page design.

Monasticism (or *monachism*, literally the act of "dwelling alone") has come to denote the way of life pertaining to persons living in seclusion from the world, under the religious vows of poverty, chastity and obedience, and subject to a fixed "rule", as monks, friars, or nuns. Eastern monasticism and Western monasticism deal with the monastic order strictly so called as distinct from the "religious orders" such as the friars, canons regular, and other more recent orders whose special work or aim, such as preaching, teaching, liberating captives, etc., occupies such a large place that many of the traditional observances of the monastic life give way to these special works.

For detailed explanations and other information on these terms, see the Catholic Encyclopedia online (www.newadvent.org/cathen/).

The Formation Process

There are several stages involved in the process of becoming a religious priest, brother or sister. Each community has its own rules, but they generally involve four stages.

The first stage involves the time period when a prospective candidate becomes acquainted with the community, and the community with the candidate. This may occur as early as high school or college years. The vocation director is usually the point of contact between the individual and the community. The candidate may spend short periods of time living with the community in order to become exposed to the spiritual and community life of the members.

The second stage begins when the candidate is ready for a more formal relationship. This usually involves full-time residency with the community and gives the candidate the opportunity to experience the life of the community. During this stage, the candidate may be continuing outside studies or employment. This stage may last one or two years.

The next stage occurs when the candidate enters the community's novitiate. This marks the official entry into the community and is a period of one to two years during which the novice spends time in prayer and study to learn more about his or her relationship with God, with the community, and with the decision to make a lifetime commitment to the religious life.

The final stage involves temporary promises. Depending on the community, promises of poverty, celibacy and obedience may be taken for periods of one to three years at a time, up to nine years. Final vows may be taken after as few as three years of temporary promises.

Men studying for the priesthood also must complete seminary training in theology before ordination.

The Diocesan Priesthood

A candidate for the diocesan priesthood must complete four years of high school, four years of college and four and a half years of graduate study in theology before ordination. A candidate may attend the college of his choice or a minor seminary to complete studies for his bachelor's degree. Graduate study is completed in residence at a major seminary.

Most diocesan priests serve in parishes. Many others serve as teachers, administrators, military chaplains, hospital chaplains, prison chaplains, and other ministries.

The call with a special tone.

When you hear God's call, you hear your own true tone...the special tone of your commitment, your courage, your love for others.

The individual tone of Holy Child Sisters can be heard throughout the world, as the Society advocates for many—most especially women and children.

Call today to learn more, your tone will fall on welcoming ears.

Carmen Torres, SHCJ
610.626.1400, x304
ctorres@shcj.org

Society of the Holy Child Jesus

An international community of women religious

AMERICAN PROVINCE

www.vocations.shcj.org

Send one of the postcards in this book for more information.

Educational Requirements

The works performed by members of the religious community usually dictate the amount of education that is required. A bachelor's degree is usually required, and often a master's. Many priests, brothers and sisters earn a doctorate degree, particularly those involved in education.

Most communities prefer candidates to complete their bachelor's degree before entering, although some communities will accept candidates after high school graduation. There are also some high school seminaries for candidates who are prepared to consider a vocation at that age. Some dioceses conduct preparatory seminaries for high school boys who are interested in the priesthood. Generally, the boys live at home while going to school.

Contact A Vocation Director

The people who are in the best position to be helpful to those who are considering a religious career or lay ministry are vocation directors. Their job is to counsel men and women about the requirements for this kind of commitment. They can suggest reading materials, arrange for visitations, answer questions and provide the spiritual guidance candidates need. Every diocese has a vocation director who can provide information about religious communities for men and women as well as information about the diocesan priesthood. A complete list of diocesan vocation directors is included in one of the following sections in this book. Most religious communities have one or more members assigned to vocations. Their names, addresses, phone numbers and e-mail addresses are included in the following sections of this book.

Vocations in the Catholic Church

"Then He said to His disciples, 'The harvest is ready but the laborers are few. Ask the harvest master to send out laborers to gather his harvest'."

Mt. 9:37-38

Many influences come together to bring it about that a woman or a man decides to become more fully involved in the ministerial life of the church. This personal commitment can be temporary or permanent, partial or complete. Whatever form this calling may take, a Catholic believes that the Holy Spirit is the source of every authentic vocation. The instruments, the human means, of His work often include the living example of persons in a given church ministry. There is also the home, the classroom, the hospital, retreat houses, religious experience, reading, friends, prayer...the Bible itself. All of these, and other things also, contribute to a church vocation.

The full and permanent commitment involved in the religious life and priesthood has long had its place in Catholic tradition. Yet these callings are by no means the only vocation: in the best sense all Christians are called to a vocation in the community. Marriage itself, for example, is certainly a vocation. We list here not simply priesthood and religious life but other possibilities for ministry in the Church. And there are others not listed here, such as sodalities, covenant communities, etc. Information about these can be secured from local pastors or chanceries, or from the National Religious Vocation Conference.

It is the Spirit that the Father has sent through Christ that is at the center of a church vocation, just as Christ Himself is the head of the Church. Hence this kind of vocation, while it is certainly a matter of professional guidance and consultation on

Care to Join Us on Pilgrimage?

Little Brothers of the Good Shepherd

...a small, pilgrim community of brothers with ministries to our brothers and sisters most in need.

Brother Bill Osmanski
680 N.E. 52nd Street
Miami, FL 33137
305.510.0039

Brother Charles Schreiner
P.O. Box 389
Albuquerque, NM 87103
505.243.4238

www.lbgs.org

Send one of the postcards in this book for more information.

WHAT ARE MONKS DOING IN THE CITY?

The Benedictine Monks of Newark Abbey have been in the center of Newark, New Jersey since 1857. What are we doing here?

- Living in community according to the Rule of St. Benedict.
- Following a daily schedule that balances prayer and work.
- Ministering to God's people through St. Benedict's Prep School, and a parish, and local pastoral assistance.
- Serving as a sign of hope and Good News in our city.

COME AND SEE!

For Further Information Write:
Director of Vocations
Br. Patrick Winbush, OSB
Newark Abbey
528 Dr. M.L. King Blvd.
Newark, NJ 07102
(973) 792-5772
www.newarkabbey.org
email: vocations@sbp.org

Send one of the postcards in this book for more information.

Presence...

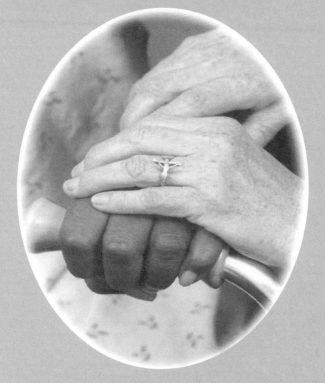

...before God, for others.

Little Company of Mary Sisters

phone 708-229-5095

vocations@lcmh.org • www.lcmh.org • www.lcmglobal.org

A Compassionate Presence in Healing Ministries

Send one of the postcards in this book for more information.

a "career" level, is also far more than that. Here the assistance of a competent spiritual director is invaluable. The work of the Spirit must be discerned. This discernment means, among other things, evaluating the qualities of a person who wishes to follow such a vocation.

The general qualifications for priesthood and the religious life (and similarly for other church-related occupations) include an appropriate level of spiritual life, emotional and physical health, and a level of intelligence and academic accomplishment consistent with the kind of life one seeks. One may enter some form of training as early as first-year high school or as late as "mid" or even later life. Most commonly, however, a man or woman enters a formation program after high school or college. The length of training varies depending upon when one enters a program, the extent of his or her background, and the specific traditions of a given community or diocese. Generally, for example, it takes the same amount of preparation to become a diocesan priest as for any other professional person: four years after college, or eight years after high school. Formal entrance into a seminary or community is often preceded by participation in an associate or affiliate program.

There is no obligation created by seeking the counsel of a trusted, knowledgeable advisor – and it is most important to do so.

A Catholic might wish to serve the Church, the people of God, in a specific, professional manner. This could be done as a diocesan priest, permanent deacon, religious brother, religious priest, religious sister, as a lay person employed in a Church ministry or engaged in volunteer work, as a member of a secular institute or by participation in any number of Church organizations.

Diocesan Priest

A diocesan priest ordinarily serves the people of God in a given area – a diocese – as a parish priest. And yet diocesan priests are also involved in administration, campus ministry, hospital and prison chaplaincy, teaching and sometimes at foreign missions. Beneath the visible surface of these ministries lies an abiding prayerful relationship with the Lord for whose sake and for whose people he ministers. Information about the diocesan priesthood can be obtained from any diocesan priest, by contacting one or more of the diocesan vocation directors listed in the **Diocesan Vocation Offices** section of this book or by contacting:

The National Conference of Diocesan Vocation Directors (NCDVD)
5400 Roland Ave., Baltimore, MD 21210
Phone: (410) 864-4111, Fax: (410) 864-4114
E-Mail: office@ncdvd.org, www.ncdvd.org

Permanent Deacon

Recently the Catholic Church restored the order of permanent diaconate. A deacon is a man 35 years of age or older, married or single, who serves the people of God in the ordained diaconal ministry. His ministry is liturgical (preaching), sacramental (except the Eucharist and Penance), pastoral and social. Inquiry about deacons' training programs can be made at the local diocesan chancery office or by contacting one of the following:

United States Conference of Catholic Bishops, Secretariat of Clergy, Consecrated Life, and Vocations
3211 4th St. NE, Washington DC 20017
(202) 541-3033
clergy@usccb.org, www.usccb.org

National Association of Diaconate Directors
7625 North High Street
Columbus, OH 43235
(614) 985-2276
naddinfo@nadd.org
www.nadd.org

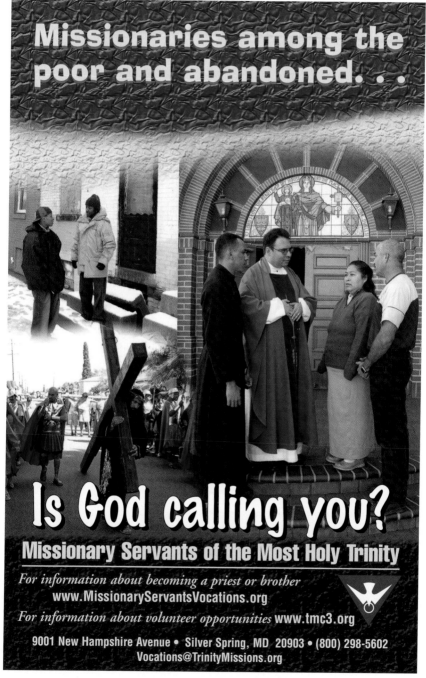

Missionaries among the poor and abandoned. . .

Is God calling you?

Missionary Servants of the Most Holy Trinity

For information about becoming a priest or brother
www.MissionaryServantsVocations.org

For information about volunteer opportunities www.tmc3.org

9001 New Hampshire Avenue • Silver Spring, MD 20903 • (800) 298-5602
Vocations@TrinityMissions.org

Send one of the postcards in this book for more information.

Missionaries of the Holy Family

We invite you to a life fully dedicated to the apostolates of the family, vocations and wherever God directs us.

Servants of God Builders of Family

Charism

The Congregation of the Missionaries of the Holy Family was founded in 1895 at Grave, Holland by Fr. Jean Berthier. He dedicated the community to the Holy Family which is "the perfect model of every religious community and of every Christian family." We seek out and foster vocations, particularly among mature adults and the poor. Our community strives to live as a family while bringing the Gospel message to areas of need.

Apostolates

Throughout the world we promote and serve the needs of Church, family, local community and our Congregation. In the North American Province (Canada, United States and Mexico) we are involved in many types of pastoral service. As priests and brothers we work in parishes, schools, hospitals and homes for the aged. Our work reflects the concern and respect we have for family life.

MSF Vocation Office
104 Cas Hills Drive
San Antonio, TX 78213
(210) 344-9145

Send one of the postcards in this book for more information..

There is a Way.

Let Him find you

and lead you to a life dedicated to Mercy, consecrated to Mary, faithful to the Magisterium, and zealous for the salvation of souls.

Whoever loses his life for my sake will find it.
—Matthew 16:25

PRIESTS & BROTHERS
Oblates of the Virgin Mary
1105 Bolyston Street, Boston, MA 02215   617.869.2429   www.omvusa.org

Send one of the postcards in this book for more information.

Religious Brother

As a male religious, a brother is a lay Christian who commits himself to Christ and the Christian community by vows of poverty, chastity and obedience. Not only is he in service to the community, he himself lives in a religious community that centers his life. It is from this root and from his own interior life that he is able to meet the needs of the Church in ministries such as teaching, social work, technical occupations, etc. The ministries of religious brothers are varied and reflect the traditions of a given community.

There are many communities of religious brothers as well as communities of priests and brothers. Often a man applies to a community with which he is familiar. Information about the brotherhood may be obtained by writing to one or more vocation directors listed in the **Religious Communities for Men** section of this book or by contacting:

The National Religious Vocation Conference (NRVC)
5401 S. Cornell Ave., Suite 207, Chicago, IL 60615-5604
Phone: (773) 363-5454
E-Mail: nrvc@nrvc.net, Web: www.nrvc.net

The Religious Brothers Conference provides advocacy for the identity and the vocation of brothers; acts as a professional and ministerial resource to its member communities and offers direct services to individual brothers. Contact:

Br. Stephen Synan, FMS, President/Executive Director
5401 S. Cornell Ave., Chicago, IL 60615-5604
Phone: (773) 595-4023, Fax: (773) 493-2356
E-Mail: rbc@ctu.edu, Web: www.brothersonline.org

Religious Priest

Some religious communities are "clerical": they include priests. What was said immediately before applies equally to priests living in religious communities. The religious priest takes vows of poverty, chastity and obedience according to the spirit of his own congregation. Being a priest he is a minister, for the Church, of the sacraments. His work generally depends upon the ministry appropriate to his community and may include teaching, overseas ministry, social work, pastoral ministry, chaplaincy, etc. A person who feels called to this life may contact any member of a community with which he is familiar, or one or more vocation directors listed in the **Religious Communities for Men** section of this book, or:

The National Religious Vocation Conference (NRVC)
(See contact information above)

Woman Religious

A woman religious is a lay person who commits herself to Christ and to the Church by vows of poverty, chastity and obedience. She lives in a religious community that follows a constantly renewed tradition, patterned on the life and teaching of the founder of the community. The work she generally does will depend upon the particular community as influenced by the needs of the Church and its people, and includes such ministries as pastoral; social service; education (in many forms and ways); hospital/medical; youth/campus; missionary; retreats/ conferences/ spiritual direction; peace and justice; evangelization/faith formation; creative expression through music, the arts, etc.; work with the poor, elderly, broken,

oppressed and distressed and so on.

The role of women in the Church is constantly developing and expanding. A significant part of that renewal is occurring within the faith communities of woman religious. Prayer and work are part of the tradition of all communities yet some are primarily contemplative while others are more active. Information about the vocation of a woman religious can be secured by contacting one or more of the vocation directors listed in the **Religious Communities for Women** section of this book or by contacting:

The National Religious Vocation Conference (NRVC)
(See contact information above)

Second-Career Vocations (Older Men and Women)

Second-career vocations are not a new trend in the Catholic Church; for instance, all the apostles were men who had previous careers before they answered the calling of Jesus Christ. Today, people from all walks of life, including retired men and women, leave successful careers as nurses, lawyers, engineers, teachers, secretaries, etc. to join or affiliate themselves with a religious community. They become priests, brothers, sisters or lay ministers with contemplative, evangelical or apostolic communities. These men and women bring a wealth of talent to religious communities whether it be management know-how, a professional background, technical skill, etc. Most religious communities listed in this publication have their own age restrictions on accepting second-career vocations. There is no set age limit; each community should be contacted to find out what age restrictions apply. This also applies to men who are interested in becoming diocesan priests. All diocesan vocation directors are listed in this publication and should be contacted directly.

Seminary programs structured to meet the needs of the second-career priestly candidate provide a unique seminary environment with a supportive peer community and experienced faculty. These seminaries are:

Sacred Heart School of Theology
7335 South Highway 100, P.O. Box 429, Hales Corners, WI 53130
(414) 529-6984; E-Mail: tknoebel@shst.edu; www.shst.edu

Holy Apostles College and Seminary
33 Prospect Hill Rd., Cromwell, CT 06416-2027
(860) 632-3010; Fax: (860) 632-3030; rector@holyapostles.edu
www.holyapostles.edu

Blessed Pope John XXIII National Seminary
558 South Ave., Weston, MA 02493-2699
(781) 899-5500; Fax: (781) 899-9057; seminary@blessedjohnxxiii.edu
http://www.blessedjohnxxiii.edu

Women who wish to enter the religious life as a second-career vocation can contact the individual communities in which they are interested. (See listings in the **Religious Communities for Women** section of this book.) Even if a community has an upper age limit, they will sometimes consider older vocations on an individual basis, after mutual discernment of candidate and congregation. It never hurts to contact them if you feel strongly attracted to that community.

Is your heart on Fire with God's Love?

"I have come to cast fire upon the earth and O how I wish it were already ablaze." -Luke 12:49

These words of Jesus led St. Vincent Pallotti to a vision of the church filled and animated by many believers using all possible means to realize the Lord's ardent desire.

We see a world today where all too often charity has grown cold and faith become lifeless. To *rekindle love* and *revive faith*, all must collaborate to live and preach the Gospel message. The Pallottine charism or inspiration is to unite all—lay faithful, religious, and clergy—in the Union of Catholic Apostolate and continually refresh their awareness of the universal call to the apostolate, making each one an apostle.

Explore the Pallottine Way of Being Church

PALLOTTINE PRIESTS AND BROTHERS

Immaculate Conception Province
New York, New Jersey and Maryland
Rev. Bernard P. Carman, SAC
1-800-APOSTLES
1-800-276-7853
vocation@sacapostles.org
www.sacapostles.org

Mother of God Province
Wisconsin and Illinois
Br. Jim Scarpace, SAC
Mr. Jeffrey S. Montoya, UAC
414-259-0688 ext. 155
Vocations@pallotti.net
www.pallottines.org

PALLOTTINE SISTERS OF THE CATHOLIC APOSTOLATE

Immaculate Conception Province
New York and New Jersey
Sr. Carmel Therese Favazzo, CSAC
845-492-5076
845-238-3917
newapostle98@yahoo.com
www.pallottinesisters.org

PALLOTTINE MISSIONARY SISTERS

Queen of Apostles Province
Missouri, Maryland and West Virginia
Sr. Lena May, SAC
314-830-9814
Vocations@pallottinespirit.org
www.pallottinespirit.org

Send one of the postcards in this book for more information.

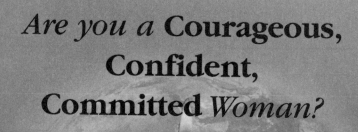

Are you a Courageous, Confident, Committed Woman?

Is there a fire burning within you? The Adorers of the Blood of Christ can provide you with helpful programs in your quest to follow Christ. LifeChoices®, our spiritual discernment program is one way to use spiritual and vocational guidance to thoughtfully explore big picture questions about how to live one's life. Also, Hearts' Journey House provides an opportunity for a lived experience to explore the life, spirit, and charism of the ASC community. Let us help you fan the flame!

For more information
on Hearts' Journey
Sister Jan Lane, ASC
1-877-236-7377 ext. 1455
lanej@adorers.org

Adorers *of the Blood of Christ*

For more information
on LifeChoices®
Sister Rita Schilling, ASC
1-877-236-7377 ext. 1409
schillingr@adorers.org

Send one of the postcards in this book for more information.

ARCHDIOCESE OF SANTA FE

With over 400 years of service to
God's people,
is God calling you to join our
historic archdiocese?

For more information about becoming a diocesan priest, contact
Fr. Michael DePalma
4000 St. Joseph's Pl. NW
Albuquerque, NM 87120
505 831-8143

Visit our website: santafevocations.org

Send one of the postcards in this book for more information.

The Carmelite Sisters for the Aged and Infirm

Have you EVER wondered about the "Call?"

. . . what it means to be
touched by a deep yearning?

Are _you_ open to the joy of sharing the gift that you are . . .

Sr. Maria Therese, O. Carm.
St. Teresa's Motherhouse
600 Woods Road
Germantown, NY 12526
(518) 537-5000
carmelitesisters.com

"The Difference is Love"
sm

Send one of the postcards in this book for more information.

DISCOVER...

...God through prayer

...balance in your life

...your place in God's plan

with the Benedictine

monks of Saint Mary's

Abbey, Delbarton.

ST. MARY'S ABBEY
at DELBARTON

Vocation Director
230 Mendham Road • Morristown, NJ 07960
(973) 538-3231, ext. 2111
e-mail: vocations@delbarton.org

www.osbmonks.org

Use the Benedictine Monks of St. Mary's Abbey postcard for more information.

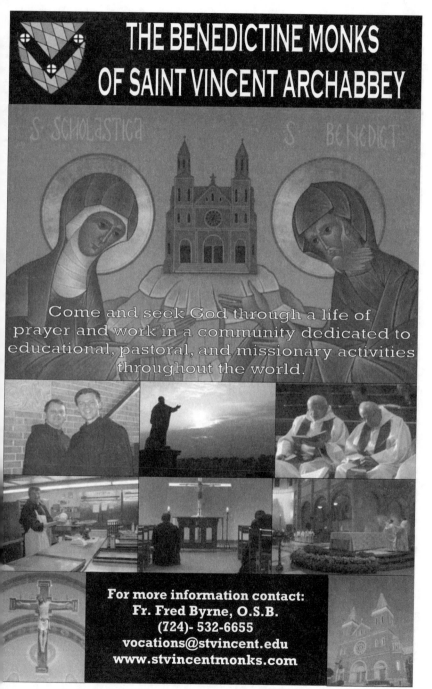

THE BENEDICTINE MONKS
OF SAINT VINCENT ARCHABBEY

Come and seek God through a life of prayer and work in a community dedicated to educational, pastoral, and missionary activities throughout the world.

For more information contact:
Fr. Fred Byrne, O.S.B.
(724)- 532-6655
vocations@stvincent.edu
www.stvincentmonks.com

Send one of the postcards in this book for more information.

Benedictine Sisters Of Corpus Christi Monastery

"What can be sweeter to us, dear brethren, than this voice of the Lord inviting us? Behold, in His loving kindness the Lord shows us the way of life."
Holy Rule of St. Benedict - Prologue

Is God calling you to a Benedictine Monastic life?

✠ Fidelity to the Pope and the Magisterium of the Church.
✠ Traditional habit.
✠ Traditional Monastic life of common life and common prayer.
✠ Primary Apostolic Divine Office sung, in English in Gregorian Chant.
✠ Other apostolates according to the needs of the Church and the talents of the individual.

We accept candidates of any age, providing they are in good health.
If you feel that God may be calling you, contact us at:

**Vocation Director
Corpus Christi Monastery
4485 Earhart Road
Ann Arbor, MI 48105
benedictines@sbcglobal.net**

Send one of the postcards in this book for more information.

Benedictine Community

"We're looking for a few good women to join us in Commitment to Community and Service."

Benedictine Programs & Services

St. Martin's Ministries

Benedictine Sisters

Contact:
Sr. Colleen Quinlivan, OSB
email: ridgelyvocations@hotmail.com
(P) 410-634-2497 ext. 1428
St. Gertrude Monastery
14259 Benedictine Lane
Ridgely, Maryland 21660
www.ridgelybenedictines.org

Send one of the postcards in this book for more information.

Send one of the postcards in this book for more information.

Love is a gift from God

How will you use your gift?

Sisters of the Blessed Sacrament

Founded by Saint Katharine Drexel

We are called to be a sign of the power of the Eucharistic Christ to effect unity and community among all people, especially among the Native American and Black peoples.

Contact: Sr. Karen Cote, SBS
1663 Bristol Pike, Bensalem, PA 19020

www.katharinedrexel.org

sbsvocof@aol.com   215-244-9900 ext: 327

Send one of the postcards in this book for more information.

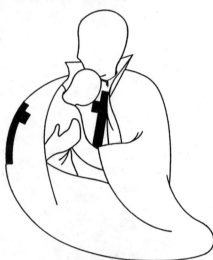

In Fraternity

In Prayer

In Service

Consider a journey
with the
Carmelite Friars,
in allegiance to
Jesus Christ

Brother Robert E. Bathe, O.Carm., Vocation Director
Carmelite Friars
P.O. Box 3079, Middletown, NY 10940
(845) 344-2225 email: ocarmvoc@frontiernet.net
www.carmelites.com

You can be Yourself

Sisters of Charity of Nazareth
www.scnfamily.org
1-800-494-1433
lukescn@comcast.net
ngsunshine@juno.com

Use the Sisters of Charity of Nazareth postcard in this book for more information.

What does it mean to be part of a community?

"It means belonging to something that is much bigger than I could ever do alone. I am a part of a group of people of all ages and backgrounds, with different histories and talents, and yes, I think we can make a difference in the world."

-Sister Chrsitine Kunze

and be One of Us !

Use the Sisters of Charity of Nazareth postcard in this book for more information.

SISTERS OF CHRISTIAN CHARITY
Mallinckrodt Convent   Mendham, N.J.

The Sisters of Christian Charity, an international, active apostolic Congregation, exist to live and make visible the love of Christ today. The charism of Blessed Pauline von Mallinckrodt, foundress, impels the Sisters to be women of deep faith who will refresh the third millennium with "joyous, youthful enthusiasm and energy, the fruit of intimacy with Jesus in the Eucharist." (SCC Documents) Like Mary, the community seeks to be open to the formative power of the Holy Spirit, which transforms it into the bread and wine of Christ's love. Pauline's Eucharistic vision leads the Sisters into the future as a community of love, a people commissioned to bring "good news to the poor... sight to the blind... liberty to captives." (Luke 4: 18)

The Eastern Province, based in Mendham, NJ, includes 27 local communities in New Jersey, New York, Pennsylvania and the Philippines. Originally founded for the education of the blind and the poor, the Sisters continue their mission in elementary and secondary schools, parish religious education programs, health care, and homemaking.

Please contact: Sisters of Christian Charity

S. Bernadette McCauley
Vocation Director (East)
Mallinckrodt Convent
Mendham, NJ 07945
(973) 543-6528 X 274
Website: www.scceast.org
Email: sbernadette@scceast.org

S. Carol Bredenkamp
Vocation Director (West)
St. Joseph Convent
1801 Forest Ave.
Wilmette, IL 60091-1533
(847) 251-5855
Email: sccvocationoffice@aol.com

Send one of the postcards in this book for more information.

The Norbertine Fathers and Brothers

We have something in Common!

Common Prayer

Common Table

Common Life

Of one mind and one heart on the way to God.

Do you have something in **Common** with us?

Contact: Vocation Director

Immaculate Conception Priory

1269 Bayview Road

Middletown, DE 19709

302-449-1840 ext. 31

The Norbertine Community
of
Immaculate Conception Priory
Nine Centuries of Praemonstratensian Tradition

Send one of the postcards in this book for more information.

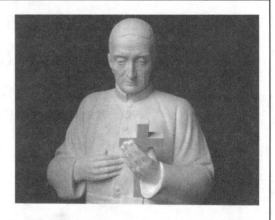

Daughters of the Charity
of the Sacred Heart of Jesus

From the Heart of God...
to the heart of the world...

In Jesus, God loves us with a human heart – one that reached out in compassion and hope towards a broken humanity.

Christ's charity – his love – compassionate and hope-giving is what we center on in our lives and in our mission.

Our name commits us to witness to God's tender love, being attentive to reveal it universally and to one another, addressing concrete needs of our times with its distresses, its challenges, and its search for meaning.

From France in 1823, to the U.S.A. in 1905, and subsequently to Canada, South Africa, Lesotho, Benin, Togo, Brazil, Madagascar and Tahiti – 1000 strong – in simplicity and love we continue to strive to meet the poor, the oppressed, and the humble of heart in their struggle and in their pain.

Are you willing to enter the 3rd Millennium by joining in a common project? A venture rooted in the original inspiration of our founders, Rose Giet and Jean-Maurice Catroux... Women living the Gospel in a diversity of apostolic commitments, but united in all that we say and do because of our bondedness in the loving Heart of Jesus...

(Please see listing under "Religious Communities for Women")

Please contact:
Vocation Director
P.O. Box 246
Milford, NH 03055-0246
Telephone 603-672-4133
E-mail: wnddr.jed@verizon.net
Web: www.fcscj.org

Send one of the postcards in this book for more information.

DOMINICAN • ROSARY
LITURGY • ROSARY
LECTIO DIVINA • WORK
COMMON LIFE • WORK

HOUSE OF PRAYER
SILENCE • STUDY
VOWS • HABIT
ENCLOSURE

Dominican Nuns of the Perpetual Rosary

Monastery of the
Immaculate Heart of Mary
1834 Lititz Pike
Lancaster, PA 17601-6585

Ph: (717) 569-2104
E-mail: monlanc@aol.com
Web: www.opnunslancaster.org

Saint Dominic
Founder, O.P. Nuns
1206

Father Damien Marie
Saintourens, O.P.
Founder of the
Dominican Sisters of
the Perpetual Rosary
1880

Send one of the postcards in this book for more information.

DOMINICAN SISTERS OF HAWTHORNE

The Eucharist nourishes
Our Consecrated Life.

The fruits of our
contemplation
overflow into our
apostolate to the
sick poor.

Study intensifies
Our prayer.

Sr. Alma Marie, Vocation Director
Dominican Sisters of Hawthorne
600 Linda Avenue
Hawthorne, New York 10532
(914) 769-4794 (0114)
e-mail: SrAlmaMarie@aol.com
www.hawthorne-dominicans.org

Use the Dominican Sisters of Hawthorne postcard in this book for more information.

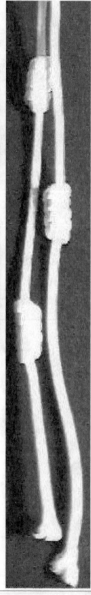

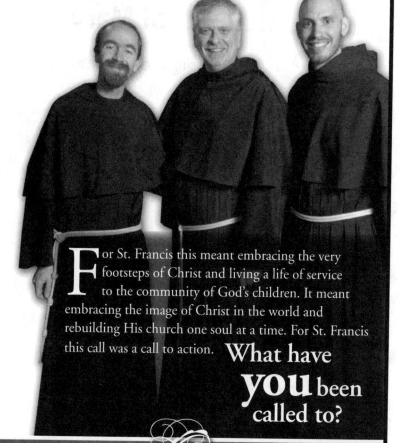

Called to Rebuild
Christ's Church...

For St. Francis this meant embracing the very footsteps of Christ and living a life of service to the community of God's children. It meant embracing the image of Christ in the world and rebuilding His church one soul at a time. For St. Francis this call was a call to action. **What have you been called to?**

Province of the Sacred Heart of Jesus – Loretto, PA

Franciscan Friars, T.O.R., Vocation Office
P.O. Box 104 • Loretto, PA 15940-0104
Phone: 814-472-8060 • E-mail: **vocationsTOR@aol.com**
www.franciscansTOR.org

Send one of the postcards in this book for more information.

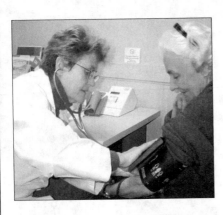

Franciscan Missionary Sisters
of the
Immaculate Heart of Mary

With Blessed Mary Catherine Troiani, our Foundress,
and Saint Francis, our Father, **we seek to follow Jesus,**
the Crucified Spouse **in a life of obedience, poverty, and**
chastity...through a life of prayer and fraternal love,
bringing the Gospel
with joy and simplicity to all...
As Missionaries through
various ministries in:
schools, hospitals,
clinics, homes for the aged,
orphanages, foreign missions,
parish work, and other works
according to our
charism and local needs.

Countries we are serving in:
USA, Brazil, China, Egypt,
Morocco, Guinea Bissau,
Ghana, Eritrea, Italy, Malta,
Israel, Palestine, Jordan,
Lebanon, Syria, Iraq

For more information contact:
Sr. Stacie Marie Gagnon, FMIHM
212 Ellis St., Glassboro, NJ 08028
Tel. (856) 881-4604   Fax: (856) 226-3098
Email: srstaciemarie@yahoo.com
And visit our <u>Website: www.fmihm.catholicweb.com</u>

Send one of the postcards in this book for more information.

FRANCISCAN MISSIONARY SISTERS
of the INFANT JESUS

"COME FOLLOW ME......."

Have you experienced a persistent attraction, a tug....to live for Jesus, to follow Him more closely, to give of yourself generously to His mission of Salvation? Jesus may be calling YOU.

We remain open to the needs of the people we serve in Africa (Cameroon, Libya), Asia (Philippines), Europe (Albania, France, Italy), South America, (Argentina, Bolivia, Brazil, Colombia, Paraguay, Peru), North America (United States)

Young women between the age of 20-35 with two years of college or equivalent work experience may seek information.

As Franciscans, we strive to live joyfully and simply, loving "Jesus in our neighbor and our neighbor in Jesus." Founded on Christmas day, 1879, we find in Jesus, the Son of God, who wanted to be born a child in order to be loved and not feared, the origin and reason of the charity, poverty and humility to which the Franciscan life pledges us. Our ministry of charity is directed to the human and Christian growth of the individual, the family and society, through education, health care, social work, and the catechetical, liturgical, pastoral ministries.

For information contact:

Vocation Director
Our Lady of the Angels
Delegation House
1215 Kresson Road
Cherry Hill, NJ 08003-2813
(856) 428- 8834
Email: fmijcomeandsee@yahoo.com

Send one of the postcards in this book for more information.

Are you being called to Religious Life?

We can help you find out.

The Franciscan Sisters of Allegany
Embracing the Challenge of the Gospel
Prayer • Community • Ministry

Sr. Mary McNally, OSF, Vocation Director
(813) 870-6314 fsavoc@aol.com
www.AlleganyFranciscans.org

Send one of the postcards in this book for more information.

**We joy in God through our Lord Jesus Christ
through whom we have received the Atonement.
Romans 5:11**

**"JOY IN GOD" is the heart of our Atonement vocation.
In Franciscan simplicity and joy,
we proclaim the Gospel message, "that all may be one."**

Franciscan Sisters of the Atonement
Vocation Ministry
41 Old Highland Turnpike
Graymoor, Garrison, NY 10524
Tel: 845-230-8231
E-mail: Vocationministry@graymoor.org
Web site www.graymoor.org

Send the convenient Franciscan Sisters of the Atonement postcard in this book for more information

Franciscan Sisters of the Poor

Called to be prophetic
witnesses of the Word,
healing our wounded world

We invite you to Join Us . . .

**We live the Gospel
We love and serve the poor
We pray and live in community**

visit us at: www.franciscansisters.org

Vocation Minister
Sr. Arlene McGowan, SFP
513-761-9040 x 112   OHIO
vocations@franciscansisters.org

Use the Franciscan Sisters of the Poor postcard in this book for more information.

Dare to be a woman of vision,
A Woman of Risk

SISTERS
of ST. FRANCIS
of the Neumann Communities

Sister Marie Joette dares to reach out in new and creative ways to provide educational opportunities for underserved children in the inner city as well as the countryside.

In addition to serving as vice principal and teacher at a grade school in Washington, D.C., Sister Marie Joette is an off-campus principal at two small schools in rural Alabama. Through her persistent and courageous efforts, these schools were established for children whose families struggle to maintain farms and rely on their children to assist with multiple tasks.

A woman of vision, inspired by the loving spirit of St. Francis, Sister Marie Joette is dedicated to making life better for thousands of children and families in need.

To read more sisters' stories, visit:
www.sosf.org

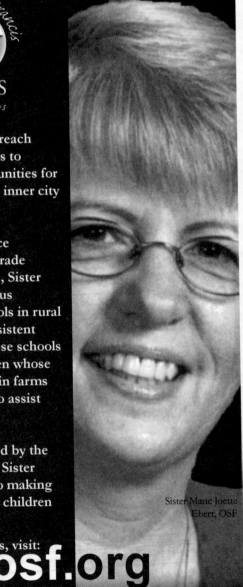

Sister Marie Joette
Ebert, OSF

Where is God calling You?

The Sisters of the Third Order of St. Francis

Since 1877, we have cared for the sick, the poor, the injured, the aged and the dying, in the spirit of Christ and after the example of St. Francis of Assisi. The times have changed, but the need for compassionate, ethical and accessible healthcare has not.

Living in community, we give ourselves to the Lord daily in our participation in the Holy Eucharist, in private and communal prayer and in our service to our sisters and to the Church.

You need not be nurses; our sisters serve in both clinical and non-clinical areas in our healthcare system.

Vocation Director: Sister Agnes Joseph Williams, O.S.F.
740 NE Glen Oak Ave., Peoria, IL 61603—(309)655-4840
vocation.info@osfhealthcare.org
Visit our website at: www.franciscansisterspeoria.org

Send one of the postcards in this book for more information.

Grey Nuns of the Sacred Heart

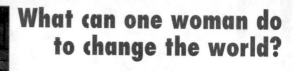

What can one woman do to change the world?

- Form community

- Know herself

- Love God

- Serve the poor

- Seek peace and work for justice

- Share in a 300 year old mission of universal compassion

Grey Nuns Motherhouse • 1750 Quarry Road • Yardley, PA 19067
PH. 215-968-4236 • www.greynun.org
Sr. Joan Daly: jdaly@greynun.org

Send one of the postcards in this book for more information.

HERMITAGE OF THE ADVENT

Reading

Hermitage of the Advent is a new contemplative community of women living the Rule of St. Benedict - seeking to be faithful to the rich values of the Monastic Tradition and, at the same time, be aware of contemporary insights.

WE SEEK TO LIVE WITH GOD
who has already found us
Singing God's praise at regular intervals
throughout the day
Hearing God's Word in Scripture,
study, events, others
Finding God's presence and love in the
silence.
Living this experience as a community

Prayer

OUR LIFE IS A BALANCED RHYTHM
Of solitude and community
Of prayer and work
Of seriousness and play
Of respect for the values of
tradition
and listening to the Spirit's
call today.

Work

Hospitality

COME AND SEE:
EXPERIENCE WHAT CANNOT BE PUT INTO WORDS.
215 HIGHLAND ST.
MARSHFIELD, MA 02050
781-319-6688
hermitage@verizon.net • www.hermitage-ofthe-advent.org

Send one of the postcards in this book for more information.

Seeking to live the vows
of authentic Franciscan life...

Franciscan Friars of the Renewal
Vocation Office: 212-281-4355
www.franciscanfriars.com

Send one of the postcards in this book for more information.

Holy Spirit Missionary Sisters

We are an international community of 3,600 religious women serving in 46 countries...

We use our gifts and talents in ways we never imagined!

Our energy to serve comes from Jesus' life-giving Spirit. People, prayer, service, joy, community living, sharing and receiving are all parts of our gospel way of life.

For more information, write or call:

Holy Spirit Missionary Sisters

Office of Vocation Ministry
319 Waukegan Road
Northfield, IL 60093

847-441-0126 ext. 704

E-mail: sspsovm@aol.com • Web-site: www.ssps-usa.org

IF YOU WANT YOU CAN FULFILL YOUR LIFE AS A MISSIONARY - HELPING PEOPLE FIND GOD'S LOVE AND PRESENCE IN THEIR LIVES.

Send one of the postcards in this book for more information.

PROVIDING
COMPASSION
and LOVE *to*
THOSE IN NEED

The Brothers of St. John of God

For the Brothers of St. John of God, their vocation means helping those who are disabled, sick or in need of compassion. It means devoting their lives to hospitality. It means experiencing community living with the opportunity to share their faith, ministry and daily lives with other men who have chosen the same vocation.

To learn more about how you can offer your unique gifts to the ministry of hospitality, contact:

Brother Thomas Osorio, O.H.
Hospitaller Brothers of St. John of God
1145 Delsea Drive
Westville Grove, NJ 08093
(856) 848-4700, ext. 163
e-mail: sjogvocationsnj@aol.com
website: www.brothersofstjohnofgod.org

The Sisters of Jesus our Hope

Proclaiming Jesus Christ and bringing hope

+

to children, youth and adults
through evangelization, catechesis
and faith formation
in a spirit of love and joy

+

Our apostolate flows from
our vowed life of communion with God
and with one another

+

Contact Vocation Director
376 Bellis Road, Bloomsbury, NJ 08804
908-995-7261
www.sistersofjesusourhope.org
E-mail: sisterjudith@sistersofjesusourhope.org

Send one of the postcards in this book for more information.

Use the convenient Josephites postcard in this book for more information.

ONE WORLD
ONE MISSION
ONE PERSON

Is it you?

One person makes a difference when the mission of Christ meets the world.

Be that person. Join us.

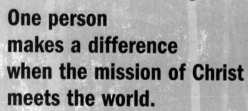

MARYKNOLL

For more information about becoming a Maryknoll Sister, contact:

Sr. Leonila Bermisa, M.M.
P.O. Box 311
Maryknoll, NY 10545
email:
Lbermisa@mksisters.org
phone:
(914) 941-7575 ext. 5676

For more information about becoming a Maryknoll Priest or Brother, contact:

Rev. Dennis Moorman, M.M.
PO Box 305
Maryknoll, NY 10545-0305
e-mail:
vocation@maryknoll.org
phone:
(914) 941-7590 ext. 2416
toll free: 1 (888) 627-9566

visit our website: www.maryknoll.org

Use the convenient Maryknoll postcard in this book for more information.

Missionaries of the Holy Family

We invite you to a life fully dedicated to the apostolates of the family, vocations and wherever God directs us.

Servants of God, Builders of Family

Charism
The Congregation of the Missionaries of the Holy Family was founded in 1895 at Grave, Holland by Fr. Jean Berthier. He dedicated the community to the Holy Family which is "the perfect model of every religious community and of every Christian family." We seek out and foster vocations, particularly among mature adults and the poor. Our community strives to live as a family while bringing the Gospel message to areas of need.

Apostolates
Throughout the world we promote and serve the needs of Church, family, local community and our Congregation. In the North American Province (Canada, United States and Mexico) we are involved in many types of pastoral service. As priests and brothers we work in parishes, schools, hospitals and homes for the aged. Our work reflects the concern and respect we have for family life.

MSF Vocation Office
104 Cas Hills Drive
San Antonio, TX 78213
(210) 344-9145

Send one of the postcards in this book for more information.

Missionaries of the Sacred Hearts of Jesus and Mary

We currently work in Italy, the United States, Argentina, Slovakia and India and have newer communities for seminarians in Nigeria and Indonesia.

"Let Us Kindle The Love Of The Sacred Hearts Of Jesus And Mary In The Hearts Of All People."

Blessed Gaetano Errico, M.SS.CC (1791-1860) Founder

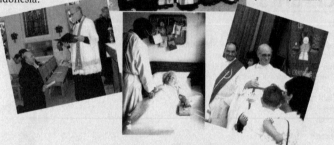

For the Honor and glory of the Sacred Hearts of Jesus and Mary...by our example, our work, our service to those in need.

Mission Statement: The Missionaries of the Sacred Hearts of Jesus and Mary is a community of priests and brothers dedicated to serving the needs of God's family while witnessing the great love present in the Sacred Hearts of Jesus and Mary through pastoral ministries, fostering of vocations to the priesthood and religious life, and active promotion of devotion to the Sacred Hearts.

We welcome you to call or write to us for more information
MISSIONARIES OF THE SACRED HEARTS
Vocation Director, 2249 Shore Road, P.O. Box 189, Linwood, NJ 08221
609-927-5600 Fax: 609-927-5262
E-mail: **mssccusa@aol.com**
Please visit our website: **www.missionofsacredhearts.org**

Send one of the postcards in this book for more information.

Pillars *of* Gentle Strength

Consider this.

If your personality evokes strength, gentleness, humility, joy, or humor,

If you are passionate about the Gospel and willing to work and live with others to inspire our Church,

If you are still searching for a commitment in the Church that will make you fully alive,

If you want to be a pillar of strength for others, ***perhaps you are a man called to live Jesus with us.***

Oblates of St. Francis de Sales are strong, gentle men who serve in parish, hospital, prison, campus, and Catholic schools ministry. Whether here in the States or in our overseas missions, we seek to live the optimistic, joy-filled spirit of St. Francis de Sales in our ministry and our community life.

For more information, please contact Fr. Kevin Nadolski, OSFS, at ***knadolski@oblates.org*** or visit us on the web at ***www.oblates.org***

Send one of the postcards in this book for more information.

Parish Visitors of Mary Immaculate

Contemplative–Missionaries: Evangelizers and Catechists

"The apostolate of the family (is) one of the priority tasks rendered even more urgent by the present state of the world"
Pope John Paul II

Holy Mass, Holy Hour, Meditation, the Rosary, Divine Office, Retreats, Spiritual Reading... provide the graces to *help families in parishes* through door-to-door evangelizing and teaching *the Faith* to adults and children.

Joyful apostles, we do the work of the Good Shepherd, seeking the strayed and the neglected to bring them back to the Church.

Please write:
Vocation Director
Parish Visitors of
Mary Immaculate
Box 658
Monroe, NY 10949
Phone: (845) 783-2251
www.parishvisitorsisters.org

Dedicated to Jesus: poor, chaste and obedient, and living a life of prayer.

Send one of the postcards in this book for more information.

Passionist Nuns

Monastic, Contemplative, Cloistered

*T*hroughout the history of the Church there have always been people who were called to leave all and live a life of prayer and solitude in union with Jesus Christ. That call continues in affluent America, in small communities such as the Passionist Nuns. Here young women seek a life of prayer and contemplative knowledge of Jesus for the glory of the Father and the good of others.

*C*onsecrating themselves totally to the mystery of the Passion and Death of Jesus, the Passionist Nuns proclaim God's redemptive love for the world by their life of prayer, penance and community. Their message is one of hope–that the Cross of Christ is a testimony of love in a world of suffering.

Passionist Nuns	*Passionist Nuns*
1151 Donaldson Highway	2715 Churchview Avenue
Erlanger, Kentucky 41018	Pittsburgh, PA 15227-2141
859-371-8568	**412-881-1155**

Send one of the postcards in this book for more information.

Could This Be Your Sign From God?

In the spirit of our founder, St. Paul of the Cross,
and sustained by our community
and prayer life, we walk with the
Crucified of Our World through our:

- Parishes
- Retreat Houses
- TV Ministry
- Parish Missions

Bring the message of Jesus' Passion to a world in need.

The Passionists

Fr. Bill Maguire, C.P.
St. Paul of the Cross Retreat Center
148 Monastery Avenue
Pittsburgh, PA 15203
412-381-1188   spoc-vocations@cpprov.org

Use the convenient Passionists postcard in this book for more information.

The Piarist Fathers
Ministers to Youth

The Piarist Fathers profess a fourth religious vow to educate youth, especially the poor. In the United States, we teach in high schools in Philadelphia and Ft. Lauderdale, we minister to the poor in Appalachia, and are very active in Hispanic Youth Ministry programs and in other educational and youth ministry apostolates.

Piarist priests and brothers instill a love and knowledge of Christ and his salvific message along with providing a quality education in the traditional academic subjects, in accordance with our mission to imbue students in Piety and Learning, as expressed by the order's motto *"Pietas et Litterae."*

Piarists care for the physical, intellectual, and spiritual dimensions of youth, and it is through this special ministry that a Piarist follows Christ's command to *"Go forth and teach all nations."*

If you can visualize yourself working in the fields of education or youth ministry, contact the Piarist Vocation Director

Rev. David B. Powers, Sch. P
99 Martha's Vineyard
Prestonsburg, KY 41653
610-564-8893 ● www.calasanz.net
E-mail: dariff@hotmail.com

Send one of the postcards in this book for more information.

SISTERS OF THE SACRED HEART OF JESUS OF RAGUSA

We were founded by
Blessed Maria Schinina in 1889 to
LOVE AND SERVE

If you are a Catholic woman between the ages of 18 – 38 and wish to consecrate yourself totally and unreservedly to the Sacred Heart of Jesus and to serve in Love, you may be called to join us...

Our Motto: Love and Reparation to the Sacred Heart

You are invited to spend a day or more with the Sisters to personally witness their lives.

Reaching out...Touching Others...
- Prayer • Teaching • Child Care Centers
- Youth Ministry • Catechetical Work
- Parish and Pastoral Work
- Missionary Work
- Nursing assistance to the sick, the lonely, the needy and the elderly

Call or write to: VOCATION DIRECTOR

5269 Lewiston Road
Lewiston, N.Y. 14092
716-284-8273
sshj_vocation@yahoo.com

94 Chapel Hill Road
North Haven, CT 06473
203-239-8012
st_frances_cabrini@sbcglobal.net

www.shvilla.org

THE CONGREGATION OF THE SACRED HEARTS OF JESUS AND MARY (SS.CC.)

Do You Have a Deep Desire for the Love of God to Be the Center of Your Life?

THE PRIESTS, BROTHERS AND SISTERS OF THE CONGREGATION OF THE SACRED HEARTS INVITE YOU:

† TO LIVE AS PART OF OUR WORLD-WIDE SPIRITUAL FAMILY CONSECRATED TO THE HEARTS OF JESUS & MARY, UNITED IN LOVE

† TO MINISTER IN PARISHES, HOSPITALS, SCHOOLS- WHEREVER PEOPLE LONG FOR COMPASSION AND DIGNITY

† TO ADORE JESUS IN HIS TABERNACLE AND IN HIS PEOPLE

Join a Religious Community inspired by the heroic witness of our SS.CC. brother, Blessed Damien of Molokai, who gave his life in service to the victims of leprosy. We celebrate his elevation to sainthood in 2009!

DO NOT HESITATE! COME AND SEE! YOU COULD BE LINKED TO GOD'S HEART IN THE WORLD

Contact Vocation Director
Fr. Richard Lifrak, ss.cc.
frlifrak@sscc.org   (508) 993-2442 x309

Congregation of the Sacred Hearts of Jesus & Mary (SS.CC.)
PO Box 111 • Fairhaven, MA 02719-0111
Phone (508) 993-2442 • www.sscc.org • (508) 996-5499 Fax

Use the Congregation of the Sacred Hearts of Jesus and Mary postcard for more information.

We Have Habits...

...Prayer...Ministry
...Generosity...Community
...Hospitality...Social Justice

CSA
Congregation of Sisters of St. Agnes
Promoting Justice, Building Community

Come and be part of the next generation of
Sisters of St. Agnes

Contact us at: CSA Office of Vocation Discernment
920.907.2310 • vocations@csasisters.org • www.csasisters.org

Send one of the postcards in this book for more information.

CONGREGATION OF THE SISTERS OF SAINT THOMAS OF VILLANOVA

The bond of our Institut is Charity *(Ange Leproust, O.S.A., Founder)*

Seek and Serve Jesus in the poor with Joy, Love and Simplicity.

- Care for the soul in distress, the needy, the poor, the lonely and the dying
- Education, Nursing Home, Hospital
- Missionary work across the world
- Community life together: prayers, meals, recreational activities and work.

Come and be part of the privilege to serve and love God in the poorest of the poor.

Hablamos Español

For more information contact:

Sister Marie Lucie Monast, S.S.T.V.
76 West Rocks Road
Norwalk, CT 06851
Phone: **203-847-2885**
Fax: **203-847-3740**
e-mail: sstv_usa@sbcglobal.net
www.sistersofsaintthomasofvillanova.com

The Motherhouse
52 Boulevard d'Argenson
92 200 Neuilly-sur-Seine
France
Phone: **011-33-1-47-47-42-20**
Fax: **011-33-1-47-47-38-00**
e-mail: stvneuilly@wanadoo.fr
www.congregation-stv.org

Respond to the call ... the deepest yearning of your heart ...

Silence Solitude Prayer...

the contemplative search for God alone

Redemptoristine Nuns live a life of charity in community as a family gathered in the name of Jesus, our Redeemer. As a contemplative monastic Order, prayer is the heart of our life. By daily celebration of the Eucharist and the Liturgy of the Hours, our adoration and prayer make our whole life a sacrifice of praise to the glory of God as intercession for the Church and the world.

Mother of Perpetual Help Monastery
P.O. Box 20 Esopus, NY 12429-0220
ContemplativeCall@hotmail.com

www.RedemptoristineNunsofNewYork.org

Send one of the postcards in this book for more information.

Sisters, Servants of the Immaculate Heart of Mary, Immaculata, PA

Is the Heart of Christ

IHM

speaking to your heart?

Consecration ~ Vows of Chastity, Poverty, Obedience

 Daily Prayer

 Community Life

Service in Catholic Education and Related Ministries

Contact: Sister Carmen Teresa Fernández, IHM
Sister Rose Bernadette Mulligan, IHM

ihmvoc@aol.com   610-889-1553

www.ihmimmaculata.org

Send one of the postcards in this book for more information.

Glory be to the Most Sacred Heart of Jesus

Is the Sacred Heart calling you?

To give glory to the Triune God in the Mystery of the Most Sacred Heart of Jesus. To live a life of prayer and loving reparation in chastity, poverty and obedience. To spread the Kingdom of love of this Heart in daily living by serving Christ in our neighbor, especially on behalf of girls, the sick, the poor, children and youth. To live in community in a spirit of Franciscan joy and simplicity...

Sister Servants of the Most Sacred Heart of Jesus
Sacred Heart Province
866 Cambria St., Cresson, PA 16630-1713
(814) 886-4223 ~ sscjusa@pngusa.net
www.sacredheartsisters.org

Send one of the postcards in this book for more information.

Say "Yes" with Mary

Sisters of the Sorrowful Mother

Serving in the United States,
Grenada, St. Lucia,
Trinidad/Tobago,
Tanzania, Africa
Dominican Republic, Austria,
Brazil, Germany and Italy

*Franciscan
women of vision,
women of compassion,
women of mission*

Vocation Director
(973) 627-0424

ssmvoc@aol.com
www.ssmfranciscans.org
40 Morris Ave., Denville, NJ 07834

Louis

Send one of the postcards in this book for more information.

Transfiguration Hermitage

- **FOLLOW:** Jesus, in this monastic way of life according to the Rule of St. Benedict.

- **PIONEER:** In a contemplative life which blends solitude and community in a healthy, environmentally friendly rural lifestyle.

- **CREATE:** Enter with us in this exciting, fresh venture as we give our lives and ourselves to the Lord.

- **PRAY:** For the needs of all people and all of creation.

- **WORK:** In a balanced, simple rhythm of manual labor, *lectio* and spiritual outreach.

- **UNITE:** Bring your heart, mind, body, spirit to integration in the One Lord.

- **CONNECT:** With your sisters in community and with all people in the heart of Jesus.

- **TRANSFORM:** The world through your life of prayer and solitude.

Contact Us

Transfiguration Hermitage
205 Windsor Neck Rd.
Windsor, Maine 04363
(207) 445-8031
www.transfigurationhermitage.org
benedicite@fairpoint.net

Send one of the postcards in this book for more information.

Order of the Most Holy Trinity

Four Pillars of Religious Life

PRAYER

COMMUNITY

SERVICE

TRADITION

Founded in 1198, the Trinitarians have worked through the centuries bringing God's liberating love to those persecuted for their faith in Christ. To find out more about our 800 years of service to the values of the Gospel and the charism of St. John DeMatha please contact us.

Fr. Carl M. Frisch, O.SS.T.
Director of Vocations
P.O. Box 5719 • Baltimore MD 21282
1-800-525-3554
Se habla español

vocations@trinitarians.org   http://www.trinitarians.org

Use the convenient Trinitarians postcard in this book for more information.

GEORGETOWN
VISITATION
MONASTERY

We invite you to learn more about our life as we strive to walk gently and humbly in the footsteps of St. Francis de Sales and St. Jane de Chantal. Come, "Live Jesus" with us!

MONASTIC PROFESSION

APOSTOLATE OF EDUCATION

**SUNG LITURGY OF THE HOURS
DAILY MASS
WEEKLY ADORATION**

**MONASTIC COMMUNITY LIFE
CONTEMPLATIVE HOSPITALITY
NEVER A DULL MOMENT**

Georgetown Visitation Monastery
1500 35th Street, NW
Washington DC 20007

www.georgetownvisitation.org
http://livejesus.blogspot.com
GVMonastery@gmail.com

"There is nothing so strong as
true gentleness and
nothing so gentle as
true strength."
St. Francis de Sales

Send one of the postcards in this book for more information.

Xaverian Brothers

CALLED PERSONALLY AND CONGREGATIONALLY TO A CONTEMPLATIVE STANCE IN THE WORLD AND TO MINISTER WITH THE POOR AND MARGINALIZED

A growing Xaverian Community in Kenya.

Members of the Xaverian Brothers Contact Program with Brother Stephen

Brother Charles encourages his math students.

After novitiate, vowed life begins with first profession.

We respond to God's call to spread the message of the gospel

For more information, contact:
Brother James Connolly, CFX
Xaverian Brothers
4409 Frederick Ave.
Baltimore MD 21229
E-mail: jconnolly@xaverianbrothers.org
Web: www.xaverianbrothers.org

Belize Bolivia Burkina Faso Canada Chile Colombia France Haiti

Clerics of St. Viator
Viatorians Around The World

Our priests and brothers ministering in parishes and schools give witness to Jesus Christ in our modern world.

Viatorians

Educators of Faith

Vocation Ministry
1212 East Euclid Avenue
Arlington Heights, IL 60004
847.637.2129
dlydon@viatorians.com
www.viatorians.com

IHS

Honduras Italy Ivory Coast Japan Peru Spain Taiwan United States

Send one of the postcards in this book for more information.

Become an
Adrian Dominican Sister!

Live Dominican Life
with us as we ...

Seek
Truth

Make
Peace

Reverence
Life

Adrian Dominican Sisters
Director of Vocations • 517-266-3537 • vocations@adriandominicans.org
www.adriandominicans.org

Send one of the postcards in this book for more information.

Questions to Ask When Discerning a Religious Vocation

Thoughtfully thinking about the questions below can help you in the process of discerning whether you are being called to a religious life as a priest, brother, or sister. Writing down the answers in a journal often helps one to reach clarity, as does discussing your thoughts with your spiritual director.

- Name the two top motivating factors for your interest in a religious vocation.
- What excites you at the prospect of ministering with and for others? Explain each.
- What, in your estimation, is the number one "mission" of the Catholic Church?
- What is the difference between serving God and being in love with God?
- What does a "personal relationship" with Jesus mean to you?
- What major events, changes, or traumas in your life trigger your attraction toward a religious vocation?
- Are you flexible and open to others of different thought, theology, practice, piety or devotion?
- Who has been a mentor or someone you would like to imitate in your ministry and why? If there are several list them all.
- Do you think the Catholic Church needs to address issues that you feel are important? What are your solutions?
- What do you think is the biggest challenge facing the Church in the 21st century and what has given you this impression?
- Please explain your idea of what "collaborative ministry" entails. Have you ever worked in this fashion (give concrete examples)?
- We face obstacles and resistance with any major decision in our lives. Name the obstacles which at present are hindering you from making an informed or a confident decision towards a religious vocation. How have you been addressing these obstacles or areas of resistance?
- Do you prefer to spend time with others or do you consider yourself a private person?
- What is the difference between being alone and being lonely?
- Reflecting on God's Word and prayer will help you with these questions. Here are some passages from Scripture relating to call, vocation, choices and journey on which you can meditate:

OLD TESTAMENT	NEW TESTAMENT
Genesis 12:1-4a (Abraham)	Matthew 16:24-28 (The Cross)
Exodus 3:10-12 & 4:1, 10-12 (Moses)	Matthew 22:1-14 (Few chosen)
Amos 7:14-15 (Amos)	Luke 4:1-13 (Temptations)
Isaiah 6:8 (Isaiah)	Luke 6:12-15 (Night in prayer)
Jeremiah 1:4-8 (Jeremiah)	Luke 9:57-62 (Requirements)
Ezekiel 3:1-4 (Ezekiel)	Luke 10:38-42 (Martha, Mary)
1 Kings 10 (Kings)	Luke 12:22-31 (Seek first)
	Luke 18:15-30 (Rich young man)
	Mark 3:13-15 (The twelve)
	Romans 8:26-31 (All things)

This article is reprinted with permission from the Diocese of Lansing website at www.dioceseoflansing.org. Lansing Catholic Diocese. All rights reserved. To contact the diocese see the listing in the section **Diocesan Vocation Offices.**

Diocesan Vocation Offices

ALABAMA

Diocese of Birmingham (D001)
in Alabama
2121 3rd Ave. North
Birmingham, AL 35203
Rev. Bryan K. Lowe,
Director of Seminarians
(256) 237-3011, ext.106
Dr. Stephen Smith, Coordinator for
Vocations, PO Box 12047,
Birmingham, AL 35202-2047
(205) 838-2184
Email: ssmith@bhmdiocese.org or
        father@
        sacredheartanniston .org
Web: www.bhmdiocese.org

Archdiocese of Mobile (D002)
6051 Old Shell Rd.
Mobile, AL 36608
Rev. Alejandro E. Valladares
(251) 343-3662
Web: www.mobilearchdiocese.org

ALASKA

Archdiocese of Anchorage (D003)
225 Cordova St.
Anchorage, AK 99501
Very Rev. Leo A. Walsh, S.T.D.
(907) 297-7770 or (907) 694-2170
Fax: (907) 279-3885
Email: lwalsh@caa-ak.org
Web:www.archdioceseof
        anchorage.org

Diocese of Fairbanks (D004)
Vocation Office
St. Nicholas Church
707 St. Nicholas Dr.
North Pole, AK 99705
Rev. Ross Tozzi, (907) 488-2595
Fax: (907) 488-9625
Email: rtozzi@parishmail.com
Web: www.cbna.info

Diocese of Juneau (D005)
Office of Vocations and Priestly
Formation
433 Jackson St.
Ketchikan, AK 99901
Rev. Edmund Penisten
(907) 225-2570
Email: fr_edmund@hotmail.com
Web: www.dioceseofjuneau.org

ARIZONA

Diocese of Phoenix (D006)
400 E. Monroe St.
Phoenix, AZ 85004
Rev. Don Kline
Office for Diocesan Priesthood
(602) 354-2004, Fax (602) 354-2442
Rev. Paul Sullivan, Associate
Vocation Director
Email: frsullivan@diocesephoenix .org
        frkline@diocesephoenix.org
Web: www.diocesephoenix.org/
        vocations

Diocese of Tucson (D007)
111 South Church Ave.
Tucson, AZ 85701
Rev. Michael Bucciarelli and
Rev. Vili Valderrama, Co-Directors
(520) 838-2531, Fax: (520) 838-2593
Vicar for Religious: Sister Rena
Cappellazzo, O.P.
(520) 838-2524 Fax: (520) 792-0291
E-mail:SrRC@diocesetucson.org
        vocations@diocesetucson.org
Web: www.diocesetucson.org

ARKANSAS

Diocese of Little Rock (D008)
2500 N. Tyler St., PO Box 7565
Little Rock, AR 72217
Rev. Msgr. Scott Friend
(501) 664-0340, Fax: (501) 664-0119
E-mail: sfriend@dolr.org
Web: www.dolr.org

CALIFORNIA

Diocese of Fresno (D009)
1550 N. Fresno St.
Fresno, CA 93703-3788
Rev. Salvador Gonzalez, Jr.
(559) 488-7424, Fax: (559) 488-7475
E-mail: vocations@dioceseof
        fresno.org
Web: www.dioceseoffresno.org

Archdiocese of Los Angeles (D010)
3424 Wilshire Blvd.
Los Angeles, CA 90010-2202
(213) 637-7248, Fax: (213) 637-6138
Rev. James Forsen
E-mail: FrJRForsen@la-archdiocese
        .org
Web: www.archdiocese.la/ministry/
        vocations/

Diocese of Monterey (D011)
PO Box 2048
Monterey, CA 93942-2048
Rev. Jose Alberto Vazquez
(831) 645-2813, Fax: (831) 373-6761
Rev. Kenneth Brown, Associate
Director, St. Patrick's Church, PO
Box 860, Arroyo Grande, CA 93421
(805) 489-2680
E-mail: vocations@dioceseof
        monterey.org
Web: www.dioceseofmonterey.org

Diocese of Oakland (D012)
2121 Harrison St.
Oakland, CA 94612
Rev. Lawrence D'Anjou
(510) 267-8356
E-mail: ldanjou@oakdiocese.org
Web: www.oakdiocese.org

Diocese of Orange (D013)
2811 E. Villa Real Dr.
Orange, CA 92867-1999
Rev. John Neneman
Rev. Jose Ferreras
Priest Vocation Coordinator
(714) 282-3033
Sister Eymard Flood, OSC,
Women's Vocations
(714) 282-3120
E-mail: jneneman@rcbo.org or
        jferreras@rcbo.org
Web: www.rcbo.org

Diocese of Sacramento (D014)
Office of Priestly & Religious
Vocations
2110 Broadway, #258
Sacramento, CA 95818
Rev. Brian Atienza, Director,
batienza@diocese-sacramento.org
Rev. Humberto Gomez
Associate Director
hgomez@diocese-sacramento.org
(916) 733-0258, Fax: (916) 733-0224
E-mail: callserve@diocese-
        sacramento .org
Web: www.diocese-sacramento.org

Diocese of San Bernardino (D015)
Vocations Office
12725 Oriole Ave.
Grand Terrace, CA 92313
Sr. Sarah Shrewsbury, O.S.C. and
Rev. Jerry Ochetti
(909) 783-1305 Fax: (909) 783-0223
E-mail: vocations@sbdiocese.org
Web: www.sbdiocese.org

Diocese of San Diego (D016)
PO Box 85728
San Diego, CA 92186-5728
Rev. Anthony Saroki, Director
(619) 291-7452
Rev. Matt Spahr, Director, Priestly
Formation, (619) 291-7446
E-mail: mspahr@diocese-sdiego.org
Sr. Jeanette Lucinio, SP, Director,
Office for Women Religious
St. Francis Center, 1667 Santa
Paula Dr., San Diego CA 92111
E-mail: asaroki@diocese-sdiego.org
Web: www.sandiegovocations.org/

Archdiocese of San Francisco (D017)
One Peter Yorke Way
San Francisco, CA 94109
Rev. Thomas A. Daly
(415) 614-5683, Fax (415) 614-5555
E-mail: dalyt@sfarchdiocese.org
Web: www.sfvocation.org

Diocese of San Jose (D018)
900 Lafayette St., Suite 301
Santa Clara, CA 95050-4966
Rev. Mark Catalana
(408) 983-0255, Fax: (408) 983-0257
Melissa A. Tamayo, Assistant
(408) 983-0155, Fax: (408) 983-0257
E-mail: frmark@dsj.org or
    tamayo@dsj.org
Web: www.dsj.org/vocations

Diocese of Santa Rosa (D019)
Mailing Address: PO Box 1297,
Santa Rosa, CA 95402-1297
985 Airway Ct
Santa Rosa, CA 95403
Rev. Thomas Diaz, Director of
Vocations and Seminarians
(707) 566-3395
Diaconate Director of Formation:
Deacon Frank Dahl, (707) 566-3371
E-mail: vocation@sonic.net
Web: www.santarosacatholic.org

Diocese of Stockton (D020)
1125 N. Lincoln St.
Stockton, CA 95203-2410
Sr. Wanda M. Billion, MSC (209)
466-0636, ext. 619
Fax (209) 463-5937
E-mail: wbillion@
    stocktondiocese. org
Web: www.stocktondiocese.org

COLORADO
(D021)
Diocese of Colorado Springs
228 N. Cascade Ave.
Colorado Springs, CO 80903
Rev. Jim Williams
(719) 636-2345 Fax: (719) 636-1216
E-mail: vocations@diocs.org
Web: www.diocs.org

Archdiocese of Denver (D022)
1300 S. Steele St.
Denver, CO 80210
Rev. Jim Crisman, Director of
Priestly Vocations
(303) 282-3429
E-mail: vocation@archden.org
Web: www.priest4christ.org

Diocese of Pueblo (D023)
1001 N. Grand Ave.
Pueblo, CO 81003
Deacon Marco D. Vegas
(719) 544-9861, ext. 116
E-mail: mvegas@dioceseof
    pueblo.com
Web: www.dioceseofpueblo.com

CONNECTICUT
Diocese of Bridgeport (D024)
Saint John Fisher Seminary
Residence, 894 Newfield Ave.
Stamford, CT 06905
Rev. Peter J. Lynch
(203) 322-5331, Fax: (203) 461-9876
E-mail: vocations@HearTheCall.org
Web: www.HearTheCall.org

Archdiocese of Hartford (D025)
467 Bloomfield Ave.
Bloomfield, CT 06002
Rev. Michael Dolan
(860) 286-7670, Fax (860) 242-9701
E-mail: vocations@stseminary.org
Web: www.vocationshartford.org

Diocese of Norwich (D026)
201 Broadway
Norwich, CT 06360-4328
Rev. Gregory P. Galvin
(860) 887-9294
E-mail: vocations@
    norwichdiocese .net
Web: www.God-calls.org

DELAWARE
Diocese of Wilmington (D027)
PO Box 2030
Wilmington, DE 19899-2030
Rev. Joseph M.P.R. Cocucci,
Director, Office of Priestly and
Religious Vocations
(302) 573-3113
E-mail: jcocucci@cdow.org

DISTRICT OF COLUMBIA
Archdiocese of Washington/ (D028)
Suburban Maryland
5001 Eastern Avenue
Hyattsville, MD 20782
Rev. Msgr. Robert J. Panke
(301) 853-4580, Fax (301) 853-7668
E-mail: Vocations@adw.org
Web: www.dcvocations.org

FLORIDA
Archdiocese of Miami (D029)
9401 Biscayne Blvd.
Miami Shores, FL 33138
Father Manny Alvarez
(305) 762-1137
E-mail: vocations@theadom.org
Web: www.miamiarch.org

Diocese of Orlando (D030)
PO Box 1800, Orlando, FL 32802
Rev. Miguel Gonzalez
(407) 246-4875;
Associate Vocation Director: Sr.
Kathleen Power, SSJ
(407) 246-4928
E-mail: mgonzalez@orlando
    diocese.org
Web: www.orlandodiocese.org

Diocese of Palm Beach (D031)
9995 N. Military Trail
Palm Beach Gardens, FL 33410
Rev. Yves Francois, Director of
Vocations/Seminarians/Religious
(561) 775-9555
E-mail: vocations@diocesepb.org
Web: www.diocesepb.org

Diocese of Pensacola-Tallahassee (D032)
11 North B Street
Pensacola, FL 32501
Rev. Msgr. Michael Tugwell
(850) 435-3500, Fax: (850) 435-3565
E-mail: vogelj@ptdiocese.org
Web: www.ptdiocese.org

Diocese of St. Augustine (D033)
11625 Old St. Augustine Road
Jacksonville, FL 32258-2060
Rev. Jason Trull
(904) 262-3200, ext 101
Fax (904) 262-0698
E-mail: vocations@dosafl.com
Web: www.dosafl.com

Diocese of St. Petersburg (D034)
6363 9th Ave. N.
St. Petersburg, FL 33710
Rev. Leonard J.M. Plazewski,
Director of Vocations
(727) 345-3452
Email: spvocation@aol.com
Web: spvocation.org

Diocese of Venice (D035)
Office of Vocations, PO Box 2006
Venice, FL 34284-2006
Rev. Gregg Caggianelli
E-mail: vocations@dioceseofvenice
    .org
Web: www.dioceseofvenice.org

GEORGIA

Archdiocese of Atlanta (D036)
680 West Peachtree St., NW
Atlanta, GA 30308-1984
Rev. Luke Ballman, (404) 888-7844
E-mail: frballman@
        calledbychrist .com
Web: www.calledbychrist.com

Diocese of Savannah (D037)
Catholic Pastoral Center
601 East Liberty St.
Savannah, GA 31401
Rev. Timothy McKeown, Vocation
Office, St. Matthew Church
221 John Paul Ave., Statesboro, GA
30458-5016
(912) 681-6726
E-mail: vocations@diosav.org
Web: www.savannahpriest.com

HAWAII

Diocese of Honolulu (D038)
1184 Bishop St., Honolulu, HI 96813
Rev. Peter Dumag
(808) 585-3343, Fax (808) 585-3384
E-mail: manao@rcchawaii.org
Web: www.catholichawaii.com

IDAHO

Diocese of Boise (D039)
804 N. 9th St., Boise, ID 83702
Rev. Jairo Restrepo, (208) 342-1328
Fax: (208) 324-4082
E-mail: jrestrepo@rcdb.org
Web: www.catholicidaho.org

ILLINOIS

Diocese of Belleville (D040)
2620 Lebanon Ave.
Belleville, IL 62221-3299
Co-Directors:
Rev. William McGhee
(618) 233-2391
Rev. Trevor Murry, (618) 932-2828
Rev. David Wilke, (618) 274-3486
E-mail: pwarner@diobelle.org

Archdiocese of Chicago (D041)
Office for Religious
www.archchicago.org/departments/
vocation/home.shtm
155 E. Superior St.
Chicago, IL 60611-2911
Rev. Joseph T. Noonan, Vocation
Director, Diocesan Priesthood
(312) 751-5240
E-mail: voac@archchicago.org
Sr. Elyse Marie Ramirez, OP,
Office for Religious, Coordinator of
Religious VocationsMinistries
E-mail: eramirez@archchicago.org
(312) 751-5245
E-mail: jnoonan@archchicago.org
Web: www.chicagopriest.org

Diocese of Joliet (D042)
402 S. Independence Blvd.
Romeoville, IL 60446-2264
Rev. Burke Masters
(815) 834-4004
E-mail: frburke23@aol.com
Web: www.vocations.com

Diocese of Peoria (D043)
419 NE Madison Ave.
Peoria, IL 61603
Rev. Brian K. Brownsey
(309) 671-1550
E-mail: frbrownsey@cdop.org
Web: www.cdop.org/vocations/

Diocese of Rockford (D044)
PO Box 7044, Rockford, IL 61125
Rev. Michael Lavan
(815) 399-4300, ext. 396
Fax: (815) 399-6085
E-mail: mail@RockVoc.org
en español: contactarnos@
        RockVoc .org
Web: www.rockvoc.org

Diocese of Springfield in Illinois (D045)
1615 W. Washington St
PO Box 3187
Springfield, IL 62708-3187
Director - Office for Vocations
Associate Director - Office for the
Diaconate and Office for Ministry
Formation: Rev. Christopher House
(217) 698-8500, ext. 182
Fax: (217) 698-8602
E-mail: vocations@dio.org
Web: www.dio.org/vocations

INDIANA

Diocese of Evansville (D046)
4200 N. Kentucky Ave.
PO Box 4169
Evansville, IN 47724-0169
Vocation Team:
Rev. Bernie Etienne
Rev. Jason Gries
Rev. Alex Zenthoefer, and
Sr. Agnes Marie Dauby
E-mail: betienne@evansville-
diocese.org,
jbgries@evansville-diocese.org,
azenthoefer@evansville-diocese
.org, amdauby@thedome.org
Web: www.evansville-diocese.org/
vocations/vocation.htm

Diocese of Fort Wayne-South Bend (D047)
114 W. Wayne St.
South Bend, IN 46601
Rev. Bernard J. Galic
(574) 234-0687, Fax (574) 232-8483
E-mail: bjgalic@earthlink.net
Web: diocesefwsb.org

Diocese of Gary (D048)
Diocese of Gary Pastoral Center
9292 Broadway
Merrillville, IN 46410
Rev. Kevin Huber
(219) 769-9292
E-mail: khuber@dcgary.org
Web: www.dcgary.org

Archdiocese of Indianapolis (D049)
Mailing address: PO Box 1410,
Indianapolis, IN 46206-1410
1400 N. Meridian St.
Indianapolis, IN 46202
Rev. Eric Johnson
800-382-9836, (317) 236-1490
Rev. Rick Nagel, Associate Director,
(317) 236-1490
E-mail: rnagel@archindy.org
        ejohnson@archindy.org or
        vocations@archindy.org
Web: www.archindy.org or
        www.heargodscall.com

Diocese of Lafayette-in-Indiana (D050)
St. Elizabeth Ann Seton Parish
10655 Haverstick Road
Carmel, IN 46033
Rev. Brian M. Doerr, (317) 873-2885
E-mail: revbdoerr@priestforever.org
Web: www.priestforever.org

IOWA

Diocese of Davenport (D051)
2706 N. Gaines St.
Davenport, IA 52804-1998
Rev. Marty Goetz, (563) 324-1911
Web: goetz@davenportdiocese.org
Web: www.davenportdiocese.org

Diocese of Des Moines (D052)
601 Grand Ave.
Des Moines, IA 50309
Rev. Chris Fontanini, Vocation
Director
Stephen Tatz, Vocations Specialist
(515) 237-5050, 5061
E-mail: cfontanini@dmdiocese.org,
        statz@dmdiocese.org
Web: www.vocationsonline.com

Archdiocese of Dubuque (D053)
Archdiocesan Center
1229 Mt. Loretta Ave., PO Box 479
Dubuque, IA 52004-0479
Rev.David A. Schatz
(Director of Vocation Awareness)
(563) 556-2580, ext. 281
Fax (563) 556-5464
Rev. Scott E. Bullock, Director of
Seminarians
(563) 556-2580, ext. 416
E-mail: dbqcvo@arch.pvt.k12.ia.us
Web: www.dbqpriesthood.com

Diocese of Sioux City (D054)
1821 Jackson St.
Sioux City, IA 51105
Rev. Brad Pelzel
(712) 233-7522, Fax: (712) 233-7598
E-mail: vocations@scdiocese.org
Web: www.scdiocese.org

KANSAS
Diocese of Dodge City (D055)
910 Central, P.O. Box 137
Dodge City, KS 67801-0137
Becky Hessman, Coordinator of
Vocations
(620) 227-1530
E-mail: bhessman@dcdiocese.org
Web: www.dcdiocese.org

Archdiocese of Kansas City (D056)
in Kansas
Catholic Church Offices
12615 Parallel Parkway
Kansas City, KS 66109-6109
Rev. Mitchel Zimmerman
(913) 721-1570, ext. 146
Fax: (913) 721-1577
E-mail: vocation@archkck.org
Web: www.kckvocations.com

Diocese of Salina (D057)
103 N. 9th, PO Box 980
Salina, KS 67402-0980
Rev. Jarett Konrade
(785) 827-8746
E-mail: vocations@
       salinadiocese.org
Web: www.salinadiocese.org

Diocese of Wichita (D058)
424 N. Broadway, Wichita, KS 67202
Rev. Mike Simone, (316) 269-3900
E-mail: frmikesimone@gmail.com
Web: www.cdowk.org

KENTUCKY
Diocese of Covington (D059)
Diocesan Curia
PO Box 15550
Covington, KY 41015-0550
Rev. Gregory J. Bach
Vocation Recruiter
(859) 392-1566
Web: www.covingtondiocese.org

Diocese of Lexington (D060)
1310 W. Main St.
Lexington, KY 40508-2040
(859) 253-1993, ext. 247
Rev. John Moriarty
E-mail: jmoriarty@cdlex.org
Web: www.cdlex.org

Archdiocese of Louisville (D061)
Maloney Center
200 So. Shelby St.

Louisville, KY 40203-2600
Rev. William Bowling
(502) 636-0296 Fax: (502) 636-2379
E-mail: vocation@archlou.org
Web: www.archlou.org

Diocese of Owensboro (D062)
Office of Vocations
600 Locust Street
Owensboro, KY 42301-2130
Rev. D. Andrew Garner
(270) 683-1545
E-mail: fr.andy.garner@pastoral.org
Web: www.owensborodio.org/
      vocations.html

LOUISIANA
Diocese of Alexandria (D063)
Vocation Office
100 1/2 Texas St.
Leesville, LA 71446
Rev. Kenneth Michiels
(318) 445-2401, ext. 211
E-mail: vocations@diocesealex.org
Web: www.diocesealex.org

Diocese of Baton Rouge (D064)
1800 S. Acadian Thruway
PO Box 2028
Baton Rouge, LA 70821-2028
Rev. Matthew P. Lorrain
Sister Lucy Silvio, CSJ, Associate
Director of Seminarians
(225) 336-8778, Fax: (225) 242-0342
E-mail: vocations@diobr.org
Web: www.diobr.org

Diocese of Houma-Thibodaux (D065)
PO Box 505, Schriever, LA 70395
Rev. Joey Pilola, Director of
Vocations
(985) 446-2606, Fax: (985) 446-6243
Rev. Mark Toups, Director of
Seminarians
(985) 414-9717, Fax: (985) 876-4171
E-mail: mtoups@htdiocese.org
       crsmith@htdiocese.org
       jpiola@aol.com
Web: www.htdiocese.org/vocations

Diocese of Lafayette (D066)
1408 Carmel Ave.
Lafayette, LA 70501
Rev. Aaron Melanon
(337) 261-5690
E-mail: jamvd123@aol.com
Web: www.dol-louisiana.org

Diocese of Lake Charles (D067)
Very Rev. Aubrey Guilbeau
Cathedral of the Immaculate
Conception
935 Bilbo St.
Lake Charles, LA 70601
(337) 436-7251
E-mail: vocations@lcdiocese.org
Web: www.lcdiocese.org

Archdiocese of New Orleans (D068)
7887 Walmsley Ave.
New Orleans, LA 70125-3496
Rev. Luis Rodriguez
Director of Vocations
Rev. Steve Bruno, Associate Director
of Vocations
(504) 861-6298, Fax: (504) 866-2906
E-mail: vocations@
       archdiocese-no.org
Web: www.vocationsoffice-no.org

Diocese of Shreveport (D069)
3500 Fairfield Ave.
Shreveport, LA 71104
Rev. David Richter
(318) 868-4441; 800-256-1542
Fax: (318) 868-4605
Web: www.dioshpt.org

MAINE
Diocese of Portland, ME (D070)
PO Box 21, Auburn, ME 04212-0021
Rev. Robert Vaillancourt
(207) 773-6471, ext. 7805
E-mail: vocations@portland
       diocese.net
Web: www.portlanddiocese.net

MARYLAND
Archdiocese of Baltimore (D071)
320 Cathedral St.
Baltimore, MD 21201-4415
Rev. Gerard Francik
(410) 547-5426, Fax (410) 234-2953
Associate Vocation Director:
Mr. Andrew Veveiros
E-mail: vocations@archbalt.org
Web: www.archbalt.org/vocations or
      www.becomeapriest.org

MASSACHUSETTS
Archdiocese of Boston (D072)
66 Brooks Dr., Braintree, MA 02184
Rev. Daniel Hennessey
(617) 746-5949, Fax: (617) 746-5468
E-mail: vocations@rcab.org
Web: www.vocationsboston.org

Diocese of Fall River (D073)
Vocation Office, PO Box 2577
Fall River, MA 02722-2577
Rev. Karl C. Bissinger, Director of
Vocations and Seminarians, and
Rev. Kevin A. Cook, Associate
Director of Vocations and
Seminarians
(508) 675-1311, Fax: (508) 679-9220
E-mail: vocations@dioc-fr.org
Web: www.fallrivervocations.org

Diocese of Springfield (D074)
PO Box 1730
Springfield, MA 01102-1730
Rev. Gary M. Dailey
(413) 452-0811, Fax: (413) 452-0678
E-mail: vocations@diospringfield.org
Web: www.myvocation.org

Diocese of Worcester (D075)
Vocation Office
51 Illinois ST., Worcester, MA 01610
Rev. Jim Mazzone, Vocation Director
(508) 340-5788, Fax: (508) 799-2368
Paula Kelleher, SSJ, Vicar for
Religious (Consecrated Life)
(508) 791-7171
E-mail: jmazzone@charter.net
Web: www.worcestervocations.com

MICHIGAN
Archdiocese of Detroit (D076)
2701 W. Chicago Blvd.
Detroit, MI 48206
Rev. Timothy Birney
(313) 237-5875, Fax: (313) 237-6070
E-mail: birney.tim@aod.org
Web: www.vocationsdetroit.org

Diocese of Gaylord (D077)
611 West North St.
Gaylord, MI 49735
Rev. Don Geyman, Delegate for
Vocations
(989) 732-5147, Fax: (989) 705-3532
E-mail: dgeyman@dioceseof
gaylord.org
Web: www.dioceseofgaylord.org

Diocese of Grand Rapids (D078)
Cathedral Square Center
360 Division Avenue S
Grand Rapids, MI 49503
Rev. Ronald D. Hutchinson, Director
of Priestly Vocations
(616) 475-1254
E-mail: rhutchinson@dioceseof
grand rapids.org
Web: www.dioceseofgrandrapids.org

Diocese of Kalamazoo (D079)
215 N. Westnedge Ave.
Kalamazoo, MI 49007-3760
Rev. John D. Fleckenstein
(269) 349-8714, ext. 242
E-mail: vocation@dioceseof
kalamazoo.org
Web: www.dioceseofkalamazoo.org

Diocese of Lansing (D080)
300 W. Ottawa St.
Lansing, MI 48933
Sr. Mary Ann Foggin, SGL
(517) 342-2506, Fax: (517) 342-2515
E-mail: mfoggin@dioceseof
lansing.org
Web: www.dioceseoflansing.org

Diocese of Marquette (D081)
117 W. Washington St.
PO Box 1000, Marquette, MI 49855
Rev. Greg Heikkala
(906) 227-9112, ext. 112
E-mail: gheikkala@dioceseof
marquette.org
Web: www.dioceseofmarquette.org

Diocese of Saginaw (D082)
5800 Weiss St., Saginaw, MI 48603
Bishop Robert J. Carlson
(989) 797-6615
E-mail: mgraveline@dioceseof
saginaw.org
Web: www.dioceseofsaginaw.org

MINNESOTA
Diocese of Crookston (D083)
1200 Memorial Dr.
Crookston, MN 56716
Rev. Vincent Miller, Vocation Director
(218) 444-4262
Rev. August Gothman, Associate
Vocation Director, (218) 281-4533
Vocation Office, (218) 281-4533
E-mail: vocations@crookston.org
Web: www.crookston.org

Diocese of Duluth (D084)
2830 E. 4th St., Duluth, MN 55812
Most Rev. Dennis Schnurr
Associate Directors:
Deacon Michael Knuth and
Rev. Richard Kunst
(218) 568-8226
E-mail: mknuth@dioceseduluth.org
Web: www.dioceseduluth.org

Diocese of New Ulm (D085)
Catholic Pastoral Center
1400 6th St. N.
New Ulm, MN 56073-2099
Rev. Todd Petersen
cell: (507) 227-2657
Blog Site: frtodd.blogspot.com and
ourmib.blogspot.com
Rev. Craig Timmerman, Associate
Director, (507) 233-9501
Sr. Margaret McHugh, DSMP,
Office of Vocations
(507) 359-2966, Fax: (507) 354-3667
E-mail: frtodd@mac.com
Web: www.ourmib.org

Diocese of St. Cloud (D086)
305 7th Ave N. Ste. 100
St. Cloud, MN 56303-3633
Rev. Gregory J. Mastey
(320) 251-5001
E-mail: gmastey@gw.stcdio.org
Web: www.stcdio.org/vocations

Archdiocese of St. Paul & (D087)
Minneapolis
2260 Summit Ave.
St. Paul, MN 55105-1094
Rev. Peter Williams
(651) 962-6890, Fax (651) 962-5790
Religious Life Liaison: Claire Roufs
E-mail: stpaulpriest@10000
vocations.org
Web: www.10000vocations.org

Diocese of Winona (D088)
Office of Vocations, Box 588
Winona, MN 55987
Rev. Thomas Melvin
(507) 454-4643, Fax: (507) 454-8106
E-mail: tmelvin@dow.org
Web: www.dow.org

MISSISSIPPI
Diocese of Biloxi (D089)
Holy Family Parish, PO Box 548
Pass Christian, MS 39571
Rev. Dennis J. Carver, Director
(228) 452-4686
Bragg Moore, Associate Director
(228) 702-2142
Rev. Tommy Conway, Vocations
Director for Irish Seminarians
(601) 736-3136
Rev. Sergio Balderas, Associate
Vocations Director, Hispanics
E-mail:dcarver@holyfamilyparish.cc
Web: www.biloxidiocese.org

Diocese of Jackson (D090)
653 Claiborne Ave.
Jackson, MS 39209-6239
Rev. Kent Bowlds, (601) 944-9844
E-mail: frkent@bellsouth.net
Web: www.jacksonvocations.com

MISSOURI
Diocese of Jefferson City (D091)
www.discoverthepriesthood.org
2207 W. Main St., PO Box 104900
Jefferson City, MO 65110-4900
Rev. Joseph Corel
(573) 635-9127, ext. 211
Fax: (573) 635-2286
E-mail: followme@diojeffcity.org
Web: www.diojeffcity.org/
vocation.htm

Diocese of Kansas City-St. Joseph (D092)
300 E. 36th St.
Kansas City, MO 64141-6037
Rev. Stephen Cook
Rev. Mathew J. Rotert, Secretary for
Seminarians
(816) 756-1850, Fax: (816) 756-0878
E-mail: vocations@diocesekcsj.org
Web: www.diocese-kcsj.org/vocation

Archdiocese of St. Louis (D093)
Office of Vocations
5200 Glennon Dr.
St. Louis, MO 63119
Rev. Msgr. Edward Rice
(314) 792-6461, Fax: (314) 792-6502
E-mail: edwardrice@archstl.org
Web: www.stlvocations.org

Diocese of Springfield- (D094)
Cape Girardeau
601 South Jefferson
Springfield, MO 65806-3143
Rev. J. Friedel
(417) 866-0841, Fax: (417) 866-1140
E-mail: jfriedel@dioscg.org
Web: www.dioscg.org

MONTANA (D095)
Diocese of Great Falls-Billings
PO Box 1399
Great Falls, MT 59403-1399
Rev. Leo McDowell
St. Francis Xavier Church
PO Box 160, Circle, MT 59215-0160
phone & fax: (406) 485-3520
(406) 974-3520 (cell)
Director of Seminarian Formation:
Rev. Jay H. Peterson, V.G., PO Box
1399, Great Falls, MT 59403-1399,
(406) 727-6683, Fax: (406) 454-3480
(406) 899-2698 (cell)
vicargeneral@dioceseofgfb.org
E-mail: vocations@frleo.org
Web: www.dioceseofgfb.org

Diocese of Helena (D096)
515 N. Ewing, Helena, MT 59601
Rev. Thomas Donnell
(406) 227-5334, ext. 106
Rev. Msgr. Kevin S. O'Neill, VG,
Director of Seminarians
St. Helena Cathedral, 530 No.
Ewing, Helena, MT 59601
(406) 442-5825
Rev. Eric Gilbaugh, Borromeo
Discernment Program
St. Helena Cathedral, 530 No.
Ewing, Helena, MT 59601
(406) 442-5825,
ericgilbaugh@hotmail.com
E-mail: thomas@sscyril.org
Web: www.diocesehelena.org/
vocations

NEBRASKA
Diocese of Grand Island (D097)
PO Box 1024
Kearney, NE 68848-1024
Rev. Jose M. Chavez
(308) 234-1539
E-mail: givocationsoffice@
hotmail.com
Web: www.gidiocese.org or
www.givocationsoffice.net

Diocese of Lincoln (D098)
St. Thomas Aquinas Church
Newman Center, 320 N. 16th St.
Lincoln, NE 68508
Rev. Robert A. Matya
(402) 474-7914, Fax: (402) 476-2620
E-mail: frmatya@usa.net
Web: www.dioceseoflincoln.org

Archdiocese of Omaha (D099)
100 North 62nd St.
Omaha, NE 68132
Rev. Paul C. Hoesing
888-303-2484, (402) 558-3100
Fax: (402) 558-3026
E-mail: vocations@archomaha.org
Web: www.omahapriests.org

NEVADA
Diocese of Las Vegas (D100-1)
PO Box 18316
Las Vegas, NV 89114-8316
Rev. Mugagga Lule
(702) 735-6044, fax: (702) 697-5917
E-mail: frmugaggalule@yahoo.com
Web: www.lasvegas-diocese.org

Diocese of Reno (D100-2)
290 South Arlington Ave., Ste. 200
Reno, NV 89501
Rev. Paul McCollum
(775) 326-9425, Fax: (775) 348-8619
E-mail: Vocations@catholicreno.org
Web: www.vocationsreno.com

NEW HAMPSHIRE
Diocese of Manchester (D101)
153 Ash St., PO Box 310
Manchester, NH 03104
Rev. Jason Y. Jalbert
(603) 669-3100, ext. 132
E-mail: jjalbert@rcbm.org
Web: www.liveinblackandwhite.com

NEW JERSEY
Diocese of Camden (D102)
631 Market St., Camden, NJ 08102
Rev. James J. Durkin
(856) 583-6170, Fax: (856) 583-1046
E-mail: jdurkin@camdendiocese.org
Web: www.camdendiocese.org

Diocese of Metuchen (D103)
The St. John Neumann Pastoral
Center
146 Metlars Lane
Piscataway, NJ 08854
Rev. Randall J. Vashon
(732) 562-2457
E-mail: vocations@diometuchen.org
Web: www.diometuchen.org/
vocations

Archdiocese of Newark (D104)
171 Clifton Ave., PO Box 9500
Newark, NJ 07104-0500
Rev. John D. Gabriel, Director of
Vocations (973) 497-4365; 4367;
4368, Fax: (973) 497-4369
E-mail: gabriejo@rcan.org
Web: www.rcan.org/vocation/
contactus.htm

Diocese of Paterson (D105)
737 Valley Rd., Clifton, NJ 07013
Rev. Thomas Fallone, Director of
Vocations
Rev. T. Kevin Corcoran, Assistant
Director of Vocations
(973) 777-2955, Fax (973) 777-4597
E-mail: vocationdirector@paterson
diocese.org
Web: www.patersondiocese.org

Diocese of Trenton (D106)
701 Lawrenceville Rd.
Trenton, NJ 08648
Rev. Msgr. Gregory Vaughan
(609) 406-7400, ext. 5698
Web: www.Godiscallingyou.com

NEW MEXICO
Diocese of Gallup (D107)
Vocations Office, PO Box 1388
Gallup, NM 87305
Rev. Matthew Keller
1-888-PRIESTHOOD
E-mail: gallupvocationsoffice@
gmail.com
Web: www.gallupvocationsoffice.
blogspot.com

Diocese of Las Cruces (D108)
1280 Med Park Dr.
Las Cruces, NM 88005
Rev. Marcos Reyna
Rev. Raymond Flores
(575) 523-7577, Fax: (575) 524-3874
E-mail: pastoralcenter@dioceseof
lascruces.org
Web: www.dioceseoflascruces.org

Archdiocese of Santa Fe (D109)
Catholic Center
4000 St. Joseph's Pl. NW
Albuquerque, NM 87120
Rev. Michael DePalma
(505) 831-8143, (505) 892-1997
E-mail: padremiked@aol.com
Web: www.santafevocations.org

NEW YORK
Diocese of Albany (D110)
Vocation Office
40 N. Main Ave.
Albany, NY 12203-2203
Sr. Rosemary Ann Cuneo, CR
rosemary.cuneo@rcda.org
Rev. David Lefort
E-mail: FrDavid@nycap.rr.com

Rev. James Walsh
E-mail: jjwalshie@aol.com
(518) 312-9397, (518) 674-3818
Web: www.albanyvocations.org

Diocese of Brooklyn (D111)
Vocation Office, 341 Highland Blvd.
Brooklyn, NY 11207
Rev. Kevin J. Sweeney
Director of Vocations
(718) 827-2454
E-mail: vocations@diobrook.org
Web: www.dioceseofbrooklyn.org/
vocations

Diocese of Buffalo (D112)
Catholic Center, 795 Main St.
Buffalo, NY 14203-1215
Rev. Walter J. Szczesny
(716) 847-5535
E-mail: wszczesny@
buffalodiocese .org
Web: www.buffalovocations.org

Archdiocese of New York (D113)
St. Joseph's Seminary, 201
Seminary Ave., Yonkers, NY 10704
Rev. Luke Sweeney, S.T. L.
Rev. Luis Saldana, S.T.D., (Cand.),
Assistant Director for Hispanics
(914) 968-1340, Fax: (914) 968-6671
Catholic Center: Sr. Deanna
Sabetta, CND, Vocations to the
Religious Life, 1011 First Ave.
18th Fl., New York, NY 10022
(212) 371-1011, ext. 2803
E-mail: vocations@archny.org
Web: www.nypriest.com

Diocese of Ogdensburg (D114)
PO Box 369, 622 Washington St.
Ogdensburg, NY 13669
Rev. Douglas J. Lucia
Rev. Bryan D. Stitt, Associate
Vocation Director
(315) 393-2920
E-mail: dlucia@dioogdensburg.org
Web: www.myvocation.net

Diocese of Rochester (D115)
Office of Priesthood Vocation
Awareness, 1150 Buffalo Rd.
Rochester, NY 14624
Rev. Timothy Horan, Director
Carol Dady, Coordinator
(585) 461-2890
E-mail: cdady@dor.org
Web: www.dor.org

Diocese of Rockville Centre (D116)
440 West Neck Rd.
Huntington, NY 11743
Rev. Brian Barr
(631) 424-9888, Fax: (631) 424-9889
Program Coordinator: Rosemary
Sullivan, (631) 424-9888
E-mail: rsullivan@drvc.org
vocations@drvc.org
Web: www.drvc.org

Diocese of Syracuse (D117)
240 E. Onondaga St., PO Box 511
Syracuse, NY 13201-0511
Rev. Joseph O'Connor, Office of
Vocation Promotion
(315) 470-1468
E-mail: joconnor@
syracusediocese .org
Web: www.vocations-syracuse.org

NORTH CAROLINA
Diocese of Charlotte (D118)
1123 S. Church St.
Charlotte, NC 28203-4003
Rev. Christopher M. Gober, (704)
370-3353 Fax: (704) 370-3379
E-mail: cmgober@
charlottediocese .org
Web: www.charlottediocese.org

Diocese of Raleigh (D119)
Office of Vocations
226 Hillsborough St. Raleigh, NC
27603, Rev. B. Edward (Ned)
Shlesinger, III 919-832-6280
E-mail: shlesinger@raldioc.org
Web: www.dioceseofraleigh.org

NORTH DAKOTA
Diocese of Bismarck (D120)
PO Box 1137
Bismarck, ND 58502-1137
Rev. Thomas J. Richter
(701) 222-3035, (701) 391-0283 (cell)
E-mail: frrichter@
bismarckdiocese .com
Web: www.bismarckvocations.com

Diocese of Fargo (D121)
100 35th Ave. N.E.
Fargo, ND 58102-1299
(701) 271-1205
E-mail: vocations@fargodiocese.org
Web: www.fargodiocese.org/
vocations/ index.htm

OHIO
Archdiocese of Cincinnati (D122)
100 E. Eighth St., Cincinnati, OH
45202, Rev. Kyle Schnippel
(513) 421-3131, Fax (513) 421-6225
E-mail: vocations@catholic
cincinnati.org
Web: www.cincinnativocations.org

Diocese of Cleveland (D123)
1404 East Ninth St. 2nd Fl.
Cleveland, OH 44114
Coordinators: Rev. Michael Gurnick,
(216) 696-6525, ext. 3410
Sr. Lenore Thomas, IHM
(216) 696-6525. ext.3460
E-mail: mgurnick@
dioceseofcleveland.org;
lthomas@diocesesofcleveland.org
Web: www.churchvocations.com;
www.clevelandcatholic
priesthood. com

Diocese of Columbus (D124)
197 E. Gay St.
Columbus, OH 43215
Rev. Jeffrey Coning
(614) 221-5565, Fax (614) 241-2572
E-mail: frjeff@seekholiness.com
Web: www.seekholiness.com

Diocese of Steubenville (D125)
Holy Name House of Formation
411 S. Fifth St.
Steubenville, OH 43952
Rev. Timothy J. Shannon
(740) 282-0646
Assistant Directors of Vocations:
Rev. Daniel Heusel
dheusel@diosteub.org
(740) 282-3631
Rev. Jason Prati
frprati@msn.org, (740) 282-3631
Rev. Mark Moore, (740) 264-4880
E-mail: diosteubhof@sbcglobal.net
Web: www.diosteub.org

Diocese of Toledo (D126)
1933 Spielbusch Ave., PO Box 985
Toledo, OH 43697-0985
Rev. Adam Hertzfeld, Director of
Vocations; Mrs. Yvonne Dubielak,
Associate Director of Vocations
(419) 244-6711 Fax: (419) 244-4791
E-mail: ahertzfeld@
toledodiocese.org or
ydubielak@toledodiocese.org
Web: www.toledovocations.com

Diocese of Youngstown (D127)
144 W. Wood St., Youngstown, OH
44503, Rev. Leo J. Wehrlin
(330) 744-8451
E-mail: lwehrlin@youngstown
diocese.org
Web: www.youngstownvocations.org

OKLAHOMA (D128)
Archdiocese of Oklahoma City
PO Box 32180
Oklahoma City, OK 73123
Rev. Lowell Stieferman
(405) 721-5651, ext. 114
E-mail: jmulligan@
catharchdiocese okc.org
Web: www.catharchdioceseokc.org

Diocese of Tulsa (D129)
St. Philip Neri Newman Center
440 S. Florence Ave.
Tulsa, OK 74104-2436
Rev. Matthew Gerlach
Vocation Director
Rev. David Medina, Assistant
Vocations Director (Spanish)
Ms. Theresa Witcher, Seminarians
Mr. Wayne Rziha, Director of
Recruitment & Promotion
(918) 599-0204, Fax: (918) 587-0115
E-mail: tulvoc@aol.com
Web: www.dioceseoftulsa.org

OREGON

Diocese of Baker (D130)
PO Box 5999, Bend, OR 97708
Rev. James Radloff, (541) 388-4004
E-mail: frradloff@
dioceseofbaker .org
Web: www.dioceseofbaker.org

Archdiocese of Portland (D131)
2838 E. Burnside St.
Portland, OR 97214
Rev. Kelly M. Vandehey (503) 233-8368 Fax: (503) 230-1477
E-mail: kvandehey@archdpdx.org

PENNSYLVANIA

Diocese of Allentown (D132)
PO Box F, Allentown, PA 18105-1538
Rev. Michael E. Mullins,
(610) 437-0755, Fax: (610) 433-7822
Web: www.beapriest.com

Diocese of Altoona-Johnstown (D133)
Prince Gallitzin Chapel House
357 St. Mary St., PO Box 99
Loretto, PA 15940-0099
Rev. Brian R. Saylor
(814) 472-5441, Fax: (814) 472-5446
E-mail: bsaylor@dioceseaj.org
Web: www.ajdiocese.org

Diocese of Erie (D134)
St. Mark Catholic Center
429 E. Grandview Blvd
PO Box 10397
Erie, PA 16514-0397
Rev. Edward M. Lohse
(800) 374-3723, (814) 824-1200
Fax (814) 824-1181
Associate Vocation Director:
Rev. Stephen J. Schreiber,
E-mail: sschreiber17@gmail.com
vocations@eriercd.org
Web: www.erievocations.org

Diocese of Greensburg (D135)
Office of Clergy Vocations
723 E. Pittsburgh St.
Greensburg, PA 15601
Rev. Larry J. Kulick, Director of
Clergy Vocations
(724) 837-0901, Fax (724) 837-0857
E-mail: lkulick@dioceseofgreens
burg.org
Web: www.dioceseofgreensburg.org

Diocese of Harrisburg (D136)
4800 Union Deposit Rd.
Harrisburg, PA 17105-2161
Rev. Raymond J. LaVoie
(717) 657-4804, ext. 282
Fax: (717) 657-4042
E-mail: vocations@hbgdiocese.org
Web: www.hbgdiocese.org/vocations

Archdiocese of Philadelphia (D137)
St. Charles Borromeo Seminary
100 East Wynnewood Rd.
Wynnewood, PA 19096-3028
Rev. Christopher B. Rogers
(610) 667-5778
E-mail: frcrogers@adphila.org
Web: www.heedthecall.org

Diocese of Pittsburgh (D138)
Saint Paul Seminary
2900 Noblestown Rd.
Pittsburgh, PA 15205
Rev. Msgr. Edward Burns
Director of Vocations - Rector
(412) 456-3048, Fax: (412) 456-3187
E-mail: vocations@diopitt.org
Web: www.diopitt.org

Diocese of Scranton (D139)
300 Wyoming Ave.
Scranton, PA 18503
Most Rev. Joseph F. Martino, D.D.,
Hist.E.D., Bishop of Scranton
Assistant Director:
Rev. Christopher Sahd
(570) 207-2226
Fax: (570) 207-2236
E-mail: Rev-Christopher-Sahd@
dioceseofscranton.org
Web: www.dioceseofscranton.org

RHODE ISLAND

Diocese of Providence (D140)
485 Mt. Pleasant Ave.
Providence, RI 02908
Rev. Michael J. Najim
(401) 831-8011
Sr. Jacqueline Dickey, S.S.Ch.,
Associate Director for Religious
One Cathedral Square, Providence,
RI 02903, (401) 278-4633
Web: www.catholicpriest.com

SOUTH CAROLINA

Diocese of Charleston (D141)
1662 Ingram Rd.
Charleston, SC 29407
Rev. Mr. Joseph F. Cahill, Director,
Office of Vocations
(800) 660-4102
(843) 402-9115, ext. 22
Fax (843) 402-9071
E-mail: joe@catholic-doc.org
Web: www.catholic-doc.org/
vocations

SOUTH DAKOTA

Diocese of Rapid City (D142)
PO Box 678, Rapid City, SD 57709
Rev. Brian P. Christensen
(605) 343-3541
E-mail: Godscall@diorc.org
Web: www.Gods-call.org

Diocese of Sioux Falls (D143)
523 N. Duluth Ave.
Sioux Falls, SD 57104
Rev. James Mason
(605) 336-8808, Fax: (605) 338-3729
E-mail: jmason@sfcatholic.org
Web: www.diocese-of-sioux-falls.org

TENNESSEE

Diocese of Knoxville (D144)
805 Northshore Drive SW
Knoxville, TN 37919
Rev. Peter Iorio, Director, (423) 290-3963; Rev. Michael Cummins,
Associate Vocation Director (for
promotion)
(423) 507-7072,
E-mail: frmc@charter.net
fatherpeteiorio@aol.com
Web: www.dioceseofknoxville.org

Diocese of Memphis (D145)
Cathedral of the Immaculate
Conception, 1695 Central Ave.
Memphis, TN 38104
Rev. Keith Stewart
Office of Vocations
St. Anne, 706 South Highland St.
Memphis, TN 38111 (901) 484-2883
Web: www.cdom.org

Diocese of Nashville (D146)
Vocation Office: 14544 Lebanon
Road, Old Hickory, TN 37138
Tom Samoray, Vocation Awareness
Young Adult Ministry, (615) 754-4107
E-mail: tsamoray@comcast.net
Web: www.NashvillePriest.com

TEXAS

Diocese of Amarillo (D147)
1800 N. Spring St., PO Box 5644
Amarillo, TX 79117-5644
Rev. Mike Colwell, JCL
(806) 383-2243, Fax: (806) 383-8452
E-mail: mcolwell@
amarillodiocese .org
Web: www.amarillodiocese.org

Diocese of Austin (D148)
PO Box 13327, Austin, TX 78711
Rev. Mike Sis
(512) 476-4888, Fax: (512) 469-9537
E-mail: fr-mike-sis@
austindiocese .org
Web: www.austindiocese.org/vocations

Diocese of Beaumont (D149)
1010 E. Virginia
Beaumont, TX 77710-7710
Rev. Shane Baxter
(409) 835-5037 or 924-4361
Fax: (409) 832-4129
E-mail: vocationsandcampus@
dioceseofbmt.org
Web: www.dioceseofbmt.org/
vocations

B-9

Diocese of Brownsville (D150)
700 North Virgen de San Juan Blvd
San Juan, TX 78589
Rev. Ignacio Tapia
(956) 781-5323, Fax: (956) 784-5081
E-mail: itapia@cdob.org
Web: www.cdob.org/vocations

Diocese of Corpus Christi (D151)
PO Box 2620
Corpus Christi, TX 78402
Rev. James Stembler
(361) 882-6191, ext. 683
Fax: (361) 882-1018
E-mail: jstembler@diocesecc.org or
vocations@diocesecc.org
Web: www.goccn.org/diocese/depts/
vocations

Diocese of Dallas (D152)
3725 Blackburn St., PO Box 190507
Dallas, TX 75219
Rev. Rodolfo Garcia
Director of Vocations
Sharon Rodriguez
Administrative Assistant
(214) 379-2860, Fax: (214) 521-0258
Rev. Anthony Lackland
Associate Director of Vocations
Daniel diSilva
Programs Coordinator
1814 Egyptian Way, PO Box 530959
Grand Prairie, TX 75050
(972) 641-4496
E-mail: rgarcia@cathdal.org
alackland@cathdal.org
ddisilva@cathdal.org
srodriguez@cathdal.org
Web: www.cathdal.org

Diocese of El Paso (D153)
499 St. Matthews St.
El Paso, TX 79907
Rev. Ben Flores
Facilitator, Vocations Office
(915) 872-8400
Web: www.elpasodiocese.org/
directory.htm

Diocese of Fort Worth (D154)
800 W. Loop 820 South
Fort Worth, TX 76108-2919
Rev. Kyle Walterscheid
(817) 560-3300, ext. 110
E-mail: kwalterscheid@fwdioc.org
Web: www.fwdioc.org

(D155)
Archdiocese of Galveston-Houston
1700 San Jacinto St.
Houston, TX 77002
Rev. Dat Hoang
Director of Vocations
Sr. Pauline Troncale CCVI
Associate Director of Vocations
(713) 652-8239, Fax: (713) 759-9151
E-mail: vocations@archgh.org
ptroncale@archgh.org
Web: www.archgh.org

Diocese of Lubbock (D156)
Catholic Pastoral Center
PO Box 98700
Lubbock, TX 79499-8700
Rev. Rene Perez, Rev. Martin Pina,
Rev. Ernesto Lopez
(806) 792-3943 ext. 230
E-mail: fr_reneperez@yahoo.com
Web: www.catholiclubbock.org/
vocations.htm

Diocese of San Angelo (D157)
804 Ford St., San Angelo, TX 76905
Rev. Barry Mclean
(325) 651-7500, Fax: (325) 651-6688
E-mail: frbarrymclean@aol.com
Web: www.san-angelo-diocese.org

Archdiocese of San Antonio (D158)
2600 W. Woodlawn Ave.
San Antonio, TX 78228-5196
Rev. Arturo Cepeda, STD
(210) 735-0553
Fax: (210) 734-4942
E-mail: acepeda@archdiosa.org
Web: www.savocations.org

Diocese of Tyler (D159)
1015 ESE Loop 323
Tyler, TX 75701-9663
Rev. Jesus R. Arroyave
(903) 534-1077, ext.171
Fax: (903) 534-1370
E-mail: vocationsoffice@
dioceseoftyler .org
Web: www.dioceseoftyler.org

Diocese of Victoria in Texas (D160)
PO Box 4070
Victoria, TX 77903-4070
Rev. Dan Morales
(361) 552-6140, Fax: (361) 552-4300
E-mail: olgulf@aol.com
Web: www.victoriadiocese.org/
vocation/vocational.htm

UTAH

Diocese of Salt Lake City (D161)
27 C St., Salt Lake City, UT 84103
Rev. Colin F. Bircumshaw
(801) 328-8641, Fax: (801) 328-9680
E-mail: cfbmann@utahweb.com
Web: www.dioslc.org

VERMONT

Diocese of Burlington (D162)
The Newman Center at UVM
390 South Prospect St.
Burlington, VT 05401-3534
Rev. Daniel E. White
(802) 862-8403
E-mail: catholic@uvm.edu
Web: www.vermontcatholic.org

VIRGINIA

Diocese of Arlington (D163)
200 N. Glebe Rd., Ste. 901
Arlington, VA 22203
Rev. Brian Bashista
(703) 841-2514
Fax (703) 841-8472
E-mail: vocations@
arlingtondiocese .org
Web: www.arlingtondiocese.org/
offices/ vocations

(D164)
Diocese of Richmond
7800 Carousel Lane
Richmond, VA 23294-4201
Rev. Michael A. Renninger
Vicar for Priestly Vocations
(804) 359-5661, ext. 207
E-mail: mrenninger@richmond
diocese.org
Web: www.richmonddiocese.org/
vocations

WASHINGTON

Archdiocese of Seattle (D165)
710 9th Ave., Seattle, WA 98104
Richard Shively
(206) 382-4595, Fax (206) 654-4654
E-mail: richs@seattlearch.org
Web: www.seattlearch.org

Diocese of Spokane (D166)
Bishop White Seminary
429 E. Sharp Ave.
Spokane, WA 99202-1857
Rev. Darrin Connall
(509) 326-3761 (phone/fax)
E-mail: vocations@dioceseof
spokane.org
Web: www.dioceseofspokane.org/
Vocations/Index.htm

Diocese of Yakima (D167)
5301A Tieton Drive
Yakima, WA 98908
Rev. Juan Flores and Rev. Wilmar
Zabala, (509) 965-7117
E-mail: info@yakimadiocese.org
Web: www.yakimadiocese.org

WEST VIRGINIA (D168)
Diocese of Wheeling-Charleston
1310 Byron St.
Wheeling, WV 26003
Rev. Paul Hudock
(304) 233-0880, ext.235
Fax: (304) 233-4086
E-mail: phudock@dwc.org
Web: www.dwc.org

WISCONSIN

Diocese of Green Bay (D169)
PO Box 23825
Green Bay, WI 54305-3825
Rev. W. Thomas Long
(920) 272-8293
E-mail: vocations@gbdioc.org
Web: www.gbdioc.org

Diocese of La Crosse (D170)
3710 East Ave. South, Box 4004
La Crosse, WI 54602-4004
Rev. Joseph Hirsch (608) 791-2666
Fax: (608) 788-8413
E-mail: jhirsch@dioceseof
lacrosse.com
Web: www.dioceseoflacrosse.com

Diocese of Madison (D171)
Bishop O'Connor Catholic Pastoral
Center
702 South High Point Rd.
Madison, WI 53719-4999
Rev. James Bartylla, Vocations
Director; Lorie Ballweg,
Administrative Assistant, 800-833-
8452, (608) 821-3088 Fax: (608)
821-3090
E-mail: vocations@straphael.org
Web: www.madisonvocations.org

Archdiocese of Milwaukee (D172)
3257 S. Lake Dr.
St. Francis, WI 53235
Rev. James E. Lobacz
Director, Vocation Office
Janice Sikora-Tabat
Vocations Services Coordinator
(414) 747-6437
E-mail: vocations@sfs.edu
Web: www.thinkpriest.org
www.archmil.org or www.sfs.edu

Diocese of Superior (D173)
St. Francis deSales
409 Summit St., Spooner, WI 54801
Rev. Andrew Ricci
(715) 635-3105, Fax: (715) 635-7341
E-mail: paparicci@gmail.com
Web: www.SuperiorVocations.org

WYOMING

Diocese of Cheyenne (D174)
Vocation Office
1800 E. Grand Ave.
Laramie, WY 82070
Rev. Raymond P. Rodriguez
(307) 745-5461
Web: www.dioceseofcheyenne.org

TERRITORIAL SEES

AMERICAN SAMOA
(D175)
Diocese of Samoa-Pago Pago
PO Box 596, PagoPago
American Samoa, 96799
Rev.Kolio Etuale
Director of Vocations
011-684-699-1402
Fax: 011-684-699-1459
E-mail: quinn@samoatelco.com

CAROLINE MARSHALL ISLANDS
(D176)
Diocese of the Caroline Islands
Vicariate Residence
PO Box 939, Chuuk, Tunnuk,
Caroline Islands, FM 96942
Rev. Julio Angkel
011-691-330-2313
E-mail: diocese@mail.fm
Web: www.dioceseofthecarolines.org

GUAM
Archdiocese of Agana (D177)
196 B Cuesta San Ramon
Agana, Guam 96910
Co-directors: Rev. Adrian Cristobal
and Rev. James Benavente
011-671-472-6116
Fax: 011-671-477-3519
www.guam.net/pub/archdiocese

MARIANA ISLANDS
Diocese of Chalan Kanoa (D178)
PO Box 500745, Saipan, MP 96950
Rev. Florentino "Nono" E. Recaido, Jr.,
01-670-322-2404
Fax: 01-670-235-3002
E-mail: nonoyerecaidojr@
hotmail.com or
nonoy_recaido@yahoo.com

PUERTO RICO
Diocese of Arecibo (D179)
Seminary of Jesus the Teacher
PO Box 2164, Arecibo, PR 613
Rev. Ovidio P erez
(787) 878-1528
E-mail: jesusmaestro1@gmail.com

Diocese of Caguas (D180)
PO Box 8698
Caguas, PR 726
Rev.Jose A. De Leon, Vicar of
Vocation
Rev. Floyd Mercado, Preseminarian
Director (787) 747-5885, ext. 243
Fax: (787) 857-3585

Diocese of Mayaguez (D181)
PO Box 2272, Mayaguez, PR 681
Rev. Orlando Rosas, Rev. Delray
Thomas Scott, Rev. Edgar Carlo,
Office of Vocations
(787) 833-5411

Diocese of Ponce (D182)
PO Box 32110
Ponce, PR 00732-2110
Rev. Msgr. Elias S. Morales
Rodriguez, Vocation Director/Rector
of Seminarians
Rev. Julio Rolon Torres, Spiritual
Director and Administrator
(787) 812-3024
phone & fax: (787) 848-4380
E-mail: meliasalvador@hotmail.com
Web: www.reginacleri.com

Archdiocese of San Juan (D183)
PO Box 11714
San Juan, PR 00922-1714
Rev. Msgr. Iván L. Huertas,
Vocations Vicar, (787) 706-9455
E-mail: vocaciones@arqsj.org
Web: www.arqsj.org

VIRGIN ISLANDS
(D184)
Diocese of St. Thomas in the Virgin Islands
Sts. Peter and Paul Cathedral
PO Box 301767
St. Thomas, VI 00803-1767
Very Rev. Neil Scantlebury
(340) 774-0201
E-mail: chancery@islands.vi
Web: www.catholicvi.com

EASTERN RITE DIOCESE
(D185)
Byzantine Catholic Eparchy of Van Nuys
c/o Holy Angels Byzantine Catholic
Church, 2235 Galahad Rd.
San Diego, CA 92123-3931
Rev. Robert M. Pipta
(858) 277-2511, Fax (858) 277-5792
Rev. Michael O'Loughlin, Asst.
Vocation Director, (303) 778-8283
E-mail: rmp.byzcath@juno.com
Web: www.eparchy-of-van-nuys.org

Eparchy of Newton (D186)
(Melkite-Greek Catholic)
3 VFW Pkwy., Roslindale, MA 2131
Rt. Rev. Philip Raczka
8525 Cole Ave., Warren, MI 48093
(586) 751-6017

B-11

Eparchy of Stamford (D187)
14 Peveril Rd.
Stamford, CT 06902-3019
Rev. Bohdan J. Danylo
(203) 324-7698
E-mail: vocstamford@netscape.net
Web: www.stbasilcollegesem.net

Diocese of St. Nicholas (D188)
in Chicago for Ukrainians
2245 W. Rice St.
Chicago, IL 60622-4858
Most Rev. Richard Seminack, D.D.
(773) 276-5080, Fax: (773) 276-6799
E-mail: sneparchy@iols.com

Byzantine Catholic Eparchy (D189)
of Passaic
St. Nicholas Byzantine Catholic
Church, 5135 Sand Lake Road
Orlando, FL 32819
Rev. Salvatore Pignato
E-mail: PassaicVocations@
  bellsouth.net

Byzantine Catholic Eparchy (D190)
of Parma
1900 Carlton Rd., Parma, OH 44134
Very Rev. Archpriest

Dennis M. Hrubiak
(216) 741-8773, Fax: (216) 741-9356
E-mail: fdhrubiak@yahoo.com
Web: www.parma.org

Ukrainian Catholic Eparchy (D191)
of St. Josaphat in Parma, Ohio
Pastoral Ministry Office
727 East Carson Street
Pittsburgh, PA 44055
Rev. Dr. Mark M. Morozowich,
Associate Dean for Seminary and
Ministerial Program
The School of Theology and
Religious Studies
The Catholic University of America,
Washington, DC 20064
(202) 319-6512 fax: (202) 319-4967
E-mail: Morozowich@cua.edu

Byzantine Catholic (D192)
Archeparchy of Pittsburgh
66 Riverview Avenue
Pittsburgh, PA 15214
Rev. Dennis M. Bogda
(412) 231-4000, ext. 20
Fax: (412) 231-1697
E-mail: vocations@archeparchy.org
Web: www.archeparchy.org

Metropolitan Archdiocese (D193)
of Philadelphia-Ukrainian
827 N. Franklin St.
Philadelphia, PA 19123-2097
Rev. Robert Hitchens, Office of
Vocations
(215) 627-0143, Fax: (215) 627-0377
E-mail: ukrmet@catholic.org or
  vocations@ukrarcheparchy.us
Web: www.ukrarcheparchy.com

Eparchy of Our Lady of (D194)
Lebanon
c/o St. Maron Church
600 University Ave. NE
Minneapolis, MN 55413
Rev. Sharbel G. Maroun
(612) 379-2758, Fax: (612) 379-7647
E-mail: abouna@stmaron.com

Eparchy of St. Maron (D195)
of Brooklyn
Our Lady of Lebanon Cathedral, 113
Remsen St., Brooklyn, NY 11201
Very Rev. James A. Root
(412) 278-0841, Fax: (412) 278-0846
Web: www.stmaron.org

Archdiocese for the Military Services

The Archdiocese for the Military Services, found wherever military personnel or diplomatic personnel are serving, is located in the Arctic Circle in Greenland and Alaska, at Antarctica, in Asia, Europe, Africa, the Far East, the Mideast, South America, and in almost every state; it serves Catholics in the Army, Navy, Air Force, Marine Corps, Coast Guard, Veterans Administration and Government Service Overseas. Its priests are loaned to the Archdiocese from almost every American diocese and from many religious institutes. For more information on serving as a priest in the military, write or call:

Rev. John McLaughlin, Jr., Vocations Office
Archdiocese for the Military Services
P.O. Box 4469, Washington, DC 20017-0469,
(202) 269-9100
Fax: (202) 269-9022,
E-mail: info@milarch.org
Web: www.milarch.org

B-12

*A man can have no greater love
then to lay down his life for his friends.
You are my friends,
if you do what I command you.
I shall not call you servants any more,
because a servant does not know
his master's business;
I call you friends,
because I have made known to you
everything I have learnt from my Father.
You did not choose me,
no, I chose you;
and I commissioned you
to go out and to bear fruit,
fruit that will last;
and then the Father will give you
anything you ask him in my name.
What I command you
is to love one another.*

John 15:13-17

Pray and Work
for Justice and Peace

Religious Communities for Men

ADORNO FATHERS (CRM) (M001)
(Clerics Regular Minor)
St. Michael's Seminary
575 Darlington Ave., Ramsey, NJ
07446, 201-327-7375
Web: www.adornofathers.org
Email: nickcapetola@cs.com
Conduct: 3 parishes, 1 house of studies.
Apostolic Work: Parish work, retreats, teaching, missions and chaplaincies
Representation: Archdiocese of Newark and in the Diocese of Charleston. Also in Italy, Germany, Congo (Africa), India and the Philippines
Vocation Director: Rev. Melvin Avilla, CRM; Superior/Rector: Rev. Nicholas Capetola, CRM

SOCIETY OF AFRICAN (M002)
MISSIONS (S.M.A.)
American Provincialate
23 Bliss Ave., Tenafly, NJ 07670
Web: www.smafathers.org
Email: deaconkm@smafathers.org, vocations@smafathers.org
Conduct: An international community of priests and lay missionaries in service of the peoples of Africa and those of African origin. Pastoral work, education, health care, formation of local clergy and lay leaders, social and agricultural development, Justice & Peace ministry, care for refugees, AIDS ministry and education, ministry among street children and handicapped people
Representation: (Arch)dioceses of Boston, Newark and Washington, DC. Missions in Angola, Benin, Central African Republic, Cote D'Ivoire, Democratic Republic of Congo, Egypt, Ghana, Kenya, Liberia, Morocco, Niger, Nigeria, Republic of the Congo, South Africa, Tanzania, Togo and Zambia
Vocation Director: Deacon Keith McKnight, SMA , 888-250-4333 (toll-free); Ms. Theresa Hicks, Director/Lay Missionaries, Society of African Missions, 256 North

Manor Circle, Takoma Park, MD
20912, (301) 891-2037
fax: (301) 270-6370,
SMAAssociation@comcast.net

ALEXIAN BROTHERS (M003-1)
(C.F.A.) (Immaculate Conception Province) 3040 West Salt Creek Lane, Arlington Heights, IL 60005
Web: www.alexianbrothers.org
Email: dmccormick@alexian.net
        emapa@alexianbrothers.net
Members: 34 Brothers
Conduct: 2 medical centers, 2 life care centers, 1 behavioral health hospital, 2 nursing homes, 1 rehabilitation hospital, 2 PACE programs, 2 AIDS ministries, 2 novitiates
Apostolic Work: Housing and all aspects of the health care field
Representation: Archdioceses of Chicago, St. Louis and Milwaukee and in the Dioceses of Knoxville, Davao, Philippines and Gyor, Hungary
Vocation Director: Bro. Daniel McCormick, C.F.A., 800-556-0332
Asst. Vocation Director: Bro. Exequiel Mapa, C.F.A.

THE APOSTLES OF (M003-2)
JESUS (A.J.) 829 Main St., Northampton, PA 18067-1838
Web: www.apostlesofJesus.org
Email: worldaj@email.com
Members: 48 Priests in US
Apostolic Work: New evangelization of Africa and the world; the service of the spiritual, pastoral and social welfare of all people with preference to the poor, in the spirit of Christ who came to serve and not be served. (Mt. 20:28)
Representation: 16 states including the Archdiocese of New York and the Diocese of Allentown. In Europe and in Africa (Ethiopia, Kenya, South Africa, Sudan, Tanzania and Uganda)
Vocation Director: Contact: Rev. Paul O. Gaggawala, A.J., (610) 502-1732, fax: (610) 502-1733

ASSUMPTIONISTS (A.A.) (M004)
(Augustinians of the Assumption)
General House: Rome
US Provincial House
330 Market St., Brighton, MA 02135
Web: www.assumption.us
Email: jlfranck@aol.com
Members: 50 Priests, 15 Brothers
Apostolic Work: Teaching (college), parishes, ecumenical work, foreign missions, campus ministry, chaplaincies, journalism, youth work, administration, preaching
Representation: (Arch)dioceses of Boston, New York and Worcester. Also in Greece, Italy, Kenya, Korea, Mexico, the Philippines, and Tanzania
Vocation Director: Fr. John L. Franck, A.A., 512 Salisbury Street, Worcester, MA 01609, (508) 767-7517

ATONEMENT FRIARS (SA) (M005)
(Franciscan Friars of the Atonement)
PO Box 300, Garrison, NY 10524
Web: www.atonementfriars
        vocations.org
Email: vocdirector@atonement
        friars.org
Members: 78 Friar-Priests, 39 Friar-Brothers, 6 men in Formation, 1 Tertiary
Conduct: 4 US and 2 Canadian parishes; 1 retreat and conference center; 1 shelter for homeless and needy men; 2 alcohol and drug rehabilitation centers; 1 library (Rome); 2 ecumenical centers (New York, Rome); 3 houses of formation; 1 novitiate
Apostolic Work: Ecumenical ministry (annual Week of Prayer for Christian Unity; ecumenical centers in U.S. and Rome; ecumenical agency staffing: U.S., Rome and London; ecumenical publications); alcohol and drug rehabilitation; parishes in the US, Canada, Japan and Rome; institutional chaplaincies (hospitals and prisons); AIDS ministries
Representation: Archdioceses of Boston, Los Angeles, New York,

and Washington, DC, and in the Dioceses of Arlington (VA), Ogdensburg (NY), Orange (CA) and Raleigh (NC); and in Canada, Great Britain, Italy and Japan.
Vocation Director: Br. John O'Hara, SA, 800-338-2620, ext. 2126, fax: (845) 424-2170

AUGUSTINIAN FRIARS (M006)
(O.S.A.) (Order of St. Augustine)
(Province of St. Thomas of Villanova) St. Thomas Monastery 800 Lancaster Avenue, Villanova, PA 19085
Web: www.augustinian.org
Email: vocations@augustinian.org
Members: 211 Friars
Conduct: Parishes, university, college, high schools, foreign missions
Apostolic Work: Friars work as active contemplatives in preaching and teaching, parish ministry and renewal, spiritual direction, counseling and liturgical arts, Hispanic ministry. In education: Theological research and the arts and sciences; secondary, college, graduate levels in teaching and administration. Foreign missions in Japan, Peru and South Africa; Formation – Pre-Novitiate: Villanova, PA; Novitiate: Racine, WI; Theological Studies: Chicago, IL
Representation: Archdioceses of Boston, New York, Milwaukee, Philadelphia, Washington, DC, Miami and Tokyo and Nagasaki, Japan; and in the Dioceses of Albany, Camden, Orlando, Venice, FL, Nagoya and Fukuoka, in Japan, Peru, and South Africa
Vocation Director: Father Kevin DePrinzio, O.S.A., (610) 519-7548

AUGUSTINIAN RECOLLECT (M007)
FATHERS (OAR)
(Province of Saint Nicholas of Tolentine – USA Delegation)
St. Anselm's Church, 685 Tinton Ave., Bronx, NY 10455
(718) 585-8666, fax: (718) 401-6686
Web: www.agustinosrecoletos.org
Email: albertofuentem@hotmail.com
Members: 22 Priests
Conduct: 12 parishes, Hispanic center
Representation: Archdioceses of New York and Newark and in the Dioceses of El Paso and Las Cruces
Vocation Director: Rev. Alberto Fuente, St. Nicholas of Tolentine Monastery, 3201 Central Ave, Union City, NJ 07087, 201-867-6535

AUGUSTINIAN RECOLLECTS (M008)
(O.A.R.) (Saint Augustine Province)
Provincial Residence: Monastery of St. Cloud, 29 Ridgeway Ave., West Orange, NJ 07052
973-731-0616, fax: 973-731-1033
Web: www.augustinianrecollects.org and www.tagastemonastery.org
Email: egonzalezoar@hotmail.com
Members: 39 Priests, 7 Brothers, 2 Permanent Deacons, 4 Postulants
Conduct: 1 pre-novitiate, 1 residence for philososphy and theological students, 7 parishes, 1 Cursillo center
Apostolic Work: Dedicated to working with the Hispanics in the US (main apostolate), pastoral ministry, retreats, charismatic renewal, Cursillos, hospital chaplaincies, youth ministry
Representation: Archdioceses of New York, Newark, Los Angeles, and Mexico City and in the Diocese of Orange, California
Vocation Director: Rev. Eliseo Gonzalez, O.A.R., Province Vocation Director, St. Augustine Priory, 400 Sherwood Way, Oxnard, CA 93033-7560
Rev. Fidel Hernandez, O.A.R., Eastern Region Vocation Promoter, St. Joseph Cursillo Center, 275 W. 230th St., Bronx, NY 10463-5319

AUGUSTINIAN FRIARS (M009)
(O.S.A.) (Order of St. Augustine)
(Province of St. Joseph in North America) Motherhouse: The Augustinian Monastery at Marylake, PO Box 333, King City, Ontario, Canada, CN L0G-1K0
(905) 833-5368
Members: 16 Priests, 17 Brothers
Apostolic Work: Parish work, retreats
Representation: Archdioceses of Toronto and Vancouver
Vocation Director: Fr. Laurence Clark, O.S.A., St. Brigid's Rectory, 300 Wolverleigh Blvd., Toronto, Ontario M4C 1S6, Canada

AUGUSTINIAN FRIARS (M010)
(O.S.A.) (Order of St. Augustine)
St. Clare of Montefalco Monastery 1401 Whittier Road, Grosse Pointe Park, MI 48230
Web: www.midwestaugustinians.org/ vocatform.html
Email: vocations@midwest augustinians.org
Members: 94 Priests, 2 Bishops, 1 Permanent Deacon, 18 Brothers
Apostolic Work: Secondary education, parochial ministry, foreign missions, retreat work, adult education, hospital chaplaincies

Representation: Archdioceses of Chicago, Detroit, Milwaukee and in the Dioceses of Ft. Worth, Hamilton, Joliet, Kalamazoo and Tulsa, with missionaries in Japan and Peru
Vocation Director: Rev. Thomas R. McCarthy, O.S.A., Augustinian Vocation Office, 7740 South Western Ave., Chicago, IL 60620 (773) 776-3044, Fax: (773) 925-2451

AUGUSTINIANS (O.S.A.) (M011)
(Order of St. Augustine)
Province of St. Augustine 1605 28th St., San Diego, CA 92102 (619) 235-0247
Web: www.osa-west.org
Email: osacole@pacbell.net
Members: 30 Priests, 9 Brothers
Conduct: High schools, parishes, housing ministry, chaplaincies to hospitals, charismatic renewal
Representation: Archdioceses of Los Angeles, Portland (OR) and San Francisco and in the Dioceses of Oakland and San Diego
Vocation Director: Fr. Thomas J.F. Whelan, OSA, 108 Cole St, San Francisco, CA 94117-1116, (415) 387-3626

BARNABITE FATHERS (M012)
AND BROTHERS (C.R.S.P.)
(Clerics Regular of St. Paul)
North American Province 981 Swann Rd., PO Box 167, Youngstown, NY 14174-0617
Web: www.catholic-church.org/barnabites
Email: pmccrsp@fatimashrine.com
Members: 15 Priests
Conduct: 1 novitiate, 1 house of studies, 3 parishes, a Spiritual Center, a Marian Shrine-Basilica, Our Lady of the Rosary of Fatima
Apostolic Work: Working with youth and young adults, teaching, retreats, spiritual direction, parishes, hospital chaplaincies, directing the National Shrine Basilica of Our Lady of Fatima, Lewiston, NY
Representation: (Arch)dioceses of Allentown, Buffalo, Philadelphia, San Diego and Hamilton, Ontario, Canada. Also ministering in Albania, Argentina, Belgium, Brazil, Chile, France, Italy, Mexico, Philippines, Poland, Rwanda, Spain and Democratic Republic of Congo, Afghanistan
Vocation Director: Rev. Peter M. Calabrese, CRSP, Very Rev. Gabriel M. Patil, CRSP, 1023 Swann Road, PO Box 167, Youngstown, NY 14174-0167, (716) 754-7489

BASILIAN FATHERS (M013)
(C.S.B.) (Congregation of St. Basil)
Motherhouse: Toronto
Cardinal Flahiff Basilian Centre, 95
St. Joseph St., Toronto, Ontario,
Canada M5S-3C2, (416) 921-6674
Web: www.basilian.org
Email: vocation@basilian.org
Conduct: 1 college, 1 university, 4
campus ministries, 6 high schools,
10 parishes
Apostolic Work: The service of the
Church in any priestly capacity but
have centered their work on
education and evangelization
Representation: US: Dioceses of
Rochester, Detroit, Gary, Galveston-
Houston, Las Cruces, Santa Fe,
and Phoenix. Also in Canada,
Colombia, Mexico and St. Lucia
Vocation Director: Rev. Dennis
Kauffman, CSB, 95 St. Joseph
Street, Toronto, Ontario M5S 2R9

BASILIAN FATHERS OF (M014)
MARIA POCH
See Eastern Catholic Religious
Communities for Men

BASILIAN ORDER OF (M015)
ST. JOSAPHAT
See Eastern Catholic Religious
Communities for Men

BASILIAN SALVATORIAN (M016-1)
FATHERS
See Eastern Catholic Religious
Communities for Men

CATHOLIC COMMUNITY (M016-2)
OF THE BEATITUDES
2924 W. 43rd Ave., Denver, CO
80211
Web: www.beatitudes.us
Email: beatitudes.denver@
gmail.com
Members: 1,500 Priests, Brothers,
Sisters, and Residential Couples
Apostolic Work: In Denver a parish,
school, retreat house, and
evangelization
Representation: Denver, Mexico,
Brazil, Peru, Canada, Israel,
Lebanon, Medjugorie, France, Italy,
Spain, Germany, Belgium, Austria,
Switzerland, Czech Republic,
Slovakia, Hungary, Norway,
Kazakhstan, China, Vietnam, New
Zealand, New Caledonia, Reunion
Island, Ivory Coast, Congo,
Democratic Republic of Congo,
Central African Republic, Gabon,
Mali
Vocation Director: Rev. Sebastien
Pelletier, Superior of the Denver
House, (720) 855-9412

BENEDICTINE CONGREGATION OF (M016-3)
OUR LADY OF MOUNTE OLIVETO
Benedictine Monastery of Hawaii
PO Box 490, Waialua, Oahu, HI
96791
Web: www.hawaiibenedictines.org
Email: monastery@hawaii
benedictines.org
Members: 5 Monks
Apostolic Work: Retreats, spiritual
direction, parish assistance, and
prayer
Representation: Diocese of Honolulu
Vocation Director: Contact: (808)
637-7887, fax: (808) 637-8601

BENEDICTINE MONKS (M017)
(O.S.B.) Saint Bernard Abbey
1600 St. Bernard Drive S.E.,
Cullman, AL 35055
Web: www.stbernardabbey.com
Email: stbernardmonastery@
yahoo.com
Members: 35
Conduct: 5 parishes; co-ed prep
school; ecumenical retreat house;
parish weekend assistance, Ave
Maria Grotto
Representation: Dioceses of
Birmingham and Mobile
Vocation Director: Contact: 800-722-
0999, ext. 137

BENEDICTINE MONKS (M018)
(O.S.B.) Subiaco Abbey
405 N. Subiaco Ave., Subiaco, AR
72865-9798
Web: www.subi.org
Email: vocation@subi.org
Members: 50 Priests and Brothers
Apostolic Work: Community life and
prayer, apostolic works of pastoral
ministry, teaching in boys academy,
retreat work, hospitality, summer
youth camps. Full complement of
manual works including farming,
vineyards and cattle ranching
Representation: Diocese of Little
Rock
Vocation Director: Br. Francis
Kirchner, O.S.B., (479) 934-1047

BENEDICTINE MONKS (M019)
(O.S.B.) Prince of Peace Abbey
650 Benet Hill Rd., Oceanside, CA
92058-1253
Web: www.princeofpeaceabbey.org
Email: vocationmonk@aol.com
Members: 25 monks, of whom 7 are
priests
Apostolic Work: Benedictine monks
seek God in worship and prayer,
work and community life in the
monastery. Prince of Peace Abbey
also runs a retreat house for guests
on the monastery land.

Representation: Diocese of San
Diego
Vocation Director: (760) 967-4200
ext. 200, vocationmonk@aol.com

BENEDICTINE MONKS (M020)
(O.S.B.) Woodside Priory
302 Portola Rd., Portola Valley, CA
94028
Web: www.woodsidepriory.com
Email: mmager@
woodsidepriory.com
Members: 3 Priests, 1 Brother
Conduct: 1 preparatory school
(grades 6-12)
Apostolic Work: Education and
related activities
Representation: Archdiocese of San
Francisco
Vocation Director: Fr. Martin Mager,
O.S.B., Superior, (650) 851-6133,
fax: (650) 851-2839

BENEDICTINE MONKS (M022)
(O.S.B.) St. Anselm's Abbey
4501 S. Dakota Ave. NE,
Washington, DC 20017
Web: http://vocations.stanselms.org
Email: vocations@stanselms.org
Members: 21 Monks, including
Priests and Brothers
Conduct: 1 high school
Apostolic Work: Centers on prayer,
both liturgical and private; on living
together in fraternal community; and
on work, especially in high-school
and university-level education,
spiritual guidance, and hospitality
Vocation Director: Father Edward
Crouzet, OSB, (202) 269-2335

BENEDICTINE MONKS (M023)
(O.S.B.) Saint Leo Abbey
PO Box 2350, Saint Leo, FL 33574
Web: www.saintleoabbey.org
Email: wellofjacob@hotmail.com
Members: 7 Priests, 8 Brothers, 1
Novice, 3 Postulants
Apostolic Work: Retreat center,
parish and mission
Representation: Dioceses of
Charlotte and St. Petersburg
Vocation Director: Br. Simon
Huggins, OSB and Br. Jacob
Tippett, OSB (352) 588-8184

BENEDICTINE MONKS (M024)
(O.S.B.) Marmion Abbey, 850
Butterfield Rd., Aurora, IL 60502
Web: www.marmion.org
Email: vbataille@marmion.org
Members: 38 Priests, 19 Brothers
Conduct: Marmion Academy and
San Jose Seminary (Primary work
is teaching)
Representation: Rockford Diocese in

B-16

IL and in Quetzaltenango Diocese in Guatemala
Vocation Director: Contact: (630) 897-7215, ext. 312

BENEDICTINE MONKS (M025)
(O.S.B.) Monastery of the Holy Cross
3111 S. Aberdeen St., Chicago, IL 60608-6503
Web: www.chicagomonk.org/vocations.htm
Email: vocations@chicagomonk.org
Vocation Director: Rev. Peter Funk, O.S.B., 888-539-4261

BENEDICTINE MONKS (M026)
(O.S.B.) St. Procopius Abbey
5601 College Rd., Lisle, IL 60532
Web: www.procopius.org
Email: gjelinek@procopius.org
Members: 40 Monks
Conduct: Praising God through the Celebration of the Eucharist and the Liturgy of the Hours; serving the Church by teaching in Benedictine University and Benet Academy, by parish work, and foreign missions in Taiwan.
Vocation Director: Bro. Guy Jelinek, O.S.B.

BENEDICTINE MONKS (M027)
(O.S.B.) St. Bede Abbey
24 West US Highway 6, Peru, IL 61354-2903
Web: www.st-bede.com
Email: frronald@st-bede.com
Members: 21 Priests, 7 Brothers
Conduct: 4 parishes, 1 high school
Representation: Diocese of Peoria
Vocation Director: Rev. Ronald Margherio, OSB, (815) 223-3140, ext. 238, fax: (815) 223-8580

BENEDICTINE MONKS (M029)
(O.S.B.) Saint Meinrad Archabbey
100 Hill Dr., St. Meinrad, IN 47577-1010, (812) 357-6611
Web: www.saintmeinrad.edu
Email: vocations@saintmeinrad.edu
Members: 1 Archbishop, 67 Priests, 21 Brothers, 4 Junior Monks, 1 Transfer
Apostolic Work: As their founding apostolate, the monks of Saint Meinrad operate a seminary for the formation of priests, permanent deacons and lay ministers, and offer pastoral assistance to local parishes. Other works inlcude a retreat center, an oblate program, Abbey Press and Abbey Caskets.
Vocation Director: Rev. Anthony Vinson, OSB; Br. Christian Raab, OSB, Associate Vocation Director

BENEDICTINE MONKS (M030)
(O.S.B.) St. Benedict's Abbey
1020 N. Second St., Atchison, KS
Web: www.kansasmonks.org
Email: jalbers@kansasmonks.org
Members: 39 Priests, 18 Brothers
Apostolic Work: Benedictine College, Maur Hill Mount Academy, parishes, mission in Brazil.
Representation: Archdiocese of Kansas City (KS). Also in Brazil.
Vocation Director: Fr. James Albers, O.S.B., (913) 360-7830

BENEDICTINE MONKS (M031)
(O.S.B.) St. Joseph Abbey
75376 River Rd., St. Benedict, LA 70457
Web: www.sjasc.edu
Email: brjude@sjasc.edu
Members: 35 Finally Professed, 6 Temporarily Professed, 3 Novices
Apostolic Work: Parishes, common prayer, college seminary, retreat house, bread program for the poor
Representation: Archdiocese of New Orleans
Vocation Director: Br. Jude Israel, OSB, (985) 892-1800

BENEDICTINE MONKS (M032)
(O.S.B.) Glastonbury Abbey, Order of St. Benedict
16 Hull St., Hingham, MA 02043
Web: www.glastonburyabbey.org
Email: oconnort@glastonburyabbey.org
Members: 10 Monks (Priests and Brothers)
Conduct: Monastery and retreat center.
Representation: Archdiocese of Boston.
Vocation Director: Fr. Thomas, osb, (781) 749-2155

BENEDICTINE MONKS (M033)
(O.S.B.) St. Benedict Abbey
252 Still River Rd., Box 67, Still River, MA 01467
Web: www.abbey.org
Email: fatherxavierosb@yahoo.com
Members: 8 Priests, 7 Brothers
Apostolic Work: Monastic life, centered on the celebration of Mass and the Divine Office in Latin to Gregorian chant, and flowing over into the dissemination of Catholic doctrine through publishing and guest apostolates
Representation: Diocese of Worcester
Vocation Director: Fr. Xavier, O.S.B., (978) 456-3221, fax: (978) 456-8181

BENEDICTINE MONKS (M034)
(O.S.B.) Saint John's Abbey
Box 2015, Collegeville, MN 56321
Web: www.abbeyvocations.com
www.saintjohnsabbey.org
Email: vocations@osb.org
Members: 101 Priests, 1 Deacon, 46 Brothers, 4 Juniors, and 1 Novice
Apostolic Work: University, graduate school of theology, seminary and preparatory school education; parochial and hospital ministry; publishing house; campus ministry, carpentry, retreats, counseling, writing, gardening, forestry.
Representation: Archdiocese of St. Paul/Minneapolis and in the Diocese of Saint Cloud. Dependent priories Japan.
Vocation Director: Br. Paul-Vincent Niebauer, O.S.B. (320) 363-2548, fax: (320) 363-2504 email: pniebauer@csbsju.edu

BENEDICTINE MONKS (M035)
(O.S.B.) Conception Abbey
PO Box 501, 37174 State Hwy. VV, Conception, MO 64433-0501
(660) 944-3100, fax: (660) 944-2800
Web: www.conceptionabbey.org
Email: monks@conception.edu
Members: 60 Monks (Priests & Brothers)
Apostolic Work: Public prayer is chanted six times daily; Conception Seminary College serves students from 28 dioceses and religious orders; Printery House publishes Christian cards, icons, and religious art; parochial and hospital ministry outside the monastery; Abbey Guest Center conducts retreats for youth and adults; work in trades and crafts
Representation: (Arch)dioceses of Kansas City (KS), Kansas City-St. Joseph, Omaha, Des Moines, Salina, Wichita, Tulsa, Oklahoma City, Cheyenne, Springfield-Cape Girardeau, Dodge City and Jefferson City
Vocation Director: Fr. Benedict Neenan, OSB, (660) 944-2857

BENEDICTINE MONKS (M036)
(O.S.B.) Saint Louis Abbey
500 South Mason Rd., St. Louis, MO 63141-8500
Web: www.stlouisabbey.org
Email: frralph@priory.org
Members: 15 Priests, 8 Brothers, 2 Novices, 2 Postulants
Apostolic Work: Own, operate and teach in boys' college prep school, grades 7-12; parish and retreat work and convent chaplaincies.
Vocation Director: Rev. Ralph Wright, O.S.B., 800-638-1527

BENEDICTINE MONKS (M037)
(O.S.B.) Mount Michael Abbey
22520 Mount Michael Rd., Elkhorn,
NE 68022-3400
Web: www.mountmichael.org/
vocation.htm
Email: hagemann_john@
hotmail.com
Members: 12 Priests, 13 Brothers
Apostolic Work: College preparatory
high school, parish assistance,
retreat work, counseling, monastic
hospitality, liturgical art
Representation: Archdiocese of
Omaha and in the Diocese of
Pueblo
Vocation Director: John Hagemann,
OSB, (402) 289-2541, ext. 1111

BENEDICTINE MONKS (M038)
(OSB) Saint Anselm Abbey
100 Saint Anselm Dr., Manchester,
NH 03102
Web: www.anselm.edu
Email: vocations@anselm.edu
Members: 30 Monks
Conduct: 1 parish, 1 college
Apostolic Work: Education and
related activities
Representation: Diocese of
Manchester
Vocation Director: (603) 641-7000

BENEDICTINE MONKS (M039)
(O.S.B.) St. Mary's Abbey, Delbarton
230 Mendham Rd., Morristown, NJ
07960
Web: www.osbmonks.org
Email: vocations@delbarton.org
Members: 45 Monks
Conduct: 1 preparatory school for
boys, 1 summer sports camp, co-ed
summer school, 1 retreat center, 2
parishes
Apostolic Work: Secondary school
teaching and administration, parish
ministry, pastoral work at local
parishes on weekends, college
campus ministry and retreat
ministry, hospital chaplaincies.
Representation: Dioceses of
Metuchen, Paterson and Trenton
and in the Archdiocese of Newark
Vocation Director: 230 Mendham
Rd., Morristown, NJ 07960, (973)
538-3231, ext. 2111, fax: (973) 538-
7109

BENEDICTINE MONKS (M039-2)
(O.S.B.) (Part of Waegwan Abbey,
Korea)
St. Paul's Abbey, Newton, NJ 07860
Web: www.osbnewton.org
Email: lumen2000@hotmail.com
Members: 14 Monks (Korean,
American, African)
Conduct: Retreat house, gift shop,

Christmas tree farm, foreign mission
Representation: Diocese of Paterson
Vocation Director: Fr. H. Peter Ahn,
O.S.B., (973) 383-2470, ext. 199,
cell: (973) 919-4946, fax: (973) 383-
5782

BENEDICTINE MONKS (M040)
(O.S.B.) Newark Abbey
528 Dr. Martin Luther King Jr. Blvd.,
Newark, NJ 07102-1314
Web: www.newarkabbey.org
Email: vocations@sbp.org
Members: 15 Priests, 4 Brothers
Conduct: 1 abbey, 1 parish, 1
preparatory high school
Representation: Archdiocese of
Newark and Archdiocese of New
York
Vocation Director: Bro. Patrick
Winbush, O.S.B., (973) 792-5772

BENEDICTINE MONKS (M041)
(O.S.B.) Mount Saviour Monastery
(Elmira)
231 Monastery Rd., Pine City, NY
14871-9787
Web: www.msaviour.org
Email: info@msaviour.org
Members: 13 Monks
Representation: Diocese of
Rochester
Vocation Director: Very Rev. James
Cronen, OSB, Prior, 607-734-1688,
fax: 607-734-1689

BENEDICTINE MONKS (M042)
(O.S.B.) Belmont Abbey
100 Belmont - Mount Holly Rd.,
Belmont, NC 28012
Web: www.belmontabbey.org
Email: abbotplacid@bac.edu
Members: 21 Monks
Apostolic Work: Teaching on the
college level, liturgical and pastoral
ministry, common prayer
Representation: Diocese of Charlotte
Vocation Director: Abbot Placid
Solari, O.S.B., (704) 461-6675, fax:
(704) 825-6242

BENEDICTINE MONKS (M043)
(O.S.B.) Assumption Abbey
PO Box A, Richardton, ND 58652
Web: www.assumptionabbey.com
Email: michael@assumption
abbey.com
Members: 32 Priests, 25 Brothers
Apostolic Work: Farm, parish work,
hospitality, teaching. Mission
community and school in Bogota,
Colombia, South America
Representation: Diocese of Bismarck
Vocation Director: Michael Taffe,
OSB, (701) 974-3315

BENEDICTINE MONKS (M044)
(O.S.B.) St. Andrew Svorad Abbey
10510 Buckeye Rd.
Cleveland, OH 44104
Web: www.bocohio.org
Email: gerardgonda@juno.com
Members: 37 Monks
Apostolic Work: Apostolic communal
life of liturgy, lectio and meditation;
active works of hospitality,
secondary education, parochial and
pastoral services
Representation: Dioceses of
Cleveland and Great Falls-Billings
Vocation Director: Rev. Gerard
Gonda, O.S.B., (216) 721-5300,
ext. 210

BENEDICTINE MONKS (M045)
(O.S.B.) St. Gregory's Abbey
1900 W. MacArthur Dr., Shawnee,
OK 74804-2403
Web: www.monksok.org
Email: vocations@stgregorys.edu
Members: 28 Monks
Apostolic Work: The monastic
community maintains its daily
prayer and common life, and the
monks, both priests and brothers,
serve principally in the following
areas: St. Gregory's University,
early child development, parishes in
Oklahoma, weekend supply work,
retreats and hospitality, and manual
labor
Representation: Archdiocese of
Oklahoma City
Vocation Director: Rev. Charles
Buckley, OSB, (405) 878-5462, fax:
(405) 878-5189

BENEDICTINE MONKS (M046)
(O.S.B.) Mount Angel Abbey
One Abbey Dr.,
St. Benedict, OR 97373
Web: www.mountangelabbey.org
Email: abbeyvocation@mtangel.edu
Members: 75 Monks
Conduct: 1 seminary, 1 retreat
house, 2 parishes
Representation: Archdioceses of
Portland, (OR) and Seattle and in
the Diocese of Cuernavaca, Mexico
Vocation Director: Fr. Joseph
Nguyen, O.S.B., (503) 845-3226

BENEDICTINE MONKS (M047)
(O.S.B.) Saint Vincent Archabbey
300 Fraser Purchase Rd., Latrobe,
PA 15650-2690, (724) 532-6655
Web: www.stvincentmonks.com
www.svamonks.blogspot.com
Email: vocations@stvincent.edu or
fred.byrne@email.stvincent.edu
Members: 170 Monks
Conduct: 1 archabbey, 3 dependent
priories, 30 parishes, 5

chaplaincies, 1 seminary, 1 college, 1 high school.
Apostolic Work: Education, foreign missions, parochial ministry and chaplaincies.
Representation: Archdiocese of Baltimore and in the Dioceses of Altoona-Johnstown, Erie, Greensburg, Harrisburg, Pittsburgh, Richmond and Savannah. Foreign missions in Taiwan and Brazil.
Vocation Director: Fr. Fred Byrne, OSB

BENEDICTINE MONKS (M048)
(O.S.B.) Portsmouth Abbey
285 Cory's Ln.,
Portsmouth, RI 02871
Web: www.portsmouthabbey.org
Email: fatherambrose@
portsmouthabbey.org
Members: 14 Monks
Apostolic Work: Boarding secondary school for boys and girls
(Portsmouth Abbey School)
Vocation Director: Rev. Ambrose Wolverton, O.S.B., (401) 683-2000

BENEDICTINE MONKS (M049)
(O.S.B.) Blue Cloud Abbey
46561 147th St., PO Box 98, Marvin, SD 57251-0098
Web: www.bluecloud.org/
assoc-cand.html
Email: vocation@bluecloud.org
Members: 13 Priests, 14 Brothers
Apostolic Work: Divine Office & common life; retreat work at Abbey; associate program (2 months); pastoral work in South Dakota and Guatemala. The Abbey invites men to explore monastic life: 2 weeks to 2 months, or for a lifetime
Representation: Dioceses of Sioux Falls, SD and Coban, Guatemala
Vocation Director: Fr. Denis Quinkert, O.S.B., (605) 398-9200, Ext. 302, fax: (605) 398-9201

BENEDICTINE MONKS (M050)
(O.S.B.)
Holy Cross Monastery
9920 North Major Dr., Beaumont, TX 77713-7618
Web: www.holycrossmonks.org
Email: porter@holycrossmonks.org
Members: 2 Monks
Apostolic Work: Retreat Center
Representation: Diocese of Beaumont
Vocation Director: Br. Michael Gallagher, O.S.B., (409) 899-3554, fax: (409) 899-3558

BENEDICTINE MONKS (M051)
(O.S.B.) Weston Priory
58 Priory Hill Rd., Weston, VT 05161-6400
Web: www.westonpriory.org
Email: vocations@westonpriory.org
Members: 14 Monks
Representation: Diocese of Burlington
Vocation Director: Contact: (802) 824-5409

BENEDICTINE MONKS (M052)
(O.S.B.)
Mary Mother of the Church Abbey
12829 River Rd., Richmond, VA 23238-7206
Web: www.richmondmonks.org/
vocations.htm
Email: frmarkpurcell@gmail.com
Apostolic Work: Celebration of the Eucharist and community prayer, teaching in high school, parochial and hospital ministry, chaplaincies and retreats
Representation: Diocese of Richmond
Vocation Director: Rev. Mark A. Purcell, OSB, (804) 784-3508, ext. 129

BENEDICTINE MONKS (M053)
(O.S.B.) Saint Martin's Abbey
5300 Pacific Ave. SE, Lacey, WA 98503-1297
Web: www.stmartin.edu/abbey
Email: vocations@stmartin.edu
Members: 34 Monks
Apostolic Work: Daily prayer and common life; St. Martin's College, parishes and hospital chaplaincies.
Representation: Archdioceses of Seattle and in the Dioceses of Portland in Oregon, Yakima and Spokane.
Vocation Director: Rev. Paul Weckert, O.S.B., (360) 491-4700

BENEDICTINE MONKS (M054)
(O.S.B.) St. Benedict's Abbey
12605 224th Ave., Benet Lake, WI 53102
Web: www.benetlake.org
Email: vocations@benetlake.org
Members: 20 Monks
Conduct: Abbey and retreat center
Representation: Archdiocese of Milwaukee
Vocation Director: Br. Michael O'Brien, OSB, 888-482-1044 (toll free) or (262) 396-4311, fax: (262) 396-4365

(M055)
BENEDICTINE MONKS - Byzantine Rite (Holy Trinity Monastery)
See Eastern Catholic Religious Communities for Men

BENEDICTINE MONKS (M056)
(O.S.B.) (Congregation of the Annunciation) St. Andrew's Abbey
PO Box 40, Valyermo, CA 93563
Web: www.valyermo.com
Email: vocations@valyermo.com
Members: 26 Monks
Apostolic Work: Retreat house, youth center, teaching, chaplaincies
Representation: Archdiocese of Los Angeles
Vocation Director: Rev. Carlos Lopez, O.S.B., (661) 944-2178, fax: (661) 944-1076

BENEDICTINE MONKS (M057)
(O.S.B.) (Olivetan Benedictines)
PO Box 298, St. David, AZ 85630
Web: www.holytrinitymonastery.org
Email: frhenri@theriver.com
Members: 2 Priests, 5 Monks, 16 Oblates Living on Property
Representation: Diocese of Tucson
Vocation Director: Fr. Henri Capdeville, O.S.B., Prior, (520) 720-4642

BENEDICTINE MONKS (M058)
(O.S.B.) (Olivetan Benedictines)
Our Lady of Guadalupe Abbey
PO Box 1080, Pecos, NM 87552
Web: www.pecosmonastery.org
Email: guestmaster@
pecosmonastery.org
Members: 4 Priests, 8 Brothers
Representation: Archdiocese of Santa Fe
Vocation Director: Br. John M. Davies, OSB, (505) 757-6415, ext. 226

BENEDICTINE MONKS (M060-1)
(O.S.B.) (Congregation of St. Ottilien for Foreign Missions)
Christ the King Priory
PO Box 528, Schuyler, NE 68661
Web: www.Benedictine
MissionHouse.com
Email: BroTobias@Benedictine
MissionHouse.com
Members: 4 Priests, 4 Brothers
Conduct: U.S. headquarters for the financial support for the Benedictine missions in Africa, Asia, the Philippines and South America. Parish assistance and a retreat center
Vocation Director: Brother Tobias Dammert, OSB, (402) 352-2177, ext. 303

BENEDICTINE MONKS (M060-2)
(O.S.B.) (Congregation of Solesmes)
Our Lady of the Annunciation of Clear Creek
5804 West Monastery Rd., Hulbert, OK 74441

B-19

Web: www.clearcreekmonks.org
Members: 32 Monks
Apostolic Work: Celebration of Divine Office and Holy Mass in Latin and sung in Gregorian Chant, retreats, hospitality
Representation: Diocese of Tulsa
Vocation Director: Father Prior, (918) 772-2454, fax: (918) 772-1044

BENEDICTINE MONKS (M061)
(O.S.B.) (Benedictines, Subiaco Congregation)
Monastery of Christ in the Desert
PO Box 270, Abiquiu, NM 87510
Web: www.Christdesert.org
Email: abbotphilip@gmail.com
Members: 30 Monks
Representation: Archdioceses of Santa Fe and Chicago. Also in Mexico
Vocation Director: (801) 545-8567

BENEDICTINE MONKS (M062)
(O.S.B.) (Sylvestrine Congregation)
St. Benedict Monastery
2711 E. Drahner Rd., Oxford, MI 48370-2815
Web: www.benedictinemonks.com
Email: saintben@core.com
Apostolic Work: Teaching, parish work and catechetical work in addition to monastic, community life and youth retreat ministry
Representation: Archdiocese of Detroit and in the Diocese of Paterson, NJ
Vocation Director: Rev. Damien Gjonaj, OSB

CONGREGATION OF THE (M063)
BLESSED SACRAMENT (S.S.S.)
(US, Province of St. Ann - Provincial Offices)
5384 Wilson Mills Rd., Highland Heights (Cleveland), OH 44143-3092
Web: www.blessedsacrament.com
Email: sssvocations@ blessedsacrament.com
Members: 56 Priests, Deacons and Brothers
Conduct: Novitiate, 6 parishes, specialized ministries
Apostolic Work: Prayer and work focused specifically on the Eucharist. Active ministry includes: staffing selected parishes, Eucharistic retreats, seminars, writing, teaching, preaching, hospital chaplains, university chaplains, counseling, spiritual direction, prayer, adoration
Representation: Archdioceses of Chicago, Galveston-Houston, New York, San Antonio and in the Dioceses of Cleveland and St. Petersburg
Vocation Director: Vocation Office

BRIGITTINE MONKS (O.Ss.S.) (M065)
(Order of the Most Holy Savior)
Priory of Our Lady of Consolation
23300 Walker Ln., Amity, OR 97101
Web: www.brigittine.org
Email: monks@brigittine.org
Members: 8 Monks
Apostolic Work: Contemplative
Representation: Archdiocese of Portland
Vocation Director: Bro. Steven Vargo, O.Ss.S., (503) 835-8080, fax: (503) 835-9662

BROTHERS OF THE (M066)
BELOVED DISCIPLE
1701 Alametos, San Antonio, TX 78201-3500
Web: www.brothersofthebeloved disciple.org
Email: GMontague@St.MaryTX.edu
Members: 4 Priests
Conduct: 1 Parish
Apostolic Work: Parish ministry, Charismatic prayer groups (English and Spanish)Young adults, Youth group, Training Programs in Ministry, Evangelization, Maturity in Relationships, and Leadership, Life in the Spirit Seminars, Eucharistic Adoration
Representation: Archdiocese of San Antonio
Vocation Director: George T. Montague, S.M., (210) 734-6727, fax: (210) 738-0698

BROTHERS OF THE CHRISTIAN (M067)
SCHOOLS FSC (DE LA SALLE CHRISTIAN BROTHERS) (F.S.C.) (CHRISTIAN BROTHERS)
Christian Brothers Conference
3025 Fourth Street NE, Suite 300, Washington, DC 20017
Founded by St. John Baptist de La Salle, we are an international institute of Brothers involved in all forms of education at the elementary, secondary, collegiate, literacy and GED levels. Brothers are teachers, social workers, religious educators, human services providers, counselors, spiritual directors, youth ministers, campus ministers, and foreign missionaries.
Web: www.lasallian.info
Email: rschieler@cbconf.org
Members: There are 800 Brothers in the United States/Toronto Region, 5,300 worldwide.
Representation: There are 6 Provinces: Baltimore, Long Island-New England, Midwest, New Orleans-Santa Fe, New York, San Francisco
Vocation Director: United States - Toronto Region: Bro. Robert Schieler, General Councilor (202) 529-0047, fax: (202) 529-0775

(M068-2)
BROTHERS OF ST. JOHN OF GOD
See Hospitaller Brothers of St. John of God

CALASANZIAN FATHERS (M069)
See Piarists

CAMALDOLESE HERMITS (M070)
(O.S.B.Cam.)
New Camaldoli Hermitage
62475 Hwy. 1, Big Sur, CA 93920
Web: www.contemplation.com
Email: vocations@ contemplation.com
Members: 26 Monks in US
Representation: Dioceses of Monterey and Oakland and in Italy, Brazil and India
Vocation Director: Fr. Michael Fish, OSB. Cam., (831) 667-0640 (tel, fax)

CAMALDOLESE HERMITS (M071)
OF MONTE CORONA
1501 Fairplay Rd., Bloomingdale, OH 43910-7971
Web: www.camaldolese.org
Members: 3 Priests, 1 Brother
Representation: Italy, Poland, Spain, Colombia and Venezuela
Vocation Director: Fr. Basil, (740) 765-4511

CAMILLIANS (O.S.Cam.) (M072)
(Servants of the Sick)
Camillian Provincialate of North American Province: St. Camillus Community, 3345 South 10th St., Milwaukee, WI 53215
Web: www.camillians.org
Email: vocations@camillians.org
Members: 10 Priests, 3 Brothers
Conduct: 3 religious houses, health center, 1 retirement center, 1 home health agency, 2 parishes and are on staff at several public and private health care institutions
Apostolic Work: Known throughout the world as Camillians, an Order founded by St. Camillus de Lellis in 1582 – caring for the sick as chaplains, counselors, nurses, doctors, psychologists, physical therapists, ethicists, health care administrators, and serving in all the fields of health care, medicine and rehabilitation.
Representation: Archdiocese of Milwaukee and in the Diocese of Worcester. Also in 40 other countries throughout the world.
Vocation Director: Fr. Albert Schempp, O.S.Cam.

CANONS REGULAR (M073)
OF PREMONTRE
See Norbertines

CAPUCHIN FRANCISCAN (M074)
FRIARS (O.F.M.Cap.)
Our Lady of Angels-Western
American Province, 1345 Cortez
Ave., Burlingame, CA 94010
(650) 342-1489
Web: www.beafriar.org
Email: beafriar@yahoo.com
Members: 60 Friars (Brothers and
Priests)
Apostolic Work: Parish ministries,
chaplaincies, high school and
college education, retreat and
renewal ministries, mission work,
social justice and peace, and similar
ministries of prayer and service
Representation: Archdioceses of Los
Angeles and San Francisco and in
the Dioceses of Oakland. Also in
Obregon, Chihuahua, Monterey,
Mexico
Vocation Director: Ron Talbott, OFM.
Cap., 200 Foothill Blvd., La
Canada-Flintridge, CA 91011, (818)
790-8215

CAPUCHIN FRANCISCAN (M075)
FRIARS (O.F.M. Cap.)
St. Francis of Assisi Friary (Capuchin
Province of Mid-America)
3553 Wyandot St., Denver, CO
80211, (303) 981-1111
Web: www.capuchins.org
Email: johnclager@aol.com
Members: 60 Friars (Priests and
Brothers)
Apostolic Work: All types of service
for the Church as parish pastors,
hospital chaplains, teachers,
counselors, preachers, with
ministries in a homeless shelter,
migrant labor camps, on college
campuses and in prisons.
Evangelization efforts in foreign
missions
Representation: Archdioceses of
Denver, Saint Louis and Kansas
City (KS) and in the Dioceses of
Colorado Springs and Salina. Also
in Mendi (Papua New Guinea),
Puerto Rico and Mexico
Vocation Director: Fr. John Lager,
ofm Cap., (303) 981-1111

CAPUCHIN FRANCISCAN (M076)
FRIARS (OFM Cap)
(Province of St. Joseph)
1740 Mt. Elliott St., Detroit, MI 48207
Web: www.capuchinfranciscans.org
Email: vocation@
capuchinfranciscans.org
Members: 200 members (Brothers
and Priests)
Apostolic Work: Serving the poor
(African-American and Hispanic
inner city ministries, Native
American missions, social justice

issues, soup kitchens), preaching
and evangelization (retreat work,
parish mission preaching, teaching),
parish ministry. Foreign missions in
Central America. Teaching (HS
Seminary)
Representation: WI: Milwaukee,
Green Bay, La Crosse, Madison,
MI: Detroit, Saginaw, Marquette; IL:
Chicago; IN: Fort Wayne/South
Bend; MT: Great Falls, and in
Central America: Nicaragua,
Honduras, Costa Rica, Panama,
Middle East
Vocation Director: John Holly, OFM
Cap, Jerome Johnson, OFM Cap,
Capuchin Vocation Office, 3407 S.
Archer Ave., Chicago, IL 60608
(773) 475-6206 Fax: (773) 847-
7409

CAPUCHIN FRANCISCAN (M077)
FRIARS (OFM Cap.)
Provincialate: Our Lady of
Guadalupe Friary
Province of the Stigmata of St.
Francis – New Jersey and Eastern
coast
PO Box 789, Union City, NJ 07087
Web: www.capuchinfriars.org
Email: capuchinlife@aol.com
Members: 50 Friars
Apostolic Work: Parish ministries,
hospital chaplaincies, preaching
apostolate, social ministry with
destitute men and women, Secular
Franciscans, foreign missions,
Hispanic ministry, AIDS ministry,
street ministry, soup kitchens and
shelters, spiritual direction
Representation: Archdioceses of
Newark and New York and in the
Dioceses of Paterson, Wilmington,
Charlotte, St. Petersburg and
Zambia, Africa. Mission in Mexico
Vocation Director: Bro. John Paul
Russo, ofm Cap., office: (201) 863-
3871; cell phone: (813) 857-5902

CAPUCHIN FRANCISCAN (M078)
FRIARS (O.F.M., Cap.)
Good Shepherd Friary, 608 Isham
St., New York, NY 10034
Web: www.capuchin.org
Email: brotimjones@yahoo.com
Province of St. Mary - New York and
New England
Capuchin Franciscan Vocation
Office, (845) 255-5680 / E-mail:
psm.vocations@capuchin.org
Members: 2 Bishops, 110 Priests, 1
Permanent Deacon, 2 Transitional
Deacons, 38 Professed Brothers, 2
Novices, 6 Postulants
Apostolic Work: Pastoral counseling,
social work, home for aged, military,
hospital and prison chaplaincies,

parish ministries, work with the
disabled, work with the dying in a
cancer hospital, preaching
apostolate, marriage encounters,
youth ministries, teach in grammar
schools, high schools, colleges and
seminary, college campus
ministries, inner-city, suburban and
rural parishes, serve the poor in
soup kitchens and assisting them
with clothing, housing and
immigration issues, outreach
program to day laborers, HIV/AIDS
ministry
Representation: Archdioceses of
New York, Boston and Hartford and
Dioceses of Portland (ME),
Manchester (NH), Burlington (VT),
Providence (RI), Fall River (MA),
Springfield (MA), Worcester (MA),
Bridgeport (CT), Norwich (CT),
Buffalo (NY), Rochester (NY),
Syracuse (NY), Ogdensburg (NY),
Albany (NY), Brooklyn (NY),
Rockville Centre (NY). Also in
Honduras in Central America, US
territory in Guam in the Marian
Islands, the Hawaiian Islands and
Ryukyu Islands in Japan.
Vocation Director: Brother Tim Jones,
O.F.M, Coordinator of Vocation
Ministry,(212) 567-1300, Email:
brotimjones@yahoo.com

CAPUCHIN FRANCISCAN (M079)
FRIARS (O.F.M. Cap.)
(Province of St. Augustine)
Provincialate220 - 37th St.,
Pittsburgh, PA 15201-5201
Web: www.capuchin.com
Email: frtomcap@yahoo.com
Members: 200 Friars (Brothers and
Priests)
Conduct: 18 friaries, 22 parishes, 1
novitiate, 1 house of studies,
hermitage, 2 foreign missions
(Papua, New Guinea and Puerto
Rico)
Apostolic Work: Parishes,
chaplaincies, inner city ministry,
work with the poor, Hispanic
ministry, justice and peace ministry,
Appalachian ministry, youth
ministry, preaching, teaching,
foreign missions
Representation: States of DC, IN,
KY, MD, OH, PA, WV as well as in
Puerto Rico and Papua, New
Guinea
Vocation Director: Brother Thomas
Betz, OFM Cap., Capuchin
Vocation Office, 915 Vine St.,
Philadelphia, PA 19107, 888-2
OFMCAP

B-21

CAPUCHIN FRANCISCAN (M080)
FRIARS (O.F.M. Cap.)
Capuchin Viceprovince of Texas
5605 Bernal Dr., Dallas, TX 75212
Web: www.capuchinosmex.com
Email: mtellitu@yahoo.com
Members: 11 Priests, 5 Brothers
Apostolic Work: Parish, renewal
movements, hospitals, preaching,
hispanic ministry, franciscan secular
Representation: (Arch)dioceses of
Dallas and Fort Worth.
Vocation Director: Fr. Mario Garcia,
OFM Cap, (214) 500-8595, (214)
637-6673

CARMELITE FRIARS (M081)
(O.Carm.) Province of St. Elias
68 Carmelite Dr., PO Box 3079,
Middletown, NY 10940
Web: www.carmelitefriars.org
Email: ocarmvoc@frontiernet.net
Members: 89 Carmelites in the
Province
Conduct: Contemplative life
Apostolic Work: Prayer is at the core
of the Carmelite spirit. To
experience God's love, to ponder
the mystery and wonder of life as
Mary our Mother did, to search for
meaning – all encompass the
contemplative dimension of
Carmelite life. We have Mary, our
Sister and Patroness, whose
example guides us in our allegiance
to her Son. With the dual spirit of
Elijah, our contemplative life is lived
in active service for the Lord. We
serve as parish priests; teachers in
grade schools, high schools,
colleges and universities; chaplains
in hospitals, mental health facilities,
nursing homes and prisons; retreat
directors, shrine directors and
campus ministers. What we do
today, we may not have done in the
past; what we do in the future, we
may not do today. Carmelites
respond to the needs of the Church,
to the People of God.
Representation: 13 Carmelite
residences in the Archdiocese of
New York and in the Dioceses of
Albany, Rochester (NY), Greenburg
(PA) and Palm Beach (FL). Also
missions in Vietnam and Trinidad
Vocation Director: Bro. Robert Bathe,
O.Carm., (845) 344-2225, fax: (845)
344-2210

CARMELITES (O. Carm.) (M082)
1313 Frontage Rd., Darien, IL 60561
Seminaries: Pre-Novitiate House in
Chicago, IL, Novitiate in Middletown,
NY, Theology at Washington
Theological Union with residence at
Whitefriars Hall, Washington, DC.
Web: www.carmelites.net

Email: carmelites@carmelites.net
Members: 204 Priests & Brothers
Apostolic Work: Community,
contemplative prayer and prophetic
ministry are the Carmelite charism.
Priests and brothers minister at 4
retreat houses, 35 parishes, 6 high
schools and various ministries in 16
dioceses throughout the United
States and Canada, with missions
in Peru and Mexico.
Representation: Archdioceses of
Boston, Chicago, Kansas City, Lima
(Peru), Los Angeles, Newark,
Toronto (Ontario, Canada), and
Washington, DC and in the
Dioceses of Joliet, Phoenix,
Sacramento, St. Catherines
(Ontario, Canada), Sicuani (Peru),
Torreon (Mexico), Tucson and
Venice (FL)
Vocation Director: Vocation Director:
Fr. Sam Citero, O. Carm., Carmelite
Vocation Office, 1600 Webster St.
NE, Washington, DC 20017, (202)
526-1221, ext. 109, fax: (202) 526-
9217

CARMELITES (HERMITS) (M082-1)
See Hermits of the Most Blessed
Virgin Mary of Mount Carmel

CARMELITE MONKS (M082-2)
**(M.CARM) (Monks of the Most
Blessed Virgin Mary of Mount
Carmel)** Carmelite Monastery, PO
Box 2747, Cody, WY 82414-2747
Web: www.carmelitemonks.org
Members: 1 Priest, 5 Monks in
Temporary Vows, 2 Novices, 5
Postulants
Apostolic Work: In a solitary
monastery under the Rocky
Mountains, the Carmelite Monks
seek to perpetuate the charism of
the Blessed Virgin Mary, living Her
life as prescribed by the Carmelite
Rule. These monks live a full
Carmelite liturgical life, with the
Divine Office and the Holy Sacrifice
of the Mass being prayed in Latin
with Gregorian Chant. Desiring to
become great saints, they have a
vehement longing to live the entirety
of the customs and charism
established by Ss. John of the
Cross and Teresa of Avila, namely:
strict monastic enclosure, two hours
of contemplative prayer daily, study
and spiritual reading, and manual
labor. The monk may aspire to be a
lay brother or a priest who
celebrates the Sacraments, gives
spiritual direction, and preaches
retreats to the Discalced Carmelite
Nuns and the monastery
retreatants. With a burning love of
God and zeal for souls, the

Carmelite monk immolates his life in
Vows of Obedience, Chastity and
Poverty. Only men between 18 and
27 who have an ardent desire for
the cloistered, monastic life and to
be spiritual fathers of souls need
inquire
Vocation Director: Rev. Daniel Mary
of Jesus Crucified, M.Carm, Prior,
(307) 645-3310

ORDER OF CARMELITES (M083)
(O. Carm.) Mt. Carmel Hermitage
244 Baileys Rd., Bolivar, PA 15923
Web: www.carmelites.com/hermits
Email: smarr@winbeam.com
Members: 2 Priests, 1 Brother
Apostolic Work: Contemplative,
semi-eremitical life
Representation: Diocese of
Greensburg
Vocation Director: Fr. Bede Mulligan,
O.Carm., Prior (724) 238-0423

CARMELITES OF MARY (M084)
IMMACULATE (C.M.I.)
Generalate: Kerala, India. North
American Headquarters
Holy Family Church, 21 Nassau
Ave., Brooklyn, NY 11222
Web: www.cmiusa.org
Email: cmiusa@hotmail.com
Members: 108 Priests in US and
Canada
Apostolic Work: Ministry to parishes,
hospitals, universities, prisons,
mission to Syro-Malabar Catholics
Representation: (Arch)dioceses of
Alexandria, Amarillo, Beaumont,
Boston, Brooklyn, Camden,
Charleston, Covington, Hartford,
Joliet, Lafayette, Lake Charles, Los
Angeles, Metuchen, Nashville, New
Ulm, New York, Philadelphia,
Rockville Centre, Sacramento,
Salina, San Angel, Shreveport,
Sioux Falls, St. Augustine, St. Paul
& Minneapolis, Tyler, Toledo and
Victoria. Also in Canada
Vocation Director: (718) 388-5145 or
4866, fax: (718) 387-1877

CARMELITES OF ST. JOSEPH (M085)
Annunciation Hermitage
1009 Oakland Ave. East
Austin, MN 55912
Web: www.carmelitesaustinmn.com
Members: 5 Hermits
Apostolic Work: A contemplative
hermit life of prayer and study,
supported by manual labor in the
silence and solitude of the
hermitage according to the Rule of
St. Albert of Jerusalem for
Carmelites.
Representation: Diocese of Winona
Vocation Director: Rev. Jon Moore,
phone and fax: (507) 437-4015

ORDER OF CARTHUSIANS (M086)
(Cart.) Carthusian Monastery Charterhouse of the Transfiguration, 1084 Ave Maria Way Arlington, VT 05250
Web: http://transfiguration. chartreux.org
Email: carthusians_in_america@ chartreuse.info
Members: 15 Members
Apostolic Work: A purely contemplative semi-eremitic order, strictly cloistered
Representation: US in the Diocese of Burlington. Also in Argentina, Brazil, England, France, Germany, Italy, Korea, Portugal, Slovenia, Spain and Switzerland
Vocation Director: Fr. Lorenzo Maria T. De La Rosa, Prior; Fr. Mary Joseph Kim, Novice Master, (802) 362-2550 fax: (802) 362-3584

THE BROTHERS OF (M087)
CHARITY (F.C.) Motherhouse: Rome American Province (Region of Our Lady of Charity)
7720 Doe Ln., Laverock, PA 19038
Web: www.brothersofcharity.org
Email: jfitzfc@aol.com
Apostolic Work: Education, special education, social work and foreign missions
Representation: Archdioceses of Philadelphia, Washington D.C. and 27 other countries
Vocation Director: Bro. John Fitzgerald, F.C., (215) 887-6361

BROTHERS OF CHRISTIAN (M088)
INSTRUCTION (FIC)
(Notre Dame Province)
Alfred, ME 04002, 207-324-0067
Web: www.ficbrothers.org
Email: gfroddy@yahoo.com
Members: 27 Members in US; 950 worldwide
Apostolic Work: Programs for academic and faith development in school, parish and retreat settings, foreign missions
Representation: Dioceses of Fall River, Ogdensburg, Portland (ME) and Youngstown. Foreign missions: Japan, Philippines, Tanzania, Uganda, Kenya, Ivory Coast, Congo, Rwanda, Burundi, Benin, Senegal, Togo, Haiti, Tahiti, Chile, Bolivia and Indonesia
Vocation Director: Contact: Br. Guy Roddy, FIC, Vocation Counselor, Walsh University, 2020 East Maple St., North Canton, OH 44720-3336, (330) 490-7064

CHRISTIAN BROTHERS (F.S.C.) (M089)
See Brothers o/t Christian Schools

CONGREGATION OF (M090)
CHRISTIAN BROTHERS (C.F.C.)
33 Pryer Terrace, New Rochelle, NY 10804
Web: www.cfcvocations.org
Email: bromaccfc@yahoo.com
North American Web: www.ercbna.org
International Web: www.edmundclt.org. Par mas informacion comunicate con: jimham78@hotmail.com.
Members: 275 Brothers In North America, 1,600 worldwide serving the people of God on six continents
Conduct: Are you called to be a Brother to the world? Blessed Edmund Rice' s founding charism gave birth to the Congregation of Christian Brothers. Edmund Rice was born in Callan, County Kilkenny, Ireland in 1762 and died in Waterford, Ireland in 1844. Realizing the effects deprivation had especially on the young people he responded to their needs. He gave up the comforts of wealth and established a school in a converted stable. Today, the Christian Brothers respond as they believe Edmund Rice would to different needs as they encounter them in different regions and different circumstances. Most Brothers live in small communities, typically of less than ten men.
Apostolic Work: The Brothers serve God's people in a variety of ways: elementary school, secondary school and college education; Youth Ministry; missionary work around the world; education services for adults (spirituality classes, workshops for teachers, English as a Second Language (ESL) instruction), parish and diocesan ministries, teaching migrant farm workers, hospital ministry (including ministering to AIDS patients), ministries with homeless people and refugees, and many other ministries serving those on the margins of society.
Representation: In North America: Canada: Archdiocese British Columbia, Newfoundland; Dominica: Diocese of Roseau; United States: Archdioceses Boston, Chicago, Detroit, Miami, Newark, New Orleans, New York, Seattle and Vancouver; and Dioceses of Brownsville, Charleston, Honolulu, Jackson, Joliet, Monterey, Orlando, Phoenix, Providence, Rochester, Tampa-St. Petersburg and Venice (FL). And on six continents.

Vocation Director: Brother James McDonald, CFC, 10001 S. Pulaski Road, Room 111, Chicago, IL, 60655-3356, (773) 429-4496, bromaccfc@yahoo.com
Para mas informacion comunicate con: Hermano Jim Hamilton, CFC, 111 East 164th St., Bronx, NY 10452, (718) 293-3993, ext. 146 jimham78@hotmail.com

CISTERCIAN (M092)
FATHERS (O.C.) Cistercian Monastery, 564 Walton Ave. , Mt. Laurel, NJ 08054
Web: www.fatimamonastery.org
Email: info@fatimamonastery.org
Members: 3 Priests, 1 Simple Vows, 1 Postulant
Conduct: Teaching, missions, parish work.
Vocation Director: Superior of Monastery, 856-235-1330

CISTERCIAN FATHERS (M093)
(O. Cist.) Cistercian Monastery of Our Lady of Dallas, 3550 Cistercian Rd., Irving, TX 75039
Web: www.cistercian.org
Email: fr-paul@cistercian.org
Members: 18 Priests, 10 Clerics, 3 Novices
Apostolic Work: Teaching and pastoral work both in college and in secondary school, parish assistance
Representation: Dioceses of Dallas and Fort Worth
Vocation Director: Rev. Paul McCormick, O. Cist., (972) 438-2044, ext. 258

CISTERCIAN ORDER (M094)
(O. Cist.) St. Mary's Cistercian Priory, 70 Schuykill Rd., New Ringgold, PA 17960
Members: 3 Priests
Conduct: A contemplative community, with intramural ecumenical activity
Vocation Director: (570) 943-2645

CISTERCIAN ORDER (M095)
(O. Cist.) Cistercian Abbey of Our Lady of Spring Bank
17304 Havenwood Rd., Sparta, WI 54656
Web: www.MonksOnline.org
Email: vocations@MonksOnline.org
Members: 3 Priests, 5 in Solemn Vows, 1 in Temporary Vows
Conduct: Contemplative monastic life
Vocation Director: Rev. Bernard McCoy, O. Cist., (608) 269-8138, fax: (608) 269-1992

CLARETIAN MISSIONARIES (C.M.F.) (M100)
(Missionary Sons of the Immaculate Heart of Mary) 205 W. Monroe St., Rm. 2905, Chicago, IL 60606
Web: www.claretianvocations.org
Email: vocations2905@
claretians.org
Members: 35 Fathers, 8 Brothers, 9 Students, 2 Novices
Conduct: USA Eastern Province, formation houses, parishes, Hispanic ministry (Casa Claret), youth ministry, Claretian Publications (U.S. Catholic, Oye), Claret Center for Resources in Spirituality, hospital ministry, campus ministry and inner-city work among the poor, elderly, hungry, immigrant and marginalized
Apostolic Work: Men, women, and couples, vowed religious and laity seek to respond to the most urgent needs of evangelization, especially in favor of the poor. Claretian priests and brothers, lay Claretians and Claretian volunteers all seek to live out this call according to their own charism.
Representation: Archdioceses of Atlanta, Chicago, and in the Dioceses of Metuchen and Springfield-Cape Girardeau. Also in Juarez, Mexico and 64 countries around the world.
Vocation Director: Eastern Province: Mario Delgado, (312) 236-7846

CLERICS OF ST. VIATOR (M101)
(C.S.V.) (Chicago Province)
1212 E. Euclid St., Arlington Heights, IL 60004
Web: www.viatorians.com
Email: dlydon@viatorians.com
Members: 80 Brothers and Priests, 56 Lay Associates
Apostolic Work: Parish ministry, education: high school and university
Representation: Archdiocese of Chicago and in the Dioceses of Joliet, Rockford, Peoria, Las Vegas, Little Rock, San Diego, Manchester, and Tucson. Foundations in Bogota, Colombia (South America) and Belize (Central America)
Vocation Director: Daniel J. Lydon, (847) 637-2129

CLERICS REGULAR OF (M102)
ST. PAUL
See Barnabite Fathers and Brothers

COLUMBAN FATHERS (M103)
(S.S.C.) (Missionary Society of St. Columban)
PO Box 10, St. Columbans, NE 68056
Web: www.columban.org
Email: vocations@columban.org
Members: 680 Priests engaged exclusively in foreign mission work
Conduct: 1 theologate, 1 pre-theology house, 1 spiritual year
Apostolic Work: Advocates of prophetic justice working alongside the poor and most marginalized people in the world; ministers of the Word and sacraments; missionary priests working in 15 countries throughout the world; creative partners with others in evangelization, community and human development, mission education and justice issues (homeless, prisoners, workers, refugees, migrants, indigenous peoples); and men of prayer committed to the mission of Jesus and God's kingdom
Representation: (Arch)dioceses of Boston, Chicago, El Paso, Los Angeles, Omaha, Providence and San Bernardino.Foreign Missions: Australia/New Zealand, Brazil, Britain, Chile, Fiji/Vanuatu, Ireland, Japan, Korea, Pakistan, Peru, Philippines and Taiwan
Vocation Director: Rev. Antonio Aguilar S.S.C., (402) 291-1920

COMBONI MISSIONARIES (M104-1)
(M.C.C.J.)
1318 Nagel Rd., Cincinnati, OH 45255
Motherhouse: Verona, Italy , General House: Rome
An international order of Priests and Brothers, working in Asia, Africa and Latin America
Web: www.combonimissionaries.org
Email: revdavemccj@gmail.com
Apostolic Work: In the footsteps of our founder St. Daniel Comboni: we proclaim the gospel with all its values throughtout the world, we live these gospel values in our daily lives, we foster the liberation of persons among neglected minorities and refugees, and we encourage local churches and people to open their hearts to the universal mission of the church.
Representation: (Arch)dioceses of Chicago, Cincinnati, Los Angeles and Newark
Vocation Director: Fr. Angel Camorlinga, MCCJ
Fr. David Bohnsack, MCCJ
Fr. Manuel Baeza, MCCJ
www.mccjvocation.com

THE COMMUNITY OF (M104-2)
THE MONKS OF ADORATION
See "T" - The Monks of Adoration
Web: www.monksofadoration.org
Email: monkadorer@verizon.net

CONGREGATION OF THE (M106)
BLESSED SACRAMENT
See Blessed Sacrament, Congregation

CONGREGATION OF (M107)
CHRISTIAN BROTHERS
See Christian Brothers, Congregation

CONGREGATION OF (M108)
HOLY CROSS
See Holy Cross Priests & Brothers

CONGREGATION OF THE (M109)
IMMACULATE HEART OF MARY
See Missionhurst Congregation of the Immaculate Heart of Mary

CONGREGATION OF (M110)
JESUS AND MARY
See Eudists

CONGREGATION OF (M111)
THE MISSION
See Vincentians

CONGREGATION OF (M112)
MISSIONARIES OF THE BLOOD OF
CHRIST See Missionaries of the
Precious Blood

CONGREGATION OF (M113)
THE PASSION
See Passionists

CONGREGATION OF THE (M114-1)
SACRED HEARTS OF JESUS AND
MARY
See Sacred Hearts Community

(M114-2)
CONGREGATION OF SACRED
STIGMATA (C.S.S.) (Stigmatine
Fathers and Brothers)
Province of the Holy Spouses, Mary and Joseph
554 Lexington St., Waltham, MA 02452-3097
Web: www.stigmatines.com
Email: geoffd@stigmatines.com, vocations@stigmatines.com
Members: 26 Priests, 1 Brother
Conduct: Retreat house, 6 parishes. Missions in Brazil, Thailand, Africa, and India
Apostolic Work: Seminary formation, spiritual direction, counseling, retreats, campus/youth/parish ministry, voluntary foreign missions, parish missions
Representation: Archdioceses of Boston and New York and in the Dioceses of Springfield (MA) and Worcester
Vocation Director: Fr. Geoffrey J. Deeker, C.S.S., (781) 209-3102

(M115)
CONGREGATION OF ST. JOSEPH
See St. Joseph, Congregation of

(M116)
CONSOLATA MISSIONARIES (I.M.C.)
Motherhouse: Rome
2301 Rt. 27, PO Box 5550,
Somerset, NJ 08875
732-297-9191
Web: www.consolata.org
Members: 1,000 Priests and
Brothers; 22 in US and Canada
Conduct: in US: 3 mission
community houses, house of
studies.
Apostolic Work: Foreign missions -
and wherever the Gospel needs to
be proclaimed and witnessed to,
especially among the poor
Representation: Archdiocese of
Washington (DC) and in the
Dioceses of Buffalo, Metuchen and
San Bernardino. Also in Argentina,
Bolivia, Brazil, Colombia, Equador,
Venezuela, Ethiopia, Guinea
Bissau, Ivory Coast, Kenya, Liberia,
Libya, Mozambique, Republic of
Congo, Somalia, Tanzania, South
Africa and Uganda, Europe (Italy,
Portugal, England, Spain,
Switzerland), Canada and South
Korea.
Vocation Director: Fr. David Gikonyo,
IMC

CROSIER FATHERS AND (M117)
**BROTHERS (O.S.C.) (Canons Regular
of the Order of the Holy Cross)** 4332
N. 24th St., Phoenix, AZ 85016-6259
Web: www.crosier.org
Email: vocations@crosier.org
Apostolic Work: The Crosiers are an
international Order of Catholic
priests and brothers, who have
served the Church since 1210 AD.
They long to imitate Christ through
the union of mind and heart in
community and through a life of
liturgical prayer and ministry. They
live for God alone by seeking to
combine contemplative routines
with a shared ministerial life. Their
value of community life is
expressed in their enthusiasm and
team approach to ministry. They
serve the needs of the Church and
society through preaching, spiritual
and liturgical formation, education,
ministry with youth, and pastoral
ministry.
Representation: Dioceses of Duluth,
Phoenix and St. Cloud. Also in
Agats, Indonesia and Rome, Italy
Vocation Director: Rev. Stephan
Bauer, OSC, 800-407-5875

DE LA SALLE (M118)
CHRISTIAN BROTHERS
See Brothers of the Christian Schools

DISCALCED CARMELITE (M126)
FATHERS (O.C.D.)
Our Lady of Mt. Carmel
Monastery/Shrine Polish Province of
the Holy Spirit
Our Lady of Mt. Carmel
Monastery/Shrine, 1628 Ridge Rd.,
Munster, IN 46321
Email: carmelmunster@yahoo.com
Members: 11 Priests, 2 Brothers
Representation: Diocese of Gary.
Vocation Director: Fr. Jack Palica,
OCD, (219) 838-7111, fax: (219)
838-7214

DISCALCED CARMELITE (M127)
FRIARS AND BROTHERS (O.C.D.)
(Oklahoma Province of St. Therese
of the Child Jesus)
5151 Marylake Dr., Little Rock, AR
72206
Provincial House, 501-888-3052
Web: www.carmeliteok.org
Email: vocations@carmelites.org
Members: 23 Priests, 2 Solemnly
Professed Brothers, 5 Students in
Vows, 1 Novice
Conduct: 1 contemplative
monastery, 1 center of adult
spirituality, 3 parishes, 1 student
house
Representation: Archdioceses of
New Orleans, San Antonio and
Oklahoma City and in the Dioceses
of Dallas and Little Rock
Vocation Director: Fr. Luis Joaquin
Castaneda, OCD, 1125 S. Walker
Ave., Oklahoma City, OK 73109

DISCALCED CARMELITE (M128-1)
FRIARS (O.C.D.) (Province of St.
Joseph of the Western US)
PO Box 3420, San Jose, CA 95156
(408) 251-1361, ext. 324
Web: www.discalcedcarmelites.com
Email: carmelitevocation@
yahoo.com
Members: 34 Priests, 6 Brothers in
Solemn Vows, 9 in Simple Vows, 5
Novices, 7 Postulants, 1 Secular
Brother
Conduct: 4 parishes, 1 retreat
house,1 institute of spirituality, 1
house of prayer, 1 novitiate, 1
house of studies, mission in
Kyengeza (Africa)
Representation: Archdioceses of Los
Angeles, Portland and Seattle and
in the Dioceses of San Bernardino,
San Jose, Santa Rosa and Tucson.
Mission in Africa
Vocation Director: Fr. Adam Gregory
Gonzales, OCD, Mount St. Joseph

Monastery, PO Box 3420, San
Jose, CA 95156, (408) 251-136,
ext. 324

DISCALCED CARMELITE (M128-2)
FRIARS (O.C.D.)
141 Carmelite Dr., Bunnell, FL 32110
Web: www.carmelitefathers.org
Email: carmelitefathers@aol.com
Members: 4 Friars
Apostolic Work: Parish work
Representation: Diocese of St.
Augustine
Vocation Director: (386) 437-2910,
fax: (386) 437-5125

DISCALCED CARMELITE (M129)
FRIARS (O.C.D.)
Province of the Immaculate Heart of
Mary, St. Florian's, 1233 So. 45th
St., Milwaukee, WI 53214
(414) 672-7212
Web: www.ocdfriarsvocation.com
Email: ocdvocation@gmail.com
Members: 1 Bishop, 60 Priests, 13
Brothers, 2 Deacons, 14 Students
Conduct: 1 Marian shrine, 1 retreat
house, 2 parishes, 1 hermitage
community, 3 formation
communities, 1 international
publication, 1 publishing house
Apostolic Work: Retreats, spiritual
direction, parishes, translation,
publication, teaching, secular order,
chaplaincies, in-house ministries:
cook, tailor, maintenance,
formation, administration. Overseas
missions in Kenya
Representation: Archdioceses of
Boston, Milwaukee, Washington,
DC, the Diocese of Wheeling-
Charleston, and Nairobi, Kenya
Vocation Director: Rev. Michael
Berry, OCD, (414) 672-7729, Fax:
(414) 383-2708

(M130)
SONS OF DIVINE PROVIDENCE
(FDP) (Don Orione Fathers)
Motherhouse: Rome
Don Orione Home
111 Orient Ave., East Boston, MA
02128
Members: 10 Priests in US
Apostolic Work: Multiple
Representation: Archdioceses of
Boston and New York and in the
Diocese of Evansville.
Vocation Director: 617-569-2100

(M132)
DIVINE WORD MISSIONARIES (SVD)
The SVD is an international,
multicultural community of over
6,000 brothers and priests working in
more than 70 countries around the
world. Our mission compels us to
minister first and foremost where the

Gospel has not yet been preached at all or only insufficiently, and where the local church is not yet viable on its own (SVD Constitutions). We have a wide variety of ministries. Formation programs include:
1) Divine Word College in Epworth, IA is the only Roman Catholic college seminary in the United States exclusively designed for missionary formation. Majors include philosophy and cross-cultural studies.
2) The Brother Formation Program allows brother candidates to attend universities or colleges to complete their specialized professional education and experience religious community life.
3) The Associate Program is a residency program for college graduates who are considering a missionary vocation. Interested men may live in a Divine Word community and participate in ministry first-hand.
4) Divine Word Theologate, Chicago, IL is the residence for seminarians completing the graduate program in theological education and ministry formation at Catholic Theological Union.
5) The Divine Word Novitiate is located in Techny, IL. For more information, please contact: Vocation Director, Divine Word Missionaries, PO Box 380, Epworth, IA 52045; 800-533-3321,
www.svdvocations.org
Vocation Office, PO Box 380, Epworth, IA 52045
Web: www.svdvocations.org
Email: svdvocations@dwci.edu
Vocation Director: Mr. Len Uhal, National Vocation Director, luhal@dwci.edu, 800-553-3321

DOMINICANS (O.P.) (M133)
(Order of Preachers)
Central Province - Province of St. Albert the Great, 1909 S. Ashland Ave., Chicago, IL 60608
Web: www.op.org/domcentral
Email: wisdomop@yahoo.com
Members: 154 Priests, 16 Professed Cooperator Brothers, 7 Novices, 15 Student Brothers
Apostolic Work: Preaching, teaching, research and writing, campus and parish ministry, social justice
Vocation Director: Fr. Andrew-Carl Wisdom, O.P., (312) 243-0011

DOMINICANS (O.P.) (M134)
(Order of Preachers)
Eastern Province
141 E. 65 St., New York, NY 10065
(212) 737-5757
Web: www.dominicanfriars.org
Email: vocations@
dominicanfriars.org

Members: 1 Archbishop, 2 Bishops, 218 Priests, 9 Cooperator Brothers, 28 Professed Clerics, 11 Novices
Conduct: 10 priories, 17 parishes, 8 houses, novitiate, foreign mission, 6 campus ministries, 1 college, house of study
Apostolic Work: Preaching, teaching, parishes, foreign missions, campus ministry, hospital chaplaincy
Vocation Director: Fr. William P. Garrott, O.P., Dominican Vocation Office, Director of Vocations, 487 Michigan Ave., NE, Washington, DC 20017-1585, 800-529-1205 toll-free

DOMINICANS (O.P.) (M135)
(Order of Preachers)
Province of the Holy Name-Western Province, 5877 Birch Court, Oakland, CA 94618-1626
Web: www.opwest.org
Email: vocations@opwest.org
Members: 120 Priests, 7 Brothers, 21 Professed Brothers, 4 Novices
Conduct: Parishes, Newman centers, retreat house, house of study, novitiate
Representation: Archdioceses of Anchorage, Los Angeles, Portland (OR), San Francisco and Seattle and in the Dioceses of Norwich, Oakland, Phoenix, Providence, Sacramento, Salt Lake City, San Bernardino, San Diego, San Jose and Tucson. Also in Germany, Guatemala, Kenya, Mexico and Rome
Vocation Director: Rev. Steven Maekawa, OP, Vocation Office, (510) 596-1821

DOMINICANS (O.P.) (M136)
(Order of Preachers)
Southern Dominican Province (Province of St. Martin de Porres) 1421 N. Causeway Blvd., Ste. 200, Metairie , LA 70001-4144
Web: www.dominicanvocations.com
Email: vocations@
dominicanvocations.com
Members: 165 Friars (Priests and Brothers)
Apostolic Work: Preaching, teaching, chaplaincies, parish and campus ministry. Missionaries: Ecuador, Cuba.
Representation: Province covers 11 southern states
Vocation Director: Fr. Charles Luke Latour, O.P., Vocation Office, (504) 837-2129, ext. 23

(M136-1)
DOMINICAN MISSIONARIES FOR THE DEAF APOSTOLATE (OP Miss.)
143 Honeysuckle Lane, San Antonio, TX 78213

Web: www.dominican
missionaries.org
Email: tomcoughlin@juno.com
Members: 6 Professed and 3 Novices
Apostolic Work: An international Dominican community for deaf and hearing men dedicated to the Deaf Apostolate in the Roman Catholic Church as priests, brothers and deacons.
Representation: Archdiocese of San Antonio and Diocese of Oakland
Vocation Director: Fr. Tom Coughlin, OP Miss., (210) 627-6303

EDMUNDITES (S.S.E.) (M137)
(Society of St. Edmund)
Edmundite Generalate, 270 Winooski Park, Colchester, VT 05439-0270
Web: www.sse.org
Email: sderesienski@smcvt.edu
Members: 40 Priests & Brothers
Apostolic Work: Evangelization of students, African-Americans, parishioners and retreatants
Representation: AL, VT, CT, LA and Venezuela
Vocation Director: Rev. Stanley Deresienski, S.S.E., (802) 654-2273, fax: (802) 654-3409

EUDISTS (C.J.M.) (M138)
(Congregation of Jesus and Mary)
Motherhouse: Rome
Eudist Community, 744 Sonrisa St., Solana Beach, CA 92075
Web: www.eudistes.org
Email: jhhcjm@aol.com
Members: 82 Priests, Deacons and Laymen in North American Province; 8 Seminarians and candidates
Apostolic Work: Parishes, young adult ministry, youth ministry, counseling, teaching apostolic word. Evangelization and formation to ministry in seminaries and diocesan institutes.
Representation: Dioceses of Buffalo, San Diego, and Phoenix
Vocation Director: Contact: (858) 755-8394

FRANCISCAN BROTHERS (M139-1)
(Congregation of the Religious Brothers of the Third Order Regular of St. Francis) Founded in 1858
Franciscan Brothers Generalate: St. Francis Monastery, 135 Remsen St., Brooklyn, NY 11201
Web: www.franciscanbrothers.org
Email: generalate@gmail.com;
LMiritello@sfponline.org
Members: 82 Brothers
Conduct: 1 college, 3 high schools,

B-26

1 summer camp/retreat center, 1 novitiate.
Apostolic Work: Secondary and higher education, educational administration, Catholic Charities, parish ministry, youth ministry, retreat ministry, counseling, health care, campus ministry, prison ministry Diocesan administration.
Representation:(Arch) dioceses of Brooklyn, Rockville Centre, Springfield-Cape Girardeau
Vocation Director: Brother Louis Miritello, OSF, St. Francis Monastery at Mt. Alvernia, 103 Prospect Road, Centerport, NY 11721, (631) 418-8522

FRANCISCAN BROTHERS (M139-2)
OF PEACE (FBP) Queen of Peace Friary, 1289 Lafond Ave., St. Paul, MN 55104-2035
Web: www.brothersofpeace.org
Email: vocation brothersofpeace.org
Members: 9 Brothers, 2 Novices, 2 Postulants
Apostolic Work: Strong Pro-Life charism; reaching out to those in crisis pregnancy, defending the vulnerable, ministering to the poor and homeless, in our friary and on the streets.
Representation: Archdiocese of Saint Paul and Minneapolis, Minnesota
Vocation Director: Bro. Joseph Katzmarek, fbp, (651) 646-8586, fax: (651) 646-9083

FRANCISCAN BROTHERS (M139-3)
OF THE EUCHARIST (F.B.E.)
173 Goodspeed Ave.
Meriden, CT 06451
Web: www.fbecommunity.org
Email: brothers@fbecommunity.org
Members: 2 Brothers
Representation: Archdiocese of Hartford
Vocation Director: Brother Leo Maneri, FBE, (203) 237-3601, fax: (203) 237-4217

FRANCISCAN BROTHERS (M140)
OF THE HOLY CROSS (F.F.S.C.)
St. James Monastery, 2500 St. James Rd., Springfield, IL 62707
Web: franciscanbrothers.net
Email: stjamesmonastery@ franciscanbrothers.net
Members: 11 Brothers
Apostolic Work: Work with disabled adults, hospital Chaplaincy, education, pastoral leadership
Representation: (Arch)dioceses of St. Louis (MO), Springfield (IL) and Madison (WI)

Vocation Director: Vocation Team, (217) 528-4757, ext. 23
(M141)
FRANCISCANS - BROTHERS OF THE POOR OF ST. FRANCIS (C.F.P.)
Provincial Office , PO Box 26022, Cincinnati, OH 45226-0022
Web: www.franciscan-brothers.net
Email: hibrothers@fuse.net
Conduct: 1 novitiate, 4 parochial schools, 1 nursing home ministry, 1 development office, pastoral ministry
Apostolic Work: Human services, especially the care and education of youth
Representation: Archdioceses of Cincinnati and Newark and in the Dioceses of Covington, Davenport, El Paso and Little Rock
Vocation Director: Bro. Edward Kesler, CFP, (513) 924-0111, fax: (513) 321-3777

FRANCISCAN FRIARS (M144)
(O.F.M.) (Province of the Assumption of the B.V.M.) Francis & Clare Friary 9230 W. Highland Park Ave., Franklin, WI 53132
Web: www.franciscan-friars.org
Email: vocationdirector@ hotmail.com
Members: 97 Priests, 1 Permanent Deacon, 42 Brothers, 1 Novice
Conduct: 12 friaries (including 1 postulancy, 1 novitiate and 1 post-novitiate residence); 18 parishes, 3 resident (retired) assistants in parishes; 13 chaplaincies; 4 social services/outreach among the poor; 5 higher education; 1 campus ministry; 1 diocesan administration; 2 bishops (1 Roman Rite, 1 Byzantine [Ruthenian] Rite); 3 foreign missionaries
Apostolic Work: Parish work; social services; retreats; teaching; institutional chaplaincies (university, Sisters' motherhouses, hospital, nursing homes); foreign missions; USA missions; urban and rural ministries; Spanish, Polish and English languages; Latino and African-American ministries; Byzantine and Roman Rites; work among the poor and marginalized
Representation: USA: Archdioceses of Milwaukee, Chicago, and Philadelphia; Dioceses of Green Bay, Gary, Joliet, Fort Wayne-South Bend, Jackson, Brownsville, Gaylord, Grand Rapids, and Scranton. Archeparchy of Pittsburgh; Eparchies of Passaic and Parma (OH).
Foreign Missions: Marrakech, Morocco; Almaty, Kazakhstan;

Guaymas, Sonora, Mexico, and Philippines
Vocation Director: Rev. Joachim Studwell, OFM (Contact - above address and email)

FRANCISCAN FRIARS (M145)
(O.F.M.), Province of the Holy Gospel 2400 Marr St., El Paso, TX 79903
Members: 3 Priests
Representation: Diocese of El Paso
Vocation Director: 915-565-2921

FRANCISCAN FRIARS (M146)
(O.F.M.) (Province of the Immaculate Conception) 125 Thompson St., New York, NY 10012, (212) 674-4388
Web: www.franciscanvoc.org
Email: Charles848@aol.com
Members: 4 Bishops, 144 Friars, 29 Brothers, 3 Permanent Deacons
Conduct: 42 parishes, 21 residence
Apostolic Work: Teaching, colleges, high school, campus ministry, hospital and school chaplaincies, pastoral counseling, parishes, soup kitchens, ecumenical work, retreats, renewals, and Christian Formation, foreign and home missions, inner-city projects, tutorial programs, Spanish and Italian speaking apostolates, special services, pilgrimages, development programs, formation and vocation apostolates, experimental communities, medical and clerical work, CCD apostolates, teenage apostolates with prisoners, mentally retarded, addicts, alcoholics, caring for the aged, Secular Franciscan apostolates, summer camps, working with the poor, Apostolate of Prayer
Representation: Archdioceses of Boston, Hartford and New York and in the Dioceses of Albany, Bridgeport, Brooklyn, Fall River, Manchester, Metuchen, Pittsburgh, Portland (ME) Trenton, Wheeling-Charleston and Youngstown. Also in Central America, Toronto (Canada) and Italy
Vocation Director: Brother Charles Gingerich, O.F.M., Franciscan Vocation Office, 459 River Rd., Andover, MA 01810-4213, toll-free: 800-521-5442 (day), 888-521-5442 (night), fax: (978) 863-0172

FRANCISCAN FRIARS (M147)
(O.F.M.) (Holy Name Province) Provincial Office, 129 W. 31st St., 2nd Floor, New York, NY 10001 (646) 473-0265
Web: www.BeAFranciscan.org
Email: vocation@hnp.org

embers: 377 Total Members; 356 Solemnly Professed, 17 Simply Professed, 1 Novice, 3 Postulants, Friar Archbishop, 280 Priests, 72 Brothers, 14 Missionaries
Conduct: 29 parishes, 4 urban ministry centers, 3 service churches, 45 community houses-residences, 10 chaplaincies, 1 military chaplain, 3 institutions of higher education, 8 campus ministries, 4 spirituality centers, 3 houses of formation
Apostolic Work: Parish ministry, social services, outreach to the poor, counseling, education, campus ministry, retreats, parish missions and days of renewal, foreign missions (Bolivia, Brazil, Japan, Peru, Taiwan and Vietnam)
Representation: Eastern Coastal States from Maine to Florida, Asia and South America
Vocation Director: Fr. Brian Smail, OFM, Franciscan Vocation Ministry, 129 West 31st Street, 2nd Floor, New York, NY 10001-3403, (800) 677-7788 (toll free) or (646) 473-0265, fax: (800) 793-7649

FRANCISCAN FRIARS (M148)
(O.F.M.) (Province of Our Lady of Guadalupe) 318 Oblate Dr., San Antonio, TX 78216-6632
Web: www.olgofm.org
Email: Aboytesofm@aol.com
Members: 40 Priests, 22 Brothers, 2 Postulants
Conduct: Parishes and missions among the culturally rich American Indian, Hispanic, and Anglo communities, retreats, social work, renewal preaching
Representation: Archdioceses of San Antonio, Santa Fe and Denver and in the Dioceses of Gallup and Las Cruces
Vocation Director: Rev. Gonzalo Moreno, OFM, Franciscan Vocation Office, (210) 366-5053

FRANCISCAN FRIARS (M149)
(O.F.M.) (Sacred Heart Province), (314) 353-3421 www.thefriars.org 3140 Meramec St., St. Louis, MO 63118-4399
Web: www.brotherfrancis.com
Email: yes@BrotherFrancis.com
Members: 300 Priests and Brothers
Apostolic Work: Work is determined by the talents and interests of the members. 48 parishes, 1 college, 2 high schools, foreign missions and work with minorities (Mexicans, Blacks, Native Americans) at home. Many engaged in special ministries; nursing care, chaplains at a variety

of institutions (hospitals, jails, etc.), teachers at other colleges and high schools, military chaplains, retreats, campus ministry, Social Justice issues, youth ministry, music ministry, etc.
Vocation Director: Br. Jack Carnaghi, OFM, 4927 N. Claremont Ave., Chicago, IL 60625 (773) 606-2769, www.franciscanvocation.com

FRANCISCAN FRIARS (M150)
(OFM) Province of St. Barbara, 1500 34th Ave., Oakland, CA 94601 (510) 536-3722
Web: www.sbfranciscans.org
Vocations Blog: http://friarsidechats.blogspot.com
Email: vocations@sbfranciscans.org
Members: 245 Friars
Apostolic Work: All honest work can be Franciscan Ministry. Parishes, retreat houses, Native American and foreign missions, education, social work, social justice, hospital chaplains, skilled trades, other professions
Representation: Archdioceses of Los Angeles, Portland (OR) and San Francisco and in the Dioceses of Fresno, Monterey, Oakland, Orange, Phoenix, Sacramento, San Diego, Spokane and Tucson. Province boundaries include WA, OR, CA, NV, AZ and NM. Also in foreign missions
Vocation Director: Fr. Chuck Talley, ofm, St Francis Friary, 1112 26th St., Sacramento, CA 95816, (916) 443-2714, national toll-free: 800-234-FRIAR

FRANCISCAN FRIARS (M151-1)
(O.F.M.) (Viceprovince of St. Casimir) Franciscan Friary, PO Box 980, Kennebunkport, ME 04046
Web: www.ofm-usa.com
Email: framon@adelphia.net
Members: 15 Priests in US and Canada
Apostolic Work: Parish work, retreats, missions, printed word apostolate
Representation: Portland, ME; St. Petersburg, FL; Toronto and Hamilton (Ontario, Canada). Main work is in Lithuania: friary, novitiate, parish, seminarians' friary
Vocation Director: (Note: candidates need to learn the Lithuanian language, as well as go to Lithuania for their formation) Fr. John Bacevicius, O.F.M., (207) 967-2011

FRANCISCAN FRIARS (M151-2)
(O.F.M.) (Order of Friars Minor) Province of Saints Francis and James, Our Lady of Guadalupe 504 E. Santa Clara St., Hebbronville, TX 78361
(361) 527-3865, fax: (361) 527-5548
Email: ofmjal@prodigy.net.mx
gpeheb@hotmail.com
Members: 3 Priests and 1 Brother
Apostolic Work: Missions in Peru, Mexico and Africa, poor parishes, schools
Representation: Diocese of Laredo. 12 dioceses in Mexico. Foreign missions in Africa (Uganda, Tanzania, Zimbabwe, Marruecos, Kenya); Peru and Israel.
Vocation Director: Belen 220, 44290 Guadalajara Jal, Mexico

FRANCISCAN FRIARS (M152)
(O.F.M.) Province of St. John the Baptist, 5000 Colerain Avenue, Cincinnati, OH 45223, 800-827-1082
Web: www.franciscan.org
Email: sjbvocations@franciscan.org
Members: 195 Friars
Apostolic Work: In the vision and the Rule of St. Francis of Assisi, one of the primary ministries of the friars is to live the Gospel life in a community of brothers.Community itself is a ministry and a witness to the world of the Reign of God coming among us. From their community lives, the friars of St. John the Baptist Province serve the poor and the middle class, heritages, farmers, Appalachians, inner city folk, suburbanites and Secular Franciscans. They minister in homes and on the streets and in the friaries; in parishes, schools, retreats, hospitals and mission lands
Representation: 11 states from Michigan to Texas and from Pennsylvania to Arizona. Also in Mexico, Japan, Jamaica, Kenya, Peru, South Africa, Germany, the Philippines and Switzerland
Vocation Director: Fr. Donald Miller, O.F.M., Vocation Office, 5000 Colerain Ave., Cincinnati, OH 45223, 800-827-1082 (toll-free)

FRANCISCAN FRIARS (M153)
(O.F.M.) (Croatian Franciscan Custody of the Holy Family) (Vice-Province of the Holy Family), 4851 S. Drexel Blvd., Chicago, IL 60615-1703, (773) 536-0552
Web: www.ofm-usa.com
Email: Sbofm25@aol.com
Members: 31 Friars
Conduct: 8 parishes, 1 friary, 6

missions in Canada

Apostolic Work: Pastoral ministry among American Croatians and other entities in the US and Canada; Croatian Franciscan Press (Chicago)

Representation: US (Arch)dioceses of Chicago, New York, Milwaukee, Detroit, St. Louis, and Canadian (Arch)dioceses of Montreal, London, Hamilton and Sault Ste. Marie

Vocation Director: Fr. Stephen Bedenikovic, O.F.M., Sacred Heart Church, 2864 East 96th St., Chicago, IL 60617, (773) 768-1423

FRANCISCAN FRIARS (M154)
(O.F.M.) (Custody of the Holy Land)
US Foundation, 1400 Quincy St. NE, Washington, DC 20017
Web: www.myfranciscan.org
Members: 97 Priests, 44 Brothers, 55 Students in Formation, 7 Novices, 35 Candidates in US and Holy Land
Apostolic Work: All areas of Church service in Washington, DC, in the Holy Land and Middle East
Vocation Director: (202) 526-6800, fax: (202) 529-9889

FRANCISCAN FRIARS OF (M155-1)
THE ATONEMENT
See Atonement Friars

FRANCISCAN FRIARS OF (M155-2)
THE IMMACULATE (F.I.)
Motherhouse and Novitiate: Marian House of Our Lady of Guadalupe, 199 Colonel Brown Rd., Griswold, CT 06351, 860-376-6840
Web: www.marymediatrix.com or www.airmaria.com
Email: ffivocations@bluemarble.net
Members: 25 Friars, 7 Novices, 4 Friaries in US, over 400 Friars worldwide
Apostolic Work: To make the Immaculate known and loved by every heart using preaching, the Sacraments, writing, music, mass media, computer, retreats, youthwork, etc.
Representation: (Arch)dioceses of Fall River, Indianapolis, Norwich, Syracuse, and LaCrosse
Vocation Director: Rev. Jacinto Mary Chapin, F.I., (812) 825-4742, 8210 West State Road 48, Bloomington, IN 47404

(M156)
FRANCISCAN FRIARS OF THE RENEWAL (COMMUNITY OF) (CFR)
St. Crispin Friary, 420 E. 156th St., Bronx, NY 10455, (718) 665-2441
Web: www.franciscanfriars.com

Conduct: The Padre Pio Shelter and The Saint Anthony Residence - short and long-term housing for men in the South Bronx; the St. Francis Youth Center; La Casa de Juan Diego - a center for evangelization, education and hospitality in Yonkers; retreats, days/evenings of recollection, parish missions, conferences, street evangelization, youth prayer festivals
Apostolic Work: Spiritual and corporal works of mercy extended toward the poor and homeless; evangelization in all forms
Representation: Archdioceses of New York and Newark. Foreign missions in London, Bradford (England) Comayagua (Honduras)
Vocation Director: Rev. Gabriel M. Bakkar, CFR, St. Joseph Friary, 523 W. 142nd St., New York, NY 10031, (212) 281-4355

FRANCISCAN FRIARS (M157)
(O.F.M. Conv.) (Order of Friars Minor Conventual)
Immaculate Conception Province
The Alibrandi Center,110 Walnut Place, Syracuse, NY 13210-2406
Web: www.franciscans.org
Email: friarmichaellor@aol.com
Members: 122 Priests and Brothers, 4 Student Friars, 3 Novices, 4 Pre-Novitiate Students
Apostolic Work: Active-contemplative men involved in parish ministry, education (secondary, college, graduate level teaching and administration), campus ministry, youth ministry, hospital chaplaincies, counseling, retreats, Secular Franciscan Order, social work, health care, manual labor, service to the poor, special education, Spanish speaking apostolates and missions in Costa Rica and Brazil. Pre-novitiate house: Washington, DC; Novitiate: Mishwaka (IN); Major Theological Seminary, WTU
Representation: Archdiocese of New York and in the Dioceses of Albany, Syracuse, Trenton, Metuchen, Charlotte and Raleigh; also in Archdioceses of Toronto and San Jose, Costa Rica and the Dioceses of Kingston, Hamilton, Ontario and Alajuela, Costa Rica
Vocation Director: Contact, (315) 475-0853

FRANCISCAN FRIARS (M158)
(O.F.M. Conv.) (Order of Friars Minor Conventual), Province of Our Lady of Consolation, Mount Saint Francis IN 47146
Web: www.franciscans.org
Email: franvoc@aol.com
Members: 100 Priests, 25 Brothers, 10 Students
Apostolic Work: Parish, retreats, education, campus, youth, counseling, chaplaincies, teaching Missions in Zambia, Africa; Central America and Denmark.
Representation: Archdioceses of Minneapolis-Saint Paul, MN, Washington, DC, Indianapolis, IN, Louisville, KY and San Antonio, TX and in the Dioceses of Cleveland and Toledo, OH, El Paso, TX, Lansing, MI, Fort Wayne, IN, Las Cruces, NM and Savannah, GA.
Vocation Director: Friar Paul Schloemer, OFM Conv., Conventual Franciscans, 6901 Dixie Hwy., Louisville, KY 40258, (502) 933-4439 or 800-424-9955, franvoc@aol.com;
Br. Tim Unser, OFM Conv., 1104 Kentucky Ave., San Antonio, TX 78201, (210) 734-4962, brtimswvoc@yahoo.com

FRANCISCAN FRIARS (M159)
(O.F.M. Conv.) (Order of Friars Minor Conventual) St. Anthony of Padua Province, USA, 12300 Folly Quarter Rd., Ellicott City, MD 21042-1419 (410) 531-1400
Web: www.franciscans.org
Email: vocations@saprov.org
Members: 120 Priests, 13 Brothers in Solemn Vows, 5 Clerics in Temporary Vows, 1 Novice, 3 Postulants
Apostolic Work: Parish ministry, secondary education, campus ministry, counselling, foreign missions, retreats, nursing
Representation: Archdioceses of Atlanta, Baltimore, Boston and Hartford and in the Dioceses of Altoona-Johnstown, Bridgeport, Brooklyn, Buffalo, Fall River, Harrisburg, Norwich, Palm Beach, Paterson, and Springfield (MA)
Vocation Director: Fr. Vincent Gluc, O.F.M. Conv., PO Box 29315, Baltimore, MD 21213, 800-937-4945

FRANCISCAN FRIARS (M160)
(O.F.M. Conv.) (Order of Friars Minor Conventual), St. Bonaventure Province , 6107 N. Kenmore Ave., Chicago, IL 60660
Web: franciscancommunity.com

Email: chicagofranciscans@
yahoo.com
Members: 40 Solemnly Professed
Friars, 9 Temporary Professed
Friars, 4 Novices, 6 Postulants
Conduct: 7 friaries/parishes, 1
shrine/retreat house
Apostolic Work: Parish, education,
counseling, catechetics,
publications, nursing and health
care, retreats, skilled trades,
institutional chaplaincies, foreign
missions, Marian and Eucharistic
Apostolate
Representation: Archdioceses of
Chicago, Detroit and Milwaukee
and in the Dioceses of Rockford
and Peoria
Vocation Director: Br. Joseph Wood,
O.F.M. Conv., (773) 764-8811 ext. 223

FRANCISCAN FRIARS (M161)
**(O.F.M. Conv.) (Order of Friars Minor
Conventual)** St. Joseph Cupertino
Province, PO Box 820, Arroyo
Grande, CA 93421-0820
(805) 489-1012
Web: www.franciscans.org
Email: calfriars@aol.com
Members: 43 Priests, 14 Brothers,
12 Seminarians, 3 Novices, 3
Postulants
Conduct: 11 parishes, 1 high school,
5 hospital chaplains, 1 military
chaplain, 12 friaries, 3 formation
houses.
Representation: Archdioceses of Los
Angeles and San Francisco and in
the Dioceses of Fresno, Monterey,
Oakland, San Bernardino and Reno
Vocation Director: Br. Christopher
Saindon, OFM Conv., 7770 St.
Bernard St., Playa del Rey, CA
90293-8370, (310) 923-2678,
brchrissaindon@franciscans.org

FRANCISCAN FRIARS, (M162)
THIRD ORDER REGULAR (T.O.R.)
(Province of the Immaculate
Conception) Provincialate
St. Bridget Friary, 3811 Emerson
Ave. N., Minneapolis, MN 55412-
2038
Web: www.franciscanfriarstor.com
Email: frpattor@hotmail.com
Members: 45 Friars in Province
(Priests and Brothers)
Apostolic Work: Parish ministry, high
school/college/graduate school
teaching, pastoral ministers,
hospital/prison chaplains, retreat
centers
Representation: Archdioceses of
Minneapolis-St. Paul and
Washington and in the Dioceses of
Altoona-Johnstown, Orlando and
Wheeling-Charleston

Vocation Director: Rev. Patrick Foley,
TOR, 800-2200TOR (220-0867) or
(612) 529-8692; (612) 229-2013
(cell)

FRANCISCANS, THIRD (M163)
ORDER REGULAR (T.O.R.)
(Province of The Most Sacred Heart
of Jesus) Vocation Office, PO Box
104, Loretto, PA 15940
Web: www.franciscanstor.org
Email: vocationsTOR@aol.com
Members: 109 Priests, 25 Brothers,
11 Friars in Formation
Apostolic Work: Parishes, high
schools, houses of formation,
Church renewal, campus ministries,
social justice, hospital chaplaincies,
home and foreign missions, 2
universities (St. Francis University
and Franciscan University of
Steubenville)
Representation: Archdioceses of
Baltimore, Philadelphia, Washington
and in the Dioceses of Altoona-
Johnstown, Arlington, Charlotte,
Fort Worth, Pittsburgh, Rockville
Centre, St. Petersburg, Sioux Falls,
Steubenville, Venice and Wheeling-
Charleston
Vocation Director: Rev. Jonathan St.
Andre, TOR, (814) 472-8060, fax:
(814) 471-1866

FRANCISCAN FRIARS, (M164)
THIRD ORDER REGULAR (T.O.R.)
Generalate: Mexico
Saint Lawrence Parish, 236 E.
Petaluma, San Antonio, TX 78221
Members: 35 Priests
Representation: Archdiocese of San
Antonio and in the Dioceses of Fort
Worth and Austin. Also in Mexico
Vocation Director: Alberto Burgos,
T.O.R., St. Francis Church, 301
Jefferson Ave., San Antonio, TX
76701

FRANCISCAN MISSIONARY (M165-1)
**BROTHERS OF THE SACRED
HEART OF JESUS (O.S.F.)**
Our Lady of the Angels Monastery,
265 Saint Joseph Rd., Pacific, MO
63069, (636) 587-2789
Web: www.franciscancaring.org
Email: fcwebsite@mindspring.com
Members: 9 Brothers
Apostolic Work: Nursing
Representation: Archdiocese of St.
Louis and in the Diocese of Joliet
Vocation Director: Br. John Spila,
O.S.F., Franciscan Caring, 300
Forby Rd., PO Box 476, Eureka MO
63025, (636) 938-5151

FRANCISCAN MISSIONARY (M165-2)
**HERMITS OF SAINT JOSEPH
(F.M.H.J.)** St. Joseph's, RR 1, Box
1590, Laceyville, PA 18623
Web: www.medugorje.com
Representation: Diocese of Scranton
Vocation Director: Fr. Pio Mandato,
FMHJ

GLENMARY HOME (M166)
MISSIONERS
PO Box 465618, Cincinnati, OH
45246-5618
Web: www.glenmary.org
Email: vocation@glenmary.org
Members: 50 Priests, 18 Brothers, 3
Men in Training
Conduct: Over 60 mission and
ministry locations. Candidacy
program and novitiate in Hartford,
KY. Theology and advanced training
at various schools/locations
depending upon individual needs of
priesthood/brotherhood candidates
Apostolic Work: Mission work with
the poor, unchurched, and Catholic
minority in the US: Appalachia,
South, and Southwest
Representation: (Arch)dioceses of
Birmingham, AL; Cincinnati, OH;
Covington, KY; Jackson, MS;
Knoxville, TN; Lexington, KY; Little
Rock, AR; Nashville, TN;
Owensboro, KY; Raleigh, NC;
Richmond, VA; Savannah, GA;
Tulsa, OK and Wheeling-
Charleston, WV
Vocation Director: 800-935-0975, fax:
(513) 874-1690

GUANELLIAN PRIESTS (M167)
AND BROTHERS
See Servants of Charity

(M168-1)
**HERMITS OF THE BLESSED VIRGIN
MARY OF MOUNT CARMEL (O. Carm)**
Mount Carmel Hermitage, PO Box
337, Christoval, TX 76935-0337
Web: www.carmelitehermits.org
Email: stellamaris@
carmelitehermits.org
Members: 5 Hermits
Apostolic Work: Contemplative
community of hermit-monks,
following the Carmelite Rule in its
eremitical form
Representation: Diocese of San
Angelo
Vocation Director: Fr. Fabian Maria,
O. Carm., (325) 896-2249, fax:
(325) 896-2265

B-30

HERMITS OF THE MOST (M168-2)
**BLESSED VIRGIN MARY OF MOUNT
CARMEL (O. Carm.)** Carmelite
Hermitage of the Blessed Virgin
Mary, 8249 de Montreville Trail, Lake
Elmo, MN 55042
Web: www.decorcarmeli.com
Email: carmelus@earthlink.net
Members: 7 Hermits
Apostolic Work: Contemplative life of
prayer, study, and labor; reverent
celebration of the liturgy and some
spiritual direction
Representation: Archdiocese of St.
Paul and Minneapolis
Vocation Director: Fr. John Burns, O.
Carm., (651) 779-7351 (tel, fax)

HOLY APOSTLES, SOCIETY (M169)
**OF THE MISSIONARIES OF THE
(M.S.A.)**
See "M" - Missionaries of the Holy
Apostles (Society of the)

HOLY CROSS BROTHERS (M170)
(C.S.C.) Eastern Province
85 Overlook Circle, New Rochelle,
NY 10804
Web: www.holycrossbrothers.org
Email: holycrossvocations@
        earthlink.net
Members: 110 Brothers
Conduct: High schools, middle
schools, social service agencies,
alternative education programs, and
missions in Kenya, Uganda, and
Tanzania
Apostolic Work: Education, spiritual
direction/retreats, parish and social
ministry, health care, foreign
missions, outreach to the homeless,
jail ministry
Representation: Archdioceses of
Hartford, New York, and
Washington, DC and in the
Dioceses of Albany, Brooklyn-
Queens, Fall River, and Wilmington
Vocation Director: Brother Jonathan
Beebe, CSC, (917) 538-7561, Fax:
(914) 632-2490
holycrossvocations@earthlink.net

HOLY CROSS BROTHERS (M171)
(C.S.C.) (Midwest Province)
Provincial House, 54515 State Rd.
933 N., PO Box 460
Notre Dame, IN 46556-0460
(574) 251-2221, fax: (574) 289-0487
Web: www.holycrossbrothers.org
        www.brothersofholycross.com
Email: cfreel@
        brothersofholycross.com
Members: 180 Brothers
Apostolic Work: Brothers are
engaged in education, campus and
youth ministry, retreat ministry,
parish and social work, health care,

work with the poor and elderly, in
trades and other areas of service in
the United States and overseas in
Bangladesh, South America, Ghana
and Liberia.
Representation: Archdioceses of
Chicago, Detroit, Los Angeles and
Miami and in the Dioceses of
Austin, Charleston, SC, Cleveland,
Evansville, Fort Wayne-South Bend,
Gary, Lansing, Peoria, IL, Phoenix,
Portland, OR, and Venice. Also in
Bangladesh, Ghana and Liberia.
Vocation Director: Bro. Chester A.
Freel, C.S.C., (574) 631-2703

HOLY CROSS PRIESTS (M174)
(C.S.C.) (Indiana Province) Provincial
Administration Center, PO Box 1064,
Notre Dame, IN 46556-1064
Office of Vocations, PO Box 541,
Notre Dame, IN 46556-0541
Web: http://vocation.nd.edu
Email: vocation.1@nd.edu
Members: 287 Priests, 15 Brothers,
38 Seminarians
Apostolic Work: University and
secondary education, preaching,
parishes, hospital chaplains, military
chaplains, scholars, authors,
publishers, social work, minorities,
counseling, psychology, music,
liturgy, inner-city, elderly, marriage
encounter, catechetical, seminary
formation, spiritual directors, youth
ministry and administration. Foreign
missionaries in Chile, South
America; Kenya, Tanzania and
Uganda, Africa; and Bangladesh,
Mexico
Representation: Austin, Boston,
Cleveland, Chicago, Colorado
Springs, Los Angeles, New Orleans,
Portland (OR) and Washington
D.C., Fort Wayne-South Bend,
Fresno, Oakland, Phoenix, and San
Bernardino
Vocation Director: Rev. Edwin H.
Obermiller, C.S.C., Rev. James T.
Gallagher, and Rev. Peter M.
McCormick, PO Box 541, Notre
Dame, IN 46556, (574) 631-6385,
Fax: (574) 631-3729

HOLY CROSS PRIESTS (M175)
AND BROTHERS (C.S.C.)
(Eastern Province), 835 Clinton Ave.,
Bridgeport, CT 06604
Web: www.holycrosscsc.org
Email: vocation.1@nd.edu
Members: 116 Priests, 12 Brothers,
2 Seminarians
Conduct: 2 colleges, retreat house,
Holy Cross Family Ministries,
Family Rosary and Family Theater,
Pastoral Institute for the Family
(US, Peru, Ireland), missionary

district of Peru, 3 houses of
formation (2 in Peru), administer or
assist in 12 parishes
Apostolic Work: University and
secondary education, campus
ministry, parishes, hospital
chaplains, health care, prison
ministry, retreat house, family
ministries, foreign missions, social
work, counseling, formation,
chaplains to Holy Cross Associates
Representation: Archdioceses of
Boston, Chicago, Hartford, Los
Angeles and New York and in the
Dioceses of Albany, Austin,
Bridgeport, Burlington, Fall River,
Fort Wayne-South Bend,
Manchester, New Orleans, Norwich,
Orlando, Portland (ME), Rochester,
St. Petersburg and Scranton.
Missionaries in Africa, Asia, Latin
America and in 3 dioceses in Peru.
Vocation Director: Rev. Edwin H.
Obermiller, C.S.C. and Rev. James
T. Gallagher, C.S.C., PO Box 541,
Notre Dame, IN 46556, (574) 631-
6385, Fax: (574) 631-3729

BROTHERS OF HOLY (M176)
EUCHARIST (F.S.E.)
General Motherhouse, PO Box 25,
Plaucheville, LA 71362
Conduct: 2 houses, 1 high school, 2
elementary schools, 1 novitiate
Representation: Diocese of
Alexandria and Baton Rouge
Vocation Director: Bro. Andre M.
Lucia, F.S.E., Superior General,
(318) 922-3630 or 3401, fax: (318)
922-3776

CONGREGATION OF THE (M177)
**MISSIONARIES OF THE HOLY
FAMILY**
See - Missionaries of the Holy
Family

SONS OF THE HOLY FAMILY (M178)
(S.F.) Generalate: Spain
(North American Vice Province) 401
Randolph Rd., PO Box 4138, Silver
Spring, MD 20904, 301-622-1184
Web: www.manyanet.org
Email: hernandoc@gmail.com
Members: 13 Priests in US
Apostolic Work: Teaching, social
work, parishes, retreats, Hispanic
ministry
Representation: Archdioceses of
Santa Fe and Washington (DC)
Vocation Director: Rev. Hernando
Cort, SF, (301) 622-1184

HOLY GHOST FATHERS OF (M179)
IRELAND (C.S.Sp.)
48-49 37th St., Long Island City, NY
11101, (718) 729-5273

Web: www.spiritans.org
Members: 65 Fathers
Representation: Archdioceses of Boston, New Orleans, New York and San Francisco and in the Dioceses of Brooklyn, Fargo, Palm Beach, Peoria and St. Augustine
Vocation Director: Laval House, Duquesne University, Pittsburgh, PA 15282

HOLY GHOST FATHERS   (M180)
See The Spiritans - Congregation of the Holy Spirit

(M181)
BROTHERS OF THE HOLY ROSARY (Congregation of Our Lady of the Rosary) Motherhouse, 232 Sunnyside Dr., Reno, NV 89503-3510, 775-747-4441
Email: bros-reno@charter.net
Apostolic Work: A small diocesan community serving the needs of the Diocese of Reno with emphasis on educational apostolate in elementary and secondary schools. Also work in the areas of CCD, adult education and parish ministry
Representation: Diocese of Reno.
Vocation Director: Bro. Philip Napolitano, F.S.R., (775) 747-4441

HOSPITALLER BROTHERS   (M182)
OF ST. JOHN OF GOD (O.H.)
Immaculate Conception Province 1145 Delsea Dr., Westville Grove, NJ 08093
Web: www.brothersofstjohnofgod.org
Email: religiousbrother@gmail.com
Members: 42 Brothers
Apostolic Work: School and vocational center for children and adults with special needs. Outreach program and pastoral counselling for the underprivileged. A worldwide Order of Brothers founded by St. John of God at Granada, Spain in 1539. A Community of Brothers sharing love, hope and respect with those who need it most. Headquarters of the Order in Rome.
Representation: Diocese of Camden
Vocation Director: Bro. Thomas Osorio, OH, 856-848-4700, ext. 163, fax: 856-848-2154

HOSPITALLER BROTHERS   (M183)
OF ST. JOHN OF GOD (O.H.)
(Our Lady Queen of Angels Province) US Provincial House 2425 S. Western Ave., Los Angeles, CA 90018-2025
Web: www.hospitallers.org
Email: sjgvocations@sbcglobal.net
Members: 3 Priests, 28 Brothers
Conduct: 2 skilled nursing facilities,

social model for alcohol rehabilitation service, 1 novitiate, 1 Christian community, co-ministry in acute care facility, 1 HIV transitional housing
Apostolic Work: Called daily to witness Christ's healing love through a community of prayer and service to God's suffering people
Representation: Archdiocese of Los Angeles and in the Diocese of San Bernadino, CA. International Headquarters of Order's 225 hospitals and schools at Tiber Island, Rome. Missions in Africa, South America, Korea, Japan, Vietnam, India, Philippines and the Holy Land.
Vocation Director: (323) 734-0233, fax: (323) 731-5987

(M184)
IDENTE MISSIONARIES (Institute Id of Christ the Redeemer) (M.Id.)
Church of Santa Maria, 2352 St. Raymond Ave., Bronx, NY 10462
Web: www.identemissionaries.org
Email: crismartin@mail.com
Members: 3 Priests, 8 Brothers, 3 Novices
Apostolic Work: Spiritual direction, parish ministry, campus ministry, youth ministry, retreat center, college/theology/pre-theology residence, house of formation, domestic and foreign missions
Representation: New York. Also in Europe, Africa, Asia and in most countries of South America
Vocation Director: Fr. Cristobal Martin, M.Id., (718) 828-2380

(M185)
BROTHERS OF THE IMMACULATE HEART OF MARY (I.H.M.)
609 N. 7th St.
Steubenville, OH 43952
Members: 3 Brothers in Apostolic Works
Apostolic Work: Parishes, CCD teachers, master of ceremonies for the bishop, retired bishop's residence
Representation: Diocese of Steubenville
Vocation Director: Brother Patrick Geary, (740) 283-2462

(M186)
INSTITUTE OF CHARITY (I.C.) (The Rosminian Priests and Brothers)
2327 W. Heading Ave.
Peoria, IL 61604
Members: 10 Priests in US; 250 Priests and Brothers worldwide
Apostolic Work: Founded to accept ANY and ALL works of charity. At present, members are involved in teaching the handicapped, parish

work, and missionary activity throughout the world
Representation: Dioceses of Peoria and St. Petersburg
Vocation Director: Fr. Paul Stiene, I.C., (309) 676-6341

INSTITUTE OF CHRIST   (M186-1)
THE KING SOVEREIGN PRIEST
6415 S. Woodlawn Ave.
Chicago, IL 60637
Web: www.institute-christ-king.org
Email: info@institute-christ-king.org
Members: 14 in the US ; Worldwide 50 priests, 12 oblates, 14 sisters, 70 seminarians
Apostolic Work: Spreading the reign of Christ in all spheres of human life by drawing from the millennial treasury of the Roman Catholic Church, particularly her liturgical tradition (extraordinary form), the unbroken line of spiritual thought and practice of her saints, and her cultural patrimony in music, art and architecture. The Institute accomplishes this primarily through a solid and well-rounded formation of its priests at its seminary in the Archdiocese of Florence. Our priests discharge their apostolic work in the churches assigned to the Institute, its schools, its missions in Africa, by preaching retreats, teaching catechesis, and providing spiritual guidance. Our sisters support the work of our priests with their prayers, and practically by making vestments and giving spiritual retreats to young women. The clerical oblates (brothers) support the apostolates according to their talents and aptitudes
Representation: Archdioceses of Chicago, Milwaukee, Newark, St. Louis; Dioceses of Oakland, San Jose, Kansas City-St. Joseph, Rockford, Green Bay, La Crosse, Belleville, and Tucson. Also in Gabon (Africa), Belgium, France, Germany, Italy, Spain, and Austria.
Vocation Director: Rev. Msgr. R. Michael Schmitz, (773) 363-7409, fax: (773) 363-7824

INSTITUTE OF THE   (M186-2)
INCARNATE WORD (I.V.E.)
Provincial Headquarters Province of the Immaculate Conception, Generalate: Rome St. Paul's Church, 113 E. 117th St., New York, NY 10035-4469
Web: www.iveamerica.org; www.ivevocations.org
Email: prov.immaculate. conception@ive.org

B-32

Representation: (Arch)dioceses of Bridgeport, Brooklyn, Fall River, New York, Philadelphia, Phoenix, San Jose and Washington. Also in Canada and Guyana
Vocation Director: Rev. Mariano Vicchi, I.V.E., phone: (301) 779-0121, e-mail: marianovicchi@ive.org

SOCIETY OF JESUS (S.J.) (M187) **(JESUITS) (The Society of Jesus in the United States)**
1016 16th Street, NW Suite 400, Washington, DC 20036
Email: vocations@jesuit.org
Members: 2,900 Priests and Brothers in the United States along with 20,000 around the world are serving God's people as Jesuits
Conduct: Men who are called to the Society of Jesus desire to be contemplatives in action combining faith and the promotion of justice. After two years as a novice, a Jesuit pronounces his solemn vows and engages in six years of philosophy and theology studies. He also engages in teaching ministry for three years. Most Jesuits receive priestly ordination after the 11 year training, but others also serve as brothers in a variety of ministries
Apostolic Work: Jesuits are best known in the fields of education (schools, colleges, universities, seminaries, theological faculties), intellectual research, and cultural pursuits. They also engage in missionary work and direct evangelization to the poor, social justice and human rights activities, interreligious dialogue, and other 'frontier' ministries. Most importantly, Jesuits continue the tradition of providing Christian retreats, based on the foundational document of Ignatius: The Spiritual Exercises. Jesuits are inspired by their motto: All for the greater glory of God
Representation: Arch(dioceses) of Allentown, Anchorage, Baltimore, Boston, Bridgeport, Buffalo, Burlington, Chicago, Honolulu, Los Angeles, Manchester, Marquette, Miami, Milwaukee, Nashville, New York, Norwich, Oakland, Philadelphia, Portland (ME), Rapid City, St. Augustine, St. Louis, St. Paul-Minneapolis, St. Petersburg, San Francisco, Scranton, Seattle, Springfield (MA), Spokane, Syracuse, Tucson, Venice, Washington, Wheeling, Worcester and others. Also, in the international field (but not limited to): Brazil, Canada, Egypt, Ethiopia, Italy,

Jamaica, Jordan, Lebanon, Mozambique, Nepal and Tanzania
Vocation Director: For more information, please contact: Vocation Director for the Society of Jesus, The Jesuit Conference, 1016 16th Street, NW, Suite 400, Washington, DC, 20036, email: vocations@jesuit.org, phone: 202-462-0400

JOSEPHITE FATHERS (M204) **(C.J.),** Novitiate, 180 Patterson Rd., Santa Maria, CA 93455
Web: www.josephiteweb.org
Email: jalbert@sjhsknights.com
Members: 10 Priests
Conduct: 2 parishes, 2 high schools
Representation: Archdiocese of Los Angeles, Belgium, England, Congo, Gabon, Cameroon
Vocation Director: Rev. Ed Jalbert, cj, (805) 937-5378

JOSEPHITE FATHERS AND (M205) **BROTHERS (S.S.J.) (St. Joseph's Society of the Sacred Heart)**
1200 Varnum St. NE, Washington, DC 20017
Web: www.josephite.com
Email: vocations@josephite.com
Members: 95 Priests, 9 Brothers
Conduct: 42 city and rural parishes, hospital and prison chaplaincies, 1 high school, 12 elementary schools, a novitiate in Baltimore, Maryland, a major seminary for graduate theology, the Josephite Pastoral Center and quarterly magazine Josephite Harvest
Apostolic Work: The Josephite Society is dedicated to a spiritual, educational and social ministry to the African-American community and has worked exclusively in the African-American community since 1871. The Josephite Society affords its members the mutual support of community life in an active ministry
Representation: Archdioceses of Baltimore, Washington and New Orleans and in the Dioceses of Arlington, Baton Rouge, Beaumont, Biloxi, Birmingham, Fort Worth, Galveston-Houston, Jackson, Lafayette, Lake Charles and Mobile
Vocation Director: Rev. Peter C. Weiss, SSJ, (202) 832-9100

(M209)
LA SALETTE MISSIONARIES (M.S.) (Missionaries of Our Lady of La Salette) (Province of Mary, Mother of the Americas) La Salette, 914 Maple Ave., Hartford, CT 06114
Web: www.lasalette.org
Email: mlsadmin@aol.com

Members: 140 Priests, 30 Brothers, 4 Oblates, 1 Scholastic
Conduct: US: 31 parishes, 4 shrines
Apostolic Work: Inner-city and suburban parishes, retreats, shrines, preaching, seminary professor, institutional and high school chaplaincies, professional counseling, spiritual direction, parish missions, foreign missions
Vocation Director: Rev. John A. Welch, M.S., (978) 342-7907, jawelchms@aol.com

LEGIONARIES OF CHRIST (M210) **(L.C.)** Territorial Directorate: Legionaries of Christ, 475 Oak Avenue, Cheshire, CT 06410
Web: www.legionofchrist.org
Email: vocation@legionaries.org
Members: Roman Catholic Congregation of priests which, since founded in 1941, has grown to over 500 Priests and 2,500 Seminarians
Conduct: Seminaries: High schools in New Hampshire, California and Ontario, Canada, for boys interested in the priesthood. Novitiate and College of Humanities in Connecticut. Philosophy in New York and Rome, Italy. Theology in Rome, Italy
Apostolic Work: Combining a deep spiritual life with an urgent apostolate (get people building Christ's Kingdom in society), the Priests engage in extensive work with lay apostolate, youth, education, family, missions, the poor, media, catechetics, and run vocation retreats for high school and college-age men
Representation: Archdioceses of Atlanta, Chicago, Denver, Detroit, Hartford, Los Angeles, New York, St. Louis and Washington and in the Dioceses of Dallas, Lincoln, Madison, Manchester, Providence, Sacramento and San Jose. Also in Canada, Ireland, Spain, France, Italy, Holland, Germany, Czechoslovakia, Poland, Brazil, Argentina, Chile, Colombia, Venezuela, Mexico and Australia
Vocation Director: Fr. Anthony Bannon, LC, 800-420-5409

LITTLE BROTHERS OF (M211) **THE GOOD SHEPHERD (B.G.S.)**
Villa Mathias, 901 Brother Mathias Place NW, Albuquerque, NM 87102
Web: www.lbgs.org
Email: info@lbgs.org
Conduct: Emergency night shelters and dining rooms, senior housing,

youth shelters, medical clinic for the homeless, hospice care, family shelters, supportive housing units, psychiatric support services, women and children's shelters-outreach service, developmentally disabled, Haitian Mission-orphanage and school
Representation: Archdioceses of Miami, FL, Santa Fe, NM, Toronto (Ontario), and Port-Au-Prince (Haiti); Dioceses of Joliet , IL, Hamilton (Ontario), Birmingham (England), and Ossory (Ireland).
Vocation Director: Br. Bill Osmanski, 680 NE 52nd St., Miami, FL 33137, (305) 510-0039; Br. Charles Schreiner, PO Box 389, Albuquerque, NM 87103 (505) 243-4238; Br. Terence Alyward, 26 Grant Ave., Hamilton, Ontario L8N 2X5, (905) 971-0868

(M212)
LITTLE BROTHERS OF JESUS
5870 Baker St., Detroit, MI 48209
Email: brosdet@yahoo.com
Apostolic Work: Contemplative life in imitation of the life of Jesus at Nazareth
Representation: Inspired by the life and writings of Charles de Foucauld, the Little Brothers seek to live as Jesus did in Nazareth. Our life is thus radically oriented to God, in the context of ordinary human life in regard to jobs, lodging, clothing, etc. Our communities are small, family size fraternities, oriented toward mutual assistance in living for God alone.
Vocation Director: (313) 849-1531

LITTLE BROTHERS OF (M213)
SAINT FRANCIS (L.B.S.F.)
General Fraternity, 785-789 Parker St., Mission Hill (Boston), MA 02120
Web: www.littlebrothersof
  stfrancis.org
Members: 4 Perpetually Professed, 2 Junior Professed
Apostolic Work: Combine contemplative life, Eucharistic Adoration and evangelical street ministry, living in radical poverty and prayerful solidarity with the poorest of Christ's poor in the ghettos, favelos or barrios of the world
Vocation Director: Br. Joseph Mary Vazquez, L.B.S.F., (617) 442-2556

MARIANISTS, SOCIETY OF (M214)
MARY (SM) Province of the US
4425 W. Pine Blvd., St. Louis, MO 63108 (314) 533-1207, ext. 225
Regional Vocation Offices:
Marianist Vocation Ministry, Alumni Hall, Room 225, University of

Dayton, Dayton, OH 45469-0323
Marianist Vocation Ministry, St. Mary's University, 251 W. Ligustrum Dr., San Antonio, TX 78228
Marianist Community, 3140 Waialae Ave., Honolulu, HI 96816-1578
Lay Members: Marianist Lay Network of North America, 1210 Fairview Ave., South Bend, IN 46614
Web: www.marianist.com/vocations
Email: cjohnson@sm-usa.org
Members: 427 Brothers, 152 Priests
Apostolic Work: Education (universities, high schools, 1 middle school), retreat and renewal work, parish work, campus ministry, youth programs in camps, home for disadvantaged youth. International missions include Kenya, India, Ireland, Malawi, Mexico, and Zambia
Representation: in the US in the Archdioceses of Baltimore, Boston, Cincinnati, Los Angeles, Miami, Philadelphia, San Francisco and St. Louis and in the Dioceses of Brooklyn, Cleveland, Honolulu, Monterey, Pittsburgh, San Antonio and San Jose
Vocation Director: National Vocation Directors: Bro. Charles Johnson, SM, 4425 W. Pine Blvd., St. Louis, MO, 63108-2301;Bro. Brian Halderman, SM;
Regional Vocation Directors:
Dayton: Bro. Tom Pieper, SM, (937) 229-2741, fax: (937) 229-2772, mvm@notes.udayton.edu
San Antonio: Sr. Gretchen Trautman, FMI, 251 W. Ligustrum Dr., San Antonio, TX 78228 (210) 431-2193
Honolulu:Bro. Dennis Schmitz, SM, (808) 735-4081, Baldschmitz@aol.com;
Lay Members: Anthony Garascia, (574) 287-0904, president@mlc-clm.org

MARIANISTS, SOCIETY OF (M215)
MARY (S.M.) (Province of Meribah)
Provincial House, 240 Emory Rd., Mineola, NY 11501
Web: www.provinceofmeribah.org
Email: frjames@chaminade-hs.org
Members: 7 Priests, 36 Brothers
Conduct: 2 high schools, 3 retreat houses, 2 grammar schools
Vocation Director: Fr. James Williams, S.M., (516) 742-5555

MARIANNHILL (M219)
MISSIONARIES (CMM)
Generalate: Rome
American Region
23715 Ann Arbor Trail, Dearborn Heights, MI 48127

Web: www.mariannhill.org
Email: vheier@juno.com
Members: 7 Priests, 3 Brothers
Conduct: Community house, parish assistance, youth retreat center
Apostolic Work: Foreign missions, parish assistance, publications - Leaves magazine, youth retreat work and vocations
Representation: Archdiocese of Detroit. Houses in Germany, Canada, Austria, Holland, Poland, Spain, Switzerland and Rome, Italy. Foreign missions in South Africa, Botswana, Zimbabwe, Zambia, Papua New Guinea, Kenya, Mozambique and Colombia
Vocation Director: Rev. Vergil Heier, CMM, (313) 561-7140, ext. 25

MARIANS OF THE (M220)
IMMACULATE CONCEPTION (M.I.C.)
Blessed Virgin Mary Province
Provincial House: (413) 298-3691
Eden Hill, Stockbridge, MA 01262
Web: www.marian.org
Email: vocations@marian.org
Members: 42 Priests, 11 Brothers, 3 Novices, 2 Postulants; approximately 500 Priests & Brothers worldwide
Conduct: 5 parishes, 1 high school totaling 6 community houses
Apostolic Work: Parishes with an emphasis on teaching and publishing. Some members working in Argentina
Representation: (Arch)dioceses of Fairbanks (AK), Chicago (IL), Joliet (IL), Norwich (CT), Portland (ME), Milwaukee (WI), Springfield (MA), Steubenville (OH) and Washington (DC). Missions in Argentina
Vocation Director: Rev. Donald Calloway, MIC, 515 Belleview Blvd., Steubenville, OH 43952, 877-261-8806

MARIST BROTHERS OF (M222)
THE SCHOOLS (F.M.S.)
Province of the United States of America, 1241 Kennedy Blvd., Bayonne, NJ 07002
Web: www.maristbr.com
Email: vocations@maristbr.com
Members: 190 Brothers in the US: Over 4,000 Brothers in 79 countries worldwide
Apostolic Work: Christian education of youth, particularly the most neglected through youth ministry, all levels of education, counseling, catechetical work, retreats, summer camps, social ministry and foreign missions
Representation: Archdioceses of Boston, Chicago, Miami, Newark,

and New York and in the Dioceses of Brooklyn, Brownsville, Laredo, Manchester, Rockville Centre, and Wheeling-Charleston. American Brothers also present in Australia, Japan, the Philippines and Rome
Vocation Director: Bro. Mike Sheerin, FMS, Marist Brothers, (201) 823-1115

MARIST FATHERS AND (M223)
BROTHERS (SM) – USA
Vocation Office - St. Peter Chanel Seminary, 2335 Warring Street, Berkeley, CA 94704
Web: www.maristsociety.org
Email: maristvocations@ sbcglobal.net
Conduct: Spirituality and Ministry: The Marists (Society of Mary) are a religious community comprised of both clerical and non-clerical members vowed to live a life of poverty, celibate chastity and obedience in accordance with their rule. As contemplatives in action they seek to lead Christ - centered community lives in the spirit of Mary. Through their life together and their spiritual practice, they interiorize the spirit of Mary and endeavor to be Mary's presence in the Church today just as she was present in the Church at its birth. They are an international congregation of about one thousand members missioned throughout the northern and southern hemispheres.
Apostolic Work: Marists are faithful to the teaching of the Church, loyal to its leaders and in cooperation with the clergy, the laity and other consecrated persons they act as instruments of Christ's mercy through evangelization, pastoral service, the education of youth and the ministerial training of clergy and laity. They serve the Church and the world in the spirit of Mary and under her leadership and name.
Representation: Marists minister in the United States and in 18 different countries.
Vocation Director: Fr. Al Dianni, SM, (Northeastern USA) 698 Beacon St., Boston, MA 02215, (617) 262-2271, Mr. Jack Ridout, TOM, 2335 Warring St., Berkeley, CA, 94704, (510) 486-1232 (toll free 866-298-3715)

MARYKNOLL FATHERS & (M226)
BROTHERS (The Catholic Foreign Mission Society of America)
(located in the Town of Ossining, NY)
PO Box 305, Maryknoll, NY 10545-0305

Web: www.maryknoll.org
Email: vocation@maryknoll.org
Members: 454 Priests and Brothers
Conduct: Maryknoll Priests and Brothers work as missionaries in 27 countries around the world, in Latin America, Asia and Africa.
Foundation: Popularly known as Maryknoll, US bishops established in 1911 as a society of secular priests and lay brothers to be an overseas mission expression of the Catholic Church of the United States.Charism/Spirit: Maryknollers are grounded in faith in Jesus Christ, particularly in the context of His mission: "Then he told them, 'Go out to the whole world and proclaim the Good News to all creation!' (Mark 16:14-15); and "Seek first the Kingdom of God and His justice" (Matt. 6:33). It is this mission of Jesus that is the foundation of Maryknoll spirituality
Apostolic Work: Maryknoll Fathers and Brothers engage in a variety of different ministries, depending on need, among people they serve, most of whom are impoverished people in Third World countries. Examples of such works are: parish ministries, teaching, setting up schools, social action and community development, health care, developing basic Christian communities, justice and peace, assisting refugees, etc. Oftentimes what Maryknollers do in witnessing to the Gospel is to respond to people's concrete needs
Vocation Director: Rev. Dennis Moorman, MM, 888-627-9566 (toll-free) or (914) 941-7590, Ext. 2416

MERCEDARIANS (M227)
See Order of the Blessed Virgin Mary of Mercy

BROTHERS OF MERCY (M228)
(F.M.M.) (American Province)
4520 Ransom Rd.
Clarence, NY 14031
Web: www.brothersofmercy.org
Email: Jude@BrothersofMercy.org
Members: 12 Brothers
Apostolic Work: Senior health care and residential services
Representation: Diocese of Buffalo
Vocation Director: Br. Jude Holzfoerster, f.m.m., (716) 759-6985, ext. 353

FATHERS OF MERCY (C.P.M.) (M229)
(Congregation of Priests of Mercy)
Generalate, 806 Shaker Museum Rd., Auburn, KY 42206
Web: www.fathersofmercy.com

Email: vocations@ fathersofmercy.com
Members: 38 Members
Apostolic Work: The propagation of the Faith and the salvation of souls through the preaching of parish missions, retreats and devotions, and the staffing of rural parishes. Strong Eucharistic and Marian devotion; unwavering loyalty to the Magisterium of the Church.
Vocation Director: Rev. Tony Stephens, CPM, (270) 542-4146, ext. 2, fax: (270) 542-4147

(M230)
MILL HILL MISSIONARIES (M.H.M.)
(St. Joseph's Missionary Society)
Regional Office, 222 W. Hartsdale Ave., Hartsdale, NY 10530-1667
Web: www.millhill-missionaries.net
Email: mhmnar@aol.com
Members: 11 Fathers, 1 Brother, 1 Associate
Conduct: 21 mission territories in Africa, Asia and South America
Apostolic Work: Foreign missions
Representation: Archdioceses of New York, Ontario, Canada
Vocation Director: Rev. Bartholomew Daly, M.H.M., Regional Representative, (212) 838-3189

MINIM FATHERS (O.M.) (M231)
US Delegation General
Motherhouse: Rome
All Saints Church, 3431 Partola Ave., Los Angeles, CA 90032
Web: www.allsaintsca.com
Email: jvega@earthlink.net
Members: 3 Priests
Representation: Archdiocese of Los Angeles
Vocation Director: Fr. Gino Vanzillotta, (323) 223-1101

MISSIONARIES OF CHARITY (M232
(M.C.) Founded by Mother Teresa of Calcutta, 1316 S. Westlake Ave., Los Angeles, CA 90006
Web: www.lamcbro.org
Members: 7 Brothers in US, 450 Brothers worldwide
Apostolic Work: Giving wholehearted and free service to the poorest of the poor. In the US: work with homeless, youth, handicapped; minister to the imprisoned and to homeless immigrants
Representation: Archdiocese of Los Angeles
Vocation Director: Bro. Bob Theis, MC, (213) 384-6116

(M233
SOCIETY OF THE MISSIONARIES OF THE HOLY APOSTLES (M.S.A.)
US Headquarters, 24 Prospect Hill Rd., Cromwell, CT 06416

mail: msa-usa-online@att.net
Conduct: 6 formation houses, 3 seminaries, 2 homes for abandoned persons, 2 retreat centers, 1 high school and assist in many parishes worldwide
Apostolic Work: Primarily the theological and spiritual preparation of adult men for the priesthood. Also involved in the education of laymen and women for positions of leadership in the Church. Concerned with the evangelization and humanization ministry in mission territories
Representation: Archdiocese of Washington (DC) and in the Dioceses of Norwich and Venice (FL). Also ministering in Africa, Brazil, Canada, Italy, Peru and Venezuela
Vocation Director: 860-632-3039, fax: 860-635-4823

MISSIONARIES OF THE (M234)
HOLY FAMILY (M.S.F.)
Servants of God - Builders of Family
Provincial House, (314) 577-6300,
fax: (314) 577-6301
3014 Oregon Ave., St. Louis, MO
63118-1498
Web: www.MSF-America.org
Email: MGalindo@MSF-America.org
Members: 29 Priests and Brothers
Conduct: Staffs 1 house of study, 1 novitiate, 9 parishes, 1 nursing home chaplaincy
Apostolic Work: Involved in a large variety of apostolates, always in an attempt to serve the Church's current needs. Work in parishes, schools and homes for the aged, reflecting the order's concern and respect for family life.
Representation: Archdioceses of Ottawa, Canada, St. Louis, MO and San Antonio, TX and in the Dioceses of Brownsville, TX, Corpus Christi, TX, Richmond, VA and Saltillo, Mexico
Vocation Director: Rev. Mario Galindo, MSF, 104 Cas Hills Dr., San Antonio, TX 78213
(210) 344-9145

MISSIONARIES OF THE (M235)
HOLY SPIRIT (M.Sp.S.)
Generalate: Mexico
US Headquarters: Christ the Priest
Province, 2336 South C St., Oxnard,
CA 93030, (805) 487-2369
Web: www.christthepriest.org
Email: plantarsemilla@yahoo.com
Members: 26 Priests, 25 Brothers, 6 Novices, 5 Postulants in US; 260 Priests, 131 Brothers, 52 Novices, 29 Postulants worldwide

Apostolic Work: Spreading the spirituality of the Cross, living the lifestyle of Christ, Priest and Victim, through spiritual direction for priests, religious men and women, and lay people; spirituality centers, seminaries and parish ministry
Representation: (Arch)dioceses of Los Angeles, Orange, Portland (OR) and Seattle. Presence in Chile, Colombia, Costa Rica, Italy, Mexico, and Spain
Vocation Director: Fr. Gerardo Cisneros, M.Sp.S., cell: (805) 889-6750

MISSIONARIES OF OUR (M236)
LADY OF LA SALETTE
See La Salette Missionaries
Web: www.lasalette.org
Email: mlsadmin@aol.com

MISSIONARIES OF THE (M237)
PRECIOUS BLOOD
See - Precious Blood

MISSIONARIES OF THE (M238)
SACRED HEART (M.S.C.)
(US Province) Provincial House
305 S. Lake St., PO Box 270,
Aurora, IL 60507-0270
Web: www.misacor-usa.org
Email: vocation@misacor-usa.org
Members: 48 Fathers, 18 Brothers, 8 Students
Conduct: 11 parishes
Apostolic Work: Christian evangelization in the US and in 54 countries around the world. In the United States, MSCs bring the love of Christ to people through their service in chaplaincies, parishes, prisons and retreats. They also work extensively in multicultural ministry including ministry to Native Americans, Hispanics, Filipinos, Indonesians and Koreans, among others. The principal mission country of the USA MSC Province is Colombia. Internationally, MSC serve in a variety of ministries, including development in Papua New Guinea, AIDS ministry in Africa and migrant ministry in Europe.
Representation: US: in the Archdioceses of Philadelphia and Chicago and in the Dioceses of Rockford, Allentown, Ogdensburg, Orange, and San Bernardino, Colombia: in the Archdiocese of Bogot, Papua New Guinea: in the Diocese of Kavieng
Vocation Director: Rev. Andrew Torma, MSC, (630) 862-0979

MISSIONARIES OF THE (M239)
SACRED HEARTS OF JESUS AND MARY (M.SS.CC.)
American Headquarters: Villa Pieta,
2249 Shore Road, Linwood, NJ
08221, Motherhouse: Naples, Italy
Web: www.missionof
sacredhearts.org
Email: mssccusa@aol.com
Members: US:8 Priests, 1 Brother, 1 Brother in Temporary Vows
Conduct: 1 parish in the Diocese of Camden, NJ; 2 parishes and a House of Studies in the Diocese of Harrisburg, PA
Apostolic Work: Inner city and suburban parishes, chaplaincies, retreats, active promotion of devotion to the Sacred Hearts of Jesus and Mary
Representation: Dioceses of Camden, NJ and Harrisburg, PA and in Italy, Argentina, India, Nigeria, Slovakia, and Indonesia
Vocation Director: (609) 927-5600, fax: (609) 927-5262

MISSIONARIES OF ST. (M240)
CHARLES/SCALABRINIANS
See - St. Charles

MISSIONARY BENEDICTINE (M241)
MONKS OF ST. OTTILIEN
See - Benedictine Monks

MISSIONARY OBLATES OF (M242)
MARY IMMACULATE (O.M.I.)
(United States Province) Central Oblate Vocation Office, 800-358-4394, English and Spanish (y en español)
327 Oblate Dr., San Antonio, TX
78216-6602
Web: www.omiusa.org
Email: vocations@omiusa.org
Members: 500 Oblate Brothers and Priests in US Province; 4,700 worldwide in 68 countries
Apostolic Work: Our Congregation is committed to carrying the Gospel of Jesus Christ to others, with a special preference for the most abandoned in our society. We work in parishes, retreat centers, shrines, educational institutions, prisons and hospital chaplaincies; on reservations with Native peoples, and with minorities as well as in foreign missions
Vocation Director: Three regional Vocation Directors:
Lowell, MA: Rev. Dwight Hoeberechts, OMI, dwightomi@juno.com
San Antonio, TX: Rev. Charlie Banks, OMI, cbanks@omiusa.org
Oakland, CA: Rev. Joe Arong, OMI, jarong5966@comcast.net

MISSIONARY SERVANTS OF (M243)
THE MOST HOLY TRINITY (S.T.)
9001 New Hampshire Ave., Silver
Spring, MD 20903
Web: www.MissionaryServants
Vocations.org
Volunteer Program-www.tmc3.org
Email: vocations@trinitymissions.org
Members: 88 Priests, 26 Brothers,
15 Student Brothers, 3 Deacons, 68
Men in Formation
Conduct: 19 parishes, 22 other
mission sites, 1 theologate, 1
novitiate, 4 pre-novitiate formation
communities in the US, Mexico,
Costa Rica and Colombia
Apostolic Work: Members answer
the pressing needs of the Church
through lay apostolic and
missionary development, inner-city
parish and social service ministry,
rural missions and retreat ministry.
Ministry with Hispanics, Native
Americans and African Americans.
Ministry to the incarcerated; alcohol,
drug and post-detention
rehabilitation ministry; youth/young
adult ministry
Representation: United States,
Puerto Rico, Mexico, Costa Rica
and Columbia
Vocation Director: Mark McGuthrie,
(800) 298-5602, (909) 659-1465

MISSIONARY SOCIETY OF (M244)
ST. JAMES THE APOSTLE
24 Clark St., Boston, MA 02109
Web: www.socstjames.com
Email: foleary@socstjames.com
Apostolic Work: An association of 40
diocesan priest volunteers, sent by
their bishops through the Society of
St. James to work in mission
parishes in South America, from 33
dioceses of the United States,
Canada, England, Scotland,
Ireland, Wales, Australia, New
Zealand and the Philippines;
serving in the Dioceses of Quito,
Santo Domingo de Los Colorados
and Guayaquil, Ecuador; Lima,
Lurin, Carabayllo, Chosica, Sicuani,
Tacna-Moquegua, Peru; and Santa
Cruz, Bolivia
Vocation Director: Rev. Msgr. Finbar
O'Leary , (617) 742-4715

MISSIONARY SOCIETY OF (M245)
ST. PAUL THE APOSTLE
See Paulist Fathers

MISSIONARY SONS OFTHE (M246-1)
IMMACULATE HEART OF MARY
See Claretian Missionaries

(M246-2)
MISSIONHURST CONGREGATION
OF THE IMMACULATE HEART of
MARY (C.I.C.M.) Motherhouse: Rome
US Province: 4651 North 25th St.,
Arlington, VA 22207-3518
Web: www.missionhurst.org
Email: provincial@missionhurst.org
Members: 43 Priests and Brothers
Apostolic Work: Parishes, hospitals,
prison ministry
Representation: Archdioceses of
Boston, New York, Philadelphia and
San Antonio and in the Dioceses of
Arlington, Brownsville and Raleigh
Vocation Director: Contact: (703)
528-3800

THE COMMUNITY OF THE (M247)
MONKS OF ADORATION
See "T" - The Monks of Adoration
Web: www.monksadoration.org
Email: monkadorer@verizon.net

MONKS OF THE MOST (M248)
HOLY TRINITY MONASTERY
See Eastern Catholic Religious
Communities for Men

MONKS OF MT. TABOR (M249)
(Holy Transfiguration Monastery)
See Eastern Catholic Religious
Communities for Men

MONTFORT MISSIONARIES (M250)
(S.M.M.) US Province: 101-18 104th
St., Ozone Park, NY 11416
Web: www.montfort
missionaries.com
Email: montfortrt@aol.com
Members: 29 Fathers, 3 Brothers
Apostolic Work: Preaching, foreign
missions, pastoral work, hospital
chaplaincies, publications
Representation: Archdioceses of
Hartford and St. Louis and in the
Dioceses of Brooklyn and Rockville
Centre. Also in Nicaragua. The
Montfort Missionaries minister in 30
countries and 11 foreign missions
Vocation Director: Fr. Roy E. Tvrdik,
SMM, (718) 849-5885, 0071

BROTHERS OF OUR LADY, (M251)
MOTHER OF MERCY (C.F.M.M.)
7140 Ramsgate Avenue, Los
Angeles, CA 90045-2249
Web: www.cmmbrothers.org
Email: asmulders@lmu.edu
Members: 3 Brothers
Conduct: 1 university
Representation: Archdiocese of Los
Angeles
Vocation Director: Bro. Anthony P.
Smulders, CFMM, (310) 338-5954

NORBERTINE FATHERS (M252)
(O. PRAEM.) (Canons Regular of
Premontre) St. Michael's Abbey
19292 El Toro Rd., Silverado, CA
92676-9710
Web: www.StMichaelsAbbey.com
Email: vocationdirector333
@yahoo.com
Members: 48 Priests, 2 Transitional
Deacons, 2 Solemnly Professed
Clerics, 8 Simply Professed Clerics
9 Novices, 1 Brother
Conduct: 1 dependent house, 1
novitiate, 1 seminary for college
resident students, 1 prep high
school, 1 summer camp, 1 pious
association
Representation: Archdiocese of Los
Angeles and in the Diocese of
Orange, San Diego, San
Bernardino, Fresno, and Rome,
Italy
Vocation Director: Rev. Justin S.
Ramos, O. Praem., (949) 858-0222
ext. 333, fax: (949) 858-0225

NORBERTINE FATHERS (M253)
(O. Praem.) (Canons Regular of
Premontre) St. Norbert Abbey
1016 North Broadway, De Pere, WI
54115-2697
Web: www.norbertines.org
Email: vocations@norbertines.org
Members: 67 Priests, 4 Brothers, 4
Seminarians
Conduct: 3 dependent priories, 1
house of studies, 1 college, 2
chaplaincies, 6 parishes
Apostolic Work: Parish work,
ecumenical work, chaplaincies,
foreign missions, campus ministry
work, retreats, teaching and
educational administration
Representation: (Arch)dioceses of
Chicago, Green Bay, Jackson,
Military Services, and Santa Fe.
Also in Peru
Vocation Director: Rev. Andrew
Cribben,O.Praem., (920) 337-4333,
fax: (920) 337-4328

NORBERTINE FATHERS (M254)
AND BROTHERS (O. Praem.)
St. Moses the Black Priory
7100 Midway Rd., Raymond, MS
39154-9611
Foundation House: St. Norbert
Abbey, DePere, WI
Web: www.norbertines.org or
www.premontre.org
Email: dewaet@netnet.net
Members: 6 Priests
Apostolic Work: Ministry primarily
among African-Americans; ministry
to the poor of any race; parishes,
education, retreats, campus
ministry, spiritual direction

Vocation Director: Onwu Akpa, O. Praem., Vocations Coordinator, Norbertines of St. Moses the Black, 601-857-0157, ext. 317 fax: (601) 857-5076

NORBERTINE FATHERS AND BROTHERS (O. Praem.) (M255)
(Canons Regular of Premontre)
Immaculate Conception Priory
1269 Bayview Rd.
Middletown, DE 19709
Members: 7 Priests
Conduct: 2 parishes
Apostolic Work: Common life, retreats, parish ministry
Representation: Archdiocese of Baltimore and in the Dioceses of Wilmington and Camden
Vocation Director: Father James D. Bagnato, O. Praem., (302) 449-1840, ext. 31

NORBERTINES (O. PRAEM.) (M256)
(Canons Regular of Premontre)
Daylesford Abbey
220 S. Valley Rd., Paoli, PA 19301
Web: www.Daylesford.org
Email: brobbt@yahoo.com
Members: 30 Priests, 3 Brothers
Conduct: 4 parishes, spirituality center
Apostolic Work: Daylesford Abbey exists to enrich the Church by our Norbertine Communio, nourished by contemplation on God's work, made visible in worship and service within the local Church
Representation: Archdiocese of Philadelphia. Also in Peru
Vocation Director: Fr. William J. Kelly, O. Praem., Vocation Minister, (610) 647-2530, ext. 115, fax: (610) 651-0219

NORBERTINE COMMUNITY (M256-1)
(O. Praem.) (Canons Regular of Prémontré) Santa Maria de la Vid Priory, 5825 Coors Blvd., SW, Albuquerque, NM 87121
Web: www.norbertinecommunity.org
Email: maesanthyg1@aol.com
Members: 12 Priests, 1 Brother, 1 Postulant, 2 Simple Vows
Apostolic Work: From a community setting, we serve parishes, hospitals, a Catholic high school, prisons, and a variety of other ministerial needs. Our ministry is broadly multi-cultural. On our 70-acre property, we also provide a Hermitage Retreat and public Theological Library.
Representation: Archdiocese of Santa Fe, New Mexico
Vocation Director: Rev. Joel Garner, O.Praem, Prior, (505) 573-4399, ext. 28, fax: (505) 873-4667

OBLATES OF ST. FRANCIS DE SALES (OSFS) (M257)
(Wilmington-Philadelphia Province)
Provincial House, 2200 Kentmere Pkwy., Wilmington, DE 19806
(302) 656-8529
Web: www.oblates.org/vocations
Email: knadolski@oblates.org
Members: 162 Priests, 15 Brothers, 3 Seminarians, 2 Novices
Conduct: 23 parishes, 1 scholasticate, 1 novitiate, 6 foreign missions, 1 university, 1 high school, 1 middle school, 5 Newman Centers, 36 community houses
Apostolic Work: High school teaching, parish work, college teaching, campus ministry, overseas missions, inner-city projects. Armed Forces chaplaincies, adult education, hospital ministry and chaplaincies, conduct retreats and parish missions
Representation: Archdioceses of Boston, Military Services, Philadelphia, Washington, DC and in the Dioceses of Allentown, Arlington, Camden, Charlotte, Harrisburg, Raleigh, Venice and Wilmington. Also in Benin, Brazil, Columbia, Ecuador, Haiti, India, Mexico, Namibia, Republic of South Africa and Uruguay
Vocation Director: Fr. Kevin Nadolski, OSFS

OBLATES OF ST. FRANCIS DE SALES (O.S.F.S.) (M258)
Toledo-Detroit Province
2043 Parkside Blvd., Toledo, OH 43607
Web: www.oblates.us
Email: mlosfs@aol.com
Members: 77 Priests and Brothers
Apostolic Work: 25 parishes including colleges; 5 high schools and 1 grade school; 6 hospitals, elderly and handicapped chaplaincies; college chaplains; 1 military chaplain; missions; prison chaplaincy; ministry to the hearing impaired; 10 community houses, 2 formation houses, 1 summer camp, and conference center
Representation: (Arch)dioceses of Buffalo, Detroit, Erie, Lansing, Miami, Military Services, Oakland, Saginaw, Salt Lake City, Stockton, Toledo and Toronto and mission regions in Brazil, Equador, Mexico, Namibia and S.W. Africa
Vocation Director: Fr. Martin Lukas, osfs

OBLATES OF ST. JOSEPH (M259)
(O.S.J.) Mt. St. Joseph Novitiate and Seminary, PO Box 547, Loomis, CA 95650-0547
(Western Province) 544 West Cliff Dr, Santa Cruz, CA 95060-0547, (831) 457-1868
Web: www.osjoseph.org
Email: vocations@osjoseph.org
Members: 14 Priests, 3 Brothers, 2 Transitional Deacons, 2 Clerical Brothers, 1 Postulant
Conduct: A religious family of priests and brothers who serve God in imitation of St. Joseph with total dedication to Jesus, special love for Mary, fidelity to the magisterial teaching of the Church, deep interior prayer life, hard work, and unshakeable trust in Divine Providence; 3 parishes; 2 houses of formation, 1 shrine
Representation: Archdiocese of Los Angeles and in the Dioceses of Fresno, Monterey and Sacramento. Also in Pennsylvania, Brazil, India, Italy, Mexico, Peru, Bolivia, Chile, Philippines, Poland, and Nigeria
Vocation Director: Fr. Philip Massetti, OSJ, (916) 652-6336, fax: (916) 652-0620

OBLATES OF ST. JOSEPH (M260-1)
(O.S.J.) Our Lady of Sorrows Province: St. Joseph Oblate Seminary, 1880 Hwy. 315, Pittston, PA 18640-9618
Web: www.oblates-stjoseph.com
Email: osjseminary@comcast.net
Members: 10 Priests
Conduct: A religious community of brothers and priests, founded by St. Joseph Marello, and working to spread the Gospel in youth ministry, catechesis and parish ministry, under the inspiration of St. Joseph. 3 parishes, 1 house of study
Representation: Diocese of Scranton.
Vocation Director: Rev. Paul McDonnell, O.S.J., (570) 654-7542, fax: (570) 654-8621

OBLATES OF THE VIRGIN (M260-2)
MARY (O.M.V.) Generalate: Rome St. Ignatius Province, 2 Ipswich St., Boston, MA 02215
Web: www.omvusa.org
Email: vocations@omvusa.org
Apostolic Work: Spiritual Exercises of St. Ignatius in the form of directed retreats and parish missions, formation of the clergy, defense of the Truth, formation of the laity, parishes, foreign missions and social communications

B-38

Representation: Archdiocese of Boston, Los Angeles and Denver and in Dioceses of Springfield-in-Illinois, Montreal (and Trois-Rivieres), Quebec, Canada. Present in Austria, France and Italy and foreign missions in Argentina, Brazil, Nigeria and the Philippines
Vocation Director: Rev. Peter Grover, OMV, and Rev. Fernando Cuenca, OMV, Our Lady of Grace Seminary, 1105 Boylston St., Boston, MA 02215, (617) 869-2429 fax: (617) 247-7576

ORATORIANS (ORAT.) (M261-1)
(Congregation of the Oratory)
The Oratorian Community of Monterey, PO Box 1688, Monterey, CA 93942
Members: 3 Priests
Representation: Diocese of Monterey
Vocation Director: Rev. Thomas A. Kieffer, Vicar, (831) 373-0476

(M261-2)
ORATORIANS (Orat.) (Diocesan Congregation of the Oratory of St. Philip Neri) 1590 Green Bay Rd., Highland Park, IL 60035-3516
Web: www.the-oratory.org
Email: oratory@the-oratory.org
Members: 2 Priests, 1 Deacon
Apostolic Work: Parishes, retreats, spiritual direction, Hispanic ministry, Catholic high school teaching, diocesan tribunal, editor
Representation: Archdiocese of Chicago
Vocation Director: Phone and Fax: (847) 432-4522

(M262)
ORATORIANS (C.O.) (Congregation of the Oratory of St. Philip Neri)
4450 Bayard St.
Pittsburgh, PA 15213
Email: davida@andrew.cmu.edu
Members: 5 Priests
Representation: Diocese of Pittsburgh
Vocation Director: Very Rev. David S. Abernethy, C.O., (412) 681-3181, ext. 222

ORATORIANS (C.O.) (M263)
(Congregation of the Oratory)
The Oratory of Rock Hill, PO Box 11586, 434 Charlotte Ave., Rock Hill, SC 29731-1586, (803) 327-2097
Web: www.rockhilloratory.com
Members: 9 Priests, 4 Brothers, 1 Novice, 1 Seminarian
Apostolic Work: 5 Parishes, retreats, campus ministry, lay ministry training, spiritual direction, nursing, Hispanic ministry
Representation: Diocese of Charleston
Vocation Director: Rev. Edward McDevitt, C.O., (803) 327-0106

ORATORIANS (C.O.) (M264)
(Congregation of the Oratory)
The Oratory of Pharr, PO Box 1698, Pharr, TX 78577, (956) 843-8217
Web: www.oratoryschools.org
Email: jlosoya@oratoryschools.org
Members: 4 Priests, 2 Seminarians
Apostolic Work: Services to the poor, Mexican-American cultural services, parish work, health, bicultural Catholic elementary and secondary schools
Representation: Diocese of Brownsville
Vocation Director: Rev. Jose Encarnacion Losoya, C.O.

THE ORDER OF THE (M265-1)
BLESSED VIRGIN MARY OF MERCY (O. de M.) (Mercedarian Friars)
One of the ancient Orders of the Catholic Church, the Mercedarian Friars were founded in 1218. The Friars honor Mary, as the foundress and mother of the work of mercy begun by Saint Peter Nolasco - the redemption of Christians in danger of losing their faith. This work of mercy is conducted in parishes, where faith is often attacked or broken due to influences and systems contrary to gospel and family values; in schools, where peer pressure and empty values threaten the faith of youth; in institutions of health care or detention, where despair and apostasy threaten one's faith in Christ; and in foreign missions, where human dignity and faith are robbed because of degrading social conditions.Men, between the ages of 18-40, who desire to live a life centered in Mary and her Son, to pray the rosary daily in common, live in community with one's "brothers" based upon the Rule of St. Augustine (prayers, meals and recreation in common), have a deep love for the Magisterium and in preserving the Faith by catechesis, are invited to contact the Director of Vocations. 6398 Drexel Rd., Philadelphia, PA 19151-2596
Web: www.orderofmercy.org
Email: vocations@orderofmercy.org
Vocation Director: Contact: (215) 879-0594

ORDER OF FRIARS MINOR (M267)
CAPUCHIN
See Capuchins

ORDER OF MINORS (M268)
FRIARS CONVENTUAL
See Franciscan Friars

(M269)
ORDER OF THE HOLY CROSS
See Crosier Fathers and Brothers

ORDER OF THE MOST (M270)
HOLY SAVIOR
See Brigittine Monks

ORDER OF THE MOST (M271)
HOLY TRINITY
See The Trinitarians

ORDER OF PREACHERS (M272)
See Dominicans

ORDER OF ST. AUGUSTINE (M273)
See Augustinians

ORDER OF ST. BENEDICT (M274)
See Benedictines

(M276)
PALLOTTINE FATHERS (S.A.C.)
(Society of the Catholic Apostolate)
Queen of the Apostles, Italian Province, Our Lady of Mt. Carmel, 448 E. 116th St., New York, NY 10029
Members: 8 Fathers, 1 Deacon
Conduct: Parishes, missionary work, diaconate director, schools
Representation: Archdiocese of New York and in the Dioceses of Albany and Pensacola-Tallahassee. Other houses, high schools and parishes in Italy and England
Vocation Director: (212) 534-0681

PALLOTTINES (S.A.C.) (M277)
(Society of the Catholic Apostolate)
(Immaculate Conception Province)
5552 Rte. 70
Pennsauken, NJ 08109
Web: www.sacapostles.org
Email: vocations@sacapostles.org
Members: 25 men in the Province; 2,400 Priests & Brothers, 1,600 Sisters, and a growing number of Lay Associates worldwide
Conduct: Lay formation programs, youth ministries, parishes, schools and foreign missions. Give: missions and retreats
Vocation Director: Rev. Bernard Carman, S.A.C., Pallottine Vocation Office, 800-APOSTLE (800-276-7853) (toll free)

PALLOTTINES (S.A.C.) (M278)
(Society of the Catholic Apostolate)
Mission House and Infant Jesus
Shrine (Infant Jesus Delegature of
the Annunciation)
Motherhouse: Poland
3452 Niagara Falls Blvd., PO Box
263, North Tonawanda, NY 14120
Members: 11 Priests
Apostolic Work: Retreats, parish
work, hospital chaplaincy, national
shrine, pro-life ministry
Representation: Dioceses of
Brooklyn, Buffalo and Rockville
Centre
Vocation Director: Rev. John
Kosiewala, S.A.C.

PALLOTTINES (Society of (M279)
the Catholic Apostolate)
Irish Province: 3352 Fourth St., PO
Box 249, Wyandotte, MI 48192
Members: 16 Priests, 1 Brother
Apostolic Work: Parishes, missions,
hospital chaplaincy
Representation: Archdioceses of
Detroit and Philadelphia and in the
Dioceses of Fort Worth, Lubbock
and Reno-Las Vegas
Vocation Director: Rev. Hubert
Flanagan, S.A.C., (734) 285-2966

PALLOTTINES (S.A.C.) (M280)
(Society of the Catholic Apostolate)
Mother of God Province
5424 W. Bluemound Rd., Milwaukee,
WI 53208-3097
Web: www.pallottines.org
Email: vocations@pallotti.net
Members: 16 Priests, 1 Brother
Conduct: 6 parishes, 1 retreat
house, 1 hospital chaplaincy, 1
health care chaplaincy, 1 high
school
Representation: (Midwest)
Represented in the Archdiocese of
Milwaukee and in the Diocese of
Springfield, IL
Vocation Director: Mr. Jeffrey S.
Montoya, UAC, (414) 259-0688,
ext. 155

PARIS FOREIGN MISSIONS (M281)
SOCIETY (M.E.P)
Headquarters: Paris
130 Ashbury St.
San Francisco, CA 94117
Members: 2 Priests
Representation: Archdiocese of San
Francisco
Vocation Director: Rev. Jacques
Didier, M.E.P., (415) 664-6747

PASSIONISTS (C.P.) (M282)
(Congregation of the Passion)
Holy Cross Province
5700 N. Harlem Ave., Chicago, IL
60631-2342
Web: www.passionist.org/vocations
Members: 68 Priests, 8 Brothers
Conduct: 4 retreat houses and 4
parishes; ministries include renewal
preaching, spiritual guidance,
chaplain ministry and parish
assistance
Representation: Archdioceses of
Chicago, Detroit, Galveston-
Houston, Los Angeles, Louisville
and San Antonio and in the
Dioceses of Birmingham and
Sacramento. Cross-cultural mission:
India
Vocation Director: Contact the
Provincial Office at the above
address

PASSIONISTS (C.P.) (M283)
(Congregation of the Passion)
(Province of St. Paul of the Cross)
Passionist Province Pastoral Center,
80 David St., South River, NJ 08882
(732) 257-7177
Web: www.thepassionists.org
Email: spoc-vocations@cpprov.org
Members: 200 Priests, 31 Brothers
Conduct: 8 monasteries, 7 retreat
houses, 10 parishes, 7 residences,
1 novitiate, 1 theologate, 1 college
residence, 1 Newman Center, 1
volunteer program, missions in the
West Indies and the Philippine
Islands
Representation: Archdioceses of
Atlanta, Baltimore, Boston, Hartford,
Newark and New York, and in the
Dioceses of Brooklyn, Metuchen,
Pittsburgh, Raleigh, Rockville
Centre, Scranton, Springfield, Palm
Beach, Wheeling and Worcester.
Also in Canada, Jamaica, W.I. and
the Philippine Islands
Vocation Director: Rev. Bill Maguire,
C.P., St. Paul of the Cross Retreat
Center, 148 Monastery Ave.,
Pittsburgh, PA 15203 (412) 381-
1188

PAULINE PRIESTS AND (M284)
BROTHERS COMMUNICATIONS
MINISTRY See Society of St. Paul

PAULINE FATHERS AND (M285)
BROTHERS (O.S.P.P.E.) (Order of St.
Paul the First Hermit)
Motherhouse: Poland
US Headquarters: The National
Shrine of Our Lady of Czestochowa
654 Ferry Rd., PO Box 2049
Doylestown, PA 18901
Web: www.czestochowa.us or
www.paulini.pl

Email: vocations@czestochowa.us
Members: 25 Priests, 5 Brothers in
the US
Apostolic Work: Contemplative order
and apostolic work especially to
foster devotion to the Blessed Virgin
Mary
Representation: (Arch)dioceses of
New York, Philadelphia, Chicago,
Orlando, Buffalo, Greensburg and
Norwich
Vocation Director: (215) 345-0607

THE PAULIST FATHERS (M286)
(C.S.P.) (Missionary Society of St.
Paul the Apostle)
The Paulists are the first community of
priests founded in the U.S. in 1858 by
Isaac Hecker. An active missionary
community serving North America.
415 W. 59th St., New York, NY 10019
Web: www.paulist.org
Email: vocations@paulist.org
Members: 150 Priests, 11
Candidates in Theology Admissions:
Formation includes 1 year novitiate
followed by theological studies in
Washington, DC including a
pastoral year
Apostolic Work: Parishes, university
ministries, adult education, retreat
and missionary preaching, Paulist
Press, Paulist Media Works, Paulist
Productions, ecumenical dialogue,
reconciliation ministries, Paulist
National Catholic Evangelization
Association, Paulist Young Adult
Ministry
Representation: 20 locations
throughout the USA and Canada.
Vocation Director: Fr. Edward C.
Nowak, C.S.P., 800-235-3456 or in
New York (212) 757-4260, fax:
(212) 445-0285

PIARIST FATHERS (Sch.P) (M288)
California's Vice-Province
3940 Perry St.
Los Angeles, CA 90063
Rev. P. Miguel Mascorro, Sch.P.,
Viceprovincial
Email: migmascorro@yahoo.com
Members: 19 Priests, 13
Seminarians
Conduct: 5 parishes, 2 grammar
schools, 4 houses of formation
Apostolic Work: Dedicated to the
education of children and youth
Representation: Archdiocese of Los
Angeles and in 34 countries around
the world
Vocation Director: Rev. Martin
Madero, Sch.P., (323) 269-2637,
maderoschp@sbcglobal.net, Casa
Calasanz (Prenoviciate), 3951
Rogers St., Los Angeles, CA 90063,
casa-calasanz@sbcglobal.net

PIARIST FATHERS AND (M289)
BROTHERS (Sch.P.)
(Province of the United States of
America),1339 Monroe St. NE,
Washington, DC 20017
(202) 529-7734
Web: www.calasanz.net
Email: dariff@hotmail.com
Members: 21 Priests
Conduct: 1 novitiate, 1 house of
studies for candidates to the
priesthood and brotherhood, 2
college preparatory schools, 1
diocesan high school, 2 missions, 3
parishes, Hungarian ministry,
Hispanic ministry
Apostolic Work: The Piarists profess
a fourth vow to educate youth.
Education for the Piarists means
the complete formation of the
person. Thus the Piarists fulfill their
vow by teaching on the elementary
and secondary levels. In addition,
they assist local parishes, conduct a
summer mission in Macuspana,
Mexico; and have an active
outreach program in Eastern
Kentucky, where they minister to
the poor in Appalachia. Their
founder, St. Joseph Calasanctius, is
the Patron Saint of Christian
Schools
Representation: Archdioceses of
Miami, Philadelphia and
Washington, DC and in the
Dioceses of Lexington, Buffalo and
Paterson
Vocation Director: Very Rev. David B.
Powers, Sch.P., 99 Martha's
Vineyard, Prestonsburg, KY 41653,
(610) 564-8893, (606) 285-3950

PIARISTS (Sch.P.) (M290)
(Calasanzian Fathers) Vice Province:
New York and Puerto Rico
Annunciation Church, 88 Convent
Ave., New York, NY 10027
Members: 20 Priests
Apostolic Work: Christian education,
youth pastoral, C.C.D. programs,
parish apostolate
Vocation Director: Fr. Felix Ganuza,
Sch.P., (212) 234-1919, fax: (212)
281-7205

PIME MISSIONARIES (M291)
**(Pontifical Institute for Foreign
Missions)** 17330 Quincy St., Detroit,
MI 48221-2765
Web: www.pimeusa.org
Email: info@pimeusa.org
Members: 500 Priests, 50 Brothers,
120 Seminarians
Conduct: 2 International Theology
(Italy and Philippines) and 3
Philosophy formation houses (Italy,
Brazil, India)

Apostolic Work: PIME is an
International Society of Apostolic
Life of priests and consecrated
laymen who dedicate their lives to
missionary activity. The Institute's
first priority is the proclamation of
the Gospel to non-Christians.
PIME's missionary activities are
consistent with the diverse
situations of the non-Christian
world, the priorities of the local
Churches and the current
understanding of evangelization. In
addition to the explicit and direct
proclamation of the Christian
message, PIME missionaries are
creative in their presence and
witness.
Living as a family of apostles in a
communion of life and activity, they
are engaged in promotion of
dialogue and understanding among
religions and cultures, human
development, justice and peace,
trade schools, hospitals and clinics,
literacy programs, community
development, pastoral care of newly
founded Catholic communities.
PIME missionaries work primarily
among non-Christians in foreign
countries. Young men who have a
deep faith in Christ and a desire to
bring that faith to people of other
cultures and traditions are likely
candidates. A desire to live the
Gospel message of Christ in
solidarity with the poor in other
countries is equally important.
The initial formation for candidates
to missionary priesthood (including
the Period of Spirituality, when
possible) will take place in the US
Region. Our formation and training
program is flexible. We try to adapt
our program to meet the needs of
each individual as much as
possible, according to one's
academic background and life
experiences. College Level
Seminarians and Post-College
Level applicants (i.e. those
candidates who need to complete
the required credits in Philosophy)
will live in one of our communities
and attend college locally.
Candidates who already have
completed Philosophy studies will
live in one of our communities for at
least six months prior to going
overseas for the Period of
Spirituality (if this is the case).
Representation: Archdiocese of
Detroit, Diocese of Paterson, N.J.
and Lansing, Mich. Worldwide: Italy,
United States, Mexico, Brazil, India,
Bangladesh, Myanmar, Thailand,
Cambodia, Philippines, Hong Kong

(China), Japan, Papua New
Guinea, Ivory Coast, Cameroon,
Guinea-Bissau, Algeria
Also see PIME Volunteers in
Volunteer Lay Ministries section.
Vocation Director: Fr. Ken Mazur
(313) 342-4066
superior@pimeusa.org
Fr. Giancarlo Ghezzi (973) 694-
1790, vocations@pimeusa.org

BROTHERS OF THE POOR (M292)
OF ST. FRANCIS
See Franciscans - Brothers of the
Poor of St. Francis

MISSIONARIES OF THE (M293)
PRECIOUS BLOOD (C.PP.S.)
100 Pelmo Cres, Toronto, Ontario,
Canada, M9N-2Y1
Web: www.cppsmissionaries.ca
Email: preciousvocations@yahoo.ca
Members: 24 Priests, 1 Brother
Apostolic Work: Mission: Founded
by St. Gaspar del Bufalo to renew
the Church through the ministry of
the Word and the proclamation of
the saving power of the Precious
Blood of Jesus Christ.Ministries:
Parishes, education, preaching
missions and retreats, foreign
missions
Representation: Archdioceses of
Toronto and Boston and in the
Dioceses of Sault St. Marie,
Ontario; St. Catharines, and
Rochester. Also in Mexico City,
Mexico; Dodoma, Morogoro
(Tanzania, East Africa)
Vocation Director: Rev. Lui Santi,
cpps, 416-531-4423

MISSIONARIES OF THE (M294)
PRECIOUS BLOOD (C.PP.S.)
Cincinnati Province - Provincial
House, 431 E. Second St., Dayton,
OH 45402-1764
Web: www.cpps-preciousblood.org
Email: vocation@cpps-
preciousblood.org
Members: 149 Priests, 28 Brothers,
1 Deacon, 32 Candidates
Apostolic Work: Mission: Founded
by St. Gaspar del Bufalo to renew
the Church through the ministry of
the Word and the proclamation of
the saving power of the Precious
Blood of Jesus Christ.Ministries:
Parishes, education, preaching
missions and retreats, foreign
missions, hospital, college and
military chaplains
Representation: Archdioceses of
Chicago, Cincinnati, San Francisco,
Guatemala City, Lima (Peru), Los
Angeles, Rome (Italy) and Santiago
(Chile) and in the Dioceses of

Cleveland, Coban (Guatemala), Columbus, Gary, Huancayo (Peru), Lafayette-in-Indiana, Oakland, Osorno (Chile), Bogota (Colombia) and Toledo
Vocation Director: Rev. Ken Schnipke, C.PP.S., (937) 228-6224

MISSIONARIES OF THE (M295) PRECIOUS BLOOD (C.PP.S.)
Kansas City Province - Provincial Office, 2130 Saint Gaspar Way, Liberty, MO 64068
Web: www.kcprovince.org
Email: voc.office@yahoo.com
Members: 1 Bishop, 49 Priests, 4 Brothers
Apostolic Work: Mission: Founded by St. Gasper del Bufalo to renew the Church through the ministry of the Word and the proclamation of the saving power of the Precious Blood of Jesus Christ.Ministries: Parishes, education, preaching missions and retreats, chaplains, foreign missions
Representation: Archdioceses of Chicago, Denver, Dubuque, Jefferson City, Kansas City in Kansas, Los Angeles, and in the Dioceses of Davenport, Des Moines, Kansas City-St. Joseph, Oakland, and San Angelo
Vocation Director: Rev. Joe Miller, C.PP.S., Sharon Crall, (816) 781-4344

PRIESTLY FRATERNITY OF (M300) SAINT PETER (F.S.S.P.)
North American Headquarters, District Superior: Fr. George Gabet, FSSP, Griffin Rd., PO Box 196, Elmhurst, PA 18416, (570) 842-4000 fax: (570) 842-4001
Web: www.fssp.com, www.fsspolgs.org
Email: vocations@fsspolgs.org
Apostolic Work: The Priestly Fraternity of St. Peter is a Society of Apostolic Life founded July 18, 1988 and officially approved by Pope John Paul II on October 18, 1988. The mission of the Fraternity is to form its members in service to the Church through the preservation and administration of Her ancient Latin liturgical traditions. Priests of the Fraternity are trained exclusively in the Extraordinary Form of the Roman Rite and offer all of the traditional sacraments to the faithful. In addition to serving at Fraternity apostolates and personal parishes, the FSSP offers retreats, hosts summer camps for youth, priest training in the Extraordinary Form, and support of homeschoolers.

Representation: In Canada: (Arch)dioceses of Vancouver, British Columbia; Hamilton, Ontario; London, Ontario; Ottawa, Ontario; St.Catharines, Ontario; Calgary, Alberta; Edmonton, Alberta; and Quebec.
In the United States: Phoenix, Arizona; Little Rock, Arkansas; Sacramento, California; Colorado Springs, Colorado; Denver, Colorado; Venice, Florida; Atlanta, Georgia; Boise, Idaho; Indianapolis, Indiana; Kansas City, Kansas; Lexington, Kentucky; Lincoln, Nebraska; Omaha, Nebraska; Paterson, New Jersey; Youngstown, Ohio; Tulsa, Oklahoma; Oklahoma City, Oklahoma; Scranton, Pennsylvania; Harrisburg, Pennsylvania; Charleston, South Carolina; Rapid City, South Dakota; Corpus Christi, Texas; Dallas, Texas; Fort Worth, Texas; Tyler, Texas; and Richmond Virginia
Vocation Director: Office: Our Lady of Guadalupe Seminary, PO Box 147, 7880 West Denton Rd., Denton, NE 68339, Rev. Joseph Portzer, FSSP, (402) 797-7700, Mr. Robert Overkamp, (402) 797-7700, ext. 35 fax: (402) 797-7705

PRESENTATION BROTHERS (M301) (F.P.M.)
Provincialate:1602 Pettis Blvd., Kissimmee, FL 34741-3117
Web: www.PresentationBrothers.com
Email: brofromknox@yahoo.com
Apostolic Work: Christian formation, primarily of youth and in particular to the poor and disadvantaged; all forms of education, both elementary and high school, retreat work, social work, pastoral ministry, youth ministry and missionary involvement
Representation: Dioceses of Orlando and Toronto. Also in Ireland, England, Trinidad, St. Lucia, Grenada, Ghana, Slovakia and Nigeria
Vocation Director: Brother Gerard Despathy, F.P.M., (407) 846-2033

THE REDEMPTORISTS, (M302) CONGREGATION OF THE MOST HOLY RDEEMER (C.Ss.R.)
(Baltimore Province) Redemptorist Provincial Residence, 7509 Shore Rd., Brooklyn, NY 11209
The Redemptorists are a community of apostolic men — followers of Jesus Christ the Redeemer and disciples of St. Alphonsus Liguori. As a religious congregation of priests and brothers, our mission is to proclaim the Good News of plentiful redemption to the poor and most

abandoned. Our work in parishes, retreat houses, parish missions, and foreign countries, as well as special apostolates, e.g., migrants, prisoners, and young adults, serves as pathways for Christ's love. Like the apostles we live and work together; we combine our prayers and deliberations, our labors and sufferings, our successes and failures, and our talents and material goods in service to the Gospel.
Web: www.redemptorists.net
Email: vocations@redemptorists.net
Members: 178 Priests, 18 Brothers, 1 Novice, 29 Students
Conduct: 34 parishes, 4 retreat houses, college residence, theology residence
Apostolic Work: Focused on preaching the Word of God, especially to the poor and most abandoned. Particular ministries include parish work, inner-city work, rural and suburban work, parish missions, foreign missions, youth ministries, AIDS ministry, and deaf ministry, as well as supplying military and hospital chaplains
Representation: Archdioceses of New York, Boston, Philadelphia, Hartford, Baltimore, and Washington as well as in the Dioceses of Albany, Brooklyn, Harrisburg, Toledo, Wilmington, Richmond, Atlanta, Charlotte, St. Augustine, Charleston, Orlando, and Venice. Also in St. Thomas, St. Lucia and Dominica
Vocation Director: Father Phil Dabney, C.SS.R., (718) 321-1394

REDEMPTORISTS (M303-1) (C.SS.R.) (Denver Province)
Denver Province, (303) 370-0035 2204 Parsons Blvd., Whitestone, NY 11357-3440
Web: http://redemptorists-denver.org
Email: vocations@redemptorists-denver.org
Members: 225 Priests, 20 Brothers, 2 Deacons
Conduct: 2 retreat houses, 1 desert house of prayer, 17 parishes, healthcare center, Liguori Publications, 2 formation houses
Apostolic Work: Preaching the gospel through parish missions, retreats publications, ministry in Afro-American, Hispanic, and Vietnamese communities, youth ministry, deaf apostolate, parishes, and foreign missions in Brazil, Nigeria and Thailand.
Representation: (Arch)dioceses of Baton Rouge, Biloxi, Chicago, Denver, Detroit, Dodge City,

Galveston-Houston, Grand Rapids, Los Angeles, Memphis, Milwaukee, New Orleans, Oakland, San Antonio, Seattle, St. Joseph-Kansas City, St. Louis, St. Paul-Minneapolis, Tucson.
Vocation Director: Fr. Tat-Thang Hoang, C.Ss.R. and Bro. Laurence Lujan, CSs.R., 2204 Parsons Blvd., Whitestone, NY 11357
718-321-1394

(M303-2)
(VIETNAMESE) REDEMPTORISTS (C.SS.R.) (Extra Patriam Vice-Province) 3912 S. Ledbetter Dr., Dallas, TX 75236
St. John Neumann Monastery, Vietnamese Redemptorist Mission also at: St. Clement Monastery, 3417 W. Little York, Houston, TX 77091
St. Gerald Majella Noviticate, 3452 Big Dalton Ave, Baldwin Park, CA 91706
Web: www.dcctdallas.org
Email: longcssr@yahoo.com or joevucssr@yahoo.com
Members: 25 Priests, 11 Professed Brothers, 16 Postulant Students
Apostolic Work: Media publications, parishes, preaching, missionary, retreats, etc
Representation: (Arch)dioceses of Dallas, Houston, Los Angeles and Tucson
Vocation Director: Rev. Dominic Nguyen Phi Long, C.Ss.R.
(972) 296-6735

(M305)
REDEMPTORISTS (EASTERN RITE)
See Eastern Catholic Religious Communities for Men

RESURRECTIONISTS (CR) (M306)
(Congregation of the Resurrection)
(United States of America Province)
7050 N. Oakley Ave.
Chicago, IL 60645
Web: www.resurrectionists.com
Email: info@resurrectionists.com
Members: 56 Fathers, 5 Brothers, 5 Professed Seminarians
Apostolic Work: Parishes, high school, retreat center, chaplaincies
Representation: Archdioceses of Chicago and St. Louis and in the Dioceses of Kalamazoo, Mobile, Pensacola-Tallahassee, Rockford and San Bernadino. Also in Bermuda
Vocation Director: Rev. Gary Hogan, C.R. and Bro. Edward Howe, C.R.
(314) 652-8814

RESURRECTIONISTS (C.R.) (M307)
(Congregation of the Resurrection)
(Ontario-Kentucky Province)
Resurrection College, 265 Westmount Rd. North, Waterloo, Ontario, Canada, N2L- 3G7
Web: www.resurrectionist.net
Email: jdonohue10@verizon.net
Members: 64 Priests (6 in US), 8 Brothers, 2 Permanent Deacons
Apostolic Work: Education of youth (high school and university as teachers and campus ministers), parish work and specialized apostolates
Representation: Archdioceses of Toronto (Ontario) and Louisville (KY) and in the Dioceses of Hamilton (Ontario) and Hamilton (Bermuda)
Vocation Director: Rev. Jim Donohue, CR, 524 North Avenue, P.O Box 246, Emmitsburg, Maryland 21727

ROGATIONIST FATHERS (M308)
AND BROTHERS (R.C.J.)
(Rogationists of the Sacred Heart of Jesus) US Delegation: 2688 S. Newmark Ave., Box 37, Sanger, CA 93657
Web: www.rcj.org
Members: 7 Priests in US
Apostolic Work: Dedicated to heed and spread the command of Jesus: Pray the Lord of the harvest to send laborers into His harvest. (Mt. 9:38). Both priests and brothers commit their lives to the education of youth, the social assistance of the underprivileged, especially children, orphans and the poor, vocation publications, parishes, missionary activities, vocation center, formation house, social services center
Representation: Archdiocese of Los Angeles and in the Diocese of Fresno. Also in Italy, Brazil, Mexico, Albania, Argentina, Africa, Spain, Poland, Philippines and India, Corea, Papua New Guinea
Vocation Director: (559) 875-2025

(M309)
ROSMINIAN PRIESTS AND BROTHERS
See Institute of Charity

BROTHERS OF THE (M310)
SACRED HEART (SC)
New England Province, Provincial House: 685 Steere Farm Rd., Pascoag, RI 02859-4601
Web: www.Brothersofthe sacredheart.org
Email: danstj@hotmail.com

Members: 70 Brothers
Apostolic Work: Christian education and related fields including teaching, counseling, social work, special education, CCD programs, religious education coordinators. Also direct and staff schools in three African countries. Admission: Post high school, college and post college levels. Minimum four years college, 18-month novitiate. Stress on closely knit community participation and life-long spiritual and academic development
Representation: Dioceses of Manchester, Providence and Hartford and in England. Also in the southern African countries of Lesotho, Zambia and Zimbabwe
Vocation Director: Br. Daniel St. Jacques, SC, (401) 678-0075 fax: (401) 568-9810

BROTHERS OF THE (M311)
SACRED HEART (S.C.)
New Orleans Province: 4600 Elysian Fields Ave., New Orleans, LA 70122
Web: www.brothersofthe sacredheart.org
Email: brochris66@hotmail.com
Members: 60 Brothers, 4 Ordained Brothers
Apostolic Work: Teacher, counselor, coach, administrator, campus ministry, chaplain, in secondary education. Also, prison ministry, parish youth ministry, college campus ministry, after school tutoring in inner city, home and foreign missionary.
Representation: Louisiana, Mississippi, Alabama, Arizona, Missouri
Vocation Director: Br. Chris Sweeney - (504)352-9940

BROTHERS OF THE (M312)
SACRED HEART (S.C.)
New York Province, Provincialate, 141-11 123rd Ave., S. Ozone Park, NY 11436, (718) 322-3309
Web: www.brothersofthe sacredheart.org
Email: mikemigacz@hotmail.com
Members: 62 Brothers
Conduct: 2 high schools, 1 house of formation, retreat center, volunteer program, 1 college
Apostolic Work: Teaching, counseling, and administering in secondary and elementary schools, religious education, youth ministry, refugee tutoring, prison ministry
Representation: Dioceses of Brooklyn, Metuchen, and Syracuse. Also in Kenya, East Africa, Phillipines

B-43

Vocation Director: Brother Michael Migacz, S.C., 1318 Court St., Syracuse, NY 13208, (732) 718-8559

PRIESTS OF THE SACRED (M313) **HEART (SCJ)** United States Province PO Box 206/RM, Hales Corners, WI 53130-0206
Web: www.scjvocation.org
Email: vocationcentral@wi.rr.com
Members: 110 Priests and Brothers in the US; 2,700 in 44 countries worldwide
Apostolic Work: The SCJs are an apostolic congregation of brothers and priests who are inspired by the mystery of God's love, expressed in the heart of Christ. Fr. Leo John Dehon, the founder, was convinced that the best way to respond to our experience of God's love is by reaching out to those around us and helping them to experience that same love in their own lives. This often means addressing the unjust situations and circumstances that prevent people from reaching their full potential. Much of the work of the Priests of the Sacred Heart in the US and around the world is with the poor, working class and outcasts. Foreign missions are available
Representation: Archdioceses of Chicago, Milwaukee and San Antonio and in the Dioceses of Green Bay, WI; Rapid City and Sioux Falls, SD; Jackson, MS; Galveston-Houston and Brownsville, TX; and St. Petersburg, FL. Foreign missions include South Africa, Congo, the Philippines, Indonesia and India
Vocation Director: SCJ Vocation Office, 800-609-5559 (toll-free) or (414) 529-4255, fax: (414) 529-3377

(M314)
SACRED HEARTS COMMUNITY (SS.CC.) (Congregation of the Sacred Hearts of Jesus and Mary) Eastern Province: Sacred Hearts Provincial House: 77 Adams St., PO Box 111, Fairhaven, MA 02719-0111
Web: www.sscc.org
Email: frlifrak@sscc.org
Members: 61 Fathers, 4 Brothers
Conduct: 1 provincial house, 1 novitiate, 1 house of formation, a center of the Enthronement of the Sacred Heart in the home, 1 retreat house, 9 parishes, 2 homes for the elderly, 16 foreign mission parishes, also seminary and formation, vocation work, parish missions, retreats of renewal, and youth

ministry.
Apostolic Work: The Sacred Hearts Community is made up of priests, sisters, brothers, and secular branch members. The three primary elements of our Gospel lifestyle are Eucharistic celebration and adoration of the Blessed Sacrament, communal life lived with a family spirit, and apostolic service to the poor and unevangelized. Members of our Congregation strive to contemplate, live cooperatively, and proclaim God's Love. The symbol of this particular orientation is that of the Sacred Heart of Jesus and the Immaculate Heart of Mary joined together, unified in suffering and joy. Like these Hearts, members of our Congregation are united and seek greater unity through Love and Compassion, which are gifts of God as well as fruits of our discipleship in common.
Representation: Archdioceses of Boston and Washington, DC and in the Dioceses of Brownsville and Fall River. Also foreign missions in Japan, Bahamas, India and the Philippines
Vocation Director: Rev. Richard Lifrak, SSCC, (508) 993-2442, ext. 309, fax: (508) 996-5499

(M315)
SACRED HEARTS COMMUNITY (SS.CC.) (Congregation of the Sacred Hearts of Jesus and Mary and of Perpetual Adoration of the Most Blessed Sacrament of the Altar) (Hawaiian Province) Sacred Hearts Center, PO Box 1365, Kaneohe, Oahu, HI 96744-1365
Members: 31 Priests, 11 Brothers
Conduct: 10 churches, 2 chaplaincies, mission-Cook Islands
Vocation Director: (808) 247-5035

(M316)
SACRED HEARTS COMMUNITY (SS.CC.) (Congregation of the Sacred Hearts of Jesus and Mary) (Western Province) Provincial Office 2150 Damien Ave., La Verne, CA 91750, (909) 593-5441
Web: www.cpl.net/~ssccwest
Email: ssccwest@cpl.net
Members: 22 Priests
Apostolic Work: Religious and academic education, parishes, chaplaincies
Representation: (Arch)dioceses of Los Angeles, San Bernardino, and Orange
Vocation Director: Rev. Michael Barry, SS.CC., Vocation Office, PO Box 668, San Dimas, CA 91773

(M317)
MISSIONARIES OF ST. CHARLES BORROMEO (C.S.) (Scalabrini Fathers and Brothers) Province of St. John the Baptist, 546 N. East Ave., Oak Park, IL 60302, (708) 386-4430
Web: www.scalabrinians.org
Email: vocations4migrants@yahoo.com
Members: 77 Fathers, 4 Brothers
Conduct: 15 parishes (US), 13 parishes, 1 mission (Canada), 2 homes for the aged, 3 centers, 5 houses of formation (US, Mexico)
Apostolic Work: Missionaries to immigrants and refugees in 29 countries
Representation: Archdioceses of Chicago, Cincinnati, Los Angeles and Vancouver and in the Dioceses of Kansas City, San Jose and Thunder Bay; in Mexico in Ciudad Juarez, Guadalajara, Zapopan, Purepero and Tijuana; in Guatemala in Guatemala City and Tecun-Uman
Vocation Director: Rev. Giovanni Bizzotto, Scalabrini House of Discernment, 10651 Vinedale St., Sun Valley, CA 91352-2825 (818) 504-9561, fax: (818) 504-9562

MISSIONARIES OF ST. (M318) **CHARLES/SCALABRINIANS (C.S.)** (Saint Charles Borromeo Province) Provincial Office: 209 Flagg Place, Staten Island, NY 10304
Web: www.scalabrinians.org
Email: saintcharlesny@aol.com
Members: 95 Fathers, 3 Brothers and 22 religious students
Conduct: 29 parishes, 7 missions, 2 homes for the aged, 4 seminaries, center for migration studies, assistance agency for migrants
Apostolic Work: Missionaries to immigrants and refugees in 30 countries
Representation: (Arch)dioceses of Boston, Brooklyn, Buffalo, New York, Palm Beach, Providence, Venice (FL) and Washington (DC). Also in eastern Canada, Columbia, Dominican Republic, Haiti and Venezuela
Vocation Director: Rev. Matthew Didone, Provincial Superior, (718) 351-8808/ (718) 351-8815 fax: (718) 667-4598

ST. COLUMBAN'S (M319) **FOREIGN MISSION SOCIETY** See Columban Fathers

SOCIETY OF ST. EDMUND (M320) See Edmundites

ST. FRANCIS XAVIER (M321)
FOREIGN MISSION SOCIETY
See Xaverian Missionaries

ST. JOHN OF GOD (M322)
BROTHERS See Hospitaller Brothers
of St. John of God

CONGREGATION OF (M323)
ST. JOSEPH (C.S.J.)
US & Mexico Vice-Province
4076 Case Rd., Avon, OH 44011
Web: www.stleonardyrc.com
Email: avon@murialdo.org,
frgiampietro@roadrunner.com
Members: 25 Priests, 6 Scholastics,
650 Priests and Brothers worldwide
Conduct: Schools, youth & retreat
centers, parishes, foreign mission
Apostolic Work: Major interest is
youth ministry in all its forms
according to times, places and
needs
Representation: (Arch)dioceses of
Cleveland and Los Angeles. Also in
Italy, Spain, Sierra Leone, Brazil,
Colombia, Albania, Argentina, Chile,
Equador, Ghana, Guinea Bissau,
Mexico, Rumania and India
Vocation Director: Fr. Giampietro
Gasparin, C.S.J., (440) 934-6270,
934-6735

ST. JOSEPH'S MISSIONARY (M324)
SOCIETY
See Mill Hill Missionaries

BROTHERS OF SAINT (M325)
PATRICK (F.S.P.) (California
Province) St. Patrick's Novitiate,
7820 Bolsa Ave., PO Box 116,
Midway City, CA 92655
Web: http://www.brothersof
stpatrick.com/
Email: brothersoc@yahoo.com
Members: 8 Brothers in US; 300
worldwide
Apostolic Work: Teaching,
counseling, administration, CCD,
youth work, hospital work
Representation: (Arch)dioceses of
Los Angeles and Orange. Also in
Ireland, Australia, Ghana, India,
Kenya and New Guinea
Vocation Director: Bro. Benedict,
FSP, (714) 897-8181,
benedict_mavelil@yahoo.co.in

ST. PATRICK FATHERS (SPS) (M326)
(St. Patrick's Missionary Society)
International Headquarters: Ireland
US Foundation: 19536 Eric Dr.,
Saratoga, CA 95070
Web: www.stpatrickfathers.org
Email: vocations@spms.org
Members: 14 Priests in US, 375
worldwide
Apostolic Work: Foreign missions
Representation: Archdioceses of
Chicago, Newark and San
Francisco and in the Dioceses of
Paterson, San Bernardino and San
Jose. Foreign mission areas:
worldwide especially Nigeria,
Cameroon, Sudan, Kenya, Uganda,
Rwanda, Zambia, Zimbabwe,
Malawi, South Africa, Brazil,
Grenada and Mexico

SOCIETY OF ST. PAUL (M327)
**(S.S.P.) (Pauline Priests and
Brothers Communications Ministry)**
2187 Victory Blvd., Staten Island, NY
10314
Web: www.vocationoffice.org
Email: vocation@stpauls.us
Members: 23 Brothers, 13 Priests in
US; 1,100 Members worldwide
Conduct: 1 novitiate, 3 houses of
formation, 7 book and
communication centers, 3 houses of
apostolate, book publishing, audio
visuals, print projects, television,
radio and video
Apostolic Work: Paulines utilize the
media of communications – press,
tapes, cassettes, videos, CCD
material and other
telecommunications to spread the
Gospel of Jesus. In the US, the
major apostolic works are Alba
House Publishing, Alba House
Audio & Video, Pastoral Life
Magazine and Alba House Book
Centers
Representation: Archdioceses of
New York, Detroit, Los Angeles, and
Miami, and in the Diocese of
Youngstown. There are over 1,100
priests and brothers located in 28
countries involved in
communications ministry
Vocation Director: Br. Richard
Brunner, S.S.P., SSP Vocation
Office, Pauline Fathers and
Brothers, (718) 982-5709

CLERICS OF ST. VIATOR (M328)
See Clerics of St. Viator

SALESIAN MONASTIC (M329)
COMMUNITY (SMC)
Salesian Monastery, HC #1, Box
455, Frantz Rd., Brodheadsville, PA
18322-9630, (570) 992-0230

Web: www.gentlestrength.org
Email: monk@epix.net
Members: 1 Solemnly Professed
Monk (perpetual private vows), 1
Solemnly Professed Nun (perpetual
private vows), 8 Monastic
Associates (through an
understanding of our charism), 381
Affiliates (through attendance at
retreats, workshops, and/or
prayerful connection).
Apostolic Work: Monastic life, Liturgy
of the Hours, use of any gift/talent
compatible with monastic life, e.g.,
pastoral care, retreat work, nursing,
medicine, manual labor.
Representation: Diocese of Scranton
Vocation Director: Abbot Brother
Bernard Seif, SMC, (570) 992-3448

SALESIANS OF DON BOSCO (M330)
(SDB) (Eastern Province)
Province of St. Philip the Apostle,
148 Main St., New Rochelle, NY
10801, (973) 761-0201
Web: www.salesianvocation.com
www.salesians.org
Email: salvoc@aol.com
Members: 152 Fathers, 12
Professed Clerics, 4 Seminarians,
26 Brothers
Conduct: Academic high schools,
junior high school, Boys' and Girls'
Club of America, youth centers,
parishes, home missions, mission
office, retreat centers, summer
camps
Apostolic Work: Salesians focus on
youth ministry, becoming friends of
Christ and friends of the young, in
the family spirit of St. John Bosco.
Their ministry expresses itself in
schools, youth centers, parishes,
retreat centers, summer camps,
missions and wherever the young
are found
Representation: Archdioceses of
Boston, Chicago, Miami, Newark,
New Orleans, New York and
Washinton (DC) in the Dioceses of
Birmingham, Columbus, Palm Beach,
Paterson and St. Petersburg and in
the Eparchy of Passaic. Also active in
120 countries around the world,
including mission areas throughout
Latin America, Asia, and Africa
Vocation Director: Rev. Franco Pinto,
SDB, Salesian Vocation Ministry,
315 Self Place, South Orange, NJ
07079, (973) 761-0201

SALESIANS OF DON BOSCO (M331)
(S.D.B.) (Western Province)
1100 Franklin St., San Francisco ,
CA 94109, (415) 441-7144
Web: www.donboscowest.org
www.salesianym.org

B-45

Email: Vocation@aol.com
Members: 86 Priests, 29 Brothers
Conduct: 7 parishes, 5 high schools, 1 seminary residence, 1 junior college, 2 retreat centers, 4 youth centers, 4 camps, 1 International House of Studies
Apostolic Work: Youth ministry (youth centers, retreats, schools, parishes)
Representation: Archdioceses of Los Angeles and San Francisco and in the Dioceses of Loredo, Monterey and Oakland
Vocation Director: Fr. Chris Woerz, SDB, Office of Vocation Ministry, PO Box 1639, Rosemead, CA 91770, (626) 280-8622, ext. 41; fax: (626) 280-1742

SALVATORIANS (Society of (M332)
the Divine Savior) (SDS)
Salvatorian Provincial Residence 1735 N. Hi-Mount Blvd., Milwaukee, WI 53208-1720
Web: www.sdsvocations.com
Email: Scott@salvatorians.com
Members: 79 Priests, 31 Brothers, 5 Clerics, 1 Novice, 142 Lay Salvatorians
Apostolic Work: Founded to use any means which the Love of Christ inspires to bring the Gospel to the world. Involved in parishes, home and foreign missions, education, hospital and military chaplaincies, youth ministry, communications, counseling, campus ministry, specialized ministries.
Representation: Archdioceses of Milwaukee, Seattle, Portland, and Washington; and in the Dioceses of Bismarck, Birmingham, Green Bay, Harrisburg, La Crosse, Nashville, Oakland, Orlando, Phoenix, St. Cloud, Sacramento, Tucson, Venice, and Wilmington. American Salvatorians are also serving in Tanzania, East Africa
Vocation Director: Father Scott Jones SDS (414) 258-1735, ext. 104 fax: (414) 258-1934

SCALABRINIAN FATHERS (M333)
AND BROTHERS
See St. Charles Borromeo, Missionararies of

SERVANTS OF CHARITY (SdC)(M334)
(Guanellian Priests and Brothers)
171 E. Michigan Ave., Grass Lake, MI 49240
Divine Providence Province India - United States - Philippines, U.S.A. Referral: Fr. Dennis M. Weber, S.C., 1799 S. Sproul Road Springfield, PA 19064
(610) 543-3380

Web: www.servantsofcharity.org
Email: fr.dweber@chs-adphila.org
Members: Priests: 32 (India) 9 (U.S.A.) 7 (Philippines)
Seminarians: 140 (India) 2 (U.S.A.) 11 (Philippines)
Conduct: Residential facilities for persons with developmental disabilities and mental retardation; homes for orphans (India) and dependent children; services for youth in need; pastoral activities in parishes, prisons and urban and rural poor areas.
Apostolic Work: Care for adults and children with developmental disabilities and mental retardation; pastoral ministry in parishes; support for troubled youth & elderly in need; pastoral ministry to visitors at our Shrine of St. Joseph in Grass Lake, MI.
Representation: Archdiocese of Philadelphia (PA), Dioceses of Lansing (MI) and Providence (RI). Also in Argentina, Brazil, Chile, Colombia, Democratic Republic of Congo, Ghana, Guatemala, India, Israel, Italy, Mexico, Nigeria, Paraguay, Philippines, Spain, Switzerland.
Vocation Director: Father Dennis M. Weber, SdC, (610) 543-3380; Father David Stawasz, SdC, (734) 475-8430, frdave@stlouiscenter.org

SERVANTS OF MARY (M336)
See Servite Friars

SERVANTS OF THE (M337)
PARACLETE (s.P.)
St. Michael's Center, 13270 Maple Dr., St. Louis, MO 63127
Web: www.theservants.org
Email: manilasp@aol.com
Members: 16 Priests, 4 Brothers, 2 Clerics, 9 Novices, 9 Postulants
Apostolic Work: Ministry to priests and religious brothers: retreats, spiritual direction, residential treatment center
Representation: Archdioceses of St. Louis and Santa Fe; Also in the Philippines
Vocation Director: (314) 965-0860

SERVANTS OF THE SICK (M338)
See Camillians

SERVITE FRIARS (O.S.M.) (M339)
(Order of Friar Servants of Mary)
United States of America Province - Provincial Center, 3121 W. Jackson Blvd., Chicago, IL 60612-2729
Web: www.servite.org
Email: arnaldosanchez@ servitesusa.org
Members: 85 Priests, 13 Brothers

Conduct: 12 communities, 8 parishes, 2 high schools, 3 shrines
Apostolic Work: Campus ministry (high school and university), hospital chaplains, prayer ministries, counseling and therapy programs, teaching, retreats and parish missions, parish ministry, Marian Center, National Shrine of Our Lady of Sorrows, National Shrine of Our Sorrowful Mother (the Grotto), National Shrine of St. Peregrine
Representation: Archdioceses of Chicago, Denver, St. Louis and Portland and in the Dioceses of Oakland and Orange. Missions in South Africa and an Australian delegation
Vocation Director: Contact: (773) 533-0360 ext. 221 or Servite Vocation Office (above address)

SMA FATHERS (M340)
See African Missions, Society of

(M341)
SOCIETY OF AFRICAN MISSIONS
See African Missions, Society of

SOCIETY OF CATHOLIC (M342)
APOSTOLATE See Pallottines

SOCIETY OF CHRIST (S.Ch.) (M343-1)
Motherhouse: Poland
American-Canadian Province
786 W. Sunset Ave.
Lombard, IL 60148
Email: SChprov@aol.com
Members: 55 Priests
Apostolic Work: Pastoral ministry to Polish Catholics worldwide: parishes, pastoral missions, ethnic radio programs, retreats
Representation: Archdioceses of Atlanta, Baltimore, Chicago, Detroit, Los Angeles, Miami, Portland (OR), St. Paul-Minneapolis, San Francisco, Seattle and Washington (DC) and in the Dioceses of Dallas, Galveston-Houston, Joliet, Phoenix, San Diego, San Jose and Toledo. Also in Canada.
Vocation Director: (630) 424-0401, fax: (630) 424-0409

SOCIETY OF THE DIVINE (M343-2)
WORD (SVP)
See Divine Word Missionaries

SOCIETY OF JESUS (M344-1)
(JESUITS) See Jesuits

SOCIETY OF MARY, (M344-2)
MARIANISTS See Marianists

(M345)
SOCIETY OF THE MISSIONARIES
OF THE HOLY APOSTLES
See Missionaries of the Holy Apostolate

SOCIETY OF OUR LADY OF (M346)
THE MOST HOLY TRINITY (S.O.L.T.)
Casa San Jose, 109 W. Ave. D, Box
152, Robstown, TX 78380
Web: www.societyofourlady.net
Email: vocations@gmail.com,
padreglenn@gmail.com
Members: 135 Priests, 6 Permanent
Brothers, 4 Deacons, 17 Novices, 7
Candidates, 75 Seminarians
Apostolic Work: Serving the neediest
of the needy - taking them to the
Trinity through Mary
Representation: 12 (Arch)dioceses in
the US; Mexico, Belize, Haiti,
Philippines, Thailand, Russia,
England, Italy, China, Papua New
Guinea
Vocation Director: Fr. Glenn Whewell,
SOLT, 109 W. Ave. D, PO Box 152,
Robstown, TX, 78380
(361) 767-9567

SOCIETY OF OUR MOTHER (M347)
OF PEACE (SMP)
Mary the Font Solitude
6150 Antire Rd., High Ridge, MO
63049-2135
Web: www.ourmotherofpeace.org
Email: frpsirangelosmp@yahoo.com
Members: US: 3 Priests, 5 Brothers
Apostolic Work: Contemplative-
apostolic balance of life in the
context of simplicity and poverty;
emphasis on solitary prayer;
apostolates of retreat work and
spiritual direction; direct
evangelization especially within the
African-American community and
among the poor
Representation: Archdiocese of St.
Louis and in the Diocese of
Springfield-Cape Girardeau. Also in
the Philippines and Nigeria
Vocation Director: Rev. Peter
Sirangelo, SMP, (636) 677-3235,
fax: (636) 677-5284

SOCIETY OF THE (M348)
PRECIOUS BLOOD
See Precious Blood, Missionaries of

SOCIETY OF ST. EDMUND (M349)
See Edmundites

ST. JOSEPH'S SOCIETY Of (M350)
THE SACRED HEART
See Josephite Fathers and Brothers

SOCIETY OF ST. SULPICE (M352)
See Sulpician Fathers, The

SOMASCAN FATHERS (C.R.S.) (M353)
610 W. Melwood, Houston, TX 77009
Web: www.somascans.org
Email: somascans@yahoo.com
Members: 11 Religious (10 Priests)

Apostolic Work: The Somascans
carry on the legacy of their founder,
St. Jerome Emiliani, the Universal
Patron of Orphans and Abandoned
Youth , in the spiritual and material
care of orphans, abandoned youth
and the poor; in the education of
youth and in pastoral ministry. In the
US, the Somascans operate Pine
Haven Boys Center, a residential
treatment center for disadvantaged
boys ages 7-15 in Allenstown, NH;
and Assumption Catholic Church
and Christ the King Church in
Houston (both parishes have a
strong presence of immigrants from
Latin America). Also in Houston, the
Fathers operate the Somascan
House of Formation.
Representation: Archdiocese of
Galveston-Houston and Diocese of
Manchester
Vocation Director: Fr. Italo Dell'Oro,
CRS, (713) 880-8243, fax: (713)
869-1491

SONS OF MARY (M354)
MISSIONARY SOCIETY (F.M.S.I.)
(Sons of Mary, Health of the Sick)
567 Salem End Rd., Framingham,
MA 01702-5599
Web: www.sonsofmary.com
Email: sonsboston@verizon.net
Members: 12 Professed
Apostolic Work: Medical, social and
catechetical
Representation: Archdiocese of
Boston. Also in the Philippines
Vocation Director: (508) 879-2541

(M355)
THE SPIRITANS - CONGREGATION
OF THE HOLY SPIRIT (C.S.Sp.)
(Holy Spirit Fathers and Brothers)
(Province of the United States East)
6230 Brush Run Rd. , Bethel Park,
PA 15102, 412-831-0302
(Province of the United States West)
1700 W. Alabama St., Houston, TX
77098-2808, (713) 522-2882
Web: www.spiritans.com
Email: vocations@duq.edu or
suazocssp@aol.com
Members: 3000 Priests and Brothers
Worldwide working in 65 countries
Apostolic Work: 1 university, 3
university chaplaincies, 1 novitiate,
hospital chaplaincies, 2 renewal
centers, 2 high schools, 17 parishes,
and missionaries serving in over 57
countries on five continents
Representation: Archdioceses of
Baltimore, Chicago, Cincinnati,
Detroit, New Orleans, New York,
Philadelphia, San Antonio, San
Diego and Washington, DC and in
the Dioceses of Alexandria,

Arlington, Charleston, Charlotte,
Erie, Little Rock, Houston,
Pittsburgh, Providence and San
Bernardino
Vocation Director: Spiritan Vocation
Office, Duquesne University, Laval
House, Pittsburgh, PA 15282, (412)
396-1666
Spiritan Vocation Office, 1700 W.
Alabama, Houston, TX 77098-2808
(713) 522-2882

STIGMATINE FATHERS (M356)
AND BROTHERS
See Congregation of the Sacred
Stigmata

THE SULPICIAN FATHERS (M357)
(S.S.) (Society of St. Sulpice)
US Province, 5408 Roland Ave.,
Baltimore, MD 21210
Web: www.sulpicians.org
Email: tulshafer@sulpicians.org
Members: 70 Priests
Apostolic Work: Educating diocesan
seminarians and priests, forming
priests for a multi-cultural church
and collaborating with seminary
programs in mission countries
Representation: Archdioceses of
Baltimore, San Antonio, San
Francisco, Washington and Los
Angeles and Lusaka, Zambia.
Canadian Province: Canada, Brazil,
Colombia and Japan. French
Province: France, Vietnam, Benin,
Cameroon
Vocation Director: Rev. Thomas R.
Ulshafer, S.S., (410) 323-5070

(M358-2)
THE MONKS OF ADORATION
PO Box 2929, Great Falls, MT 59403
Web: www.monksofadoration.org
Email: monkadorer@verizon.net
Members: 2 Monks
Apostolic Work: A semi-
contemplative monastic community
dedicated to adoration of the Most
Blessed Sacrament done in a spirit
of and offer for Eucharistic
Reparation offered to the Sacred
Heart of Jesus and the Immaculate
Heart of Mary. Rule of St. Augustine
Works include writing books and
articles, publishing booklets and
"The Tabernacle" (a small
magazine); as well as sacred study,
manual labor, cooking, gardening
and maintaining our Catholic
bookstore. Faithful to the Holy
Father and bishop, gray habit,
Liturgy of the Hours and Rosary,
individual silent times of adoration
before the Blessed Sacrament.
Various apostolic works to help the
poor.
Vocation Director: Brother Craig

HEATINE FATHERS (C.R.) (M359)
rovincial House, St. Andrew
eminary, 1050 S. Birch St., Denver,
O 80222
Members: 17 Priests, 5 Clerics
Conduct: 9 parishes, 1 house of
rmation, 1 provincial house
Apostolic Work: Parish work,
etreats, working with Spanish
peaking, other special Hispanic
ninistries.
Representation: (Arch)dioceses of
Denver, New York and Pueblo.

RAPPISTS (O.C.S.O.) (M360)
Cistercians of the Strict Observance)
bbey of New Clairvaux, Box 80,
ina, CA 96092-0080
Web: www.newclairvaux.org
mail: godseeking@
newclairvaux.org
Members: 24 in Community, 7
riests
Vocation Director: Father Paul Mark
chwan, (530) 839-2161

RAPPISTS (O.C.S.O.) (M361)
Cistercians of the Strict Observance)
st. Benedict's Monastery
012 Monastery Rd.
Snowmass, CO 81654
Web: www.snowmass.org
mail: mikamonk@rof.net
Members: 11 Monks, 2 Juniors, 1
Novice, 1 Postulant, 1 Oblate
Vocation Director: Fr. Micah, (970)
27-3311, ext. 29

TRAPPISTS (O.C.S.O.) (M362)
Cistercians of the Strict Observance)
Monastery of the Holy Spirit
2625 Hwy. 212 S.W., Conyers, GA
0094-4044
Web: www.trappist.net
Email: michael@trappist.net
Members: 45 Monks, 24 Priests, 3
Novices, 1 Junior, 2 Observers, 1
Transfer
Representation: Archdiocese of
Atlanta
Vocation Director: Bro. Michael
Lautieri, O.C.S.O., (678) 964-2018
or (770) 851-9673

TRAPPISTS (O.C.S.O.) (M363)
Cistercians of the Strict Observance)
New Melleray Abbey, 6632 Melleray
Circle, Peosta, IA 52068
Web: www.newmelleray.org
Email: frsteve@newmelleray.org
Apostolic Work: Contemplative
community of monks, brothers and
priests
Vocation Director: Fr. Stephen
Verbest, (563) 588-2319, ext. 138

TRAPPISTS (O.C.S.O.) (M364)
(Cistercians of the Strict Observance)
Our Lady of Gethsemani Abbey
3642 Monks Rd., Trappist, KY 40051
Web: www.monks.org
Email: gethvoc@juno.com
Members: 14 Priests, 47 Brothers
Vocation Director: (502) 549-3117

TRAPPISTS (O.C.S.O.) (M365)
(Cistercians of the Strict Observance)
Saint Joseph's Abbey, 167 North
Spencer Rd., Spencer, MA 01562
Web: spencerabbey.org
Email: vocation@spencerabbey.org
Members: 60 Monks (Brothers and
Priests)
Apostolic Work: A contemplative
monastic community living a hidden
life of work and prayer
Vocation Director: Fr. James
Palmigiano, O.C.S.O.
(508) 885-8700, ext. 518

TRAPPISTS (O.C.S.O.) (M366)
(Cistercians of the Strict Observance)
Assumption Abbey, Route 5, Box
1056, Ava, MO 65608-5608
Web: www.assumptionabbey.org
Email: avavocations@hughes.net
Members: 6 Priests, 12 Monks
Apostolic Work: A Trappist-Cistercian
community of 15 Monks in the
Ozark foothills of S.W. Missouri
dedicated to the contemplative
monastic life and supported by own
manual labor
Vocation Director: Bro. Francis
Flaherty, o.c.s.o., (417) 683-5110

TRAPPISTS (O.C.S.O.) (M367)
(Cistercians of the Strict Observance)
Abbey of the Genesee, 3258 River
Rd., Piffard, NY 14533
Web: www.geneseeabbey.org
Email: Vocations@
GeneseeAbbey.org
Members: 33 Monks (21 Brothers, 12
Priests)
Apostolic Work: Contemplative
monastic community according to
the Rule of St. Benedict living a life
of prayer, lectio divina and work.
Representation: Diocese of
Rochester, NY
Vocation Director: Br. Anthony Weber,
O.C.S.O., (585) 243-0660, ext. 19

TRAPPISTS (O.C.S.O.) (M368)
(Cistercians of the Strict Observance)
Our Lady of Guadalupe Abbey
9200 NE Abbey Rd.
Lafayette, OR 97127
Web: www.trappistabbey.org
Email: community@
trappistabbey.org
Members: 10 Priests, 19 Brothers

Vocation Director: Br. Mark Filut,
O.C.S.O., (503) 852-7174, 0107

TRAPPISTS (O.C.S.O.) (M369)
(Cistercians of the Strict Observance)
Mepkin Abbey, 1098 Abbey Rd.,
Moncks Corner, SC 29461
Web: www.mepkinabbey.org
Email: kevin@mepkinabbey.org
Members: 24 Monks (14 Brothers, 10
Priests)
Apostolic Work: Contemplative
monastic community called to seek
the face of God together in a life of
liturgical prayer, simple manual
labor and meditation
Vocation Director: Fr. Kevin, o.c.s.o.,
(843) 761-8509, fax: (843) 761-6719

TRAPPISTS (O.C.S.O.) (M370)
(Cistercians of the Strict Observance)
Abbey of Our Lady of the Holy Trinity
1250 South 9500 East, Huntsville,
UT 84317
Web: www.holytrinityabbey.org
Email: hta@xmission.com
Members: 21 Monks, Priests and
Brothers
Apostolic Work: Contemplative
monastic community
Vocation Director: Fr. Charles
Cummings, ocso, (801) 745-3784

(M371)
TRAPPISTS (O.C.S.O.)
(Cistercians of the Strict Observance)
Abbey of Our Lady of the Holy
Cross, 901 Cool Spring Ln.,
Berryville, VA 22611-2700, (540)
955-1425
Web: www.hcava.org
Members: 22 Solemnly Professed,
11 Priests, 1 Simply Professed
Apostolic Work: Contemplative
monastic community
Vocation Director: Fr. James
Orthmann, OCSO

THE TRINITARIANS (O.SS.T.) (M373)
(Order of the Most Holy Trinity)
(Province of the Immaculate Heart of
Mary) Provincial Office, PO Box
5719, 8400 Park Heights Ave.,
Baltimore, MD 21282-0719
Web: www.trinitarians.org
Email: vocations@trinitarians.org
Members: 78 Priests and Brothers
Conduct: 8 parishes, 17 community
houses, 1 high school, 1 retreat
house, 2 foreign missions
Apostolic Work: Parish ministry,
youth ministry, hospital chaplaincy,
pastoral counseling, ministry to
minorities, secondary, college and
graduate level education, retreats,
prison ministry, campus ministry,
promoting social justice,

international release of Christian captives, missions
Representation: Archdioceses of Baltimore, San Antonio, Houston, Philadelphia, Washington, DC and Los Angeles and in the Dioceses of Dallas, Trenton and Victoria. Internationally in Spain, Italy, France, Poland, Mexico, Colombia, Peru, Bolivia, Madagascar, Canada, the Congo, India and other countries.
Vocation Director: Fr. Carl Frisch, O.SS.T., (410) 484-2250 or 1-800-525-3554

TRINITY MISSIONS (S.T.) (M374)
See Missionary Servants of the Most Holy Trinity

VERONA FATHERS (M375)
See Comboni Missionaries

VIATORIANS (M376)
See Clerics of St. Viator

VINCENTIANS (C.M.) (M377)
(Congregation of the Mission)
American Spanish Branch
Holy Agony Church, 1834 3rd Ave., New York, NY 10029
Members: 4 Fathers
Conduct: 1 church
Representation: Archdiocese of New York

VINCENTIANS (CM) (M378)
(Congregation of the Mission)
Eastern Province, 500 E. Chelten Ave., Philadelphia, PA 19144
Web: www.vincentians.net
Email: vocations@vincentians.net
Members: 159 Fathers, 11 Brothers, 24 Seminarians
Conduct: 15 parishes, 2 universities, 2 seminaries, 2 retreat houses, 2 youth and young adult centers
Apostolic Work: Catholic education, priestly formation, parishes, missions in Panama, preaching, service to the poor, youth work
Representation: 21 (Arch)dioceses
Vocation Director: Rev. Aidan Rooney, C.M., Vincentian Vocation Ministry, 8000 Utopia Pkwy., Queens, NY 11439, (718) 990-1823

VINCENTIANS (C.M.) (M379)
(Congregation of the Mission)
Midwest Province, 13663 Rider Trail North, Earth City, MO 63045
Web: www.vincentian.org
Email: vocations@vincentian.org
Members: 100 Priests, 16 Brothers
Apostolic Work: Clerical and lay formation, Catholic education, preaching parish missions, parishes, chaplaincies, foreign missions and

service to the poor.
Representation: 17 (Arch)dioceses
Vocation Director: 1-800-DEPAUL1 (337-2851)

VINCENTIANS (C.M.) (M380)
(Congregation of the Mission)
New England Province, 234 Keeney St., Manchester, CT 06040-7048
Email: nepcm1@cox.net
Members: 26 Priests, 1 Brother, 1 Seminarian
Conduct: 7 parishes
Apostolic Work: Mission preaching, parochial apostolate
Representation: Archdiocese of Hartford and in the Dioceses of Bridgeport, Brooklyn, and Manchester, NH
Vocation Director: Rev. Eugeniusz Kotlinski, CM, (203) 323-4967, fax: (203) 327-2229

VINCENTIANS (C.M.) (M381)
(Congregation of the Mission)
(Southern Province) 3826 Gilbert Ave., Dallas, TX 75219-4346
Web: www.cmsouth.org
Email: cmsouth@sbcglobal.net
Members: 19 Priests, 1 Brother
Conduct: Preaching missions in parishes, conducting continuing clergy education, parish work, home mission team, parishes in 8 cities
Apostolic Work: A mobile community dedicated to instructing and ministering to the poor
Representation: Archdiocese of New Orleans and in the Dioceses of Dallas, Gallup, Evansville, and Little Rock
Vocation Director: Rev. David Nations, C.M., (314) 703-6987, 800-DEPAUL-1(337-2851) fax: (314) 344-2989 e-mail: vocations@vincentian.org

VINCENTIANS (C.M.) (M382-1)
(Congregation of the Mission)
Vincentian Fathers-Eastern Province of Philadephia
118 Congress St., Brooklyn, NY 11201-6045
Email: guadarrama72@hotmail.com
Members: 2 Priests
Conduct: Centro de Evangelizacion, "San Vicente de Paul", Cursillo Movement, Jornada Movement
Representation: Diocese of Brooklyn
Vocation Director: Rev. Jesus Guadarrama, C.M., (718) 624-5670, fax: (718) 624-5806

VINCENTIANS (C.M.) (M382-2)
(Congregation of the Mission)
Province of the West, 420 Date St., Montebello, CA 90640

Web: www.vincentian.org
Email: vocations@vincentian.org
Members: 26 Priests, 1 Brother, 1 Deacon, 2 Students in Formation
Conduct: Evangelization of the poor, priestly formation, home missions, parish ministry, foreign mission, hospital chaplaincies, retreat and evangelization centers
Apostolic Work: Serving the needs of the Church in the spirit of St. Vincent de Paul
Representation: Archdiocese of Los Angeles and in the Dioceses of Phoenix, Stockton and Gallup
Vocation Director: Rev. David Nations, C.M., (314) 703-6987, 1-800-DEPAUL-1(337-2851) fax: (314) 344-2989

VOCATIONIST FATHERS (S.D.V.) (M384)
(Society of the Divine Vocations)
90 Brooklake Rd
Florham Park, NJ 07932
Web: www.vocationist.org
Email: info@vocationist.org
Apostolic Work: The Vocationist Fathers are a Community of Priests and Brothers who strive to search, recruit and guide vocations to religious life and the priesthood. They pursue this goal through their work in parishes, missions and special vocation houses called Vocationaries
Representation: (Arch)dioceses in Italy, Brazil, Argentina, Madagascar, Colombia, Ecuador, England, Indonesia, Nigeria, Philippines and India. In the US in the (Arch)dioceses of Newark and Paterson
Vocation Director: Fr. Vernon M. Kohlmann, SDV, (973) 966-6262

XAVERIAN BROTHERS (C.F.X.) (M386)
Xaverian Brothers Generalate, 4409 Frederick Ave., Baltimore, MD 21229
410-644-0034, fax: 410-644-2762
Web: www.xaverianbrothers.org
Email: jconnolly@xaverianbrothers.org
Members: 220 Brothers
Conduct: Schools in Belgium and the United States; missions and schools in Bolivia, Democratic Republic of Congo, Haiti, Kenya and Lithuania
Apostolic Work: Education in elementary, high school and colleges, DRE and parish ministers, CCD, catechetical centers, counselors (alcoholic, career, personal), social ministry, educational specialists in prison ministry, hospital chaplaincy, centers for the homeless

Representation: Archdioceses of Baltimore, Boston, Chicago, Los Angeles, Louisville, Newark, New York and Washington and in the Dioceses of Arlington, Brooklyn, Charleston, Richmond, Wilmington and Worcester and in the Dioceses of Aiquile, Bolivia, Hinche, Haiti, Lubumbashi, Republic of Congo, Bungoma, Lodwar, Nyeri, Kenya and Vilna, Lithuania
Vocation Director: Bro. James Connolly, C.F.X., 4409 Frederick Ave., Baltimore, MD, 21229

(M387)
XAVERIAN MISSIONARIES (s.x.)
US Provincial Office(973) 942-2975
12 Helene Court, Wayne, NJ 07470
Web: www.XavierMissionaries.org
Email: pino.ma@gmail.com
Conduct: In the US: 4 vocation and mission education centers, and 1 international theology community
Apostolic Work: Pastoral and community work, education, leadership training, social work and justice & peace work in poor, non-Christian and cross-cultural situations
Representation: Archdioceses of Boston, Chicago, Milwaukee and New York and in the Diocese of Paterson (NJ). Also in Asia: Bangladesh, Japan, Indonesia, Philippines and Taiwan. In Europe: Great Britain, Italy and Spain. In Latin America: Brazil, Colombia and Mexico. In Africa: Burundi, Cameroon, Chad, D.R. Congo, Sierra Leone and Mozambique
Vocation Director: Fr. Joe Matteucig, sx, Vocation Office, 101 Summer St., Holliston, MA 01746

EASTERN CATHOLIC COMMUNITIES FOR MEN

BASILIAN FATHERS (ME001)
BASILIAN ORDER OF ST. JOSAPHAT (O.S.B.M.)
Assumption of B.V.M. Province
29 Peacock Lane, Locust Valley, NY 11560
Email: psandrick@aol.com
Members: 3 monasteries, 7 parishes, 2 parochial schools
Apostolic Work: The order works in the USA and throughout the world mainly among Ukrainians
Representation: Ukrainian Catholic Eparchies of St. Nicholas in

Chicago and Stamford
Vocation Director: Rev. Philip Sandrick, O.S.B.M., 29 Peacock Lane, Locust Valley, NY 11560, (516) 609-3262; in Canada: Rev. Eugene Rychlak, O.S.B.M., 737 Bannerman Ave., Winnipeg R2X 1J9, Canada, (204) 582-6695

BASILIAN FATHERS OF (ME002)
MARIA POCH (O.S.B.M.)
329 Monastery Ln., Matawan, NJ 07747-9703
Apostolic Work: Retreat center, area social center, pilgrimage shrine
Vocation Director: Rev. Joseph Erdei, O.S.B.M., Rev. Basil Rakaczy, (732) 566-8445, fax: (732) 566-8762

BASILIAN SALVATORIAN (ME003)
FATHERS (B.S.O.)
Motherhouse: Lebanon.
American Headquarters:
St. Basil Seminary, 30 East St., Methuen, MA 01844
Web: www.saintbasils.org
www.stbasilartstudio.org
Email: stbasil@comcast.net
Members: 12 Priests in US
Conduct: Seminary, novitiate, retreat center, 4 parishes
Apostolic Work: Specialize in parishes, ecumenical activities, Cursillos, Teen Encounters, retreats, prison ministry, teaching, special ministries
Representation: (Arch)dioceses of Boston, Cleveland, Newton, and Miami. Also in Canada
Vocation Director: Rev. Larry Tumminelli, bso, (978) 683-2471

HOLY TRINITY (ME007)
MONASTERY-BENEDICTINE
MONKS - Byzantine Rite
Holy Trinity Monastery
PO Box 990, Butler, PA 16003-0990
Email: hegmenleo@aol.com
Members: 5 Priests, 3 Brothers
Conduct: throughout the Byzantine Metropolitan Province of Pittsburgh
Apostolic Work: Hospitality, private retreats, parochial work, and Eastern Christian religious articles
Vocation Director: Fr. Leo R. Schlosser, O.S.B., 724-287-4461, fax: 724-287-6160

HOLY TRANSFIGURATION (ME008)
MONASTERY - MONKS OF MT. TABOR
17001 Tomki Rd., PO Box 217, Redwood Valley, CA 95470-0217
Web: www.byzantines.net/ monastery
Email: mttabor@pacific.net
Apostolic Work: Contemplative; retreats, hospitality to all visitors, church unity, iconography, book writing
Representation: (Arch)diocese of St. Nicholas in Chicago
Vocation Director: (707) 485-8959, fax: (707) 485-1122

(ME009)
HOLY TRANSFIGURATION SKETE
Ukrainian Catholic Monastery
6559 State Hwy. M26, Eagle Harbor, MI 49950
Web: www.societystjohn.com
Email: skete@societystjohn.com
Members: 4 Consecrated Monks, 1 Novice
Conduct: Diocese of St. Nicholas in Chicago
Apostolic Work: Contemplative
Vocation Director: Fr. Basil, (906) 289-4484 or 4386, fax: (906) 289-4388

(ME010)
MARONITE MONKS OF ADORATION
Most Holy Trinity Monastery, 67 Dugway Rd., Petersham, MA 01366
Web: www.MaroniteMonks.org
Members: 9 Priests, 9 Brothers
Apostolic Work: Contemplative life of prayer and reparation
Representation: Diocese of St. Maron (USA)
Vocation Director: Rev. Michael Gilmary Cermak, MMA, (978) 724-3347

(ME011)
UKRAINIAN REDEMPTORISTS
St. Joseph Monastery
250 Jefferson Ave., Winnipeg, MB, Canada, R2V-0M6
Web: www.yorkton redemptorists.com
Email: ukryvm@mts.net
Apostolic Work: Parish work, missions, retreats, teaching and formation work, inner-city ministry, Blessed Vasyl Velychkovsky Martyr's Shrine
Representation: Serve in US and Canada
Vocation Director: Vocation Ministry Director, 204-339-5737, fax: 204-339-1062

Lord, Are You Calling Me?

GOD'S CALL
How do I know if God is calling me?
How can I tell?
Who can help me?
Where do I go?
When will I know?
What will I do?

Step One
Ask yourself, first of all, how am I doing with my very first vocation: my Baptismal Call.

Am I really a loving and faithful daughter or son of God?

Do I worship God at liturgy, keeping the Lord's day?

Do I use my gifts to pray, to read, to serve, to sing, to play music, to be a greeter, usher, sacristan, etc.?

Is Jesus alive in me? Am I alive in Him? Am I living His Gospel?

Is my life giving witness to His presence in me?

Do I take pride and find joy in my union with Jesus Christ?

Am I a true dwelling place of the Holy Spirit?

Is prayer important in my life?

Do I really try to love others?

Forgive them?

Speak well of them?

Pray for them?

Do I enjoy learning about my faith and religion?

Am I involved in things that help people?

Step Two
Do I have a desire to serve?

Do I have an attraction to doing something with my life?

Have I always wanted to be like someone I admired and respected in ministry or religious life?

Do I feel driven to help people or to make the world a better place?

What do I see myself doing with my life?

What do other people think I would be good at?

Step Three
Pray over your calling and talk to God about it and LISTEN.

Make a retreat. Spend a weekend in a seminary, a convent, a monastery, or a vocation awareness program.

Also talk about it with others: friends, parents, your pastor, sisters, priests, brothers, teachers, mentors, your own sister or brother - anyone you trust and who knows you well.

Learn about how other people have found their calling.

Find a spiritual director to help you. Search this *Guide* or visit www.ReligiousMinistries.com to identify communities which best suit your particular talents and abilities.

Step Four
Take a deep breath.
Pray.

Now call, write, or email the vocations director in the religious community or diocese in which you have an interest.

Step Five
Give it a try.
You will never know if you have a vocation to be a priest, a sister, a brother, a deacon, or a lay minister unless you actually test and try it.

Religious Communities for Women

ADORERS OF THE BLOOD (W001)
OF CHRIST (A.S.C.)
An international community
US Region Vocation Office, 1400 S.
Sheridan, Wichita, KS 67213-1394
Web: www.adorers.org
Email: ascvocations@adorers.org
Members: More than 350 U.S.
Sisters, 370 Associates
Apostolic Work: If you're reading
this, you may be wrestling with
questions about your vocation and
how God is calling you to live your
life. We offer a spiritual discernment
program – LifeChoices® – that is
designed to help women and men
discern their vocation. Regardless
of whether you are being called to
marriage, single or religious life,
LifeChoices®; can help in your
search for a life filled with meaning,
purpose and holiness. Use the
contact information below if you'd
like to know more.

If you feel called to religious life,
then we invite you to consider the
Adorers of the Blood of Christ. The
Adorers primary mission is to bring
the reconciling presence of the
Blood of Jesus into our world.
We live this out through prayer and a
variety of ministries including:
EDUCATION: classroom teachers,
principals, professors, tutors and
instructors in day care centers;
preschool; universities and colleges;
and secondary and elementary
schools; in HEALTH CARE:
hospitals, day care centers, home
care, skilled care facilities for the
elderly, and alternative health care
modalities; in PASTORAL WORK:
parish administrators, directors of
religious education/ parish school of
religion, hospital/ nursing home
chaplains, retreat and spiritual
directors; in SOCIAL JUSTICE:
homeless shelters, food pantries and
soup kitchens, and national Office of
Justice and Peace; and in other
ministries where the Holy Spirit
draws us to serve.

Representation: The Adorers' United
States Region Office is in St. Louis,
4233 Sulphur Ave, St. Louis, MO
63109 and Centers in Ruma,
Illinois; Wichita, Kansas; Columbia,
Pennsylvania; and missions in
Guatemala, Korea and Bolivia.
Vocation Director: For more infor-
mation on a religious vocation,
contact Sister Jan Lane 877-236-
7377 ext 1455, lanej@adorers.org.
For more information on
LifeChoices® contact Sister Rita
Schilling 877-236-7377 ext 1409,
schillingr@adorers.org.

SISTERS ADORERS OF THE (W004)
PRECIOUS BLOOD (A.P.B.)
700 Bridge St., Manchester, NH
03104-5495
Email: pbsisters1898@yahoo.com
Members: 29 Professed Sisters
Apostolic Work: Cloistered,
contemplative
Representation: Diocese of
Manchester
Vocation Director: Sister Mary Clare,
A.P.B., Superior, (603) 623-4264,
669-2879

SISTERS ADORERS OF THE (W006)
PRECIOUS BLOOD (A.P.B.)
166 State St., Portland, ME 04101
Email: sraloysius@verizon.net
Apostolic Work: Cloistered,
contemplative
Representation: Diocese of
Portland, ME
Vocation Director: Sr. Mary Aloysius,
APB, (207) 774-0861

SISTERS ADORERS OF THE (W007)
PRECIOUS BLOOD (A.P.B.)
Precious Blood Monastery
5400 Fort Hamilton Pkwy., Brooklyn,
NY 11219
Web: www.catholic.org/macc
Members: 12 Nuns
Apostolic Work: Cloistered,
contemplative
Representation: Diocese of Brooklyn
Vocation Director: (718) 438-6371

SISTERS ADORERS OF THE (W008)
PRECIOUS BLOOD (A.P.B.)
Precious Blood Monastery, 400 Pratt
St., Watertown, NY 13601-4238
Web: www.sisterspreciousblood.org
Email: smarilyn@twcny.rr.com
Apostolic Work: Cloistered,
contemplative, intercessory prayer
Representation: Diocese of
Ogdensburg
Vocation Director: Director of Novices,
(315) 788-1669, fax: (315) 779-9046

ANGELIC SISTERS OF (W009)
ST. PAUL (A.S.S.P.), 770 Washington
St., Easton, PA 18042-4342
Members: 4 Sisters in US, 350
worldwide
Apostolic Work: Teaching, mission
work, parish work, C.C.D. teaching,
social work, youth group coordinator
Representation: Diocese of
Allentown (PA)
Vocation Director: Sister Teresa
Bianco, ASSP, (610) 258-7792

(W010)
ANTONINE SISTERS (MARONITE)
See Eastern Catholic Religious
Communities for Women

APOSTLES OF THE SACRED (W011)
HEART OF JESUS (A.S.C.J.)
Mount Sacred Heart Provincialate
295 Benham St., Hamden, CT 06514
Web: www.ascjus.org
Email: vocations@ascjus.org
Members: 145 Sisters in the United
States, 1400 worldwide
Apostolic Work: Teaching in high
schools, elementary schools,
schools for children who are
mentally handicapped or learning
disabled, kindergartens and day
nurseries; Pastoral Ministry; Social
Services; Health Care; Legal
Services to the Poor
Representation: (Arch)dioceses of
Bridgeport, Greensburg, Hartford,
New York, Pensacola/Tallahassee,
and St. Louis. Also in Africa,
Albania, Argentina, Brazil, Chile,
Italy, the Philippines, Switzerland,

Uruguay, Mexico and Taiwan
Vocation Director: Sr. Susan Marie Krupp, A.S.C.J., Apostles of the Sacred Heart of Jesus Vocation Office, 800 Montebello Camp Rd., Imperial, MO 63052, (314) 620-8847

RELIGIOUS OF THE (W012)
ASSUMPTION (R.A.), Provincial House,11 Old English Road, Worcester, MA 01609, (508) 793-1954
Web: www.assumptionsisters.org
Email: info@assumptionsisters.org
Members: 26 Sisters in the US; 1,300 Sisters worldwide
Apostolic Work: Teaching, catechetics, campus ministry; retreats, ecumenical work, pastoral ministry, justice and peace work, counseling, spiritual direction in Europe, USA, Africa, Central and South America and Asia
Representation: (Arch)dioceses of Philadelphia, Las Cruces and Worcester and in 35 foreign countries
Vocation Director: Mary Ann Azanza, R.A., 11 Old English Rd., Worcester, MA 01609, (508) 793-1954, fax: (508) 791-2936

(W013)
SISTERS OF THE ASSUMPTION OF THE B.V. (S.A.S.V.)
Motherhouse: Nicolet, Quebec, Canada, 156 Granite St., Leominster, MA 01453
Web: www.sasv.ca
Email: cpimleysasv@yahoo.com
Members: 600 Sisters
Apostolic Work: Education, pastoral ministry, campus ministry, retreat/ spiritual direction, missionaries, hospital chaplaincy, elder care, music, art, advocacy for women, youth and the impoverished, SASV Associates.
Representation: New England (USA), Canada, Brazil, Japan, Equador, Haiti
Vocation Director: Sr. Catherine Pimley, (978) 537-1224

(W014-1)
AUGUSTINIAN CONTEMPLATIVE NUNS (O.S.A.), Augustinian Monastery, 440 N. Marley Rd., New Lenox, IL 60451
Web: www.augustiniannuns.com
Email: s.marygrace.osa@ sbcglobal.net
Apostolic Work: Augustinian Nuns seek God and follow Jesus within a communal context which is wholly oriented to a contemplative life of prayer
Vocation Director: Sister Mary Grace, O.S.A., Prioress, 815-463-9662

AUGUSTINIAN RECOLLECT (W014-2)
SISTERS (O.A.R.), Motherhouse: Mexico, St. Leo's Convent, 121 Myrtle Ave., Irvington, NJ 07111
Email: ugurecsisnj@aol.com
Apostolic Work: Contemplative, centered around prayer and devotion/dedication to the worship of Christ in the Blessed Sacrament. Make vestments, art work, pottery, baking
Representation: Archdiocese of Newark
Vocation Director: Sr. Beatriz, OAR, (973) 374-6397, fax: (973) 372-0356

AUGUSTINIAN SISTERS (W015)
(O.S.A.), Servants of Jesus and Mary St. John Convent, Brandenburg, KY 40108-0108
Web: www.asjm.org (overseas)
Email: sisters4@bbtel.com
Members: 350 Sisters worldwide; 4 Sisters in US
Representation: Archdiocese of Louisville
Vocation Director: (270) 422-4935

(W016-1)
BASILIAN NUNS AND SISTERS
See Eastern Catholic Religious Communities for Women

CATHOLIC COMMUNITY (W016-2)
OF THE BEATITUDES
2924 W. 43rd Ave., Denver, CO 80211, (720) 855-9412
Web: www.beatitudes.us
Email: beatitudes.denver@gmail
Members: 1,500 Priests, Brothers, Consecreted Nuns, and Married Couples
Apostolic Work: In Denver a parish, school, retreat house, and evangelization
Representation: Denver, Mexico, Brazil, Peru, Canada, Israel, Lebanon, Medjugorie, France, Italy, Spain, Germany, Belgium, Austria, Switzerland, Czech Republic, Slovakia, Hungary, Norway, Kazakhstan, China, Vietnam, New Zealand, New Caledonia, Reunion Island, Ivory Coast, Congo, Democratic Republic of Congo, Central African Republic, Gabon, Mali
Vocation Director: Rev. Sebastien Pelletier, Superior of the Denver House

(W016-3)
BENEDICTINE CONGREGATION OF OUR LADY OF MOUNTE OLIVETO
Benedictine Monastery of Hawaii, PO Box 490, Waialua, Oahu, HI 96791-0490

Web: www.hawaiibenedictines.org
Email: monastery@hawaii benedictines.org
Members: 4 Sisters
Apostolic Work: Retreats, spiritual direction, parish assistance, and prayer
Representation: Diocese of Honolulu
Vocation Director: (808) 637-7887, Fax (808) 637-8601

BENEDICTINE NUNS (O.S.B.) (W017-1)
Abbey of St. Walburga
32109 N. U.S. Hwy. 287, Virginia Dale, CO 80536-8942
Web: www.walburga.org
Email: aswvocations@ix.netcom.com
Members: 22 Nuns
Apostolic Work: Full monastic office in English, Latin Gregorian Chant for Sunday mass, life of prayer interwoven with compatible work (guest house, farm and gardens, altar bread distribution, arts and crafts.)
Representation: Archdiocese of Denver
Vocation Director: Sister M. Pauline Laplante, O.S.B., (970) 472-0612

BENEDICTINE NUNS (O.S.B.) (W017-2)
St. Scholastica Priory, Box 606, 271 N. Main St., Petersham, MA 01366-0606
Web: www.stscholasticapriory.org
Email: sspriory@aol.com
Members: 9 Nuns in Solemn Vows
Apostolic Work: Prayer. Cloistered
Vocation Director: Sr. Mary Angela Kloss, O.S.B., (978) 724-3213

BENEDICTINE NUNS (O.S.B.) (W018)
St. Emma Monastery, 1001 Harvey Ave., Greensburg, PA 15601-1494
Web: www.stemma.org
Email: vocations@stemma.org
Members: 8 Nuns, 3 Temporarily Professed, 1 Novice
Apostolic Work: Monastic life
Representation: Diocese of Greensburg
Vocation Director: Mother Mary Anne Noll, O.S.B. (724) 834-3060, fax: (724) 834-5772

BENEDICTINE NUNS OF (W019)
THE CONGREGATION OF SOLESMES (O.S.B.), US Foundation, Monastery of the Immaculate Heart of Mary, 4103 VT Rte. 100, Westfield, VT 05874, 802-744-6525
Web: www.ihmwestfield.com or www.solesmes.com
Email: monastery@ ihmwestfield .com
Members: 11 Professed Nuns, 1

Temporary Professed, 1 Novice, 3 Postulants
Apostolic Work: Divine Office, in Latin with Gregorian Chant, according to the Rule of Saint Benedict and the Vatican II Constitution on the Liturgy
Representation: Diocese of Burlington. 24 monasteries of monks and 8 monasteries of nuns in 11 countries
Vocation Director: Mother Maria-Magdalen Grumm, O.S.B., Subprioress

BENEDICTINE NUNS OF THE (W020)
PRIMITIVE OBSERVANCE (O.S.B.)
Abbey of Regina Laudis, 273 Flanders Rd., Bethlehem, CT 06751
Web: www.abbeyofreginalaudis.com
Members: 29 Perpetually Professed, 4 Temporary Professed, 4 Novices, Postulant
Conduct: Cloistered. 1 Abbey
Representation: Archdioceses of Hartford and Seattle
Vocation Director: Rt. Rev. Mother David Serna, O.S.B., Abbess, (203) 266-7727

BENEDICTINE SISTERS (W021)
(O.S.B.), Sacred Heart Monastery, 916 Convent Rd., Cullman, AL 35055
Web: www.shmon.org
Email: vocations@shmon.org
Members: 46 Sisters,1 Postulant
Apostolic Work: Varies. As a monastic community, prayer and community are the primary work. Beyond these, each Sister engages in a ministry which allows her to live this life of prayer and community
Representation: Dioceses of Birmingham and Orlando
Vocation Director: Sister Magdalena Craig, O.S.B., (256) 734-2199

BENEDICTINE SISTERS (W022)
(OSB), St. Scholastica Monastery, PO Box 3489, 1301 S. Albert Pike, Fort Smith, AR 72913-3489
Web: www.stscho.org
Email: vocationdirector@stscho.org
Members: 72 Sisters
Apostolic Work: Essential ministry is to seek God in community and to praise God through a balanced life of prayer, work and leisure. Sisters are involved in teaching, retreat work, spiritual direction, pastoral care, parish work, youth ministry, social work, and service to one another in community
Representation: Diocese of Little Rock
Vocation Director: Sister Kimberly Rose Prohaska, OSB, (479) 783-4147

BENEDICTINE SISTERS (W023)
(O.S.B.), St. Lucy's Priory, 19045 E. Sierra Madre, Glendora, CA 91741
Web: www.stlucys.com
Members: 14 Sisters
Apostolic Work: Education, pastoral ministry
Representation: Archdioceses of Los Angeles and San Diego
Vocation Director: Sr. Elizabeth Brown, O.S.B., Prioress, (626) 335-1682, fax: (626) 963-9398

BENEDICTINE SISTERS (W024)
(O.S.B.), Holy Spirit Monastery 22791 Pico St., Grand Terrace, CA 92313-5725
Web: www.holyspiritmonastery.org
Email: hsmonastery@prodigy.net
Members: 6 Sisters
Apostolic Work: Early childhood/training, parish administration, counseling, retreats, spiritual direction, religious education and monastery works
Representation: Diocese of San Bernardino
Vocation Director: Sr. Mary Ann Schepers, OSB, Prioress, (909) 783-4446, fax: (909) 783-3525

BENEDICTINE SISTERS (W025)
(O.S.B.), Benet Hill Monastery 2555 N. Chelton Rd., Colorado Springs, CO 80909-1399
Web: www.benethillmonastery.org
Email: info@benethillmonastery.org
Members: 39 Sisters
Apostolic Work: Seeking God in the monastic community, praise of God in liturgy and serving in the area of each Sister's giftedness and the needs of the People of God
Representation: Archdioceses of Denver and Santa Fe and in the Dioceses of Colorado Springs and Pueblo. Also in Jamaica
Vocation Director: Sister Clare Carr, O.S.B., Sister Mary Colleen Schwarz, O.S.B., 719-633-0655

BENEDICTINE SISTERS (W026)
(O.S.B.), Our Lady of Mount Caritas Monastery, 54 Seckar Rd., Ashford, CT 06278
Web: www.mountcaritas monastery .org
Members: 4 Sisters
Apostolic Work: Contemplative prayer
Representation: Diocese of Norwich
Vocation Director: Rev. Mother Mary Peter, O.S.B., Prioress, (860) 429-7457

BENEDICTINE SISTERS (W027)
(OSB), Monastery of St. Gertrude 465 Keuterville Road, Cottonwood, ID 83522
Web: www.stgertrudes.org
Email: vocation@stgertrudes.org
Members: 60 Professed members, 4 Temporary professed, 3 Novices
Apostolic Work: In 1882, our foundresses Mother Johanna Zumstein, Rosalia Ruebli and Magdalene Suter came from Sarnen, Switzerland to establish a presence in the United States. In 1909, Mother Hildegard Vogler moved the motherhouse from Colton, WA to our present location in Cottonwood, Idaho. We invite you to join us as we celebrate 100 years "at home" in Idaho. As Benedictine women, we welcome God's transforming power in ourselves and our world. We seek God together through monastic profession and respond in healing hospitality, grateful simplicity and creative peacemaking. We gather daily to pray the Liturgy of the Hours and celebrate the Eucharist, practice individual prayer, reflective reading and contemplation. Prayer is central to our lives and is the base for which our ministries emerge. Our ministries include education, administration, health care, parish and pastoral work, music, social work, historical museum, retreat and spirituality ministries and land stewardship.
Representation: (Arch)dioceses of Boise, Seattle and Spokane
Vocation Director: Sr. Janet M. Barnard, OSB, (208) 962-5024

BENEDICTINE SISTERS (W028)
(O.S.B.), St. Scholastica Monastery 7430 N. Ridge Blvd., Chicago, IL 60645-1913
Web: http://www.osbchicago.org.
Email: bcoffey@osbchicago.org
Members: 54 Sisters
Apostolic Work: We are Benedictine women called to seek God in prayer and community, serving where there is need. We sponsor an academy for young women and serve the church and society in a variety of ways. We work in all areas of education, social service, pastoral ministry, spiritual development, and health care. We minister to the elderly, to homeless men and women, and the mentally ill, and underlying all we do is our desire to live the Gospel command to love God and neighbor. Women 20-50 who wish to seek God in an active

monastic community by living a balanced life of prayer, work, and leisure are invited to contact us.
Representation: Archdiocese of Chicago
Vocation Director: Sr. Benita Coffey, O.S.B., 7430 North Ridge Boulevard, Chicago, IL 60645; (773) 764-2413, ext. 327

BENEDICTINE SISTERS (W029)
(O.S.B.), Sacred Heart Monastery 1910 Maple Ave., Lisle, IL 60532
Web: www.shmlisle.org
Email: ckouba@shmlisle.org
Members: 32 Sisters
Conduct: Senior citizen residence, education, pastoral ministry in parishes, administrators, counseling, nursing to elderly, ministry to Hispanics, Lectio Divina centering prayer groups, transitional housing for the poor, community support services, and domestic services
Apostolic Work: Living in a monastic life of seeking God in prayer and work, focusing on mission of hospitality especially to the elderly in our Villa Center
Representation: Diocese of Joliet
Vocation Director: Sister Christine Kouba, OSB, (630) 725-6050, 725-6065, fax: (630) 725-6020

BENEDICTINE SISTERS (W030)
(O.S.B.), St. Mary Monastery, 2200 88th Ave. W., Rock Island, IL 61201
Web: www.smmsisters.org
Email: rbussan@smmsisters.org
Members: 58 Sisters
Apostolic Work: Monastic community: primary ministry of seeking God in community through a balanced life of prayer and work; extending through ministries of prayer, spiritual direction, pastoral ministry, education, social work and outreach to the poor. We invite you to come and experience who we are as Benedictine monastic women
Representation: Primarily in the Diocese of Peoria, IL
Vocation Director: Sr. Bobbi Bussan, O.S.B., 800-650-1257 or (309) 283-2300

BENEDICTINE SISTERS (W032-1)
(OSB), Monastery Immaculate Conception, 802 E. 10th St., Ferdinand, IN 47532-9239
Web: www.thedome.org/vocations
Email: vocation@thedome.org
Apostolic Work: We are monastic women seeking God through the Benedictine tradition of community life, prayer, hospitality and service to others. By our life and work, we

commit ourselves to be a presence of peace as we join our sisters and brothers in the common search for God. We minister in education, parish ministry, religious education, counseling, retreat work, spiritual direction, social services and health care. We do not identify with one specific ministry; rather we respect each individual's gifts as given by God. We encourage women, ages 18-40, who earnestly seek God and want to live a balanced life of prayer and work to inquire about our monastic lifestyle. At the time of entrance, women must be between 21 and 40 and have at least two years of work experience or college.
Representation: Dioceses of Evansville, Owensboro, Joliet and Belleville and Archdioceses of Louisville, Indianapolis and Washington D.C. Also in Rome and Peru.
Vocation Director: Sister Agnes Marie Dauby and Sister Michelle Catherine Sinkhorn, 800-738-9999

BENEDICTINE SISTERS (W033)
(O.S.B.), Mount St. Scholastica 801 S. 8th St., Atchison, KS 66002
Web: www.mountosb.org
Email: vocation@mountosb.org
Members: 160 Sisters, 1 Scholastic, 1 Novice, 1 Postulant
Apostolic Work: A monastic community rooted in community life, prayer and ministry to God's people. Flowing from prayer and community, sponsored ministries include Sophia Spirituality Center, Mount Conservatory of Music, women's centers in Atchison and Kansas City, Benedictine College, Donnelly College and Maur Hill-Mount Academy. Sisters also work in the areas of counseling, health care, parish ministry and education at all levels
Representation: Archdiocese of Kansas City and in the Dioceses of Kansas City-St. Joseph and Des Moines. Also in Mineiros, Brazil
Vocation Director: (913) 360-6200 or 6219 (vocation office), fax: (913) 360-6190

BENEDICTINE SISTERS (W034)
(O.S.B.), Mt. Tabor Benedictines, 150 Mt. Tabor Rd, Martin, KY 41649-1649
Web: http://www.mounttabor.net
Email: mtabor150@hotmail.com, carolynmt@hotmail.com
Members: 6 Sisters
Apostolic Work: A monastic ecumenical community of women challenged by the Gospel and the

Benedictine tradition: to nurture the giftedness of each person, to serve the community through teaching, counseling, outreach to the poor, social work, agricultural work, care of the sick, parish and retreat work, liturgical prayer, ecumenism and sharing resources as well as other traditional and creative ministries.
Representation: Diocese of Lexington
Vocation Director: Sr. Carolyn Lambert, OSB, (606) 886-9624

BENEDICTINE SISTERS (W035)
(OSB), St. Walburg Monastery 2500 Amsterdam Rd., Covington, KY 41017-1017
Web: www.stwalburg.org
Members: 71 Sisters
Conduct: 1 academy (K-12); Montessori school (3-5 years old); center of spirituality (retreats, spiritual direction, hospitality and volunteer service programs)
Apostolic Work: We are a Benedictine community of monastic women who celebrate the presence of Jesus Christ in community, prayer and work. The Liturgy of the Hours, Eucharist, personal prayer and reading are the foundations of our spirituality. We work as church ministers serving old and young, sick and poor, strangers and guests. Our common search for God enables us as community to create spaces of peace and justice. We are spiritual and retreat directors, teachers, social workers, counselors, nurses and administrators. Women who want to strengthen their faith and discern a call to serve God are welcome to spend time with the community.
Representation: Archdiocese of Cincinnati, OH and the Dioceses of Covington, Lexington, KY and Pueblo, CO
Vocation Director: Sr. Cathy Bauer, OSB, email: bauerosb@yahoo.com; phone: (859) 331-6324

BENEDICTINE SISTERS (W036-1)
(O.S.B.), St. Gertrude Monastery 14259 Benedictine Lane, Ridgely, MD 21660-1044
Web: www.ridgelybenedictines.org
Email: ridgelyvocations@hotmail.com
Members: 27 Professed Sisters
Apostolic Work: Prayer and community life. A sister with the prioress discerns a ministry of service.

Presently sisters are involved in the Benedictine Programs for developmentally disabled children, elementary and high school teaching, religious education, nursing, social work, pastoral ministry, ministry with the poor and social justice efforts
Representation: Diocese of Wilmington, DE
Vocation Director: Sr. Colleen Quinlivan, O.S.B., (410) 634-2497, ext. 1428 fax: (410) 634-1410

BENEDICTINE SISTERS (W036-2)
(O.S.B.), Corpus Christi Monastery 4485 Earhart Rd., Ann Arbor, MI 48105-9710
Email: benedictines@sbcglobal.net
Members: 4 Sisters, 5 Associates
Apostolic Work: Various works compatible with monastic schedule; sing Divine Office in Gregorian Chant in English; daily Eucharistic Adoration
Representation: Diocese of Lansing
Vocation Director: Mother Regina Mary, O.S.B.(734) 995-3876, fax: (734) 930-9471

BENEDICTINE SISTERS (W037)
(O.S.B.), Mount Saint Benedict Monastery, 620 Summit Ave., Crookston, MN 56716-2799
Web: www.msb.net
Email: ademers@msb.net
Members: 88 Sisters
Apostolic Work: The primary work of the Benedictine is to seek God in community through prayer and service. The Sisters work in health care, education, pastoral care, parish ministry, retreat work, social work, domestic services, arts and crafts.
Representation: Primarily in the Dioceses of Crookston (MN) and Brownsville (TX)
Vocation Director: Sr. Anne DeMers, OSB, (218) 281-3441 fax: (218) 281-6966

BENEDICTINE SISTERS (W038)
(O.S.B.), St. Scholastica Monastery 1001 Kenwood Ave., Duluth, MN 55811-2300
Web: www.duluthbenedictines.org
Email: mcshambour@duluthosb.org
Members: 121 Sisters
Apostolic Work: We are Benedictine monastic women who seek God together in Community. Our lives are centered around the Eucharist and the Liturgy of the Hours, grounded in liturgical and personal prayer, – in Lectio Divina – (holy reading), with time for silence and solitude, for ministry, study, and leisure. Our core monastic values of hospitality and stewardship, peace and justice, stability and attentive listening, together with the Gospel and the Rule of St. Benedict, guide our communal life and our ministries. We invite women to join us in permanent vowed membership or to experience monastic life by living with us for six months to a year or longer in our volunteer residential Benedictine Associate program.
Representation: Dioceses of Duluth and Phoenix and Archdioceses of Chicago and St. Paul-Minneapolis
Vocation Director: For more information, to arrange a visit, or for a copy of our film "Sing a New Song"; contact Sr. Mary Catherine Shambour, O.S.B., 1001 Kenwood Ave., Duluth, MN 55811-2300 (218) 723-6646; e-mail: mcshambour@ duluthosb.org; website: www.duluthbenedictines .org

BENEDICTINE SISTERS (W039)
(O.S.B.), Saint Benedict's Monastery 104 Chapel Lane, St. Joseph, MN 56374-0220
Web: www.sbm.osb.org
Email: mholicky@csbsju.edu
Members: 315 Sisters
Apostolic Work: Seeking God especially in the context of Monastic Community, Liturgy of the Hours, and serving in whatever area the giftedness of the sisters and the needs of the people require
Vocation Director: S. Mary Catherine Holicky, O.S.B., (320) 363-7180

BENEDICTINE SISTERS (W040)
(OSB), St. Paul's Monastery 2675 Larpenteur Ave. E., St. Paul, MN 55109-5097
Web: www.stpaulsmonastery.org
Email: srmarie@stpauls monastery.org
Members: 60 Sisters
Apostolic Work: Seeking God in monastic life, Liturgy of the Hours and contemplation; parish and liturgical ministry, education, spiritual direction, retreats, psychotherapy, pastoral care of the aged, child care, health care, food management, and other ministries needed by the people
Representation: Archdiocese of St. Paul/Minneapolis
Vocation Director: Sister Marie Fujan, OSB, (651) 777-8181

BENEDICTINE SISTERS (W041)
(O.S.B.), Our Lady of Peace Monastery, 3710 W. Broadway, Columbia, MO 65203-0116
Web: www.benedictinesister.org
Email: olpvoc@juno.com
Representation: Dioceses of Jefferson City and Springfield-Cape Girardeau
Vocation Director: Sister Joyce McNerney, O.S.B., (573) 819-2373 or (573) 446-2300

BENEDICTINE SISTERS (W044)
(O.S.B.), Saint Walburga Monastery 851 N. Broad St., Elizabeth, NJ 07208-2539
Web: www.catholic-forum.com/ bensisnj
Email: srmariette@aol.com
Members: 45 Sisters, 1 Novice
Apostolic Work: The Sisters are monastic women who seek God in community through Gospel values and the Rule of Saint Benedict. In active lives balanced with prayer, they witness to Jesus Christ through hospitality, community, and service in education, health care and spirituality
Representation: Archdioceses of New York and Newark
Vocation Director: Sister Mariette Therese Bernier, OSB, (908) 352-4278, ext. 274

BENEDICTINE SISTERS (W046)
(O.S.B.), Annunciation Monastery 7520 University Dr., Bismarck, ND 58504
Web: www.annunciation monastery.org
Email: vocations@annunciatio nmonastery.org
Members: 70 Sisters
Apostolic Work: The Sisters' commitment to seek God through prayer and community life overflows into ministries of education, health care, campus and parish ministry, social work and whatever best suits the talents of the Sister and the needs of the people of the area
Vocation Director: Sister Kathleen Atkinson, osb, (701) 255-1520

BENEDICTINE SISTERS (W047)
(O.S.B.), Sacred Heart Monastery, PO Box 364, Richardton, ND 58652
Web: www.sacredheart monastery.com
Email: vocations@sacredheart monastery.com
Members: 25 Sisters

Apostolic Work: Parish ministry, hospital chaplains, social work, spirituality center, monastery works, raising llamas
Representation: Diocese of Bismarck
Vocation Director: Sr. Patti Koehler, OSB, (701) 974-2121.

BENEDICTINE SISTERS (W049)
(O.S.J.), St. Joseph Monastery
2200 S. Lewis Ave., Tulsa, OK 74114
Web: www.stjosephmonastery.org
Email: srveronica@
    montecassino.org
Members: 23 Sisters
Apostolic Work: Monastic community life and prayer, 1 private school grades pre-school through 8th grade coeducational.Other ministries: nursing, teaching, social services, pastoral ministry, catechetics, campus ministry, and Benedictine Oblates
Representation: Archdiocese of Oklahoma City and in the Dioceses of Lincoln and Tulsa
Vocation Director: Sr. Veronica Sokolosky, OSB, (918) 742-4989

BENEDICTINE SISTERS (W050-1)
(O.S.B.), Queen of Angels Monastery
840 S. Main St., Mt. Angel, OR 97362
Web: www.benedictine-srs.org
Email: smarietta@juno.com
Members: 39 Sisters
Apostolic Work: Seek God in a balanced life of prayer and work, simplicity, hospitality and service. Community ministries include a retreat and renewal center and a homeless shelter; individual ministries include teaching, pastoral care, health care, spiritual direction and parish work
Representation: Primarily in rural Oregon
Vocation Director: Sister Marietta Schindler, (503) 845-6141, fax: (503) 845-6585

BENEDICTINE SISTERS (W051)
(O.S.B.), Mount St. Benedict Monastery, 6101 East Lake Road, Erie, PA 16511
Web: www.eriebenedictines.org
Email: vocations@mtstbenedict.org
Members: 107 Sisters
Apostolic Work: Are you longing to deepen your relationship with God? Do you want to make a difference in our world? Do you want to meet others who share your faith and values? If so, we invite you to experience our life as monastic women who follow the Rule of St. Benedict. This ancient rule offers a way of life vital for our time: a way of living that calls us to a communal life of prayer and ministry; that gives witness, in a world of violence and inequality, to the values and teach-

ings of Jesus the Christ. Visit our website. Explore with us how our life of community, prayer, and ministry may be what you are seeking.
Representation: Diocese of Erie
Vocation Director: Vocation Ministry: Sr. Janet Goetz, O.S.B. (814) 899-0614 ext. 2424

BENEDICTINE SISTERS (W053)
(O.S.B.), St. Joseph Monastery
303 Church St., St. Marys, PA 15857
Web: www.osbnuns.org
Email: benedictinevocations@
yahoo.com, srjohnpaul@yahoo.com
Members: 21 Sisters
Apostolic Work: Education, retreats, office work, tutoring, transcribing books for the blind, music, art, recycling, farming, religious education, counseling and ceramics
Representation: Diocese of Erie
Vocation Director: Sister John Paul, O.S.B. (814) 834-2267

BENEDICTINE SISTERS (W054)
(OSB),St. Martin Monastery, 2110 St. Martin's Dr., Rapid City, SD 57702
Web: www.blackhillsbenedictine.com
Email: marg@blackhills
    benedictine.com
Members: 31 Members
Conduct: Retreat center. Also involved in religious education, pastoral ministry, counseling, hospital chaplaincy, home health care, spiritual direction, directed retreats
Representation: Diocese of Rapid City and Santiago, Chile
Vocation Director: Sr. Margaret Hinker, (605) 343-8011

BENEDICTINE SISTERS (W055)
(O.S.B.), Mother of God Monastery
110 28th Ave. SE #214, Watertown, SD 57201
Web: www.watertown
    benedictines.org
Email: vocations@dailypost.com
Members: 65 Sisters
Apostolic Work: We are a community of monastic women rooted in the peaceful prairie land of rural South Dakota. We are focused on seeking God through our daily monastic prayer and community life. From these flow our commitment to serving God's people. We invite women who desire to joyfully seek God in community to journey with us.
Vocation Director: Adrienne Kaufmann, OSB, (605) 886-4159

BENEDICTINE SISTERS (W056)
(O.S.B.), Sacred Heart Monastery
1005 West 8th St., Yankton, SD 57078
Web: www.yanktonbenedictines.org
Email: eoconnor@mtmc.edu

Members: 129 Sisters, 5 in formation
Apostolic Work: Prayer and the building of community are central to the Benedictine way of life and from this all other ministries flow. Individual and communal gifts and resources are used for the building of God's kingdom in a variety of ways. Ministry is characterized by a continual openness and response to the changing needs of the area and the times
Representation: (Arch)dioceses of Sioux Falls and Rapid City, SD; Omaha, Lincoln, and Grand Island, NE
Vocation Director: Sr. Eileen O'Connor, (605) 668-6017 and Sr. Barbara McTague, (605) 668-6008

BENEDICTINE SISTERS (W057)
(O.S.B.), St. Scholastica Monastery
416 W. Highland Dr., Boerne, TX 78006
Web: www.boernebenedictines.com
Email: khiggins@ktc.com
Members: 18 Sisters
Apostolic Work: Education, health care, pastoral outreach, community development, public policy, retreat
Representation: Dioceses of San Antonio and Laredo.
Vocation Director: Sr. Kathleen Higgins, O.S.B., (830) 816-8504, 249-2645

BENEDICTINE SISTERS (W058-1)
(O.S.B.), St. Benedict Monastery
17825 South Western St., Canyon, TX 79015
Web: www.osbcanyontx.org
Email: nuns@osbcanyontx.org
Members: 3 Final Professed, 2 Postulants
Apostolic Work: The primary ministry is to seek God through monastic life: community, Liturgy of the Hours, contemplation and work
Vocation Director: Sister Marcella Schmalz, OSB, (806) 655-9317

BENEDICTINE SISTERS (W058-2)
(O.S.B.), Mount Benedict Monastery, 6000 South 1075 East, Ogden, UT 84405
Web: www.mbmutah.org
Email: vocations@mbmutah.org
Members: 8 Sisters
Apostolic Work: Parish ministry, campus ministry, health care ministry, chaplaincy services, RCIA, retreat work, spiritual direction, and liturgical music
Representation: Diocese of Salt Lake City
Vocation Director: Sister Marilyn Mark, OSB, (801) 479-6030, fax: (801) 479-4997

BENEDICTINE SISTERS (W059)
(O.S.B.), St. Placid Priory, 500
College St., NE, Lacey, WA 98516
Web: www.stplacid.org/
vocations.html
Email: vocations@stplacid.org
Members: 18 Sisters
Apostolic Work: Ministries, within a
rich Benedictine tradition, include
spiritual direction, operating a
retreat center and bookstore,
healing touch, teaching, study,
liturgical preparation, and welcom-
ing guests into St. Placid's
Representation: Archdiocese of
Seattle
Vocation Director: Monika Ellis, OSB,
(360) 438-2595

BENEDICTINE SISTERS (W060)
(O.S.B.), St. Bede Monastery, PO
Box 66, 1190 Priory Rd., Eau Claire,
WI 54702-0066
Web: www.saintbede.org
Email: vocation@saintbede.org
Members: 32 Sisters
Apostolic Work: Seeking God in
monastic community life; serving
guests in retreat/conference center;
working in pastoral ministry, educa-
tion, health care, parish adminis-
tration, fundraising and spiritual
direction
Representation: Wisconsin, Texas
and Kentucky
Vocation Director: Contact: Sister
Marjorie Hill, (715) 834-3176

BENEDICTINE SISTERS (W062-1)
OF BALTIMORE (O.S.B.)
Emmanuel Monastery, 2229 W.
Joppa Rd., Lutherville, MD 21093-
4601
Web: www.emmanuelosb.org
Email: pkirk@emmanuelosb.org
Members: 14 Sisters
Apostolic Work: Committed to
seeking God in a communal way of
life as we respond through prayer
and ministry. Ministries include
education, parish, justice and
peace, soup kitchen, community
organizing, retreats/ spiritual
direction, administration, office
work, hospital and hospitality.
Representation: Archdioceses of
Baltimore and Newark.
Vocation Director: Sr. Patricia Kirk,
OSB, (410) 821-5792

BENEDICTINE SISTERS (W062-2)
OF FLORIDA (O.S.B)
Holy Name Monastery, PO Box
2450, St. Leo, FL 33574-2450
Web: www.floridabenedictines.com
Email: vocation@saintleo.edu
Members: 19 Sisters, 1 Volunteer
Apostolic Work: Educational,
pastoral and community services,
alleviating the hungers of the
human family

Representation: Diocese of St.
Petersburg
Vocation Director: Sister Mary David
Hydro, O.S.B. (352) 588-8320

BENEDICTINE SISTERS OF (W063-1)
PERPETUAL ADORATION (OSB)
Benedictine Monastery, Tucson
Monastery, 800 N. Country Club Rd.,
Tucson, AZ 85716.
San Benito Monastery, Box 510,
Dayton, WY 82836
31970 State Highway P, Clyde, MO
64432-8100
Web: www.benedictinesisters.org
Email: vocation@benedictine
sisters.org
Members: 93 Sisters
Apostolic Work: We are a contemplative monastic community with a
special dedication to the Eucharist.
Our life is guided by the tradition
and wisdom of the Rule of Saint
Benedict. We serve the Church
through a ministry of prayer,
support ourselves by work within
the enclosure of the monastery and
strive to witness to God's presence
in the world through our prayer and
community life and by offering a
welcoming and peaceful space to
those who visit. If you're a woman
between the ages of 18 and 40 and
drawn to a life of prayer, we invite
you to contact us
Representation: Dioceses of Kansas
City-St. Joseph, Tucson, and
Casper
Vocation Director: Sister Ruth Elaine
Starman, O.S.B. (660) 944-2221 or
877-632-6665 (toll-free)

BENEDICTINE SISTERS (W063-2)
OF PITTSBURGH (OSB)
4530 Perrysville Ave., Pittsburgh, PA
15229-2296
Web: www.osbpgh.org
Email: listening@osbpgh.org
Members: 60 Sisters, 4 in formation
Apostolic Work: Our monastic life
compels us to daily seek God in
Community and Prayer as our chief
occupation. Nourished by the Word
of God and our life together we
then respond to the needs of our
world through education ministry,
parish ministry, social justice, senior
services, transitional housing for
women with dependent children,
foster parenting, visual arts, liturgy
and music, counseling, spiritual
direction and spirituality programs.
We seek to be sign that peace and
peacemaking is possible in an ever-
chaotic world.
Representation: Dioceses of
Greensburg and Pittsburgh
Vocation Director: Sister Barbara
Jayne Vopat, OSB, (412) 931-2844,
ext. 118

BENEDICTINE SISTERS (W064-1)
OF VIRGINIA (O.S.B.)
St. Benedict Monastery, 9535 Linton
Hall Rd., Bristow, VA 20136-1217
Web: www.osbva.org
Email: vocations@osbva.org
Members: 34 Sisters
Apostolic Work: Education, pastoral
care, retreat programming, adult
literacy, transitional housing for
homeless women and children, low-
fee counseling for Catholic schools,
families and individuals
Representation: Dioceses of
Richmond and Arlington
Vocation Director: Sr. Vicki Ix, OSB,
(703) 298-5337

BENEDICTINE SISTERS (W064-2)
OF THE BYZANTINE RITE
See Eastern Catholic Religious
Communities for Women

BENEDICTINE SISTERS (W065)
(OSB), (Olivetan Benedictine Sisters)
Holy Angels Convent
1699 CR 766 - PO Drawer 130,
Jonesboro, AR 72403-0130
Web: www.olivben.org
Email: vocations@olivben.org
Members: 37 Sisters, 7 Junior
Sisters, 1 Novice, 1 Postulant
Apostolic Work: Teaching in schools,
parish religious education (at all
levels), teaching music, hospital
ministries, pastoral care ministry,
day care ministry, ministry to the
Hispanic and Black communities,
prison ministry.
Representation: Dioceses of Little
Rock and Fort Worth
Vocation Director: Sister M. Therese
Johnson, O.S.B., vocations cell-
phone: (870) 273-6872 (or) convent
telephone: (870) 935-5810. Fax:
(870) 935-4210

BENEDICTINE SISTERS (W066-1)
(O.S.B.), (Olivetan Benedictines)
Our Lady of Guadalupe Abbey
PO Box 1080, Pecos, NM 87552-1080
Web: www.pecosmonastery.org
Email: guestmaster@pecos
monastery.org
Members: 6 Sisters
Apostolic Work: Retreat ministry,
spiritual direction, school for
charismatic spiritual directors
Representation: Archdiocese of
Santa Fe
Vocation Director: Formation
Director, (505) 757-6415, 757-6600,
ext. 225, fax: (505) 757-2285

CONGREGATION OF THE (W066-3)
BENEDICTINES OF JESUS
CRUCIFIED (O.S.B.), Monastery of
the Glorious Cross, 61 Burban Dr.,
Branford, CT 06405-4003

Web: www.benedictinesjc.org
Email: monasterygc@juno.com
Members: Approximately 100 Sisters in Congregation, 18 in US
Apostolic Work: A Benedictine contemplative monastic community open to women with certain physical limitations as well as those in good health. Good psychological and emotional balance is essential
Representation: Motherhouse/ International Novitiate, 3 other monasteries in France and 1 in Japan.
Vocation Director: Sr. M. Zita Wenker, OSB, (203) 315-9964

SISTERS OF ST. BENEDICT (W067) **(OSB)**, Our Lady of Grace Monastery, 1402 Southern Ave., Beech Grove, IN 46107-1197
Web: www.benedictine.com
Email: nicolette@benedictine.com
Members: 76 Sisters, 2 in Formation
Apostolic Work: Teaching, administration, health care, directors of religious education, parish ministry, youth ministry, music ministry, retreat/education center.
Representation: Archdiocese of Indianapolis and in the Dioceses of Evansville and Dayton, Ohio
Vocation Director: Sr. Nicolette Etienne, OSB, (317) 787-3287, ext. 3032, fax: (317) 780-2368

MISSIONARY BENEDICTINE (W068-1) **SISTERS (O.S.B.)**
See "M"- Missionary Benedictine

TRANSFIGURATION (W068-2) **HERMITAGE (O.S.B.)**, 205 Windsor Neck Rd., Windsor, ME 04363
Web: www.transfiguration hermitage.org
Email: benedicite@fairpoint.net
Apostolic Work: Contemplative (Benedictine)
Representation: Diocese of Portland (ME)
Vocation Director: Sr. Elizabeth Wagner, (207) 445-8031

BERNARDINE FRANCISCAN (W069) **SISTERS (O.S.F.)**, (United States Province), 450 St. Bernardine St., Reading, PA 19607-1737
Web: www.bfranciscan.org
Email: FollowFrancis@ bfranciscan.org
Members: Over 450 Sisters and 100 Associates worldwide
Apostolic Work: In 1894 Mother Veronica and four daring women left their European cloister and responded to the call to serve the immigrant Church in the US. Today, Bernardine Franciscan Sisters and Lay Associates reach out in the name of Jesus to God's people across the continental United States, Puerto Rico, Brazil, the

Dominican Republic and Liberia (West Africa).
Rooted in contemplative prayer and trusting in Divine Providence, we strive to create communities of love and service wherever we minister: early childhood, all levels of education, catechetics, retreat centers, health care, parish and diocesan ministries as well as with, and on behalf of, the poor - especially women and children.
The Gospels, Francis and Clare permeate our Formation Programs for both Sisters and Lay Associates. Do you have a Franciscan heart? Are you willing to journey in faith and joy, sister and servant to all? If so, contact us
Vocation Director: S. Shaun Kathleen Wilson, OSF, Office of Vocations, (610) 777-2967

SISTERS OF BETHANY (W070) **(C.V.D.)**, 850 N. Hobart Blvd., Los Angeles, CA 90029
Members: 14 Sisters in US
Conduct: Religious education, social service and 1 women's residence
Representation: Archdiocese of Los Angeles
Vocation Director: Sr. Florelia Salazar, C.V.D., (323) 665-6937, fax: (323) 664-0754

BETHLEMITA DAUGHTERS (W071) **OF THE SACRED HEART OF JESUS (BethL.)**, St. Joseph Residence, 330 W. Pembroke Ave., Dallas, TX 75208
Email: srab@stjr.org
Members: 6 Sisters in US
Apostolic Work: Teaching, mission work, social work, work with the elderly in Central and South America, Canary Islands, Italy, Africa, India and in the US in the Diocese of Dallas only
Representation: Diocese of Dallas
Vocation Director: Sister Adelaide Bocanegra, (214) 948-3597

SERVANTS OF THE (W072) **BLESSED SACRAMENT (S.S.S.)** American Regional House, 101 Silver St., Waterville, ME 04901, 207-872-7072
Web: www.blesacrament.org
Email: servantsinfo@ blesacrament.org
Members: 13 Sisters in US
Apostolic Work: Eucharistic contemplative life & adoration of the Blessed Sacrament and sharing of prayer life with laity
Representation: Dioceses of Portland (ME) and Pueblo
Vocation Director: Sr. Kathryn Kelm, SSS, (207) 872-7072

SISTER SERVANTS OF THE (W073) **BLESSED SACRAMENT (S.J.S.)**
Motherhouse: Mexico
Province: United States of America 3173 Winnetka Dr., Bonita, CA 91902, (619) 267-0720
Charism: Adoration of the Blessed Sacrament and Education
Web: www.siervasdejesussacra mentado.org
Email: sjsusprovince@ sdcoxmai.com
Apostolic Work: Education
Representation: Archdiocese of Los Angeles and Dioceses of Fresno, Sacramento and San Diego
Vocation Director: Sister Aurora Lopez, SJS, Provincial, Sister Maria Paz Uribe, SJS, Provincial, Fax: (619) 276-0920

SISTERS OF THE BLESSED (W074) **SACRAMENT (SBS)**
Motherhouse, 1663 Bristol Pike, Bensalem, PA 19020-5796
Web: www.katharinedrexel.org
Email: sbsvocof@aol.com
Members: 200 (multi-racial, multi-cultural)
Apostolic Work: Share the Gospel message with the poor and oppressed, especially among Black and Native American peoples and challenge the deeply rooted injustice in the world today through a life of prayer, community and service. The SBS are involved in education, parish ministry, religious instruction, social and health services and spiritual ministries. They minister in the inner cities, rural areas, on Native American reservations, as well as in Haiti.
Representation: Archdioceses of Atlanta, New York, Philadelphia, Boston, New Orleans, Santa Fe and Washington (DC) and in the Dioceses of Baton Rouge, Birmingham, Evansville, Lafayette, Memphis, Gallup, Tucson and Palm Beach. Also in Haiti.
Vocation Director: Sister Karen Cote, (215) 244-9900 Ext. 327

CONGREGATION OF BON (W075) **SECOURS (CBS)**, 1525 Marriottsville Rd., Marriottsville, MD 21104, An International Congregation of Sisters
Web: www.bonsecoursvocations.org
Email: cbsvocations@bshsi.org
Members: 400 Sisters worldwide, 20 in Formation, 75 Associate Members, Lay Ministry Volunteers and Coworkers
Apostolic Work: Do you keep feeling God calling you to something more? If you wonder about religious life as a Sister, a simple call or email can begin your journey to know God's desires for you. As part of your discovery, it is very important to

seek a community where your unique gifts can be used.
The Sisters of Bon Secours is an international congregation founded in 1824. Our charism of COMPASSION, HEALING and LIBERATION impels us to provide "Good Help to those in need "with a particular compassion for the poor, the sick and the dying.
We are nourished by prayer and community life. Each Sister contributes her unique gifts and talents to the Bon Secours mission of Compassion, Healing, and Liberation.
Our ministries include health care: medical, hospitals, nursing homes for the elderly, and visiting nursing; hospital chaplaincy; social work: case management, and human services; rural area and inner city work; community-based outreach programs to the poor, ranging from housing to drop-in centers; spiritual direction; counseling; immigration; communications; foreign missions; education/teaching; and retreat ministry.
In continuity with our foundress' innovative spirit, our vision brings compassionate healing and wholeness beyond the walls of tradition to a world in need of healing.
Representation: US headquarters in Baltimore, Maryland, with convents in South Carolina, Michigan, Kentucky, New York, New Jersey, Virginia, Florida, and international provinces in France, Ireland, England, Scotland, Peru and a mission in South Africa.
Vocation Director: Sr. Pat Dowling, CBS, 877-742-0277 (toll-free) or (410) 442-3172

BRIGITTINE SISTERS (W076)
(O.SS.B.), Convent of St. Birgitta
4 Runkenhage Rd., Darien, CT 06820
Web: www.birgittines-us.com
Email: convent@birgittines-us.com
Members: 10 Sisters
Apostolic Work: Guest house, private retreats, active contemplative life, semi-contemplative life.
Representation: Diocese of Bridgeport. Houses in 16 foreign countries, missions in India (16 houses) and Mexico (5 houses)
Vocation Director: Sr. M. Eunice Kulangarathottiyil, O.SS.S., Superior, (203) 655-1068

(W076-1)
BYZANTINE NUNS OF ST. CLARE
See Eastern Catholic Religious Communities for Women

CABRINI SISTERS (W076-2)
See Missionaries of the Sacred Heart of Jesus

CAMALDOLESE NUNS (W077-2)
Transfiguration Monastery, 701 N.Y. Rte. 79, Windsor, NY 13865-9230
Web: www.catholic.org/macc
Email: bendon@dep.tds.net
Apostolic Work: Contemplative community
Representation: Diocese of Syracuse
Vocation Director: 607-655-2366

CANOSSIAN DAUGHTERS (W078-1)
OF CHARITY (FdCC) (Canossian Sisters), Provincial House
5625 Isleta Blvd. S.W., Albuquerque, NM 87105
Web: www.canossiansisters.org
Email: fdccvocations@aol.com
Members: 3,500 Sisters worldwide
Apostolic Work: Discovering God's love in contemplation of Christ crucified, St. Magdalene of Canossa opened herself to the poorest. In Mary, at the foot of the Cross, she found the model of steadfast faith and ardent charity. Today's Canossian Sisters work as pastoral ministers in parishes, schools, retreat and youth centers; live in a community of faith and spiritual growth; mutually accept one another in love, sharing all; are part of the international family of 4,000 sisters, lay associates, oblates, and volunteers; serve the Church in 30 countries spanning 6 continents, including 7 communities in North America; and give special attention to education, evangelization, pastoral care of the sick, formation of the laity, and spiritual exercises
Representation: Archdioceses of Santa Fe and San Francisco and in the Diocese of Sacramento and in Canada, Mexico and 7 African countries, 3 South American countries, Australia, 10 Asian countries and 6 European countries
Vocation Director: Canossian Sisters, (505) 873-2059

CAPUCHIN POOR CLARES (W078-2)
St. Veronica Giuliani Monastery
816 Jefferson St., Wilmington, DE 19801-1432
Web: www.capuchinpoorclares.org
Email: capuchinpoorc@comcast.net
Members: 12 Sisters
Apostolic Work: Cloistered, contemplative; cook meals for shelters for the homeless, sew vestments, clerical work
Representation: (Arch)dioceses of Wilmington, Denver, Pueblo, Amarillo and Alamo, Texas
Vocation Director: Sr. Carmen Quiroz, (302) 654-8727

CARMELITE COMMUNITY (W079-1)
OF THE WORD (C.C.W.)
Incarnation Center, 394 Bem Rd., Gallitzin, PA 16641
Web: www.ccwsisters.org
Members: 17 Sisters
Apostolic Work: Religious and academic education (all levels), pastoral ministry, family life ministry, ministry to the imprisoned, the homeless and the literal poor, evangelization, Catholic Charities, operate family soup kitchen
Representation: Diocese of Altoona-Johnstown
Vocation Director: (814) 886-4098

CARMELITE HERMIT OF (W079-2)
THE TRINITY (C.H.T.)
Mount Carmel Hermitage, 4270 Cedar Creek Rd., Slinger, WI 53086-9372
Web: www.carmelitehermit. homestead.com
Email: jmjose@catholic.org
Members: 1 Professed Hermit
Apostolic Work: Prayer, facilities for private retreats, spiritual guidance, religious publications
Representation: Archdiocese of Milwaukee
Vocation Director: Sister Joseph Marie, C.H.T.

MISSIONARY CARMELITES (W080)
OF ST. TERESA (C.M.S.T.)
Motherhouse: Mexico City
Provincialate, 9548 Deer Trail Dr., Houston, TX 77038
Email: hfamprovcmst@yahoo.com
Members: 66 Sisters in US, 670 worldwide
Apostolic Work: Education, health care, pastoral ministry, spirituality, pastoral clinic, spirituality and missions
Representation: Archdioceses of Oklahoma City and Galveston-Houston; Dioceses of Little Rock, Beaumont. Also in Stockholm, Sweden; Mexico, South America, Central America
Vocation Director: Sr. Guadalupe Flores (281) 445-5520 and Sr. Elsa Galdeano, (281) 820-8961

CARMELITE NUNS, (W082)
DISCALCED (O.C.D.), 716 Dauphin Island Pkwy., Mobile, AL 36606
Members: 4 Nuns
Vocation Director: Mother Marie Therese of Jesus, O.C.D., Prioress

CARMELITE NUNS, (W083)
DISCALCED (O.C.D.), Monastery of St. Teresa of Jesus, 7201 W. 32nd St., Little Rock, AR 72204
Web: http://www.littlerockcarmel.org
Email: lrcarmel@comcast.net

B-60

Members: 14 Nuns
Vocation Director: Sr. Mary Alice Grace, OCD, Monastery of St. Teresa of Jesus, (501) 565-5121

CARMELITE NUNS, (W084)
DISCALCED (O.C.D.), Carmel of St. Teresa, 215 E. Alhambra Rd., Alhambra, CA 91801
Email: teresacarm@aol.com
Members: 16 Nuns
Vocation Director: Sister Maria, O.C.D, (626) 282-2387

CARMELITE NUNS, (W085)
DISCALCED (O.C.D.), Monastery of Our Lady and St. Therese 27601 Hwy. 1, Carmel, CA 93923
Web: www.carmelitesistersbythe sea.net
Email: teresitaocd@catholic.org
Members: 10 Nuns
Apostolic Work: Cloistered, contemplatives
Vocation Director: Mother Teresita, O.C.D., Prioress, (831) 624-3043, fax: (831) 624-5495

CARMELITE NUNS, (W086)
DISCALCED (O.C.D.), 6981 Teresian Way, PO Box 1720, Georgetown, CA 95634
Web: www.carmelitemonastery.com
Members: 15 Nuns
Vocation Director: Mother Christine, OCD, Prioress, (530) 333-1617

CARMELITE NUNS, (W087)
DISCALCED (O.C.D.), Carmelite Monastery of Christ, the Exiled King, 68 Rincon Rd., Kensington, CA 94707-1047
Members: 4 Nuns

CARMELITE NUNS, (W088)
DISCALCED (O.C.D.), Carmelite Monastery of the Trinity, 5158 Hawley Blvd., San Diego, CA 92116-1934
Web: www.carmelsandiego.com
Email: carmelsd@sbcglobal.net
Members: 14 Nuns, 2 in Formation
Apostolic Work: Contemplative community
Vocation Director: Sister Yvonne Hanke, O.C.D., (619) 280-5424, ext. 111

CARMELITE NUNS, (W089)
DISCALCED (O.C.D.), Carmelite Monastery of Cristo Rey, 721 Parker Ave., San Francisco, CA 94118-4227
Members: 16 Nuns
Apostolic Work: Cloistered contemplatives
Vocation Director: Sr. Mary of the Sacred Heart, OCD, (415) 387-2640, fax: (415) 751-5330

CARMELITE NUNS, (W090)
DISCALCED (O.C.D.), Carmelite Monastery of the Mother of God, 530 Blackstone Dr., San Rafael, CA 94903
Web: www.motherofgodcarmel.org
Email: srdol@motherofgod carmel.org
Members: 6 Nuns, 1 Novice
Apostolic Work: Contemplative prayer for the Church; special emphasis to pray for the people of Russia
Vocation Director: Mother Dolores Sullivan, O.C.D., Prioress, (415) 479-6872

CARMELITE NUNS, (W091)
DISCALCED (O.C.D.), Carmelite Monastery of the Infant Jesus 1000 Lincoln St., Santa Clara, CA 95050-5050
Email: santaclaracarmel@ sbcglobal.net
Members: 13 Solemnly Professed
Vocation Director: Sr. Irene of Jesus, O.C.D., Prioress, (408) 296-8412

CARMELITE NUNS, (W093)
DISCALCED (O.C.D.), Carmel of the Holy Spirit, 6138 S. Gallup St., Littleton, CO 80120-2702
Members: 11 Nuns
Vocation Director: Mother Gemma Marie of the Passion, Prioress, (303) 798-4176

CARMELITE NUNS, (W094)
DISCALCED (O.C.D.), Our Lady of Confidence Monastery, 11 W. Back St., Savannah, GA 31419-3219
Web: www.savannahcarmel.org
Email: carmelite@savannah carmel.org
Members: 4 Nuns
Apostolic Work: Contemplative life of prayer
Vocation Director: Vocation Directress, (912) 925-8505

CARMELITE NUNS, (W095)
DISCALCED, 1101 N. River Rd., Des Plaines, IL 60016
Members: 14 Nuns
Vocation Director: Mother Marie Andre of the Holy Spirit, Prioress, (847) 298-4241

CARMELITE NUNS, (W097)
DISCALCED (O.C.D.), St. Joseph's Monastery, 59 Allendale, Terre Haute, IN 47802
Web: www.heartsawake.org
Email: vocations@heartsawake.org
Members: 11 Professed, 1 Novice
Apostolic Work: A purely contemplative apostolate, excluding all forms of active ministry. Member of a worldwide order composed of

almost 800 monasteries, represented in over 60 dioceses in the US
Vocation Director: Sister Mary Helen Nixon, O.C.D., (812) 299-1410, ext. 202 cell (812) 239-2924

CARMELITE NUNS, (W098)
DISCALCED (O.C.D.), Carmel of the Queen of Heaven, 17937 250th St., Eldridge, IA 52748-2748
Email: solitude@netins.net, carolocd@juno.com
Members: 10 Nuns
Apostolic Work: Prayer
Vocation Director: Sister M. Carol, O.C.D., (563) 285-8387, fax: (563) 285-7467

CARMELITE NUNS, (W099)
DISCALCED (O.C.D.), Monastery of the Discalced Carmelite Nuns 2901 S. Cecelia St. Sioux City, IA 51106
Web: www.carmelsc.org
Email: carmelsc@msn.com
Members: 9 Nuns
Apostolic Work: Contemplative prayer
Vocation Director: Vocation Directress, (712) 276-1680

CARMELITE NUNS, (W100)
DISCALCED (O.C.D.), Carmelite Monastery, 1740 Newburg Rd., Louisville, KY 40205-1292
Members: 10 Professed Nuns
Apostolic Work: Prayer and penance
Vocation Director: Mother Francis, O.C.D., Prioress

CARMELITE NUNS, (W101)
DISCALCED (O.C.D.), Monastery of St. Joseph and St. Teresa, 73530 River Rd., Covington, LA 70435
Web: www.covingtoncarmelite.org
Email: covingtoncarmel@aol.com
Members: 11 Nuns, 2 Junior Professed, 2 Novices
Vocation Director: Sister Edith Turpin, OCD, (985) 898-0923, fax: (985) 871-9333

CARMELITE NUNS, (W102)
DISCALCED (O.C.D.), Monastery of Mary, Mother of Grace, 1250 Carmel Dr., Lafayette, LA 70501-5299
Web: www.lafayettecarmelites.org
Email: lafcarmel@catholic.org
Members: 15 Nuns
Vocation Director: Sister Mary John Billeaud, OCD, (337) 232-4651, fax: (337) 232-3540

CARMELITE NUNS, (W103)
DISCALCED (O.C.D.), Carmelite Monastery, 1318 Dulaney Valley Rd., Baltimore, MD 21286-1399
Web: www.geocities.com/baltimore carmel
Email: coletteackerman@baltimore carmel.org

Members: 17 Nuns
Apostolic Work: Carmelite tradition centered in contemplation and community. Shared vibrant liturgical life
Vocation Director: Sr. Colette Ackerman, (410) 823-7415

CARMELITE NUNS, (W104-1)
DISCALCED (O.C.D.), Carmelite Monastery, 5678 Mt. Carmel Rd., La Plata, MD 20646-3625
Web: www.erols.com/carmel-of-port-tobacco
Email: steresa@erols.com
Members: 17 Nuns
Apostolic Work: Cloistered, contemplative
Representation: Archdiocese of Washington, DC
Vocation Director: Mother Virginia Marie, OCD, (301) 934-1654

CARMELITE NUNS, (W104-2)
DISCALCED (O.C.D.), 61 Mt. Pleasant Ave., Boston (Roxbury), MA 02119
Web: carmelitesofboston.org
Email: carmelitesofboston@earthlink.net; bostoncarmel@juno.com
Members: 10 Nuns
Apostolic Work: Contemplative prayer
Vocation Director: Sr. Bernadette Therese, OCD, (617) 442-1411

CARMELITE NUNS, (W105)
DISCALCED (O.C.D.), 15 Mount Carmel Rd., Danvers, MA 01923
Members: 14 Professed Nuns, 1 Novice
Conduct: Cloistered
Vocation Director: Sister Michael of Christ the King, OCD (978) 774-3008

CARMELITE NUNS, (W106)
DISCALCED, Carmelite Monastery (Grand Rapids), 4300 Mt Carmel Dr. NE, Ada (Parnell), MI 49301-9784
Web: www.carmelitenuns.org
Members: 13 Cloistered Nuns, 2 Externs
Vocation Director: Contact: (616) 691-7625

CARMELITE NUNS, (W107)
DISCALCED (O.C.D.), Monastery of St. Therese of the Child Jesus 35750 Moravian Dr., Clinton Township, MI 48035-2138
Web: www.rc.net/detroit/carmelite
Email: carmelctwp@sbcglobal.net
Members: 6 Nuns, 1 Novice, 1 Extern Sister
Apostolic Work: Cloistered contemplatives
Vocation Director: Mother Mary Elizabeth, O.C.D., 586-790-7255

CARMELITE NUNS, (W108)
DISCALCED (O.C.D.), Monastery of the Holy Cross, Hwy. U.S. 2, PO Box 397, Iron Mountain, MI 49801-0397
Members: 17 Cloistered Nuns, 2 Externs
Apostolic Work: Contemplative prayer for the Church
Vocation Director: Mother Pauline Marie, O.C.D., Prioress, (906) 774-0561

CARMELITE NUNS, (W109)
DISCALCED (O.C.D.), Monastery of the Infant Jesus of Prague 3501 Silver Lake Rd., Traverse City, MI 49684-8949
Web: www.carmelitenuns stjoseph.org
Email: carmeltc@charter.net
Members: 4 Solemnly Professed, 2 Sisters in Formation
Vocation Director: Mother Mary of Jesus, O.C.D., Prioress, (231) 946-4960

CARMELITE NUNS, (W110)
DISCALCED (O.C.D.), Carmel of Our Lady of Divine Providence, 8251 De Montreville Trail N., Lake Elmo, MN 55042-9547
Vocation Director: Mother Marie of the Incarnation, OCD, Prioress (651) 777-3882

CARMELITE NUNS, (W111)
DISCALCED (O.C.D.), 2155 Terry Rd., Jackson, MS 39204
Web: www.jacksoncarmel.org
Email: jm2155dt@aol.com
Members: 7 Nuns
Vocation Director: Sister Margaret Mary, OCD, Prioress, (601) 373-1460

CARMELITE NUNS, (W112)
DISCALCED (O.C.D.), Monastery of the Sacred Heart and St. Joseph 2201 W. Main St., Jefferson City, MO 65109
Members: 10 Nuns
Vocation Director: Mother Prioress, 573-636-3364

CARMELITE NUNS, (W113)
DISCALCED (O.C.D.)
Carmel of St. Joseph, 9150 Clayton Rd., St. Louis County, MO 63124
Web: www.stormpages.com/mtcarmel
Email: stlouiscarmel@sbcglobal.net
Members: 9 Professed Nuns, 1 Professed Extern, 2 Postulants
Apostolic Work: Prayer and penance, lived in a cloistered, contemplative community
Vocation Director: Mother Mary Joseph, O.C.D., Prioress, (314) 993-4394, fax: (314) 993-5039

CARMELITE NUNS, (W115-1)
DISCALCED (O.C.D.), Carmel of Jesus, Mary and Joseph, 9300 W. Agnew Rd., Valparaiso, NE 68065
Members: 13 Professed Nuns, 10 Novices, 6 Postulants
Apostolic Work: Cloistered contemplatives
Vocation Director: Mother Teresa of Jesus, O.C.D., Prioress

CARMELITE NUNS, (W115-2)
DISCALCED (O.C.D.), Monastery of Our Lady of the Mountains, 1950 La Fond Dr., Reno, NV 89509-3099
Email: clasachse@carmelofreno.net
Members: 17 Nuns
Vocation Director: Sr. Carol, O.C.D., (775) 323-3236

CARMELITE NUNS, (W115-3)
DISCALCED (O.C.D.), 275 Pleasant St., Concord, NH 03301-2509
Email: vocationcarmel.concordnh@verizon.net
Members: 10 Nuns
Apostolic Work: Contemplative community
Representation: Diocese of Manchester
Vocation Director: Sr. Louise Aylward, ocd, (603) 225-5791

CARMELITE NUNS, (W116-1)
DISCALCED (O.C.D.), The Carmelite Monastery of Mary Immaculate and St. Mary Magdalen, 26 Harmony School Rd., Flemington, NJ 08822
Web: www.FlemingtonCarmel.org
Members: 16 Nuns, 2 Novices
Apostolic Work: Cloistered contemplatives
Vocation Director: Mother Anne, O.C.D., Prioress

CARMELITE NUNS, (W116-2)
DISCALCED (O.C.D.), Monastery of the Most Blessed Virgin Mary of Mount Carmel, 189 Madison Ave., Morristown, NJ 07960-6101
Members: 12 Nuns
Vocation Director: Mother Therese, OCD, Prioress, (973) 539-0773, fax: (973) 984-0509

CARMELITE NUNS, (W117)
DISCALCED (O.C.D.), Discalced Carmelite Monastery, 49 Mount Carmel Rd., Santa Fe, NM 87505-0352
Members: 9 Nuns
Apostolic Work: Contemplative community
Vocation Director: Mother Rose Teresa, O.C.D., Prioress, (505) 983-7232

B-62

CARMELITE NUNS, (W118)
DISCALCED (O.C.D.), Carmel of the
Incarnation, 89 Hiddenbrooke Dr.,
Beacon, NY 12508-2230
Web: www.carmelitesbeacon.org
Email: beaconcarmel@optonline.net,
srmarita@yahoo.com
srmichaelene@yahoo.com
Members: 21 Professed Nuns
Apostolic Work: Contemplative
Vocation Director: Sr. Marita Biscotti,
OCD, Sr. Michaelene Devine, OCD,
845-831-5572

CARMELITE NUNS, (W118-1)
DISCALCED (O.C.D.), Monastery of
Our Lady of Mount Carmel and
St. Joseph, 361 Highland Blvd.,
Brooklyn, NY 11207-1910
Members: 7 Professed Nuns
Vocation Director: Contact: Mother
Maria Luz of the Holy Spirit,
Prioress, (718) 235-0422

CARMELITE NUNS, (W119)
DISCALCED (O.C.D.)
Monastery of Discalced Carmelites
75 Carmel Rd., Buffalo, NY 14214
Members: 11 Cloistered Nuns
(Professed), 2 Extern Sisters
(Professed), 1 Postulant
Apostolic Work: Prayer
Vocation Director: Mother Miriam of
Jesus, O.C.D., (716) 837-6499

CARMELITE NUNS, (W122-1)
DISCALCED (O.C.D.), 1931 W.
Jefferson Rd., Pittsford, NY 14534
Web: www.carmelitesofrochester.org
Members: 13 Nuns, 1 Postulant
Apostolic Work: Apostolate of prayer
and penance lived in strict enclosure
Vocation Director: Mother John, OCD

CARMELITE NUNS, (W122-2)
DISCALCED (O.C.D.), Carmel of Holy
Family, 3176 Fairmount Blvd.,
Cleveland Heights, OH 44118-4199
Web: www.clevelandcarmel.org
Email: sisters@clevelandcarmel.org
Members: 14 Nuns

CARMELITE NUNS, (W123)
DISCALCED (O.C.D.), Carmel of St.
Joseph, 20000 N. County Line Rd.,
Piedmont, OK 73078
Web: www.okcarmel.org
Email: vocation@okcarmel.org
Members: 11 Nuns
Apostolic Work: Cloistered,
contemplative
Vocation Director: Sister Donna
Ross, OCD

CARMELITE NUNS, (W124)
DISCALCED (O.C.D.), Carmel of
Maria Regina, 87609 Green Hill Rd.,
Eugene, OR 97402
Web: http://home.attbi.com/
~heartof mary1/
Members: 7 Nuns
Apostolic Work: Prayer and sacrifice
for the Church and the whole world
Vocation Director: Mother Elizabeth
Mary, O.C.D., Prioress, (541) 345-
8649, fax: (541) 345-4857

CARMELITE NUNS, (W125)
DISCALCED (O.C.D.), Carmelite
Monastery, 70 Monastery Rd.,
Elysburg, PA 17824-9697
Web: www.carmelelysburg.org
Email: carmelelysburg@
carmelelysburg.org
Members: 14 Nuns
Apostolic Work: Contemplative
religious life
Vocation Director: 570-672-2935,
fax: 570-672-0278

CARMELITE NUNS, (W126)
DISCALCED (O.C.D.), Monastery of
Holy Family, 510 E. Gore Rd., Erie,
PA 16509
Apostolic Work: Cloistered
contemplatives
Vocation Director: Mother Emmanuel,
Prioress, (814) 825-0846 fax: (814)
825-0865

CARMELITE NUNS, (W127)
DISCALCED (OCD), Carmel of the
Assumption, 5260 Center Dr.,
Latrobe, PA 15650-5204
Web: www.latrobecarmel.org
Email: carmelite.monastery@
verizon.net
Members: 12 Nuns
Apostolic Work: A cloistered
contemplative community
Vocation Director: Sr. Marie Elizabeth
Krug, OCD

CARMELITE NUNS, (W128)
DISCALCED (O.C.D.), Carmel of St.
Therese of Lisieux, PO Box 57,
Loretto, PA 15940-0057
Members: 10 Professed Nuns
Vocation Director: Mother John of the
Cross, O.C.D., Prioress, (814) 472-
8620

CARMELITE NUNS, (W129)
DISCALCED (O.C.D.), Carmelite
Monastery, 66 Ave. & Old York Rd.,
Philadelphia, PA 19126
Members: 8 Professed Nuns
Apostolic Work: A life of prayer and
penance for the needs of the
universal Church, especially for the
sanctification of priests. Papal
enclosure is maintained

Vocation Director: Mother Barbara of
the Holy Ghost, O.C.D., Prioress,
215-424-6143

CARMELITE NUNS, (W130)
DISCALCED (O.C.D.), Monastery of
Our Lady of Mount Carmel and St.
Therese of the Child Jesus, 25
Watson Ave., Barrington, RI 02806
Web: www.barringtoncarmel.full
channel.net
Email: vilmaseelaus@juno.com
Members: 15 Nuns
Vocation Director: Sister Vilma
Seelaus, O.C.D.

CARMELITE NUNS, (W131-1)
DISCALCED (O.C.D.), Monastery of
the Most Holy Trinity, 5801 Mt.
Carmel Dr., Arlington, TX 76017
Web: www.carmelnuns.com
Email: arcarmel@ix.netcom.com
Members: 11 Nuns, 1 Novice, I
Postulant
Vocation Director: Mother Maria of
Jesus Crucified, O.C.D., Prioress,
(817) 468-1781

CARMELITE NUNS (O.Carm.) (W131-2)
Monastery of Our Lady of Grace
6202 CR 339 Via Maria, Christoval,
TX 76935-3023
Web: http://carmelnet.org/christoval/
christoval.htm
Email: desertcarmel@carmelnet.org
Members: 4 Professed, 1 Junior
Professed
Apostolic Work: A life of loving
prayer, fed by silence, solitude,
challenging and joyful community
support. We place our hearts in that
of Mary, following in the footsteps of
her Son toward deeper union with
God for the life of the world.
Carmelite motto: "I have been most
zealous for the Lord, the God of
Hosts". (1 Kings 19:10)
Vocation Director: Contact:
(325) 853-1722

CARMELITE NUNS, (W132)
DISCALCED (O.C.D.), Monastery of
Discalced Carmelites, 600 Flowers
Ave., Dallas, TX 75211-4413
Members: 12 Nuns
Vocation Director: Mother Juanita
Marie, O.C.D., Prioress,
(214) 330-7440

CARMELITE NUNS, (W133)
DISCALCED (O.C.D.), Carmel of the
Most Holy Trinity, 1100 Parthenon Pl.,
New Caney, TX 77357-3276
Web: www.icansurf.com/ocdnew
caney
Email: carmelitesnctx@icansurf.net
Members: 8 Nuns
Vocation Director: Sr. Mary Ann
Harrison, OCD, Novice Mistress,
(281) 399-0270

CARMELITE NUNS, (W134)
DISCALCED (O.C.D.), Monastery of
the Infant Jesus of Prague and Our
Lady of Guadalupe, 6301 Culebra
Ave. at St. Joseph's Way, San
Antonio, TX 78238-4909
Web: www.carmelsanantonio.org
Email: cuocd@dcci.com
Members: 10 Nuns
Vocation Director: Sr. Corinne Uher,
OCD., (210) 680-1834

CARMELITE NUNS, (W135)
DISCALCED (O.C.D.), Carmel of the
Immaculate Heart of Mary, 5714
Holladay Blvd., Salt Lake City,
UT 84121-1599
Web: http://www.carmelslc.org
Email: carmelsl@xmission.com
Members: 8 Nuns
Apostolic Work: Contemplation
Vocation Director: Sister Maureen,
OCD, 801-277-6075, fax: 801-277-
4263

CARMELITE NUNS, (W137)
DISCALCED (O.C.D.), 2215 N.E.
147th St., Shoreline, WA 98155
Email: seattlecarm@comcast.net
Members: 9 Nuns, 2 Novices, 1
Postulant
Representation: Archdiocese of
Seattle
Vocation Director: Sr. Sean
Hennessy, OCD

CARMELITE NUNS, (W138)
DISCALCED (O.C.D.), Monastery of
the Holy Name of Jesus, 6100
Pepper Rd., Denmark, WI 54208
Email: dcn@pngusa.net
Members: 10 Professed, 1 Novice
Vocation Director: Contact: (920) 863-
5055

CARMELITE NUNS (W139-1)
(O. Carm.), Carmel of the Sacred
Heart, 430 Laurel Ave., Hudson, WI
54016-1688
Web: www.pressenter.com/~carmelit/
Email: carmelit@pressenter.com
Members: 6 Nuns
Apostolic Work: In a life of contem-
plative prayer centered on Jesus
Christ and in union with Mary, the
Carmelite listens in silence and
responds in joyful service, supported
by the warmth of a caring
community
Representation: Diocese of Superior, WI
Vocation Director: Sister Lucia La
Montagne, O. Carm., (715) 386-2156

CARMELITE NUNS, (W139-2)
DISCALCED (O.C.D.), Carmel of
Mother of God, W267 N2517
Meadowbrook Rd., Pewaukee,
WI 53072-4528
Web: www.geocities.com/
pewaukee carmel

Email: pewaukeecarmel@aol.com
Members: 8 Nuns
Apostolic Work: Cloistered, contem-
plative nuns living a life of prayer for
the Church and the world
Vocation Director: Sr. Margaret, OCD,
Prioress, (262) 691-0336, fax: (262)
695-0143

CARMELITE NUNS OF THE (W140-1)
ANCIENT OBSERVANCE (O. Carm.)
Carmel of Mary, 17765-78th St. SE,
Wahpeton, ND 58075-9310
Email: carmelofmary@gmail.com
Members: 9 Solemn Professed, 1
Junior Professed
Apostolic Work: Contemplative
prayer, Liturgy of the Hours in
Gregorian Chant, Papal Enclosure,
in the solitude of a rural setting
Representation: Diocese of Fargo
Vocation Director: Contact: (701) 642-
2360

CARMELITE NUNS OF (W140-2)
THE BYZANTINE RITE, DISCALCED
See Eastern Catholic Religious
Communities for Women

CARMELITE NUNS CALCED (W141)
(O.Carm.), 3551 Lanark Rd.,
Coopersburg, PA 18036-9324
Apostolic Work: Cloistered. Contem-
plation, Adoration of the Blessed
Sacrament
Representation: Dioceses of
Allentown, Fargo and Superior
Vocation Director: Sister Marie
Charlette, O. Carm.

CORPUS CHRISTI (W142)
CARMELITE SISTERS (O. Carm.)
Motherhouse: Trinidad, WI
Regional House, 412 W. 18th St.,
Kearney, NE 68847
Web: www.corpuschristi
carmelites.org
Email: brownun@yahoo.com
Members: 8 Sisters in US, 100
worldwide
Apostolic Work: Catechetics, care of
the elderly, Christian unity, schools
for mentally and physically
challenged children
Representation: Dioceses of Grand
Island and Providence. Also in
England, South America and 6
Caribbean islands in the West Indies
Vocation Director: Sister Emerentiana
Pouliot, O.Carm., (308) 237-2287,
fax: (308) 236-9380

CARMELITE SISTERS FOR (W143)
THE AGED AND INFIRM (O. Carm.)
St. Teresa's Motherhouse, 600
Woods Rd., Germantown, NY 12526
Web: www.carmelitesisters.com
Email: vocation@carmelite
sisters.com
Members: 220 Sisters, 2 Novices

Conduct: Homes for the aged
Representation: Archdioceses of
Boston, Cincinnati, New York and
Philadelphia and in the Dioceses of
Albany, Altoona-Johnstown, Bridge-
port, Brooklyn, Columbus, Coving-
ton, Davenport, Joliet, Harrisburg,
Palm Beach, Scranton and Syracuse.
Also in Ireland
Vocation Director: Sister Maria
Therese, O. Carm., (518) 537-5000

CARMELITE SISTERS, (W144)
**INSTITUTE OF THE SISTERS OF OUR
LADY OF MT. CARMEL (O. Carm.)**
Motherhouse: Rome
US Headquarters, 5 Wheatland St.,
Peabody, MA 01960
Web: www.carmelitepreschool.com
Email: carmelite@verizon.net
Members: 20 Nuns (in US)
Apostolic Work: Religious education,
nursing, teaching
Representation: Archdioceses of
Boston and Washington (DC) and in
the Diocese of St. Augustine
Vocation Director: Sr. Kathleen
Bettercourt, O.Carm, (978) 531-
4733, fax: (978) 531-2468

CARMELITE SISTERS OF (W145)
CHARITY (CCV), Generalate: Rome
Motherhouse: Spain, 1222 Monroe
St., NE, Washington, DC 20017-2507
Apostolic Work: Ministry in health,
education, parish, prison, immigra-
tion and social services
Representation: Archdiocese of
Washington and in the Diocese of
Brooklyn
Vocation Director: Sr. Maureen Foltz,
Provincial

CARMELITE SISTERS OF (W146)
**THE DIVINE HEART OF JESUS
(Carmel D.C.J.),** 1230 Kavanaugh Pl.,
Wauwatosa, WI 53213
Web: www.carmelitedcjnorth.org
Email: carmeliteec@aol.com
Members: 94 Sisters in US; 527
worldwide
Conduct: 2 homes for youth, 10
homes for the aged, 4 day nurser-
ies, mission work in Africa, Brazil,
Iceland, Nicaragua and Venezuela
Representation: Archdioceses of
Milwaukee, St. Louis and San
Antonio and in the Dioceses of Gary,
Grand Rapids, Owensboro and San
Diego
Vocation Director: Sr. Maria
Giuseppe, Northern Province, (616)
453-7715
Sr. Mary Joseph, Central Province,
(314) 965-7616
Sr. M. Michelle, Southwestern
Province, (619) 466-3116

B-64

CARMELITE SISTERS OF (W147)
THE MOST SACRED HEART OF
LOS ANGELES (O.C.D.),
Motherhouse, 920 East Alhambra
Rd, Alhambra, CA 91801-1801
Loretto Convent, 1200 Fourteenth
St., Douglas, AZ 85607, (520) 364-
7571
Saint Theresa Convent, 1253
Anastasia Ave., Coral Gables, FL
33134, (305) 448-0662
Holy Name of Jesus Convent, 4040
Pierce St., Wheat Ridge, CO 80033,
(303) 422-6419
St. Teresa Benedicta of the Cross
Convent, 838 Lawson Ave., Steuben-
ville, OH 43952, (740) 282-3070
Saint Teresa of the Andes Convent,
16607 SW 103 Lane, Miami, FL
33196, (305) 388-7751
Santa Teresita Medical Center, 819
Buena Vista St., Duarte, 91010,
(626) 359-3243
Mount Carmel in the Desert, 17862
Queensglen Ave., Palmdale, CA
93591, (661) 264-2811
Web: www.carmelitesistersocd.com
Email: vocations@carmelite
sistersocd.com
Members: 132 Professed Sisters, 2
Novices, 2 Postulants, 4 Candidates
Conduct: 6 grammar schools, 1 high
school, 1 medical center, 2 skilled
nursing facilities for the care of the
aged, 3 nursery schools with day
care center and kindergarten, 2
retreat houses, 1 evangelization
center
Vocation Director: Sister Grace
Helena, O.C.D., (626) 300-8938

CARMELITE SISTERS OF (W148)
ST. THERESE OF THE INFANT
JESUS (C.S.T.), Villa Teresa
1300 Classen Dr., Oklahoma City,
OK 73103
Web: www.oksister.com/
vocations.htm
Email: SrSylvia@OKSister.com
Members: 21 Sisters
Apostolic Work: Education (early
childhood: 2 1/2-year olds to 4th
grade, high school, college), parish
ministry, youth, senior citizens,
social service, pantry for homeless
Representation: Archdiocese of
Oklahoma City.
Vocation Director: Sister Sylvia
Negrete, C.S.T., Vocation Minister,
(405) 232-7926 (h);
(405) 470-6554 (w)

CARMELITES: SISTERS OF (W151)
OUR LADY OF MT. CARMEL (O. Carm.)
Generalate, PO Box 476, Lacombe,
LA 70445, (504) 882-7577
Web: http://home.bellsouth.net/p/
PWP-mountcarmel
Email: carmelitevoc@earthlink. net
Members: 80 Professed Sisters in
US; 20 in the Philippine Islands

Apostolic Work: Education, health
care, social work, parish and
campus ministry, day care, art,
prison ministry, lay Carmelites,
retreat and spiritual direction
Representation: Archdioceses of
Chicago and New Orleans and in
the Dioceses of Houma-Thibodaux
and Lafayette. Also in the Philippine
Islands
Vocation Director: Sr. Angele M.
Sadlier, O.Carm, 4200 Courtland
Dr., Metairie, LA 70002-3111, (504)
455-3107

SISTERS OF THE CATHOLIC (W152)
APOSTOLATE, See Pallotine Sisters

CENACLE SISTERS (r.c.) (W153)
(Congregation of Our Lady of the
Retreat in the Cenacle), North
America Province, The Cenacle, 513
Fullerton Pkwy., Chicago, IL 60614
Web: www.cenaclesisters.org
Email: vocations@cenacle
sisters.org
Apostolic Work: "Awakening and
deepening faith – in the form of
retreats, spiritual direction, educa-
tion in the faith, or other spiritual
ministries...to honor and be atten-
tive to the Spirit's action in others as
well as in ourselves. Ministry flows
out of prayer and community life,
and it necessarily leads back to
prayer and community..."
Representation: Several archdioceses and dioceses across the
United States and in British
Columbia
Vocation Director: Sr. Janice
Bemowski, r.c, 513 W. Fullerton
Pkwy, Chicago, IL 60614

SISTERS OF CHARITY OF (W154)
THE BLESSED VIRGIN MARY
(B.V.M.), Mount Carmel, 1100
Carmel Dr., Dubuque, IA 52003
Web: www.bvmcong.org
Email: newmember@bvmcong.org
Members: 560 Sisters

SISTERS OF CHARITY OF (W155)
CINCINNATI (S.C.)
Motherhouse, 5900 Delhi Rd., Mount
St Joseph, OH 45051
Web: www.srcharitycinti.org
Email: janetsc@juno.com
Members: 450 Sisters
Apostolic Work: Ministering as
educators, healthcare professionals
pastoral and social service workers;
sponsoring institutions and programs
with particular concern for building a
more just society through advocacy
and providing direct service to poor
populations.
Representation: (Arch)dioceses of
Brownsville, Cincinnati, Cleveland,
Colorado Springs, Columbus,
Covington, Denver, Detroit, El Paso,

Helena, Indianapolis, Kalamazoo,
Lansing, Lexington, Little Rock,
Louisville, Memphis, Newark, New
York, Oakland, Orlando, Pueblo,
Saginaw, St. Petersburg, San Fran-
cisco, Santa Fe, Toledo, Washing-
ton, DC and Wilmington. Also in
Guatemala and Mexico
Vocation Director: Sister Janet
Gildea, S.C., (915) 525-5882

SISTERS OF CHARITY OF (W156)
HALIFAX (S.C.H.), Motherhouse:
Mount Saint Vincent, 150 Bedford
Hwy., Halifax, Nova Scotia B3M 3J5
Canada, 800-371-9613
26 Phipps St., Quincy, MA 02169
Web: www.schalifax.ca
Email: smaruzzo@schalifax.com
Apostolic Work: All areas of educa-
tion, pastoral ministry, social
services, health care, earth ministry,
social justice, community service/
outreach
Representation: Primarily in Massa-
chusetts, New York and Nova
Scotia. Also in other parts of US,
Canada, Bermuda, Peru and the
Dominican Republic
Vocation Director: Contact: S.
Maryanne Ruzzo, (617) 471-1827,
ext. 15

SISTERS OF CHARITY OF (W157)
THE IMMACULATE CONCEPTION
(S.C.I.C.), Motherhouse/Novitiate:
Italy. US Foundation Immaculate
Virgin of Miracles, 268 Prittstown
Rd., Mount Pleasant, PA 15666
Web: www.vernamontessori
school.org
Email: vmsami@zoominternet.net
Apostolic Work: (in US) 1 Montessori
school (which includes Children's
House PK-K) and Elementary
(grades 1-6). Now also offering
Middle School (grades 7-8).
Religious education, pastoral
ministry, parish work
Representation: Diocese of Greens-
burg (PA), Italy, Israel, Lebanon,
Switzerland, Albania, Turkey, Libya,
Kenya, Tanzania, Mexico and
Argentina
Vocation Director: Sr. Angelina
Grimoldi, Local Superior,
(724) 887-6753, 887-8810
fax: (724) 887-2977

SISTERS OF CHARITY OF (W158)
THE INCARNATE WORD (C.C.V.I.)
U.S. Province, 3200 McCullough,
PO Box 15378, San Antonio, TX
78212-8578
Web: www.amormeus.org
Email: join_incarnateword@
amormeus.org
Members: 457 Sisters, 226 Associ-
ates, 8 Lay Missionaries
Apostolic Work: Serving the

Christian community in Catholic schools, hospitals, children's centers, and as parish workers and in various ministries in the United States, Guatemala, Mexico, Peru and Zambia (Africa)
Representation: United States, Guatemala, Mexico, Region of Peru, Zambia
Vocation Director: New Membership Team Office, (210) 734-8310 or (800) 497-4363

SISTERS OF CHARITY OF (W159)
THE INCARNATE WORD, Houston
Motherhouse, 6510 Lawndale Ave., PO Box 230969, Houston, TX 77223-0969
Web: www.sistersofcharity.org
Email: mtheriot@ccvi-vdm.org
Members: 174, 100 Associates
Apostolic Work: Direct services in hospitals, clinics, schools, spirituality centers, social services, children's centers, homes for the elderly and abandoned. Systemic change via Corporate Social Responsibility, and Legislative and Community Advocacy.
Representation: United States, El Salvador, Guatemala, Ireland, and Kenya, Africa
Vocation Director: Sr. Maura Theriot, CCVI, Sr. Mary Patricia Driscoll, CCVI, and Sr. Kim-Phuong, CCVI, (713) 928-6053

SISTERS OF CHARITY OF (W160)
LEAVENWORTH (SCL)
Motherhouse, 4200 S. 4th St., Leavenworth, KS 66048-5054
Web: www.scls.org
Email: ssmith@scls.org
Members: 310 Sisters
Apostolic Work: Health care: hospitals and clinics for the uninsured poor. Education: college, high school, elementary. Pastoral ministry: parish associates, administrators, religious education, spiritual direction, campus ministry, and youth ministry. Social services: Catholic Charities, AIDS ministry, social justice. Foreign missions: Peru
Representation: Archdioceses of Kansas City (KS), Los Angeles, Denver, and in the Dioceses of Kansas City, (MO), Helena, Great Falls-Billings, Pueblo and Cheyenne. Also in Peru
Vocation Director: Sister Sharon Smith, SCL, (913) 758-6522

SISTERS OF CHARITY OF (W161)
MONTREAL (Grey Nuns) (S.G.M.)
Regional Office, 10 Pelham Rd., Lexington, MA 02421-2173
Web: www.sgmlex.org
Email: nscmty@wildblue.net

Apostolic Work: As an apostolic community, the Sisters serve those persons in need, especially the most forsaken, with compassionate love, through various ministries, as the care of the sick, the homeless and abandoned children; also, as pastoral ministers; handcrafting for the poor and by trying to alleviate the social injustices of our day
Representation: Maine, Massachusetts, New Hampshire, South America, and throughout Canada
Vocation Director: Sister Marie Mansfield, S.G.M., (781) 674-7401

SISTERS OF CHARITY OF (W164)
NAZARETH (SCN)
General Motherhouse: PO Box 9, Nazareth, KY 40048
Web: www.scnfamily.org
Email: ngsunshine@juno.com
Members: 680 Sisters worldwide
Apostolic Work: Through diverse ministries in education, health care, administration, law, pastoral ministry, communications, social service/action and advocacy for the poor, abused, homeless and addicted, the Sisters care for the earth and work for justice in solidarity with oppressed peoples, especially the economically poor and women. Currently there are 66 in initial formation (7 in the US/Belize and 59 in India)
Representation: Archdioceses of Boston, Chicago, Cincinnati, Louisville, Miami, Philadelphia and Washington, DC and in the Dioceses of Baton Rouge, Charleston, Columbus, Jackson, Jacksonville, Knoxville, Lexington, Little Rock, Memphis, Oakland, Owensboro, Providence, Richmond, San Jose, Steubenville and Worcester. Also in India, Nepal and Botswana, Africa; and Belize, Central America
Vocation Director: Sr. Luke Boiarski, SCN, (502) 348-1581, E-mail: lukescn@scnazarethky.org

SISTERS OF CHARITY OF (W165)
OTTAWA (S.C.O.) (Grey Nuns of the Cross), St. Joseph Province, 559 Fletcher St., Lowell, MA 01854-3434
Web: www.soeursdelacharite ottawa.com
Email: prleblanc2@comcast.net
Members: 25 Sisters in the US; 650 worldwide
Apostolic Work: Teaching, foreign missions: (South Africa, Japan, Central Africa, Brazil, Cameroon, Haiti, Thailand), nursing, care of the aged, parish work and social work
Representation: Archdiocese of Boston
Vocation Director: Provincial Administration, (978) 458-4472

SISTERS OF CHARITY OF (W166)
OUR LADY OF MERCY
May Forest Motherhouse
424 Fort Johnson Rd., PO Box 12410, Charleston, SC 29422
Members: 22 Sisters
Apostolic Work: Parish ministry, social service, Hispanic ministry
Representation: Diocese of Charleston
Vocation Director: Sr. Bridget Sullivan, (843) 795-2866, fax: (843) 795-6083

SISTERS OF CHARITY OF (W166-1)
OUR LADY, MOTHER OF THE CHURCH (S.C.M.C.), Holy Family Motherhouse, 54 West Main St., Baltic, CT 06330-0691
Web: www.sistersofcharity.com
Email: Motherhouse@sistersof charity.com
Members: Our members include 71 Sisters from various states and nations.
Apostolic Work: The Sisters of Charity of Our Lady, Mother of the Church is an active/contemplative institute of Pontifical Right. Our motto: To Jesus through Mary, signifies our prayer and devotion to the Immaculate Heart of Mary. In light of our precious heritage we live our vowed life in community, with the Eucharist at the heart of our varied apostolates. We, though founded principally to teach the young and to care for the elderly, have also made ourselves available to meet other needs of the Church, such as nursing, Hispanic ministry, family shelter for the homeless, and food pantry. We accept applicants ages 18-35 and consider others on an individual basis
Representation: Archdioceses of Hartford, CT and St. Paul, MN and in the Dioceses of Norwich, CT and Madison, WI
Vocation Director: Sr. Mary Jacinta, S.C.M.C., (860) 822-8241

SISTERS OF CHARITY OF (W167)
OUR LADY, MOTHER OF MERCY (S.C.M.M.), Motherhouse: Netherlands Provincial House: 32 Tuttle Pl., East Haven, CT 06512
Web: www.sistersofcharity.net
Email: scmm@comcast.net
Members: 14 Sisters in US, 800 worldwide
Conduct: Motherhouse: Netherlands
Apostolic Work: Works of charity
Representation: Archdioceses of Detroit, Hartford and St. Paul-Minneapolis and in the Diocese of San Diego
Vocation Director: Contact: www.sistersofcharity.net

SISTERS OF CHARITY OF (W169)
ST. AUGUSTINE (C.S.A.)
Motherhouse: Mt. Augustine
5232 Broadview Rd., Richfield, OH
44286-9608
Web: www.srsofcharity.org
Email: scw@srsofcharity.org
Members: 67 Sisters, 43 Associates
Apostolic Work: Education; pastoral
ministry: parish associates, spiritual
direction, directors of religious
education; health care: hospitals,
nursing home administration, AIDS
ministry, pastoral care, social
services, homeless, Catholic
Worker houses, CSA Health
System, foundations
Representation: Dioceses of
Cleveland, Charleston, Lexington
and Youngstown
Vocation Director: Sr. Catherine
Walsh, CSA, (330) 659-5100, 4161

SISTERS OF CHARITY OF (W170)
SAINT ELIZABETH (S.C.)
Convent of Saint Elizabeth
PO Box 476, Convent Station, NJ
07961-0476
Web: www.scnj.org
Email: vocations@scnj.org
Members: 439 Sisters
Apostolic Work: College, academies,
high schools, elementary schools,
special education schools, hospi-
tals, child care, long term care
nursing home, adult literacy
programs, homes for aged and
retired sisters, novitiate, parish work
Vocation Director: Sr. Patricia
Dotzauer, S.C., (973) 290-5331

SISTERS OF CHARITY OF (W171)
**ST. HYACINTHE (S.C.S.H.) (Grey
Nuns),** General House: Canada
US Regional Administration
98 Campus Ave., Lewiston,
ME 04240
Web: www.scsh.ca
Email: sr.beaudoin@cgocable.ca
Members: 10 Sisters in US
Apostolic Work: Hospital, nursing
homes, home for the aged
Representation: Dioceses of
Manchester and Portland (ME)

SISTERS OF CHARITY OF (W172)
ST. JOAN ANTIDA (SCSJA)
Regina Mundi, 8560 N. 76th Pl.,
Milwaukee, WI 53223
Web: www.scsja.org
www.suoredellacarita.org
Email: srtheresa@scsja.org
Members: 37 Sisters in the United
States Province; approximately
2,700 Sisters in 7 European, 6
African, 4 Asian, 4 Middle East and
4 South American countries
Apostolic Work: Teaching, nursing,
pastoral work, parish work, social
work, jail ministry and missionary
work

Representation: Archdiocese of
Milwaukee and in the Dioceses of
Amarillo and Gallup in the US
Vocation Director: Sister Mary
Theresa Rozga (414) 354-9233

SISTERS OF CHARITY OF (W173)
ST. LOUIS (S.C.S.L.), Local Community, Our Lady of Victory Convent,
4907 So. Catherine St., Plattsburgh,
NY 12901-3658
Members: 7 Sisters in US, 645
worldwide
Apostolic Work: Teaching: elementary, secondary, CCD; Nursing: in
nursing homes for the aged and
hospitals; retreat, parish and social
work
Representation: Diocese of
Ogdensburg
Vocation Director: Sister Bernadette
Ducharme, SCSL, (518) 563-7410
(tel, fax)

SISTERS OF CHARITY OF (W174)
ST. VINCENT DE PAUL (S.V.Z.)
US Foundation, 171 Knox Ave.,
West Seneca, NY 14224
Email: milosrdnice@adelphia.net
Members: 12 Sisters in the US
Apostolic Work: Nursery schools,
CCD, parish services, hospital and
health services
Representation: Diocese of Buffalo
and in Oakville, Hamilton, Canada

SISTERS OF CHARITY OF (W175)
NEW YORK (S.C.), 6301 Riverdale
Ave., Bronx, NY 10471
Web: www.scny.org
Email: vocationsc@scny.org
Apostolic Work: The Sisters of
Charity of New York are a group of
400 religious women who seek to
reveal God's love in their varied
ministries with and for people who
are poor. Founded by St. Elizabeth
Ann Seton in 1809 in Emmitsburg,
MD, the community adopted a
modified rule of St. Vincent de Paul.
The congregation was established
in New York City in 1817 in response
to Bishop John Connolly's request
for assistance in caring for the
orphans. While the majority of the
members still serve in the New York
Archdiocese, the congregation is
represented in 8 other localities as
well. The Sisters are engaged in
traditional ministries of education,
health care and social service as
well as in a wide variety of other
compassionate and effective
responses to the signs of the times,
including pastoral ministry and
Guatemalan missions
Vocation Director: Sr. Maria Iglesias,
SC, (718) 543-5131

SISTERS OF CHARITY OF (W176)
SETON HILL (S.C.), De Paul Center,
463 Mt. Thor Rd, Greensburg,
PA 15601
Web: www.scsh.org
Email: mobrien@scsh.org;
rachelwv2001@yahoo.com
Members: 503 Sisters
Apostolic Work: Prayer, service and
life in community are the primary
principles upon which the Sisters
carry out their mission, which is to
reveal the reality and beauty of
God's love to people in need. The
Sisters administer and staff educa-
tional institutions from preschools
through universities; offer religious
education and formation; chap-
laincy, counseling, pastoral and
social services
Representation: primarily in the
dioceses of western Pennsylvania,
West Virginia and Arizona. The
Korean Province offers opportunities for foreign mission work.
Vocation Director: Maureen O'Brien,
SC Fidelis House, 120 Underwood
Ave., Greensburg, PA 15601 (724)
454-8601
Rachel Blais, SC, 740 Elysian Ave.,
Morgantown, WV 26501

SISTERS OF CHRISTIAN (W177)
**CHARITY (S.C.C.) (Daughters of the
Blessed Virgin Mary of the
Immaculate Conception),**
Eastern Province: Mallinckrodt
Convent, 350 Bernardsville Rd.,
Mendham, NJ 07945
Western Province: 2041 Elmwood
Ave., Wilmette, IL 60091-1533,
847-920-9341
Web: www.scceast.org
Email: sbernadette@scceast.org
Members: 350 Sisters in US; 700
worldwide
Apostolic Work: Eastern Province:
Teaching, retreat ministry, cate-
chetics, nursing, health services,
special care for the poor
Western Province: Academic
education, care of abused and
neglected children, religious
education, parish ministry, social
service and prayer ministry, and
ministry to Native Americans
Representation: Eastern Province:
Archdioceses of Newark, New York
and Philadelphia and in the
Dioceses of Allentown, Camden,
Harrisburg, Metuchen, Paterson
and Scranton; Western Province:
Archdioceses of Chicago, New
Orleans, St. Louis and Santa Fe
and in the Dioceses of Jefferson
City, Lansing and Tucson. Also
provinces in Germany, Chile,
Uruguay and Argentina with houses
in Italy and the Philippines

Vocation Director:
Eastern Province: Sr. Bernadette
Mc Cauley, S.C.C., 973-543-6528,
sbernadette@scceast.org
Western Province: Sr. Carol
Bredenkamp, S.C.C., 1801 Forest
Ave., Wilmette, IL 60091-1533

CISTERCIAN NUNS (O.Cist) (W180-1)
Valley of Our Lady Monastery
E. 11096 Yanke Dr., Prairie du Sac,
WI 53578-9737
Web: www.nunocist.org
Email: vocations@nunocist.org
Members: 13 Solemnly Professed
Nuns, 5 Junior Professed Nuns, 2
Novices, 1 Postulant
Apostolic Work: Contemplative
The Order of Citeaux is one of the
Church's ancient monastic orders.
The primary sources of Cistercian
monasticism are the Sacred
Scriptures, the Rule of St. Benedict,
the traditions of the Desert Fathers,
and the spirituality of our own 12th
century Fathers. Our daily life is a
balanced alternation between the
Divine Office prayed in Latin with
Gregorian Chant, lectio divina, and
manual labor. Silence, solitude in
community, ascetic practices, the
cultivation of continual interior
prayer, together with the monastic
vows of obedience, stability, and
unceasing conversion, are the
means by which we hope to attain
to purity of heart, tranquility of mind
and spriritual union with God.
Monastic life is a radical
participation in the self-emptying of
Christ which transforms humanity
and the cosmos into the New
Creation.
Requirements for candidacy: age
20-35 with two years of college or
work experience, possession of
good physical and psychological
health, emotional maturity, and the
desire to fullfill God's will.
Representation: Diocese of Madison
Vocation Director: Sr. Aleydis
Johnson, O.Cist.

CISTERCIAN NUNS OF (W180-2)
THE STRICT OBSERVANCE
See "T" - Trappistines

CLARETIAN MISSIONARY (W181-1)
**SISTERS (R.M.I.) (Religious of Mary
Immaculate, Claretian Missionary
Sisters)**
18450 N.W. 12th Ave., Miami, FL
33169-3169,(305) 652-4593
also at 7080 SW 99 Ave., Miami, FL
33173, (305) 274-6148
7700 W. Lake Dr., West Palm
Beach, FL 33406, (561) 433-4731
and PO Box 516, Mayo, FL 32066-
0516, (386) 294-2126

Web: www.claretiansisters.org
Email: vocations@claretian
sisters.org
Members: 11 Sisters in US; 524
Sisters worldwide
Apostolic Work: Missions, education,
youth, migrant, social and parish
ministry. Theological formation in
seminaries and institutes
Representation: Archdiocese of
Miami and in the Dioceses of Palm
Beach and St. Augustine

COLUMBAN SISTERS (W181-2)
See "M" - Missionary Sisters of St.
Columban

COMBONI MISSIONARY (W182-1)
SISTERS (C.M.S.)
US Headquarters, 1307 Lakeside
Ave., Richmond, VA 23228-4710
Web: www.combonisrs.com
Email: cmsusacommunity@
verizon.net
Members: 1,650 Sisters
Apostolic Work: Foreign missions in
Africa, Latin America, and Middle
East, mission education and JPIC
office in US. Their charism is to
share with the poorest of the poor
God's love: to initiate and/or to
collaborate in the building and
strengthening of the local Christian
community through their lives,
words and works in schools,
catechetical and pastoral centers,
hospitals, dispensaries and leprosy
centers; by fostering Christian
family life and women's promotion
and education; by collaborating in
the formation of native clergy,
sisters and laity; by working, living
and dying for the realization of
peace and justice with the poor
Representation: Archdioceses of
Philadelphia and Baltimore and in
the Diocese of Richmond. The
entire international community is
represented in 33 different countries of the world
Vocation Director: Contact: (804)
262-8827

COMMUNITY OF THE (W182-2)
HOLY SPIRIT (C.H.S.)
6151 Rancho Mission Rd #205, San
Diego, CA 92108, (619) 584-0809
Members: 14 Sisters
Apostolic Work: Education, health
care, social services
Representation: Dioceses of
Oakland, Orange, Portland, Reno-
Las Vegas, San Diego, San Jose
and Wichita

COMMUNITY OF THE (W183-1)
MOTHER OF GOD OF TENDERNESS
See Eastern Catholic Religious
Communities for Women

COMMUNITY OF THE (W183-3)
RESURRECTION, PO Box 284,
Casco, ME 04015-0284
Web: http//w3.ime.net/~sisterop
Email: comres1@juno.com
Members: 4 Sisters, 1 Novice
Apostolic Work: Rooted in the
Dominican tradition and spirituality
of contemplative prayer. Dedicated
to the service of women in need.
Representation: Diocese of
Portland (ME)
Vocation Director: Sr. Renata
Camenzind, phone & fax: (207)
627-7184

COMPANY OF MARY (W184-1)
(O.D.N.), Motherhouse, 16791 E.
Main St., Tustin, CA 92780-4034
Web: www.Lestonnac.org
Email: kschneider62@adelphia.net
Members: 65 Sisters in US; 2,236
worldwide in 27 countries
Apostolic Work: Educators in the
faith through: pre-schools to high
school, free clinic, detention minis-
try, social service, retreat centers,
parish ministry, residences for
women, diocesan offices.
Representation: Archdiocese of Los
Angeles and in the Dioceses of
Orange, San Bernardino and Tucson.
Vocation Director: Sister Kathy
Schneider, ODN, (714) 558-1340,
Fax (714) 835-0648

THE COMPANY OF THE (W184-2)
SAVIOR (C.S.), 820 Clinton Ave.,
Bridgeport, CT 06604-6604
Members: 82 Sisters, 3 Novices
Representation: Diocese of
Bridgeport
Vocation Director: Sr. Constanza
Lopez, (203) 368-1875

(W185-1)
CONGREGATION OF THE CENACLE
See Cenacle, Congregation of the

CONGREGATION OF (W185-2)
THE DIVINE SPIRIT (C.D.S.)
409 W. Sixth St., Erie, PA 16507-6507
Members: 37 Sisters
Apostolic Work: Parish schools,
CCD centers, home for senior
citizens
Representation: Dioceses of Erie
and Youngstown
Vocation Director: (814) 455-3590

CONGREGATION OF (W185-3)
THE INFANT JESUS, See - Infant
Jesus, Congregation of the

CONGREGATION OF (W185-4)
NOTRE DAME (CND) (Blessed Sacrament Province), 30 Highfield Road, Wilton, CT 06897
(203) 762-4304
Web: www.cnd-m.com
Email: cndsusa@sbcglobal.net
Members: 150 Sisters; 1,300 worldwide
Apostolic Work: Teachers, social workers, school administrators, diocesan personnel, lawyers, counselors, parish ministers, retreat directors, campus ministers, college professors, chaplains and advocates for peace and nonviolence
Representation: (Arch)dioceses of Albany, Boston, Bridgeport, Brooklyn, Charlotte, Chicago, Hartford, Joliet, Newark, New York, Oklahoma City, Providence, Rapid City, Richmond, and Scranton. Also in Cameroon, Canada, El Salvador, France, Guatemala, Honduras, and Japan
Vocation Director: Sr. Peggy Doyle, Sr. Lucille Cormier

RELIGIOUS MISSIONARIES (W185-5)
OF ST. DOMINIC, RMSD (O.P.)
Motherhouse: Rome, Italy
2237 Waldron Rd., Corpus Christi, TX 78418-8418
Web: www.crmsdusadelegation.org
Members: 24 Sisters in US, 635 Sisters worldwide
Apostolic Work: Schools, religious education for Catholic students in public schools, day care centers, youth ministry, hospitals, residences for women college students, retreat house, pastoral work, senior care homes
Representation: Archdiocese of Los Angeles and Diocese of Corpus Christi. Also in Italy, Spain, Portugal, Philippines, Cambodia, Taiwan, Thailand, Japan, Korea, Guam and Chile
Vocation Director: Vocation Promoter, (361) 937-5978

CONGREGATION OF THE (W185-6)
SISTERS OF JESUS CRUCIFIED
See "J" - Jesus Crucified, Congregation of the

CONGREGATION OF THE (W185-7)
SISTERS OF OUR LADY OF MERCY
See "O" - Our Lady of Mercy, the Congregation of the Sisters of

CONSOLATA MISSIONARY (W186)
SISTERS (MC), PO Box 371, Belmont, MI 49306-9710, (616) 361-2072
Web: www.consolatasisters.org
Email: mcregus@consolatasisters.org
Members: Total members in Congregation: just under 800, 21

Sisters in US
Apostolic Work: Primary work is evangelization among the poor which is carried out by ministries of teaching, nursing, social work, and pastoral ministry.
Representation: Michigan and Alabama, in 8 African countries, in 5 South American countries, in 5 European countries, and 1 Asian country
Vocation Director: Sr. Zelia M. Cordeiro, MC, PO Box 97, Belmont, MI 49306-0097, (616) 361-9609, Fax (616) 361-2049

CORDI-MARIAN SISTERS (W186-1)
11624 W. Culebra Rd., #501, San Antonio, TX 78253, (210) 798-8220, fax: (210) 798-8225
Web: www.cordi-marian.org
Email: mjaime@cordi-marian.org
Members: 30 Sisters, 2 Novices
Apostolic Work: Retreats, catechetical or religious education instructors, advocacy. The spreading of the Word through all media.
Representation: Illinois, Missouri, and Texas
Vocation Director: Sister Alicia Macias, MC-M, Formation House, 2902 Morales St., San Antonio, TX 78207, amacias@cordi-marian.org

CONTEMPLATIVE SISTERS (W187-1)
OF THE GOOD SHEPHERD
See "G" - Good Shepherd, Sisters of the

SISTERS OF THE CROSS (W187-2)
OF THE SACRED HEART OF JESUS (R.C.S.C.J.), Motherhouse: Mexico
US Foundation, 1320 Maze Blvd., Modesto, CA 95351-5351
Email: sistersofthecross@sbcglobal.net
Members: 350 Sisters, 9 Novices, 11 Postulants
Apostolic Work: Contemplative Perpetual Adoration
Representation: Diocese of Stockton. Also in Rome, Guatemala, Costa Rica, Mexico, Spain and El Salvador
Vocation Director: Sr. Gabriela Silva, rcscj, (209) 526-3525

DAUGHTERS OF CHARITY (W188)
OF THE MOST PRECIOUS BLOOD (D.C.P.B.), Generalate: Rome
1482 North Ave., Bridgeport, CT 06604
Members: 18 Sisters in US
Apostolic Work: Education of the youth, care for the sick and the elderly.
Representation: Dioceses of Albany, Bridgeport and Paterson.
Vocation Director: Sr. Alfonsa Kunnel, D.C.P.B., Superior, (203) 334-7000

DAUGHTERS OF THE (W189)
CHARITY OF THE SACRED HEART OF JESUS (F.C.S.C.J.)
US Provincialate: Mount Sacred Heart, 26 Amherst St., Milford, NH 03055
Founded in France in 1823: Motherhouse in La Salle-de-Vihiers (Angers); Generalate in Montgeron (Paris)
Web: www.fcscj.org
Email: wnddr.jed@verizon.net
Members: 43 Sisters (US); 1,200 in 10 countries worldwide
Apostolic Work: Day care and education of children, youth and adults, health care, geriatric care, hospice, pastoral ministry, community service, retreat work, foreign missions
Representation: Archdiocese of Boston and in the Dioceses of Burlington, Fall River, Manchester, and Ogdensburg. Present in France, Canada, Lesotho, the Republic of South Africa, Togo, Benin, Madagascar, Brazil and Tahiti
Vocation Director: (603) 672-4133

DAUGHTERS OF CHARITY (W190)
OF ST. VINCENT DE PAUL (D.C.)
(Province of the West), 26000 Altamont Rd., Los Altos Hills, CA 94022-4317
Web: www.christurgesus.org
Email: SrTrangTruong@dochs.org
Members: 129 Sisters; 21,000 worldwide
Apostolic Work: Elementary schools, high school, adult education (Healthcare career colleges, English Language Learners), elder care (residential care, senior citizen nutrition program), day care, hospitals/ healthcare, Native American ministry, parish ministry, prison ministry, Catholic Charities, food bank, residential programs for at-risk children and at-risk families, Vincentian Marian Youth, Vincentian Service Corps West.
Representation: Archdioceses of Los Angeles, San Francisco and Anchorage and in the Dioceses of Gallup, Phoenix, Salt Lake City and San Jose; foreign missions in Kenya, Magadan (Russia) and the Cook Islands
Vocation Director: Sr. Trang Truong, D.C., (650) 949-8890

DAUGHTERS OF CHARITY (W191)
OF ST. VINCENT DE PAUL (D.C.)
(East Central Province) Mater Dei Provincialate, 9400 New Harmony Rd., Evansville, IN 47720-8912
Web: www.doc-ecp.org/
Email: smb@doc-ecp.org

Members: 142 Sisters in Province; 20,000 Sisters worldwide
Apostolic Work: Sisters minister in elementary, high schools and universities, religious education, parish ministry, skilled nursing facilities, multi-hospital system, clinics, day care and neighborhood services, services and residences for the aged, social services and Catholic Charities offices, prison ministry, advocacy, homeless shelters, children's residence, home for retired Sisters, rural ministry and outreach services
Representation: Archdioceses of Chicago, Detroit, Indianapolis, Milwaukee and Mobile and in the Dioceses of Belleville, Birmingham, Evansville, Nashville, Jackson, and Saginaw. Also in 2,424 communities in 94 countries
Vocation Director: Sister Mary Beth Kubera, D.C., Vocation Coordinator, (812) 963-7556 Fax (812) 963-7526

DAUGHTERS OF CHARITY (W192)
Emmitsburg Province-Southeast
333 South Seton Ave., Emmitsburg, MD 21727, (301) 447-3121
Web: www.thedaughtersof
charity.org
Email: dcvoc@doc.org
Members: 266
Apostolic Work: 3 high schools, 4 elementary schools, 5 hospitals, 4 ministry with the aged, 2 homes for unmarried mothers, 1 day care, 11 parish and social services, 3 Hispanic ministry, 2 soup kitchens, 3 diocesan work, 1 St. Elizabeth Seton Shrine and overseas missions.
Representation: Archdioceses of Baltimore and Washington and in the Dioceses of Charleston, St. Augustine, Pensacola-Tallahassee, Raleigh, Richmond, Savannah and Wheeling-Charleston
Vocation Director: Sister Denise LaRock, 1201 South Caton Avenue, Baltimore, MD 21227, (410) 646-2074

DAUGHTERS OF CHARITY (W193)
OF ST. VINCENT DE PAUL (D.C.)
West Central Province, 4330 Olive St., St. Louis, MO 63108
Web: www.daughters-of-charity.org
Email: tdaly@dcwcp.org
Members: 200 Sisters
Apostolic Work: parochial schools, high schools, hospitals, leprosarium, psychiatric hospitals, parish ministry, social service centers, day care centers, clinics, prison ministries, homes for aged, homes for children, shelter for women, neighborhood centers, Catholic Charities

offices, refugee resettlement, senior citizens programs, higher education, diocesan offices, youth programs, HIV-AIDS ministry
Representation: Archdioceses of New Orleans, St. Louis and San Antonio and in the Dioceses of Austin, Baton Rouge, Brownsville, Dallas, El Paso, Kansas City, Little Rock, St. Joseph, San Angelo, Springfield-Cape Girardeau
Vocation Director: Sr. Teresa Daly, D.C., (314) 533-4770, ext. 103

DAUGHTERS OF CHARITY (W194)
OF ST. VINCENT DE PAUL (D.C.)
(Northeast Province) Provincialate: De Paul Provincial House, (518) 462-6430
96 Menand Rd., Albany, NY 12204
Web: www.dc-northeast.org
Email: srmarydc@yahoo.com
Members: 171 Sisters
Apostolic Work: Campus ministries, child care centers, day care centers, elementary school, shelters, general hospitals and clinics, high schools, homes for special needs children, parish visiting, multi-service center, neighborhood centers, pastoral/parish ministries, social work with Catholic Charities, visiting home nursing, psychiatric care, geriatric care
Representation: Archdioceses of Boston, New York and Philadelphia and in the Dioceses of Albany, Allentown, Bridgeport, Brooklyn, Buffalo, Greensburg, Metuchen, Ogdensburg, Syracuse and Wilmington. Also in Canada
Vocation Director: Sr. Mary Frate, D.C., De Paul Provincial House, 96 Menands Road, Albany, NY 12204-1499, (607) 341-1849

DAUGHTERS OF THE (W195)
CROSS OF LIEGE (F.C.)
Principal House: St. Bernard's Convent, 165 W. Eaton Ave., Tracy, CA 95376-5376
Also St. Joseph's Convent, 1168 S. Country Club, Stockton, CA 95204.
Web: www.daughtersofthe
cross.org.uk/
Email: srjudefc@hotmail.com
Members: 7 Sisters in the US
Apostolic Work: Serving the weak and poor in healthcare education and social ministries
Representation: Diocese of Stockton and in many countries worldwide
Vocation Director: Sr. Marlene, F.C., (209) 835-7391

DAUGHTERS OF DIVINE (W197)
CHARITY (F.D.C.), (Holy Trinity Province) St. Elizabeth's Briarbank 39315 Woodward Ave., Bloomfield Hills, MI 48304-5024

Web: www.godslovefdc.org
Members: 16 Sisters
Conduct: 1 grammar school, 1 residence for women, 1 home for the aged in the Midwest
Representation: Archdiocese of Detroit and in the Diocese of Ft. Wayne-So. Bend. Also on the East and West coasts of the US, Europe, No. and So. Brazil, Bolivia, Albania, Ukraine, Uganda (Africa), Switzerland and Ecuador
Vocation Director: Sister M. Innocentia, F.D.C., (248) 644-1011 or 644-8052 Fax (248) 644-1596

DAUGHTERS OF DIVINE (W199)
CHARITY (F.D.C.), St. Joseph Province, Provincial House, 850 Hylan Blvd., Staten Island, NY 10305, (718) 727-5700
Web: www.godslovefdc.org
Email: srmarieclairefdc@aol.com
Members: 30 Sisters in St. Joseph Province, 1,254 Sisters Worldwide
Apostolic Work: Education (elementary and secondary), religious education, residence for young women in NYC, pastoral ministry
Representation: Archdiocese of New York and in the Dioceses of San Bernardino and San Diego
Vocation Director: Sister Marie Claire Weaver, St. Mary's Residence, 225 E. 72nd St., New York, NY 10021 (212) 249-6850, Fax: (212) 249-4336

DAUGHTERS OF DIVINE (W200)
CHARITY (F.D.C.), (St. Mary Province) Provincial Motherhouse Leonora Hall Convent, 39 N. Portage Path, Akron, OH 44303-1183
Email: smcoffelt1@hotmail.com
Members: 17 Sisters
Apostolic Work: Elementary education, home for young women, home for well elderly men and women, pastoral ministry, catechetical, work with the deaf
Representation: Archdioceses of Milwaukee and New York and in the Diocese of Cleveland
Vocation Director: (330) 867-4960, Fax (330) 876-6334

DAUGHTERS OF THE (W202)
HEART OF MARY (D.H.M.)
Provincial House, 1339 Northampton St, Holyoke, MA 01040-1900, (413) 532-7406
Web: www.dhmna.org
Email: pgaudet@dhmna.org
Members: 50 Professed Sisters USA; 1,650 worldwide
Apostolic Work: Ministries are diversified according to gifts of individual women committed to Gospel values in the service of the Church.

Representation: Archdioceses of Chicago, New York, Philadelphia, St. Louis and St. Paul-Minneapolis and in the Dioceses of Buffalo, Ogdensburg, Springfield (MA)
Vocation Director: Marian Center, 1365 Northampton St., Holyoke, MA 01040 (413) 534-4502

DAUGHTERS OF THE (W203)
HOLY SPIRIT (D.H.S.), 152 Prospect St., Moosup, CT 06354-1441
Web: www.daughtersoftheholy spirit.org
Email: tvanassedhs@att.net
Members: 1,300 Sisters
Apostolic Work: Education: pre-school through college; hospital and home nursing; pastoral work; migrant ministry; campus ministry; hospital chaplaincy; prison work; advocacy in the name of justice; home missions in the US; foreign missions in Chile, Peru, Nigeria, Cameroon, Burkina-Faso and Romania. Serving in NY, New England, Alabama, California, Pennsylvania and Virginia
Vocation Director: (East Coast) Sr. Therese Vanasse, DHS, (860) 564-2243

DAUGHTERS OF MARY (W205)
AND JOSEPH (D.M.J.), Provincialate, 5300 Crest Rd., Rancho Palos Verdes, CA 90275-5004
Web: www.dmjca.org
Email: frances_fisher@sbcglobal.net
Conduct: 1 novitiate, 1 retreat center, 3 grammar schools, 1 high school, 11 parish ministry, 3 health ministry, 2 African missions
Apostolic Work: Education, parish ministry, retreat ministry, counseling, Hispanic ministry
Representation: Archdioceses of Los Angeles and San Francisco and in the Dioceses of Monterey, Oakland, San Bernardino and San Diego.
Vocation Director: Sr. Frances Fisher, DMJ, (818) 243-5664

DAUGHTERS OF MARY (W206)
HELP OF CHRISTIANS (F.M.A.)
See "S" - Salesian Sisters of St. John Bosco

CONGREGATION OF THE (W208)
DAUGHTERS OF MARY IMMACULATE (Marianists) (F.M.I.)
See - Marianist Sisters

DAUGHTERS OF MARY OF (W209)
THE IMMACULATE CONCEPTION (D.M.), Motherhouse of the Immaculate Conception, 314 Osgood Ave., New Britain, CT 06053
Web: www.crossfire.org/ daughtersofmary

Email: dmvocdir18@yahoo.com
Members: 38 Sisters
Apostolic Work: 2 parochial schools, 1 home for the aged, 3 residences for women, 1 reading clinic, 2 skilled care facilities
Representation: Archdioceses of Boston, Hartford and New York and in the Diocese of Springfield
Vocation Director: Sister Mary Joseph Zimmerman, D.M., (413) 967-5032

DAUGHTERS OF OUR (W209-1)
LADY OF THE GARDEN (F.M.H.)
Convent of Our Lady of the Garden 124 Rivington Avenue, Staten Island, NY 10314
Web: www.sistersolg.org
Email: sr_ines@sistersolg.org
Members: 11 Sisters
Apostolic Work: Education, parish, missions, nursing and social work.
Representation: Archdiocese of New York
Vocation Director: Sister Ines Aparicio, FMH, Superior, (718) 448-3408

DAUGHTERS OF OUR (W210)
LADY OF THE HOLY ROSARY (F.M.S.R.), 1492 Moss St., New Orleans, LA 70119
Web: www.dongmancoi.org
Email: fmsrusa@dongmancoi.org
Members: 55 Sisters in US
Apostolic Work: Education of young people, especially the poorest. Parish ministry, nursing and counseling, and CCD. Ministry to both Vietnamese and American
Representation: (Arch)dioceses of New Orleans, Houma-Thibodaux, Shreveport, Charleston, Mobile, Oklahoma City, and in Mississippi
Vocation Director: Sr. Sandy Nguyen, F.M.S.R., (504) 486-0039

DAUGHTERS OF OUR (W211)
LADY OF MERCY (D.M.)
Provincial House and Novitiate Villa Rossello, 1009 Main Rd., Newfield, NJ 08344-5203
Email: dmnewfield@yahoo.com
Members: 60 Sisters
Apostolic Work: Education, parish ministry, catechesis, counseling, ministry to elderly, foreign missions
Representation: (Arch)dioceses of Camden, Harrisburg and Scranton. Also in Italy, South America (Argentina, Bolivia, Brazil, Peru, Chile), Germany, Africa, India, Romania, Jamaica, Haiti and the Dominican Republic
Vocation Director: (856) 697-2983

DAUGHTERS OF OUR (W212)
LADY OF THE SACRED HEART (F.D.N.S.C.), Provincial: Ireland St. Francis de Sales Convent, 424 E. Browning Rd., Bellmawr, NJ 08031
Web: www.religiouslife.com/ w_dolshbellmawr.phtml
Members: 11 Sisters in US, 1,800 Sisters worldwide
Apostolic Work: Teaching, pastoral ministry
Representation: Diocese of Camden
Vocation Director: Sr. Patricia Burns, FDNSC, (856) 931-8973

CONGREGATION OF THE (W213-1)
DAUGHTERS OF ST. FRANCIS OF ASSISI (D.S.F.), American Province 507 N. Prairie St., Lacon, IL 61540
Web: www.laconfranciscans.org
Email: sradriana@mtco.com
Members: 14 Sisters
Apostolic Work: Health care, pastoral ministry, and nursing
Representation: Dioceses of Peoria and Springfield-Cape Girardeau.
Vocation Director: Sr. Adriana Zdila, D.S.F., (309) 246-2175

DAUGHTERS OF (W213-2)
ST. JOSEPH (F.S.J.)
Provincial House: Mexico
US Foundation, 6677 Del Rosa Ave., San Bernardino, CA 92404-2404
Email: daughtersjoseph@ netzero.net
Members: 5 Sisters; 800 worldwide
Apostolic Work: Carrying the specific spirituality of Nazareth: work-prayer, especially with working women and laborers
Representation: Diocese of San Bernardino and in Mexico, Guatemala, Colombia, Argentina, Uruguay, Paraguay, Brazil, Africa, Spain, Portugal and Italy
Vocation Director: Sr. Josephine Ornelas, (909) 888-4877, fax: (909) 888-4387

DAUGHTERS OF ST. MARY (W214)
OF PROVIDENCE (D.S.M.P.) (The Guanellian Sisters)
Motherhouse: Daughters of St. Mary of Providence, 4200 N. Austin Ave., Chicago, IL 60634
Web: www.daughtersofstmaryof providence.com
Email: dsmpnovchi@sbcglobal.net
Members: 100 Sisters in US; 1,000 Sisters worldwide
Conduct: Prayer Life: Divine Office, mass, rosary, meditation, holy hours, recollection days, yearly retreat for a week, spiritual reading, Stations of the Cross
Apostolic Work: Residential facilities for developmentally disabled, parish work, nursing homes, retreat center, respite care, religious education, youth ministry

Representation: Archdioceses of Boston, Chicago and Philadelphia and in dioceses in Minnesota, South Dakota and Canada. Also in India, Italy, Mexico, the Philippines and South America
Vocation Director: Sr. Barbara Moerman, D.S.M.P., (773) 205-1645 or (773) 545-8300

DAUGHTERS OF ST. PAUL (W215) **(F.S.P.),** US/Toronto Province 50 Saint Paul's Ave., Boston, MA 02130
Web: www.daughtersofstpaul.org
Email: vocations@pauline media.com
Members: 144 in US; 2,607 worldwide
Apostolic Work: We are missionary sisters who live in the spirit of St. Paul the Apostle, proclaiming the Gospel through the mass media. Daily Eucharistic adoration and reflection on the Word of God sustains our life and mission. Our apostolate of media evangelization includes: radio, Internet, music, art and design, writing, publishing, media education workshops, Pauline Books and Media Centers and more. We are present in 52 countries.
Representation: Archdioceses of Boston, Chicago, Los Angeles, New Orleans, Miami, New York, Philadelphia, St. Louis, San Antonio and San Francisco and in the Dioceses of Arlington, Charleston, Honolulu, Memphis, Metuchen and San Diego. Also in Canada
Vocation Director: Sr. Margaret Michael, fsp, Vocation Office, 4403 Veterans Memorial Blvd., Metairie, LA 70006, (504) 887-7635

DAUGHTERS OF WISDOM (W216) **(D.W.),** International Congregation: Motherhouse: France Generalate: Italy
(US Province) Provincial House 385 Ocean Ave., Islip, NY 11751-4600
Web: www.daughtersofwisdom.org
Email: vocation@daughtersof wisdom.org
Members: 107 Sisters in US; 1,975 Sisters worldwide
Apostolic Work: Minister to a world broken by injustice and violence, especially to women, children and those displaced by war, oppression and poverty. Serving in rural communities and in the inner city to those lacking education, health care and basic human resources
Representation: Archdioceses of Hartford and in the Dioceses of Arlington, Brooklyn, Charleston, Portland (ME), Raleigh, Richmond,

Rockville Centre, St. Petersburg, and Wheeling. Also in Africa, Asia, Canada, Europe, Haiti and South America
Vocation Director: Sr. Lucy Clynes, DW, Daughters of Wisdom, (631) 277-2660, vocation@daughtersofwisdom.org

SISTER DISCIPLES OF (W217-1) **THE DIVINE MASTER (S.D.D.M.)** 3700 North Cornelia Ave., Fresno, CA 93722, (559)275-1656
Web: www.pddm.us
Email: sddmsiny@aol.com
Members: 48 Sisters in the US
Apostolic Work: Contemplative-active life style, Perpetual Adoration, collaboration with the priesthood, liturgical apostolate
Representation: In 27 nations throughout the world and in the Archdioceses of Boston, New York, Los Angeles, Fresno and San Jose
Vocation Director: Sr. Mary Peter Mendes, SDDM, 60 Sunset Ave., Staten Island, NY 10314, (718) 494-8597, SrPeterM@aol.com

DISCIPLES OF THE LORD (W217-2) **JESUS CHRIST (D.L.J.C.),** PO Box 64, Prayer Town, TX 79010-0064
Web: www.dljc.org
Email: dljcvocations@gmail.com
Members: 32 Sisters
Apostolic Work: Contemplative community with evangelistic apostolates: retreat work, Catholic Charismatic Renewal prayer groups, music ministry, university ministry, foreign mission, youth ministry. The sisters follow the Rule of the Third Order Regular of Saint Francis of Assisi
Representation: Dioceses of Amarillo. Also in Monterrey, Mexico
Vocation Director: Sister Juliana, DLJC, (806) 534-2312, ext.32, fax: (806) 534-2223

SISTERS OF THE DIVINE (W218-1) **COMPASSION (R.D.C.)** Motherhouse and Novitiate Good Counsel Convent, 52 N. Broadway, White Plains, NY 10603
Web: www.divinecompassion.org
Email: sisters@divine compassion.org
Members: 96 Sisters
Apostolic Work: Education, health care, counseling, social service, parish ministry, migrant ministry, rural outreach, spiritual development
Representation: Mostly in the Archdiocese of New York
Vocation Director: Office of Mission and Charism, (914) 798-1109, fax: (914) 949-5169

DIVINE MERCY (O.L.M.) (W218-2) See Our Lady of Mercy, The Congregation of the Sisters of

COMMUNITY OF DIVINE (W219) **PROVIDENCE (C.D.P.),** 5 Cygnet Ln., Valley Cottage, NY 10989
Email: shenchy@aol.com
Apostolic Work: House of prayer and hospitality, building Christian community through associate membership, retreats, spiritual direction, teaching, ministry to the sick
Representation: Archdiocese of New York
Vocation Director: Sister Catherine Reddy or Sister Gloria Jean Henchy, (845) 268-6314

CONGREGATION OF DIVINE (W220) **PROVIDENCE (CDP) SAN ANTONIO, TX,** Generalate: Our Lady of the Lake Convent, 515 S.W. 24th St., San Antonio, TX 78207-4619
Web: www.cdptexas.org
Email: elsacdp@aol.com, vocationministry@cdptexas.org
Members: 275 Sisters
Apostolic Work: Education: college, secondary and elementary; pastoral services, parish ministry, hospitals and clinics, hospice, social services, diocesan offices, retreats, counseling, spiritual direction, music
Representation: Archdioceses of Chicago, Denver, Los Angeles, Milwaukee, New Orleans, Oklahoma City, St. Louis, San Antonio, San Francisco, Seattle and Washington and in the Dioceses of Alexandria, Austin, Baton Rouge, Colorado Springs, Corpus Christi, Dallas, El Paso, Fort Wayne-So. Bend, Fresno, Galveston-Houston, Lafayette, (LA), Lake Charles, Laredo, Raleigh, St. Petersburg, San Angelo, San Bernardino, Springfield-Cape Girardeau, Tucson, Tulsa and Victoria. Also in Ghana and Mexico
Vocation Director: New Membership Team: Sister Elsa E. Garcia, CDP, Sister Gloria Ann Fiedler, CDP, (210) 434-1866, ext. 1130, 1155, 1135

DAUGHTERS OF DIVINE (W221) **PROVIDENCE (F.D.P.)** Motherhouse: Italy US Delegation, 74684 Airport Rd., Covington, LA 70435
Email: divineprovidence@ netzero.net
Members: About 300 Sisters worldwide; 4 in the US
Apostolic Work: Ministry: Education through catechesis, parish ministry, service to the sick, the elderly and the poor. Since 1832 the Congrega-

tion has been dedicated to spreading the message of God's Divine Providence following the example of its foundress, Venerable Maria Elena Bettini
Representation: Archdiocese of New Orleans. Also serving in Italy, Mexico, Chile, India and Poland
Vocation Director: Sr. Barbara Dichiara, FDP, Vocation Directress, (985) 809-8854, fax: (985) 809-8836

SISTERS OF DIVINE (W222)
PROVIDENCE (C.D.P.)
St. Anne Convent, 1000 St. Anne Dr., Melbourne, KY 41059
Web: www.cdpkentucky.org
Email: vocation@cdpkentucky.org
Members: 140 Professed Sisters
Apostolic Work: Education (Montessori, elementary, secondary, college), social services, religious education, pastoral ministry (parish, hospital), health care, foreign missions, peace and justice ministry, retreat ministry
Representation: (Arch)dioceses of Cincinnati, Covington, Duluth, Indianapolis, Lexington, Louisville, Manchester, New York, Toledo and Washington (DC) and Wheeling-Charleston. Also in Latacunga, Ecuador
Vocation Director: Sister Fidelis Tracy, CDP(859) 441-0700, ext. 324

SISTERS OF DIVINE (W225)
PROVIDENCE (C.D.P.)
Providence Heights
Marie de La Roche Province, Pittsburgh, PA
9000 Babcock Blvd., Allison Park, PA 15101
Web: www.divineprovidenceweb.org
Email: cdpjudith@hotmail.com
Members: 265 Sisters, 180 Associates
Apostolic Work: Higher education, high schools, elementary schools, religious education and special education, pastoral ministry, campus ministry, social service, hospital, clerical, pastoral care, House of Prayer, day care, ministry with the aging, social concerns, health care, foster care, retreat ministry, psychological counseling and therapy, advocacy, ministry with refugees, Hispanic ministry, ministry with the homeless; missionary work
Representation: Dioceses throughout the US. Also in Puerto Rico and Santo Domingo
Vocation Director: Sister Judith Connor, CDP, (412) 318-3327 Fax: (412) 635-5416

SISTERS OF THE DIVINE (W226)
REDEEMER (S.D.R.)
Divine Redeemer Motherhouse
999 Rock Run Rd.
Elizabeth, PA 15037
Web: www.sistersofthedivine redeemer.org
Email: sisrosemarysdr@aol.com
Members: 22 Sisters
Apostolic Work: Witness to God's redeeming love through care of the sick, the poor, and the elderly; education, domestic service, parish ministry, retreat work and pastoral care
Representation: Archdiocese of Philadelphia and in the Diocese of Pittsburgh
Vocation Director: Sister Joanne Tricsko, S.D.R., (412) 751-8600

SISTERS OF THE DIVINE (W227)
SAVIOR, See - Salvatorians

CLOISTERED (W228)
DOMINICAN NUNS (O.P.)
Monastery of the Infant Jesus
1501 Lotus Ln., Lufkin, TX 75904-2699
Web: www.nunslufkin.op.org
Email: info@nunslufkin.op.org
Members: 29 Sisters
Vocation Director: Sr. Mary Thomas, (936) 634-4233

DOMINICAN (W229)
CONTEMPLATIVE SISTERS, O.P.
Monastery of the Heart of Jesus, 155 Church St., Lockport, LA 70374-2552
Members: 5 Professed Sisters
Conduct: Cloistered Monastic Life. Application requirements: Single women under age 35 in excellent health
Representation: Diocese of Houma-Thibodaux
Vocation Director: Vocation Directress, 985-532-2411

DOMINICAN NUNS (O.P.) (W230)
Corpus Christi Monastery
215 Oak Grove Ave., Menlo Park, CA 94025-3272
Web: www.nunsmenlo.org
Email: vocationsmenlo@comcast .net
Members: 16 Sisters
Apostolic Work: Contemplative Solemn liturgy, community life, solitude, study, work, adoration of the Blessed Sacrament
Vocation Director: Sr. Mary, (650) 322-1801, ext 1

DOMINICAN NUNS (O.P.) (W231)
Our Lady of Grace Monastery
11 Race Hill Rd., North Guilford, CT 06437-1099
Web: www.op-stjoseph.org/nuns/ olgrace

Email: olgracevocations@juno.com
Members: 35 Nuns, 2 in Formation
Apostolic Work: Dominican Monastic Life: a way of living out the invitation to follow Jesus Christ more closely. It is a way of life constituted by a whole body of common activities - time tested and proven practices - which help our entire being to collaborate in our spiritual quest. These practices or observances are: common life, liturgy and prayer, solemn vows, and the study of sacred truth. These are helped by enclosure, silence, the habit, work, and penitential practices. The monastery has perpetual adoration of the Blessed Sacrament.
Vocation Director: Sister Maria Christi, O.P., (203) 457-0599

DOMINICAN NUNS (O.P.) (W232)
2636 Monastery Rd., Linden, VA 22642
Web: www.lindenopnuns.org
Members: 6 Solemnly Professed Nuns, 1 Temporary Professed, 3 Postulants
Apostolic Work: Cloistered contemplative life: Fidelity to the Holy Father, choral celebration of the Divine Office, daily exposition of the Blessed Sacrament. A life lived in community, balanced with lectio divina, private prayer, silence, study and work
Vocation Director: (540) 635-3259

DOMINICAN NUNS (O.P.) (W233)
Province of St. Joseph, Mother of God Monastery, 1430 Riverdale St, West Springfield, MA 01089-4698
Web: www.op-stjoseph.org/nuns/ ws/index.htm
Email: monasteryws@comcast.net
Apostolic Work: Monastic contemplative life with perpetual adoration of the Blessed Sacrament. 20 nuns daily celebrating the entire Liturgy of the Hours and having as the focal point of the day the solemn and joyful celebration of the Eucharistic Liturgy. Devotion to Mary, Mother of God, especially through praying the Rosary, is characteristic of the community
Vocation Director: Sister Mary of the Pure Heart, O.P., (413) 736-3639, fax: (413) 736-0850

DOMINICAN NUNS (O.P.) (W234)
Monastery of the Blessed Sacrament, 29575 Middlebelt Rd., Farmington Hills, MI 48334
Web: www.opnuns-fh.org
Email: vocdir@sbcglobal.net
Members: 40 Sisters, 5 in Formation
Apostolic Work: The Sisters' monastic contemplative vocation balances a life of solitude with life in

B-73

community. The whole of their life is aimed at the continual remembrance of God, especially through liturgical/personal prayer, study and work
Vocation Director: Sister M. Peter, O.P., (248) 626-8253

DOMINICAN NUNS (O.P.) (W236)
Monastery of Our Lady of the Rosary, 543 Springfield Ave., Summit, NJ 07901-4498
Web: www.nunsopsummit.org or www.monialesop.blogspot.com
Email: vocations.summit@op.org
Members: 15 Solemnly Professed, 5 Novices, 2 Postulants
Representation: Archdiocese of Newark
Vocation Director: Sr. Mary Catharine, OP, (908) 273-1228

DOMINICAN NUNS, (W237)
CLOISTERED (O.P.)(Nuns of the Order of Preachers), Corpus Christi Monastery,1230 Lafayette Ave., Bronx, NY 10474-5399
Web: http://bronxop.org
Email: vocations@bronxop.org
Members: 13 Sisters
Apostolic Work: Perpetual Adoration of the Most Blessed Sacrament, Contemplatives
Vocation Director: Vocation Contact: Sr. Marie, O.P., (718) 328-6996

DOMINICAN NUNS (O.P.) (W238)
Monastery of Mary the Queen, 1310 W. Church St., Elmira, NY 14905-1998
Web: www.op.org/maryqueen/
Email: maryqueenop@gmail.com
Members: 12 Nuns
Apostolic Work: We have dedicated ourselves to the following of Jesus Christ within the monastic, contemplative tradition given to us by St. Dominic. We do this principally through: Prayer offered both in a common liturgy, and in solitude which issues from an attentive listening to the Lord speaking in the Scriptures and the study of sacred truth; Community life marked by a freedom of spirit arising from our poverty, chastity, and obedience, a common labor and a sisterly love; An Apostolic Spirit which finds expression in a joyful hospitality and a universal solidarity with all people in their needs
Vocation Director: Novice Directress, (607) 734-9506

DOMINICAN NUNS OF THE (W239)
PERPETUAL ROSARY (O.P.)
Dominican Monastery of St. Jude, PO Box 170, Marbury, AL 36051
Web: www.stjudemonastery.org
Email: stjudemonastery@aol.com

Members: 8 Sisters
Apostolic Work: Following the tradition established by St. Dominic in 1207, the nuns live a life of contemplation in the monastic tradition. This small community preaches the Gospel by the witness of their lives; they serve God by living out their vows of poverty, chastity and obedience and adoration of the Blessed Sacrament and devotion to Our Lady. Along with daily celebration of the Eucharist, the nuns commit ourselves to praying the Liturgy of the Hours in English and Latin
Vocation Director: Mother Prioress, (205) 755-1322

DOMINICAN NUNS OF (W240)
PERPETUAL ADORATION (O.P.)
Monastery of the Angels, 1977 Carmen Ave., Los Angeles, CA 90068
Web: www.op-stjoseph.org/ nuns/angels
Email: monastery1977@att.net
Members: 23 Sisters
Apostolic Work: A cloistered community observing norms of a full contemplative life
Vocation Director: Sister Mary Pia, O.P., (Director/Novice Mistress), (323) 466-2186 ext 45

DOMINICAN NUNS OF THE (W241)
PERPETUAL ROSARY (O.P.)
Monastery of the Dominican Nuns of the Perpetual Rosary, 605 14th and West Sts., Union City, NJ 07087
Members: 3 Professed Sisters
Conduct: Cloistered
Vocation Director: Mother Mary Jordan, O.P., (201) 866-7004

DOMINICAN NUNS OF THE (W242)
PERPETUAL ROSARY (O.P.)
Monastery of the Perpetual Rosary, 1500 Haddon Ave., Camden, NJ 08103-3112
Conduct: 6 Nuns
Vocation Director: Mother Mary of the Immaculate Heart, O.P., Prioress

DOMINICAN NUNS (W243)
(Nuns of the Order of Preachers)
Monastery of Our Lady of the Rosary, 335 Doat St., Buffalo, NY 14211-2199
Web: www.dominicannunsof buffalo.org
Email: monasteryvoc@opnuns.org
Members: 22 Nuns, 2 Externs, 1 Simple Vows, 2 Novices, 1 Postulant
Apostolic Work: Contemplative: Divine Office, Eucharistic Adoration and Rosary
Vocation Director: Sr. Mary Lucy, O.P., (716) 892-0066

DOMINICAN NUNS OF THE (W244)
PERPETUAL ROSARY (O.P.)
802 Court St., Syracuse, NY 13208
Email: violetbop@juno.com
Members: 11 Sisters
Apostolic Work: Contemplative community
Vocation Director: Sister Bernadette Marie, OP, Prioress, (315) 471-6762

DOMINICAN NUNS OF THE (W245)
PERPETUAL ROSARY (O.P.)
Monastery of the Immaculate Heart of Mary,1834 Lititz Pike, Lancaster, PA 17601-6585
Web: www.opnunslancaster.org
Email: monlanc@aol.com
Members: 11 Nuns, 1 Aspirant
Apostolic Work: Contemplative monastic life
Vocation Director: Mother Prioress, (717) 569-2104

DOMINICAN SISTERS OF (W248)
ADRIAN (O.P.), Motherhouse 1257 E. Siena Heights Dr., Adrian, MI 49221-1793, (517) 266-3400, fax: (517) 266-3545
Web: www.adriandominicans.org
Email: vocations@adrian dominicans.org
Members: 1,000+ Vowed members and associates
Apostolic Work: Education at all levels, pastoral work, health care, social work, direct social action, legal assistance, community development, theology, preaching and the fine arts
Representation: 37 states, the Dominican Republic, Puerto Rico and South Africa
Vocation Director: Sister Durstyne Farnan, OP 866-774-0005 toll-free or (517) 266-3537, fax: (517) 266-3524

DOMINICAN SISTERS OF (W249)
AKRON (O.P.), Our Lady of the Elms Motherhouse, 1230 W. Market St., Akron, OH 44313-7108
Web: www.akrondominicans.org
Email: btbaltrinic@akronop.org
Members: 75 Sisters
Apostolic Work: Education on all levels preschool through college including religious education and earth education; pastoral ministry in parishes, counseling. Hospital ministry, hospice ministry, ministry to elderly and shut-ins. Preaching, parish life coordinator and spiritual direction. Library work, clerical, administration, director of parish outreach and computer design; Tanzania missions, East Africa.
Representation: Archdioceses of Denver, Portland (OR), and Seattle and the Dioceses of Cleveland,

Dodge City, Fort Wayne-South Bend, Phoenix, Toledo, and Youngstown
Vocation Director: Sister Bernadine Baltrinic, O.P., (330) 836-4908

DOMINICAN SISTERS OF (W250) **AMITYVILLE (O.P.)**, Queen of the Rosary Motherhouse, 555 Albany Ave., Amityville, NY 11701
Web: www.amityvilleop.org or www.catholicdominicansisters.org
Email: erldop@amityop.org
Members: 500 Sisters
Apostolic Work: Teaching, hospital ministry, parish ministry, communications and media, congregational service, counseling, religious education, campus ministry, social work, law, medicine, preaching teams and others
Representation: Archdiocese of New York and in the Dioceses of Brooklyn and Rockville Centre (NY City). Also in Puerto Rico
Vocation Director: Sr. Ancilla Keinberger, O.P., (631) 842-6000, ext. 220, fax: (631) 841-3424

DOMINICAN SISTERS OF (W251-1) **BLAUVELT (O.P.)**, Motherhouse: Convent of St. Dominic, 496 Western Hwy., Blauvelt, NY 10913-2097, (845) 359-5600
Web: www.opblauvelt.org
Email: mconnolly@opblauvelt.org
Members: Vowed, Associate Membership, Dominican Lay Volunteers
Apostolic Work: Education, college, high schools, elementary, child care, developmentally challenged, migrant children, pastoral, social work, health care, preaching ministry, outreach to homeless and those with AIDS
Representation: (Arch)dioceses in New York, New Jersey, Providence, RI and St. Petersburg, FL
Vocation Director: Sister Michaela Connolly, O.P., (845) 359-5600 or 0696, fax: (845) 359-5773

DOMINICAN SISTERS, (W251-2) **CABRA (O.P.) (Our Lady of the Rosary)**, Regional House 6315 Caldwell Dr., New Orleans, LA 70122
Web: www.cabraop.org
Email: fquinn@cajun.net
Members: 6 Sisters in US; 500 Sisters worldwide
Apostolic Work: A variety of educational ministries, pastoral work, spiritual direction, retreats, community organizing
Representation: Archdiocese of New Orleans

DOMINICAN SISTERS OF (W252-1) **CALDWELL, NEW JERSEY (O.P.)**
Motherhouse: 1 Ryerson Ave., Caldwell, NJ 07006, (973) 403-3331 Vowed, Associate Relationship, Dominican Lay Volunteers
Web: www.caldwellop.org
Email: ktuite@caldwell.edu
Members: 170 Sisters
Apostolic Work: Education at all levels, pastoral ministry, health and human services, campus ministry, preaching and earth study (Genesis Farm)
Representation: Archdiocese of Newark and in six other dioceses in the US. Also in the Dominican Republic
Vocation Director: Sr. Kathleen Tuite, OP, (973) 618-3534

DOMINICAN SISTERS OF (W252-2) **CHARITY OF THE PRESENTATION OF THE BLESSED VIRGIN (O.P.)**
Motherhouse: France 3012 Elm St., Dighton, MA 02715
Web: www.dominicansistersofthe presentation.org
Email: srfaye@cox.net
Members: 39 Sisters in US; 2,737 worldwide
Apostolic Work: In US: Hospital, caring for the aged, rural health, pastoral care, education, parish ministry, house of studies, home health care, social work, ministry to immigrants and Hispanics; Abroard: Missions in Korea and Honduras
Representation: Archdiocese of Washington, DC and the Dioceses of Brownsville, Fall River, Providence, and Sacramento
Vocation Director: Sr. Faye Medina, OP, (508) 669-5460
Sr. Marina Mejia, O.P., Provincial Superior, (508) 669-5425

DOMINICAN SISTERS OF (W255) **GRAND RAPIDS (OP)**, Motherhouse Marywood, 2025 E. Fulton St., Grand Rapids, MI 49503-3895
Web: www.GRDominicans.org
Email: ksleziak@grdominicans.org
Members: 290 Sisters
Apostolic Work: Education at all levels, parish and campus ministry, health care, social service, liturgy, social justice ministries, retreat work, diocesan personnel
Representation: 6 Michigan Dioceses, New Mexico and 17 other states. Foreign missions in Chimbote (Peru) and Honduras
Vocation Director: Katheryn Sleziak, OP, 800-253-7343, (616) 643-0378, fax: (616) 454-6105

DOMINICAN SISTERS OF (W256) **GREAT BEND (OP)**, 3600 Broadway, Great Bend, KS 67530-3692
Web: www.ksdom.org
Email: teriop@msn.com
Members: 105 Sisters
Apostolic Work: Teaching, parish ministry, religious education, pastoral care, nursing, care of aging, home health, holistic health, social service, foreign missions, retreat and spirituality center, permaculture farming, presence with and housing for the poor
Representation: (Arch)dioceses of Denver, Dodge City, Kansas City in Kansas, Phoenix, Pueblo, St. Louis, St. Paul-Minneapolis, Salina, San Angelo, Springfield-Cape Girardeau and Wichita. Also in Africa.
Vocation Director: Sister Teri Wall, OP, (303) 922-2997

DOMINICAN SISTERS OF (W257-1) **HAWTHORNE (O.P.) (Servants of Relief for Incurable Cancer)**
Motherhouse and Novitiate: Rosary Hill Home, 600 Linda Ave., Hawthorne, NY 10532
Web: www.hawthorne-dominicans.com
Email: SrAlmaMarie@aol.com
Apostolic Work: Dedicated to the care of incurable cancer patients
Representation: Archdioceses of Atlanta, New York, Philadelphia and St. Paul, U.S. and Archdiocese of Kisumu, Kenya
Vocation Director: Sister Alma Marie Borja, O.P., (914) 769-4794 or 0114

DOMINICAN SISTERS OF (W257-2) **HOPE (O.P.)**, 299 N. Highland Ave., Ossining, NY 10562-2327
Web: www.ophope.org
Email: jmarchesani@ophope.org
Members: 228 Sisters
Apostolic Work: We, Dominican Sisters of Hope, are called to preach the Gospel to our world. In communion with all Creation, we commit our lives to the transforming power of Hope. Our Sisters minister wherever they have discerned a call to serve others. As followers of St. Dominic, we strive to embrace the values of prayer, study and common life for the sake of mission.
Representation: 20 states and Puerto Rico
Vocation Director: Sr. Janet Marchesani, O.P., (845) 452-3484, fax: (914) 941-1125

DOMINICAN SISTERS OF (W258) **HOUSTON (O.P.)**, Congregation of the Sacred Heart, 6501 Almeda Rd., Houston, TX 77021-2095
Web: www.houstonop.org
Email: pcasey@domhou.org
Members: 100 Sisters

B-75

Apostolic Work: Education at all levels, pastoral work, health care, social work, direct social action, theology, preaching and the fine arts, foreign mission
Representation: Archdioceses of Indianapolis, Los Angeles, St. Louis, San Antonio and the Dioceses of Austin, Beaumont, Brownsville, Corpus Christi, Galveston-Houston, Houma-Thibodaux, San Angelo, San Bernardino, and San Jose. Also in Guatemala and Kenya.
Vocation Director: Contact: Sr. Pat Casey, O.P., (713) 440-3706

DOMINICAN SISTERS (O.P.) (W259)
(Congregation of the Immaculate Conception)
Motherhouse: Cracow, Poland
Provincial House: Rosary Hill, 9000 W. 81st St., Justice, IL 60458
Web: www.sistersop.com
Email: justice@sistersop.com
Members: 29 Sisters in US; approximately 400 worldwide
Apostolic Work: Evangelization, teaching, health care
Representation: (Arch)diocese of Chicago, Milwaukee and Little Rock. Also in Calgary, Canada; Poland, Italy, Russia, Ukraine, Belaruss, and Cameroon, Africa
Vocation Director: Sr. Margaret Lekan, OP, (708) 458-3040

DOMINICAN SISTERS OF (W260-2)
MISSION SAN JOSE (O.P.)
Dominican Convent, 43326 Mission Blvd., Fremont, CA 94539
Web: www.msjdominicans.org
Email: msjhelena@msjdominicans.org
Members: 229 Sisters, 3 Novices, 2 Candidates, 1 Pre-Candidate
Conduct: Junior college, high schools, elementary schools, school of music
Apostolic Work: Preachers of the Good News of Jesus Christ through the ministry of Christian education in elementary, high schools and colleges, campus ministry, parish ministry, pastoral ministry in hospitals, prisons, social justice and other ministries
Representation: Archdioceses of Los Angeles and San Francisco and in the Dioceses of Oakland, Orange, San Jose and Tucson. Also in Mexico and Germany.
Vocation Director: S. Helena Im, O.P., (510) 657-2468

DOMINICAN SISTERS OF (W261)
NASHVILLE (O.P.)
General Motherhouse
St. Cecilia Convent, 801 Dominican Dr., Nashville, TN 37228-1909

Web: www.nashvilledominican.org
Email: vocation@op-tn.org
Members: 220 Sisters; 80 in Formation
Conduct: 1 college, 3 academies, 5 high schools, 24 elementary schools, 2 private elementary schools, 2 private kindergartens
Representation: Archdioceses of Atlanta, Baltimore, Cincinnati, New Orleans, St. Paul/Minneapolis and Washington, DC and the Dioceses of Arlington, Birmingham, Charleston, Denver, Lafayette, Memphis, Knoxville, Nashville, Providence, Richmond and Rome, Italy
Vocation Director: Sr. Mary Emily, O.P., (615) 256-0147

DOMINICAN SISTERS OF (W263)
OAKFORD (O.P.), US Regional Center, 980 Woodland Ave., San Leandro, CA 94577, 510-638-2822
Web: www.oakforddominicans.org
Email: jomin@sfhs.com
Members: 20 Sisters in US
Conduct: 1 regional center, 1 novitiate. Serve in health care, social work, parishes, spiritual direction
Representation: Dioceses of Oakland, Phoenix, San Bernardino, San Jose and Tucson. Serve in South Africa, Germany and England
Vocation Director: Sr. Jodi Min, OP, Dominican Sisters of Oakford, 327 Woodland Park, San Leandro, CA 94577, (510) 635-1480

DOMINICAN SISTERS OF (W264)
OXFORD, 775 W. Drahner Rd., Oxford, MI 48371-4866
Web: www.domlife.org/oxford
Email: gpoore@umich.edu
Members: 34 Sisters
Apostolic Work: Education, health care, pastoral ministry, child care, retreats, preaching, spiritual direction, peace and justice
Representation: Archdioceses of Chicago and Milwaukee and the Dioceses of Detroit and Saginaw, MI.
Vocation Director: Sr. Gene Poore, OP, Vocation Minister, (248) 628-2872

DOMINICAN SISTERS OF (W265)
THE PERPETUAL ROSARY (O.P.)
(Cloistered, Contemplative)
217 North 68th St., Milwaukee, WI 53213-3928
Web: www.op-milwaukee.org
Email: DomSisters@wi.rr.com
Members: 10 Professed Sisters
Vocation Director: Sr. Mary M. John Krupo, O.P., (414) 258-0579

DOMINICAN SISTERS OF (W267)
RACINE (O.P.)
Siena Center, 5635 Erie St., Racine, WI 53402-1900
Web: www.racinedominicans.org
Email: vocations@racinedominicans.org
Members: 172 Members
Apostolic Work: Education, health care, pastoral ministry, retreats and spiritual direction, art and music, social services, counseling, prison ministry and social justice concerns
Representation: 10 states
Vocation Director: Sister Karen Vollmer, O.P., (262) 639-4100, ext. 1274

DOMINICAN SISTERS OF (W268)
THE ROMAN CONGREGATION (O.P.)
Provincial Residence, 123 Dumont Ave., Lewiston, ME 04240-6107, (207) 782-3535, fax: (207) 782-0435
Web: www.dominicanromanusa.org
Email: moniqueb@megalink.net-e-mail
Members: 19 Sisters in US; 500 worldwide
Apostolic Work: Education at all levels, parish and pastoral ministries, mission work on the Navajo Reservation, health care, ministry to the poor and needy
Representation: Archdioceses of New York and Chicago and the Dioceses of Davenport, Gallup, Phoenix, Portland, ME. In countries of US, Canada, Brazil, Belgium, Sweden, France, Italy, Switzerland, Benin, Japan, Spain, Chile
Vocation Director: (Maine) Sr. Christine Plouffe, OP, Dominican Sisters, 61 Lisbon Rd., Sabattus, ME 04280

DOMINICAN SISTERS OF (W270)
ST. CATHERINE DE' RICCI (OP)
131 Copley Rd., Upper Darby, PA 19082
Web: www.catherinedericciop.org
Email: cealop1@verizon.net
Members: 72 Sisters
Apostolic Work: Retreat ministry, religious education, parish ministry, pastoral counseling, ministry with the poor, social services
Representation: (Arch)dioceses of Baltimore, Detroit, Miami, Philadelphia and Santa Fe and in the Dioceses of Albany, Orlando and 10 other dioceses
Vocation Director: Sr. Cecilia Warner, OP, (215) 635-6027

DOMINICAN SISTERS OF (W271)
ST. CATHARINE, KENTUCKY (O.P.)
St. Catharine Motherhouse, 2645 Bardstown Rd., St. Catharine, KY 40061, (859) 336-9303

Web: www.opkentucky.org
Email: budkaop@juno.com
Members: 189 Sisters
Apostolic Work: The Dominican charism of preaching the Word of God is lived by the Sisters in their ministries as educators, health-care providers, advocates for the homeless, pastoral ministers in parishes and retreat centers, counselors and through other ministries that address contemporary needs
Representation: (Arch)dioceses of Boston, Brooklyn, Chicago, Grand Island, Louisville, Memphis and Omaha; in about 17 other dioceses in lesser numbers
Vocation Director: For more information: Sister Mary Ann Budka, OP, (859) 262-5771

DOMINICAN SISTERS OF (W272)
ST. CATHERINE OF SIENA (O.P.)
119 Brooks St., Taos, NM 87571
Email: taosop@aol.com
Members: 14 Sisters
Apostolic Work: Education, healing ministry, care of the aged, social services, parish ministry, ministry to Hispanic peoples
Representation: Archdioceses of Milwaukee and Santa Fe and the Dioceses of Baker, San Jose, and Fresno
Vocation Director: Contact: (575) 751-1237

DOMINICAN SISTERS OF (W273)
ST. MARY OF THE SPRINGS (O.P.)
St. Mary of the Springs, 2320 Airport Dr., Columbus, OH 43219-2098
Web: www.columbusdominicans.org
Email: vocations@columbus
 dominicans.org
Members: 243 Sisters, 175 Associates
Conduct: 2 colleges, high schools, elementary schools, 3 learning centers, parish ministry, involvement in many aspects of pastoral ministry. Foreign mission - Chimbote, Peru, and Honduras
Apostolic Work: Diversified ministries which include education at all levels, parish ministries, health care, spirituality ministry, social work, foreign missions, chaplaincy, ecological farming
Representation: (Arch)dioceses in Colorado, Connecticut, Indiana, Iowa, Louisiana, Maryland, Michigan, Missouri, New Mexico, New York, Ohio, Pennsylvania, Rhode Island, Washington State, West Virginia and Wisconsin. Also in Peru, South America, Honduras, and Africa
Vocation Director: Sr. Cathy Arnold, OP, (614) 416-1056

DOMINICAN SISTERS OF (W274)
SAN RAFAEL (O.P.)
Motherhouse, 1520 Grand Ave., San Rafael, CA 94901-2236
Web: www.sanrafaelop.org
Email: pfarrellop@sanrafaelop.org
Members: 120 Sisters
Apostolic Work: Education, health care, retreat ministry, parish ministry, social service and pastoral care
Representation: Archdiocese of San Francisco and the Dioceses of Oakland, Reno, Sacramento, San Jose, Santa Rosa and Stockton
Vocation Director: Sister Patricia Farrell, O.P., (415) 453-8303, 257-4939

DOMINICAN SISTERS OF (W275)
SINSINAWA (O.P.) (Sinsinawa Dominican Congregation of the Most Holy Rosary), Dominican Motherhouse, The Mound, 585 County Rd. Z, Sinsinawa, WI 53824-9701
Web: www.sinsinawa.org
Email: member@sinsinawa.org
Members: 600 Sisters
Apostolic Work: Educational, pastoral, health care and social service ministries
Representation: 35 states, Europe, South and Central America and Trinidad
Vocation Director: Initial Membership Office, (608) 748-4411, ext. 279

DOMINICAN SISTERS OF (W276)
SPARKILL (O.P.) (Dominican Congregation of Our Lady of the Rosary), Dominican Convent, 175 Rte. 340, Sparkill, NY 10976-1047
Web: www.sparkill.org
Email: mcburke@sparkill.org
Members: 382 Sisters
Apostolic Work: Elementary schools, high schools, college, child care, housing, foreign missions, nursing, religious education, pastoral ministry, secretarial, administration, campus ministry, health related, counseling, aging, art, communication, handicapped, Native American missions
Representation: largely in the US with a mission in Pakistan
Vocation Director: Sister Mary Carol Burke, O.P., (845) 359-4025, fax: (845) 359-4118

DOMINICAN SISTERS (O.P.) (W277)
(St. Mary's New Orleans)
Motherhouse, 7300 St. Charles Ave., New Orleans, LA 70118, (504) 861-8183
Web: www.dominican-sisters.net/ stmarys
Email: mcdaniop@aol.com
Members: 40 Professed Sisters

Formation Orientation: National common novitiate: St. Louis. Affiliation possible (6 mo. to 2 yrs.)
Apostolic Work: Education: all phases and levels; spiritual direction, sponsorship of two retreat centers and a private high school; presence to the elderly and those under hospice care; pastoral ministry; ministry to the deaf and to those mentally challenged
Representation: Archdiocese of New Orleans and the Diocese of Baton Rouge
Vocation Director: Sister Mary C. Daniel, OP, 7320 St. Charles Ave., New Orleans, LA 70118, (225) 294-5794 (tel, fax)

DOMINICAN SISTERS OF (W279)
SPRINGFIELD (O.P.), Sacred Heart Convent, 1237 West Monroe St., Springfield, IL 62704
Web: www.springfieldop.org
Email: SLorik@spdom.org
Members: 254 Professed Sisters, 1 in Formation in US; 1 in Formation in Peru
Apostolic Work: We preach the Gospel of Jesus among the unserved and underserved through education, parishes and pastoral ministry, and healthcare. Living in community and praying daily the Liturgy of the Hours are the foundation of our life together in the U.S. and in Peru, where we've served since 1965 and where we have a house of formation. A 100-acre farm in Springfield serves as a spirituality center and model for organic gardening and Earth's sustainability.
Representation: 5 states and in Peru: in the Archdioceses of Chicago, Lima (Peru) and Detroit and in the Dioceses of Dubuque, Huancayo (Peru), Jackson, Joliet, Peoria, Rockford, Springfield-in-Illinois, and Superior
Vocation Director: Sister Lori Kirchman, O.P., (217) 787-0481

DOMINICAN SISTERS OF (W280)
TACOMA (O.P.), Tacoma Dominican Center, 935 Fawcett Ave. S., Tacoma, WA 98402-5605
Web: www.tacoma-op.org
Email: gretta@tacoma-op.org
Members: 69 Sisters, 1 Novice
Apostolic Work: Education, parish ministry, nursing, campus ministry, mental health, L'Arche Assistants, literacy programs, pastoral care, social workers, care for the elderly and orphans, sponsors of affordable housing.
Representation: Archdiocese of Seattle and the Dioceses of Baker, Fresno, CA; Spokane, WA, Yakima,

WA; Oakland, Fresno, and San Diego, CA.
Vocation Director: Sister Gretta Woodlock, OP, (253) 272-9688

EUCHARISTIC FRANCISCAN (W281)
MISSIONARY SISTERS (E.F.M.S.)
Our Lady's Convent, 943 S. Soto St., Los Angeles, CA 90023, (323) 264-6556
Novitiate: Nativity Convent, 1421 Cota Ave., Torrance, CA 90501, (310) 328-6725
Mission Centers: Blessed Sacrament Convent, 1205 N. San Joaquin St., Stockton, CA 95202, (209) 462-3906
St. Francis Convent, 302 W. 24th St., Tyler, TX 75702, (903) 526-4005
Email: efms@earthlink.net
Members: 26 Sisters
Apostolic Work: Adoration of the Blessed Sacrament, catechetical ministry at all levels, parish ministry (social work), education, secretarial work, multi-cultural ministry, retreats, out-reach programs and diocesan work
Representation: Archdiocese of Los Angeles and in the Dioceses of Stockton and Tyler (TX).
Vocation Director: Sister Gloria DeJesus, (209) 462-3906

EUCHARISTIC MISSIONARIES (W282)
OF ST. DOMINIC (O.P.), Administrative Offices, 2645 Bardstown Rd., St. Catharine, KY 40061-9435, (859) 336-9303, Ext. 383
Web: www.emdsisters.org
Email: SrKatOP@aol.com, EMDOffice@aol.com
Members: 33 Sisters
Apostolic Work: Health care, home visitation, religious education, spiritual direction, social work, parish administration, pastoral services, work with the terminally ill and the elderly, prison ministry, Maya ministry
Representation: Archdiocese of New Orleans and Louisville, and the Dioceses of Beaumont, Biloxi, Detroit, Houma-Thibodaux, Lafayette, Tucson and West Palm Beach
Vocation Director: Sr. Kathy Broussard, O.P., 5660 Bancroft Dr., New Orleans, LA 70122, (504) 452-2858

FAITHFUL COMPANIONS (W283)
OF JESUS (F.C.J.) (Society of the Sisters, Faithful Companions of Jesus), Generalate in England; Provincialate in Toronto, Canada Saint Philomena Convent, 324 Cory's Lane, Portsmouth, RI 02871, (401) 683-2222
Web: www.fcjsisters.org

Email: gemtfcj@aol.com
Members: 17 Sisters in US; 325 Sisters worldwide
Apostolic Work: Companioning with Jesus and one another, the Sisters strive to answer the "I thirst" of Jesus in the world today. They are involved in various ministries including: education in all forms; retreat work; parish ministry; prison ministry; hospital chaplaincy; ministry to the elderly; and missionary work. The Faithful Companions of Jesus are deeply rooted in Ignatian spirituality and are located throughout the world in 16 countries, including Romania, Indonesia, the Philippines, Argentina and Bolivia
Representation: (Arch)dioceses of Birmingham, Brooklyn, Fall River, Providence, Raleigh and San Francisco
Vocation Director: Sr. Gemma Tucciarone, F.C.J., 350 Mt. Pleasant Ave., Providence, RI 02908, (401) 274-6578

FELICIAN SISTERS (C.S.S.F.) (W284)
Immaculate Conception Province - Provincial House
Immaculate Conception Convent, 260 S. Main St., Lodi, NJ 07644
Web: www.feliciansisters.org
Email: feliciansisters@hotmail.com
Members: 165 Sisters in the Province
Apostolic Work: Primary work: education on all levels: elementary schools, high schools, college, school for exceptional children, religious education offices, a reading center and child care centers. Also: nursing home, infirmary, diocesan offices, urban youth center, retreat center, home for children and pastoral assistants/associates
Representation: Archdioceses of Newark and Philadelphia and the Dioceses of Metuchen, Paterson and Wilmington
Vocation Director: Sister Judith Marie Blizzard, C.S.S.F., Director of Vocation Ministries, (973) 473-7447, ext. 130, fax: (973) 473-7126

FELICIAN/FRANCISCAN (W285)
SISTERS (C.S.S.F.)
Our Lady of the Angels Province - Motherhouse and Novitiate, (860) 745-7791, 4946, fax: (860) 741-0819
Centralized Novitiate - (860) 745-3484
Our Lady of the Angels Convent, 1315 Enfield St., Enfield, CT 06082
Web: www.feliciansisters.org
Email: stalprov@aol.com
Members: 86 Sisters
Apostolic Work: Ministry in fields of

health and education, adult day care, pastoral care. Also missionary work, e.g. Africa, Brazil
Representation: Archdioceses of Boston, Hartford and New York and the Dioceses of Albany, Manchester, Norwich, Portland (ME), Providence and Springfield
Vocation Director: Sister Mary John Fryc, C.S.S.F., St. Adalbert Convent, 856 Atwells Ave., Providence, RI 02909-2523, (401) 831-3336, fax: (401) 351-9306

FELICIAN SISTERS (C.S.S.F.) (W286)
Immaculate Heart of Mary Province - Provincial House, Villa Maria, 600 Doat St., Buffalo, NY 14211
Web: www.cssfbuffalo.org
Email: vocations@cssfbuffalo.org
Members: 182 Sisters in the Province
Apostolic Work: Institutions include a college. Felicians minister in education on the elementary, high school and college levels; also involved in religious education, pastoral ministry, retreat work, nursing, counseling, special education and prison ministry
Representation: Dioceses of Buffalo, Rochester and Syracuse
Vocation Director: Vocation Team Representative, Sister M. Renée Kurczaba, CSSF, (716) 892-4141, ext. 114, fax: (716) 892-4177

FELICIAN FRANCISCAN (W287)
SISTERS (C.S.S.F.), Our Lady of Sacred Heart Province - Provincial House, 1500 Woodcrest Ave., Coraopolis, PA 15108-3099
Web: www.felicianspa.org
Email: faithbala@yahoo.com
Members: 90 Sisters in the Province, international Franciscan community of 12 provinces
Apostolic Work: Private high school, elementary schools, religious education centers, home for exceptional children, nursing home, assisted living facility. Engaged in adult education, youth ministry, health care, social ministry, retreats, parish ministry, tutoring, outreach to the poor, home visiting and also other spiritual and corporal works of mercy
Representation: Dioceses of Altoona-Johnstown, Charleston, Greensburg, Harrisburg and Pittsburgh
Vocation Director: Sister Mary Faith Balawejder, C.S.S.F., (412) 424-4697, fax: (412) 264-7047

FELICIAN SISTERS (W288)
(Congregation of the Sisters of St. Felix) (C.S.S.F.), Presentation of the Blessed Virgin Mary Province -

Motherhouse and Novitiate
Presentation of the B.V.M. Convent,
36800 Schoolcraft Rd., Livonia, MI
48150
Web: www.felicianslivonia.org
Email: smdesales@felician
  slivonia.org,
  cssf@felicianslivonia.org
Members:172 Sisters in the Province
Apostolic Work: 1 university, 2 high
schools, 7 elementary schools, 5
religious education centers, 1
Montessori center, 1 day care
center, 1 nursing home, 1 assisted
living center, community outreach
programs, 1 hospice in-patient
facility and home care program, 2
retreat centers, 2 child care centers,
1 prayer center, 4 parochial pastoral
centers, foreign missions in Brazil
and Kenya, 1 senior clergy residence, Archdiocesan Delegate for
Consecrated Life, chaplain for
Livonia Police Department
Representation: Archdiocese of
Detroit and the Dioceses of Lansing, Saginaw, and Fort Wayne-
South Bend. Also in Rome, Italy
Vocation Director: Sister Mary De
Sales Herman, CSSF,
(734) 591-1730

FELICIAN SISTERS (C.S.S.F.) (W289)
Mother of Good Counsel Province -
Provincial and Novitiate
Mother of Good Counsel Convent,
3800 W. Peterson Ave., Chicago, IL
60659-3116
Web: www.felicianschicago.org
Email: smarybeth@felicians
  chicago.org,
  cssf@felicianschicago.org
Members: 259 Sisters in the
Province
Apostolic Work: Instruction and
administration in elementary
schools, child development center,
hospitals, senior living centers,
assisted-living facility for the elderly,
skilled-care facilities, counseling
program for high-risk children, teens
and parents, social service especially among the poor, youth ministry,
pastoral ministry, religious education, evangelization, diocesan work,
domestic service, clerical work,
foreign missions in Brazil and
Kenya
Representation: Archdioceses of
Chicago and Milwaukee and the
Dioceses of Green Bay, La Crosse,
Belleville, Joliet and Rockford. Also
in Rome, Brazil, Poland and 7 other
North American provinces
Vocation Director: Sister Mary Beth
Bromer, C.S.S.F., (773) 463-3020
ext. 1391

FELICIAN SISTERS (C.S.S.F.) (W290)
Assumption of the B.V.M. Province
4210 Meadowlark Ln. S.E., Rio

Rancho, NM 87124
Email: cssfrrnm@nm.net
Members: 68 Sisters
Conduct: high school, grammar
schools, Christian Doctrine classes,
religious education centers, coun-
seling, youth ministry, adult educa-
tion, pastoral ministry, missionary
ministry, domestic service, Eucha-
ristic ministry, home visiting and
other spiritual and corporal works of
mercy
Representation: Archdioceses of Los
Angeles and San Antonio and the
Dioceses of Laredo and San
Bernardino. Also in Mexico
Vocation Director: Sister Carol Marie
Wiatrek, 505-892-8862

FILIPPINI SISTERS (M.P.F.) (W291)
(Religious Teachers Filippini)
See - Religious Teachers Filippini

FILIPPINI SISTERS (M.P.F.) (W292)
(Religious Teachers Filippini)
Queen of Apostles Province -
Provincial House
474 East Rd., Bristol, CT 06010
Email: itflower@erols.com
Members: 27 Sisters
Conduct: 4 grammar schools, 1
Montesorri Pre-School, 1 mission,
4 religious education centers, 1
shrine
Representation: Archdiocese of
Hartford and the Dioceses of
Bridgeport, Orlando and Providence
Vocation Director: Sister Frances
Stavalo, M.P.F, (860) 584-2138, fax:
(860) 582-1119

FRANCISCAN HANDMAIDS (W293-1)
**OF THE MOST PURE HEART OF
MARY (F.H.M.),** 15 W. 124th St., New
York, NY 10027, (212) 289-5655
Email: handmaidsofmary@aol.com
Members: 25 Sisters
Conduct: 1 nursery; St. Edward
Food Pantry; altar bread; FHM
Associates
Apostolic Work: Teaching, pastoral
work, social work, religious instruc-
tion, retreat work
Representation: Archdiocese of New
York
Vocation Director: Sr. Vincent Marie,
F.H.M., Vocation Directress, 6581
Hylan Blvd., Staten Island, NY
10309, 718-984-1625

FRANCISCAN HOSPITAL (W293-2)
SISTERS (O.S.F.)
See "H" - Hospital Sisters of the
Third Order of St. Francis

FRANCISCAN HOSPITALLER (W294)
**SISTERS OF THE IMMACULATE
CONCEPTION (F.H.I.C.)**
St. Joseph Novitiate, 300 S. 17th St.,

San Jose, CA 95112, 408-998-2896,
fax: 408-998-3407
Members: 20 Sisters
Apostolic Work: Schools, hospitals,
social work, parish
Representation: Dioceses of Fresno,
Monterey and San Jose. Also repre-
sented in Portugal, Brazil, India,
Spain, Philippines, Italy, Angola,
Mozambique, South Africa and
Mexico
Vocation Director: Sr. Acacia Moises,
1441 Berkeley Dr., Los Banos, CA
93635, (209) 827-8933

FRANCISCAN MISSIONARIES (W295)
**OF THE IMMACULATE HEART OF
MARY (F.M.I.H.M.)**
Motherhouse in Cairo, Egypt
General House in Rome, Italy
St. Bridget Convent, 206 Ellis St.,
Glassboro, NJ 08028
Web: www.fmihm.catholicweb.com
Email: srstaciemarie@yahoo.com
Members: Small presence in New
Jersey, USA; 600 Sisters worldwide
Apostolic Work: Teaching, foreign
missions, parish work, nursing,
social services, and other ministries
according to need and our charism
Representation: Brazil, China, Egypt,
Morocco, Guinea Bissau, Ghana,
Eritrea, Italy, Malta, Israel, Pales-
tine, Jordan, Lebanon, Syria, Iraq
Vocation Director: Sister Stacie Marie
Gagnon, F.M.I.H.M., (856) 881-
4604, fax: (856) 226-3098

FRANCISCAN MISSIONARIES (W296-1)
OF MARY (F.M.M.), (Provincial House)
Institute of Franciscan Missionaries
of Mary, 399 Fruit Hill Avenue, North
Providence, RI 02911-2842
Web: www.fmm.org
  www.fmmusa.org
Email: aliciaalambra82152@
  yahoo.com, fmmvoc@aol.com
Members: Over 7,400 Sisters
worldwide, 140 in US
Conduct: Prayer life includes daily
Adoration of the Blessed Sacrament
Apostolic Work: Medical, educa-
tional, social work, pastoral care
and parish ministry as well as
special ministries among the poor
and marginalized in 76 countries
throughout Africa, Asia, Europe,
Latin America, North America and
Oceania
Representation: in the US (Arch) dio-
ceses of New York, Chicago, Boston,
Rhode Island, Texas, New Mexico,
Georgia, and Florida
Vocation Director: Sr. Alicia Alambra,
FMM, (401) 353-5800, (401) 353-
9412

FRANCISCAN MISSIONARIES (W296-2) **OF OUR LADY (O.S.F.)**, 4200 Essen Ln., Baton Rouge, LA 70809
Web: www.fmolsisters.com
Email: lynne.barre@ololrmc.com
Members: 22 Sisters in the US
Apostolic Work: Health care ministry, serving the poor in various ministries. Missionary work in Haiti
Representation: Dioceses of Baton Rouge, Lafayette (LA) and Shreveport.
Vocation Director: (225) 926-1627

FRANCISCAN MISSIONARIES (W297) **OF THE SACRED HEART**
See "F" - Franciscan Sisters of Peekskill

FRANCISCAN MISSIONARY (W298) **SISTERS FOR AFRICA (F.M.S.A.)**
American Headquarters
172 Foster St., PO Box 35095, Brighton, MA 02135
Web: www.fmsa.net
Email: brightonsisters@yahoo.com
Members: 5 Sisters
Apostolic Work: An international and completely missionary Congregation working solely in Africa in education, refugee services, healthcare projects; ministry to patients with AIDS and their families; behavior change programs, adult literacy programs, vocational training of those in need, rehabilitation of handicapped children, and fostering vocations to the religious life
Representation: Archdiocese of Boston and in 8 foreign countries
Vocation Director: Sr. Mary Ryan, fmsa, Mission Procurator, (617) 254-4343, fax: (617) 787-8007

FRANCISCAN MISSIONARY (W299) **SISTERS OF ASSISI (SFMA)**
1039 Northampton St., Holyoke, MA 01040-1320
Web: www.sistersofassisi.org
Email: sistersofassisi@comcast.net
Apostolic Work: Pastoral work, teaching, nursing, social work, ministry of care/bereavement, ministry of care/homebound, religious education, adult faith formation and domestic work
Representation: (Arch)dioceses of Springfield and New York. Also missions in Brazil, China, Croatia, Italy, Japan, Kenya, Korea, the Philippines, Romania, Russia, United States and Zambia
Vocation Director: Sister Cordilia Munthali, SFMA, (413) 532-8156, fax: (413) 534-7741

FRANCISCAN MISSIONARY (W301-1) **SISTERS OF THE IMMACULATE CONCEPTION (O.S.F.)**
Provincial House, 13367 Borden Ave., Unit A, Sylmar, CA 91342-2804, 818-364-5557
Web: www.franciscansistersofthe immaculateconception.com
Email: comeandseeosf@yahoo.com
Members: 113 Sisters
Conduct: Provincial home, 1 novitiate, 1 home for the aged, 2 grammar schools, 1 preschool, 2 hospitals, 1 retreat house, 2 houses in catechetical and pastoral ministries, 1 home for senior citizens, 1 medical clinic for the poor
Representation: Archdioceses of Los Angeles and the Dioceses of Orange and Gallup. Also in Mexico
Vocation Director: Sister Cristina Knoell, OSF, 11306 Laurel Canyon Blvd., San Fernando, CA 91340-4317, (818) 365-7739, (818) 822-9142

FRANCISCAN MISSIONARY (W301-2) **SISTERS OF THE INFANT JESUS (F.M.I.J.)**, Motherhouse in Assisi (Italy) - Generalate in Rome Delegation (Regional) and Formation House, 1215 Kresson Rd., Cherry Hill, NJ 08003-2813
Web: www.cmswr.org/member_ communities/FMSIJ.htm
Email: mijcomeandsee@ yahoo.com, fmijusdel@yahoo.com
Apostolic Work: Education, health care, pastoral assistance to elderly, youth; catechesis and other services to evangelization
Representation: on 5 continents and 13 countries
Vocation Director: Sister Dianna Higgins, fmij, (856) 428-8834, fax: (856) 848-6049

FRANCISCAN MISSIONARY (W302) **SISTERS OF OUR LADY OF SORROWS (OSF)**, 3600 S.W. 170th Ave., Beaverton, OR 97006-5099
Web: www.olpretreat.org
Email: sisters@olpretreat.org
Members: 50 Sisters
Representation: Archdioceses of Portland (OR) and Vancouver, Canada and the Dioceses of Gallup and Monterey. Also in Hong Kong and Taipei, Taiwan
Vocation Director: Sister Anne Marie Warren, OSF, (503) 649-7127, fax: (503) 649-8382, e-mail: franmisisters@yahoo.com

FRANCISCAN SERVANTS (W303) **(O.S.F.)(Holy Child Jesus)**
Regional Motherhouse, 109 Route 156, Yardville, NJ 08620, (609) 585-4660
Email: srantoniavm@aol.com
Members: 18 Sisters

Apostolic Work: Health care, social services, education
Representation: Archdiocese of Newark and the Diocese of Trenton

FRANCISCAN SISTERS OF (W304) **ALLEGANY, NY (O.S.F.)**
St. Elizabeth Motherhouse, Allegany, NY 14706
Web: www.AlleganyFranciscans.org
Email: fsavoc@aol.com
Members: 350 Sisters
Apostolic Work: The Franciscan Sisters of Allegany seek to live the Gospel and witness to God's love in the Franciscan tradition by living as sisters with all creation and by joyfully serving others, especially those who are poor and marginalized. Our charism is that of Francis Assisi: to live the Gospel life in the spirit of love, joy, simplicity, and hospitality. Supporting each other in community and prayer, together we use our varied gifts and talents to care for God's people. Some of the many ways we serve are as teachers, nurses, social workers, directors of religious education, doctors, accountants, artists, pastoral ministers, administrators, lawyers, counselors, liturgists, spiritual directors, musicians, massage therapists, librarians, environmentalists, chaplains and justice advocates
Representation: Represented in the Archdioceses of New York, Boston, Hartford, Newark, Philadelphia, Miami and Wilmington and in the Dioceses of Buffalo, Syracuse, Albany, Rockville Centre, Paterson, Brooklyn, Metuchen, Trenton, Camden, Palm Beach, Venice, St. Petersburg, Gallup and Spokane. Also in Jamaica, Brazil, Bolivia, and Peru
Vocation Director: Vocation Minister: Sr. Mary McNally, OSF, 2924 W. Curtis St., Tampa, Fl 33614, (813) 870-6314, Fax: (813) 350-9533

FRANCISCAN SISTERS OF (W305) **THE ATONEMENT (S.A.)**, 41 Old Highland Turnpike, Graymoor, Garrison, NY 10524-9717
Web: www.graymoor.org
Email: vocationministry@ graymoor.org
Apostolic Work: Religious education, social services, pastoral ministry, retreat and guest house ministry.
Representation: (Arch)dioceses of Boston, Bridgeport, Detroit, Monterey, Newark, New York and Washington, DC and in 15 other dioceses in the United States. Also in Brazil, Canada, Japan, Ireland and Italy
Vocation Director: Vocation Ministry, (845) 230-8231

FRANCISCAN SISTERS OF (W308)
CHICAGO (O.S.F.), 11500 Theresa
Dr., Lemont, IL 60439
Web: www.chicagofranciscans.org
Email: kdoloriaosf@cs.com
Members: 68 Professed Sisters
Apostolic Work: Ministry to the poor,
the sick and elderly; religious
education; pastoral ministry and
evangelization; counseling and
social services; liturgy and parish
ministry
Representation: Archdiocese of
Chicago and the Dioceses of
Cleveland, Gary, Joliet, Lafayette,
Louisville and San Antonio
Vocation Director: Sr. Doloria Kosiek,
O.S.F., 3115 N. Karlov Ave., Chicago,
IL 60641-5436, (773) 202-0310

FRANCISCAN SISTERS OF (W309)
CHRISTIAN CHARITY (O.S.F.)
Holy Family Convent, 2409 South
Alverno Rd., Manitowoc, WI 54220
Web: www.fscc-calledtobe.org
Email: vocations@
    fscc-calledtobe.org
Members: 350 Sisters
Apostolic Work: Catholic education,
Catholic health care, and service to
our sisters in community
Representation: (Arch)dioceses of
Chicago, Columbus, Green Bay,
Honolulu, Jackson, Lincoln,
Marquette, Milwaukee, Omaha,
Phoenix, Steubenville and Tucson
Vocation Director: Vocation
Directress, (920) 682-7728

(W310)
SCHOOL SISTERS OF ST. FRANCIS
OF CHRIST THE KING (SSFCR)
Mt. Assisi Convent, 13900 Main St.,
Lemont, IL 60439
Web: www.lemontfranciscans.org
Email: vocareosf@yahoo.com
Members: 54 Sisters in America;
1,100 Sisters worldwide
Apostolic Work: 1 academy, 2
grammar schools, 1 home for the
aged, a house of prayer. Also serve
as Directors of Religious Education,
liturgy directors, nurses and in other
pastoral capacities
Representation: Archdiocese of
Chicago and the Diocese of Joliet
Vocation Director: Contact: (630)
257-7524

FRANCISCAN SISTERS OF (W311)
THE HOLY FAMILY OF DUBUQUE, IA
(O.S.F.), 3390 Windsor Ave., Dubuque,
IA 52001-1311
Web: www.osfdbq.org
Email: millern@osfdbq.org
Members: 340 Vowed Members, 108
Franciscan Associates
Apostolic Work: "Rooted in the
Gospel and in the Spirit of Saint

Francis and Saint Clare the Sisters
of St. Francis live in right relationship with all creation."
We express our love of God by our
commitment to prayer and service,
and by collaborating with others in
forming community. We have a
deep reverence for all creation and
a commitment to peace and justice.
We serve in a variety of ministries
as educators, health care workers,
retreat and prayer ministers, pastoral
ministers, caretakers among the
elderly, social workers, peace and
justice advocates, counselors,
dietary and clerical workers, artists
and musicians-wherever the needs
of God's people call for a compassionate and loving response.
Representation: 29 dioceses and 20
states in the US.
Vocation Director: Sr. Nancy Miller,
OSF, (563) 583-9786

FRANCISCAN SISTERS OF (W312)
THE EUCHARIST (F.S.E.)
Motherhouse, 405 Allen Ave.,
Meriden, CT 06451
Web: www.fsecommunity.org
Email: fseinfo@fsecommunity.org
Members: 77 Sisters, 3 Novices, 3
Postulants
Apostolic Work: Dedicated to the
sacredness of human life, the
Community's mission is carried out
through programs of counseling,
education, health care, music, land
experience and service to families
and the elderly
Representation: Archdioceses of
Hartford, Indianapolis, Portland and
Washington (DC) and the Dioceses
of Arlington, Boise, Duluth,
Galveston-Houston and Grand
Rapids. Also in Rome and Assisi,
Italy; Jerusalem; and Jamaica,
West Indies
Vocation Director: Sister Barbara
Johnson, F.S.E., (203) 238-2243

SISTERS OF ST. FRANCIS (W313)
OF THE IMMACULATE HEART OF
MARY (O.S.F.), Motherhouse,
St. Francis Convent, PO Box 447,
Hankinson, ND 58041-0447, (701)
242-7195
Web: www.fargodiocese.org/
    vocations/sfc
Email: osfhank@rrt.net
Members: 35 Sisters, 1 Postulant
Apostolic Work: Health care, care for
elderly and handicapped, retreats,
education, pro-life work, parish
work, social service and domestic
work
Representation: North Dakota and in
Germany, Brazil, India, Spain and
Switzerland
Vocation Director: Sister M. Jean
Louise Schafer, OSF, 301 Fourth St.

SE, Rugby, ND 58368-1821, (701)
776-6866; Sister Donna Welder, St.
Francis Provincial Motherhouse, PC
Box 447, Hankinson, ND 58041-
0447, (701) 242-7195

SISTERS OF ST. FRANCIS (W315-1
OF THE HOLY CROSS, 3110 Nicolet
Dr., Green Bay, WI 54311-7212
Web: www.gbfranciscans.org
Email: vocations@gbfranciscans.org
Members: 75 Sisters, 38 Associates
Apostolic Work: We serve as parish
leaders, educators (elementary,
high school, college), health care-
givers, youth ministers, minority and
environmental advocates, social
workers, literacy tutors, retreat
directors, artists and in other minis-
tries that promote understanding
and peace
Representation: Primarily in the
Diocese of Green Bay (NE
Wisconsin)
Vocation Director: Director of
Vocation Ministries, (920) 468-4737

SISTERS OF ST. FRANCIS OF (W317)
THE IMMACULATE CONCEPTION
(O.S.F.), Immaculate Conception
Convent, 2408 W. Heading Ave.,
West Peoria, IL 61604
Web: www.westpeoriasisters.org
Email: srpaulav@yahoo.com
Members: 42 Sisters
Apostolic Work: Teaching, parish
work, care of the elderly, religious
education, social work, Right to Life
movement, hospital chaplaincy,
teen and adult retreat programs,
spiritual direction, permanent
diaconate program, TEC program.
Ministries based in Midwest
Vocation Director: Contact, (309)
674-6168, fax: (309) 674-2006

FRANCISCAN SISTERS OF (W318
THE IMMACULATE CONCEPTION AND
ST. JOSEPH FOR THE DYING (O.S.F.)
1249 Josselyn Canyon Road,
Monterey, CA 93940
Members: 5 Sisters
Apostolic Work: Convalescent
hospital, home visiting
Representation: Diocese of Monterey
Vocation Director: Sr. M. Constance,
O.S.F., Superior, 831-375-8680

FRANCISCAN SISTERS OF (W319)
LITTLE FALLS, MINNESOTA (OSF)
St. Francis Convent, 116 8th Ave.
SE, Little Falls, MN 56345-3597
Web: www.fslf.org
Email: vocations@fslf.org
Members: 190 sisters
Apostolic Work: Following the spirit
of Saints Francis and Clare of
Assisi, living the Gospel life in
continual conversion through faithfu

B-81

prayer, simple living, caring community, reverencing and preserving all of God's creation and by seeking solidarity with persons who are poor
Representation: 9 states. Also in Ecuador and Mexico
Vocation Director: Sister Grace Skwira, OSF, (320) 632-0652 or 2981, fax:(320) 632-1714

SISTERS OF ST. FRANCIS OF (W320) **THE MARTYR ST. GEORGE (F.S.G.M.)**
Province: St. Elizabeth, St. Francis Convent, 1 Franciscan Way, PO Box 9020, Alton, IL 62002-9020
Web: www.altonfranciscans.org
Email: vocations@alton franciscans.org
Members: 151 Professed Sisters, 7 Novices, 5 Postulants
Apostolic Work: Teaching, nursing, social work, day care for children, parish work, youth ministry, missions in Brazil, secretarial and domestic work, adoration of the Blessed Sacrament
Vocation Director: Sister M. Consolata Cruz, FSGM, (618) 463-2757, fax: (618) 465-5064

FRANCISCAN SISTERS OF (W321) **MARY (FSM)**, 1100 Bellevue Ave., St. Louis, MO 63117-1826
Web: www.fsmonline.org
Email: sschwartz@fsmonline.org
Members: 128 members
Apostolic Work: Increasingly varied but emphasizing compassionate presence, healing, health promotion, restoration, health education and social ministry. Focus is on wholeness of relationships and life, including communal and congregational life. Members serve in hospitals, clinics, birthing centers, parishes, chaplaincies, hospices, homes, women's drop-in centers of hospitality, counseling situations, group dynamics, organizational development, social ministry settings, retreats, pastoral care, etc. Emphasis is given to the care of women and children and all those on the margins of society
Representation: Archdioceses of Chicago, Cincinnati, Milwaukee, and St. Louis and the Dioceses of Brownsville, Charleston, Corpus Christi, Gallup, Jefferson City, Madison, Springfield, MO, and Tucson
Vocation Director: Contact: Sr. Sandra Jean Schwartz, FSM, FSM Leadership Team,(314) 768-1828

SISTERS OF ST. FRANCIS (W322) **OF MARY IMMACULATE (OSF)**
1433 Essington Rd., Joliet, IL 60435
Web: www.jolietfranciscans.org
Email: bkwiatkowski@joliet franciscans.org
Members: 215 Professed Sisters
Apostolic Work: All levels of education (pre-school through adult), health care, parish ministry, campus ministry, social services, religious education, elder care, holistic health, music and art specialists.
Representation: 8 Archdioceses, 21 Dioceses in the US and Brazil
Vocation Director: Sister Barbara Kwiatkowski, OSF (815) 725-8735, x115

FRANCISCAN SISTERS (W323) **OF MARY IMMACULATE (F.M.I.)**
Province of St. Francis, U.S.A. St. Francis Convent, 4301 NE 18th St., Amarillo, TX 79107-7220
Email: srinesfmi@yahoo.com, retreatsfmi@yahoo.com
Members: Congregational Members: 683. Members in this Province: 42
Apostolic Work: The mission of our Congregation demand that we live our consecration according to the spirit of the Beatitudes, in a profound experience of faith, being witnesses of the Kingdom, living the motto of Mother Caritas (Our Foundress); "All for the love of God and as He wills it." We express our congregational mission by contributing specifically to the work of Evangelization in the Church through:
a. Educational Work
b. Missionary Work
c. Social Work
Our Charism is a gift of the Holy Spirit to live and announce the Gospel as minor sisters, in permanent availability to the will of God, incerted in a needy world.
The identity of our Congregation is to live the Love of God and of neighbor, according to the Gospel, in Chastity, Poverty and Obedience, after the exemple of St. Francis of Assisi, following the humble crucified Christ, in a constant attitude of Conversion, animated by the spirit of contemplation, poverty and humility, lived in fraternity.
Representation: in U.S.A Province: Archdiocese of Los Angeles, CA and Diocese of Amarillo, TX. Out of USA: Mexico, Costa Rica, Panama, El Salvador and Colombia Countries in other Provinces: Guatemala, Ecuador, Peru, Nicaragua, Honduras, Cuba, Switzerland, and MISSION ADGENTES: In West Africa (Mali and Benin)

Vocation Director: Sr. Ines Lopez, fmi, (806) 383-5769, fax (806) 383-6545

SISTERS OF ST. FRANCIS (W324) **OF MILLVALE, PA**
See "M" - Millvale Franciscans

FRANCISCAN SISTERS OF (W325) **OLDENBURG (O.S.F.)**
Motherhouse and Novitiate: Sisters of St. Francis, PO Box 100, Oldenburg, IN 47036-0100, 812-934-2475, fax: 812-933-6403
Web: http://oldenburg franciscans.org
Email: vocations@ oldenburgosf.com
Members: 268 Sisters, 2 in Formation, 284 Associates
Apostolic Work: Elementary, secondary, college, and religious education and administration; campus ministry, pastoral and hospital ministry; daycare; spiritual direction and retreat ministry; counseling; social work; nursing; library science; clerical and supportive services; African-American, Native American, Hispanic and Appalachian ministries, and wherever the gifts of the Sisters are needed
Representation: Archdioceses of Cincinnati, Detroit, Indianapolis, Los Angeles, St. Louis and in the Dioceses of Buffalo, Evansville, Cheyenne, Gallop, Great Falls-Billings, Lexington, Springfield, and Wheeling. Foreign missions in Papua New Guinea
Vocation Director: Sr. Joan Miller (812) 933-6417

FRANCISCAN SISTERS OF (W326) **OUR LADY OF PERPETUAL HELP (O.S.F.)**, 335 South Kirkwood Rd., St. Louis, MO 63122-6117
Web: www.franciscan sisters-olph.org
Email: srmarcy@fsolph.org
Members: 110 Sisters and 1 in pre-novitiate
Apostolic Work: Education, health care, pastoral ministry, social service, contemporary needs of the Church
Representation: (Arch)dioceses of Austin, Belleville, Charleston, Chicago, El Paso, Grand Rapids, Kansas City, Lafayette, IN, Las Cruces, Milwaukee, Omaha, Pueblo, Rockford, Rockville Centre, St. Louis, St. Petersburg, Santa Fe, Shreveport, Springfield (IL), Springfield-Cape Girardeau, Toledo
Vocation Director: Marcy Romine, OSF, (314) 965-3700, ext. 3054, fax: (314) 965-3710

FRANCISCAN SISTERS (W327-1)
OF PEACE (F.S.P.), 20 Ridge St.,
Haverstraw, NY 10927-1198
Web: www.fspnet.org
Members: 87 Sisters; co-founded in 1986
Apostolic Work: Education (pre-school through college), pastoral and campus ministry, prison ministry, religious education, spiritual direction, counselling, health care, day care, working with the poor and homeless
Representation: (Arch)dioceses of Albany, Chicago, New York, Newark, Paterson, Rockville Centre, San Francisco and Tucson
Vocation Director: Ann Smith, FSP, (845) 942-2527, ext.100

FRANCISCAN SISTERS OF (W327-2)
PEEKSKILL (F.M.S.C.) (Franciscan Missionaries of the Sacred Heart)
Mount St. Francis, 250 South St., Peekskill, NY 10566-4419
Web: www.cmswr.org/member_
communities/FMSH.htm
Email: sajfmsc@mail.com
Members: 54 Sisters in US; 782 worldwide
Apostolic Work: Education, religious education, parish ministry, nursing, prison ministry and community service
Representation: Archdioceses of Newark and New York and the Diocese of Brooklyn. Also in 21 countries in Europe, Africa, South America and Asia
Vocation Director: Sister Anne Matthew Carlone, F.M.S.C., Vocation Directress, (914) 737-3373, E-mail: srannemcarlone@optonline.net

FRANCISCAN SISTERS, (W328-1)
T.O.R. OF PENANCE OF THE SORROWFUL MOTHER, Motherhouse Our Lady of Sorrows Monastery, 369 Little Church Rd., Toronto, OH 43964
Web: www.torsisters.org
Email: vocations@torsisters.org
Members: 21 Professed Sisters, 5 Novices, 2 Postulants
Apostolic Work: Contemplative/active; emphasis on prayer and Eucharistic adoration, with works of mercy which include care for the poor, catechetical, retreat work, parish missions and youth ministry
Vocation Director: Sr. Thérése Marie, TOR, (740) 544-6204, fax: (740) 544-5543

FRANCISCAN SISTERS OF (W328-2)
PERPETUAL ADORATION (F.S.P.A.)
St. Rose Convent, 912 Market St., La Crosse, WI 54601-8800
Web: www.fspa.org

Email: membership@fspa.org
Members: 340 Sisters, 200 Lay Affiliates
Apostolic Work: Perpetual Adoration of the Blessed Sacrament since 1878. Members synthesize prayer and action through work in diversified ministries including education, health care, social services and pastoral ministry. The Community operates four spirituality centers; two have a strong emphasis on ecology. Members work with people of various needs in prisons, immigrant services and intercultural awareness programs – wherever their talents and the world's needs meet
Representation: 40 dioceses in the US and in Africa, Canada, El Salvador, Guam and Mexico
Vocation Director: Sister Dorothy Dunbar, (888) 683-FSPA (3772)

SISTERS OF ST. FRANCIS (W329)
OF PERPETUAL ADORATION (O.S.F.)
Mt. Saint Francis, 7665 Assisi Heights, Colorado Springs, CO 80919
Web: www.nunsarewe.org
Email: frances@stfrancis.org
Members: 70 Sisters (Colorado Springs Province)
Apostolic Work: Perpetual adoration of the Blessed Sacrament, ministry to the sick, the elderly, the poor; parish ministry; hospital chaplaincy; facilitation of individual and family wellness; and justice and peace work. In all ministry, special emphasis on working with women and children
Representation: Primarily the Archdioceses of Denver, Omaha and Sante Fe and the Dioceses of Colorado Springs, Grand Island and Lincoln
Vocation Director: Sister Frances Sedlacek, osf, Vocation Minister, (719) 955-7015

SISTERS OF ST. FRANCIS (W330)
OF PERPETUAL ADORATION (O.S.F.)
St. Francis Convent, 1515 Dragoon Trail, PO Box 766, Mishawaka, IN 46546-0766
Web: www.ssfpa.org
Email: srlois@yahoo.com
Members: 130 Sisters (in Province)
Apostolic Work: Perpetual adoration of the Blessed Sacrament, health-care, education and other ecclesial ministries
Representation: (Arch)dioceses of Fort Wayne-South Bend, Lafayette in Indiana, Gary, Indianapolis and Chicago
Vocation Director: Sr. Lois DeLee, O.S.F., (574) 259-5427

SISTERS OF ST. FRANCIS (W331)
OF PHILADELPHIA (O.S.F.) (Glen Riddle Franciscans), Our Lady of Angels Convent, 609 S. Convent Rd., Aston, PA 19014
Web: www.osfphila.org
Email: vocations@osfphila.org
Members: 625 Sisters
Conduct: Prayer ministry, health care, education (all levels), parish and diocesan ministry, spiritual and pastoral care; ministry with the homeless, the poor, persons with AIDS, immigrants and refugees; counseling, advocacy, leadership in national religious organizations, services to the elderly.
Apostolic Work: Committed to the needs of others, especially those who are economically poor, marginal and oppressed. Willing to take necessary risks to be a healing, compassionate presence in our violent world.
Representation: 24 states and in Africa, Ireland, and Puerto Rico
Vocation Director: East Coast Director: Sr. Mary Beth Antonelli, OSF, Our Lady of Angels Convent, 609 S. Convent Rd., Aston, PA 19014, (610) 558-6789, e-mail: vocations@osfphila.org
West Coast Directors: Sr. Patricia Novak, OSF, 2408 SE 16th Ave., Portland, OR 97214, (503) 233-1878, e-mail:srpatriciaosf@juno.com or vocations@osfphila.org

SISTERS OF ST. FRANCIS (W332)
OF THE PROVIDENCE OF GOD, PITTSBURGH (O.S.F.)
3603 McRoberts Rd., Pittsburgh, PA 15234-2398
Web: www.osfprov.org
Email: vocations@osfprov.org
Members: 85 Sisters in US, 145 Sisters worldwide
Apostolic Work: Education, child care, health care, social services, pastoral ministry, prison ministry, catechetical work, campus ministry, retreat and spiritual direction ministry
Representation: 6 dioceses in US. Also in Brazil, Bolivia and Lithuania
Vocation Director: Life Futuring Minister, (412) 885-7407

FRANCISCAN SISTERS (W332-1)
OF THE IMMACULATE, 8220 W. State Road 48, Bloomington, IN 47404, (812) 825-4642, ext. 240 or 825-1991
Web: www.marymediatrix.com
Email: materdomini@
bluemarble.net
Members: 10 Sisters, 1 Postulant, Novices in Italy
Apostolic Work: Mass Media

(publishing religious books, magazines, etc.), teaching, Marian catechism, distributing miraculous medals, rosaries, religious articles, animation of the liturgy and every technological advance, placed at the service of the Immaculate.
Vocation Director: Sr. Ma. Consolatrice Scozzare, 106 Bullard St., New Bedford, MA 02746

FRANCISCAN SISTERS OF (W333)
THE POOR (S.F.P.), US Area Office: 60 Compton Rd., Cincinnati, OH 45215-5105, 513-761-9040, 1-877-761-9040, fax: 513-761-6703, Email: sfpusarea@fuse.net
Web: www.franciscansisters.org
Email: vocations@franciscan sisters.org
Members: 155 Sisters
Apostolic Work: We are women who have heard the call from Christ to "heal my wounds in the poor and suffering." We walk in the footsteps of St. Francis of Assisi, committed to a Gospel way of life. An international congregation in the geographical areas of United States, Brazil, Italy and Senegal, we respond to people in need through our healing presence and diversity of gifts. Sisters in the United States are involved in pastoral/spiritual ministry, parish work, health care, social outreach and work directly with the poor and homeless. Prayer, contemplation and community are central to our lives. You are welcome to "come and see!"
Representation: Archdioceses of New York, Newark, Detroit and Cincinnati and in four dioceses in the United States. Present also in Brazil, Italy and Senegal.
Vocation Director: Vocation Minister: Sr. Arlene McGowan, SFP, 60 Compton Rd., Cincinnati, OH 45215-5199, (513) 761-9040, ext 112, vocations@franciscansisters.org

FRANCISCAN SISTERS OF (W334)
THE RENEWAL (C.F.R.), Our Lady Queen of Angels Convent, 232 E. 113th St., New York, NY 10029
Web: www.franciscansisterscfr.com
Apostolic Work: Evangelization and work with the very poor
Representation: Archdiocese of New York
Vocation Director: Sr. Francis Teresa O'Donnell, CFR, (212) 831-3334

FRANCISCAN SISTERS OF (W336)
ROCHESTER, MN (O.S.F.), 1001 14th St. NW, Ste. 100, Rochester, MN 55901-2525
Web: www.rochesterfranciscan.org
Email: ann.redig@myclearwave.net

Members: 279 Members, 96 Cojourners
Apostolic Work: We Franciscan Sisters and Cojourners(Associates) of Rochester, MN believe as St. Francis did: that we are all brothers and sisters, one family under God. With a rich spiritual heritage and the strength of prayer and community, we choose ministries guided by societal needs and the call to justice. You will find us across the United States and in Colombia, in inner cities and rural areas, responding to the call to justice and peace; we are teachers, nurses, spiritual directors, artists, writers, administrators, religious educators, counselors, social workers, therapists, and healers of creation. We believe in the empowerment of women and the worth and dignity of every person. We learn as we teach, are healed as we heal others and are changed as we pray and act with compassion. We hope to join with others in creating with compassion a just and loving global community.
Representation: Congregational Administrative Offices, Motherhouse and Retirement Center located in Rochester, Minnesota. Sisters minister in 19 States in the USA, in Bogota Colombia SA
Vocation Director: Ann Redig osf, Central Minister of Incorporation and Rochester Franciscan Life Teams (RFLT) 507-282-7441/ 1-888-277-4741

FRANCISCAN SISTERS OF (W337)
THE SACRED HEART (O.S.F.)
Motherhouse: St. Francis Woods 9201 W. St. Francis Rd., Frankfort, IL 60423-8335
Web: www.fssh.net
Email: vocations@fssh.net
Members: 105 Professed, 8 in Formation
Apostolic Work: Education, health care, parish ministry, retreat ministry, social services, spiritual direction and missions
Representation: Indiana, Illinois and California. Also in Brazil
Vocation Director: Sr. Lovina Francis Pammit, OSF, (815) 464-3873

FRANCISCAN SISTERS OF (W338)
SAINT ELIZABETH (F.S.S.E.)
Motherhouse: Rome
499 Park Rd., Parsippany, NJ 07054-1736
Web: www.franciscansisters.com
Email: sr_cathylynn@yahoo.com
Members: 55 Sisters in USA
Apostolic Work: (in US) 1 novitiate, 1 elementary school, 4 pre-schools, 1

early childhood Montessori school, 1 elementary Montessori school, 4 mission houses, 1 infirmary and parish work
Representation: Archdiocese of Newark and in the Dioceses of Paterson and St. Petersburg. Also, throughout Italy, Panama, India, Philippines, Ethiopia and Indonesia
Vocation Director: Contact: (973) 539-3797

FRANCISCAN SISTERS OF (W339)
ST. JOSEPH (H.F.S.J.)
Motherhouse: Mexico
Ave. Revolucion No. 431, Delegacion, Benito Juarez, Mexico, 3801
Members: 6 Sisters
Apostolic Work: Ministry in domestic areas
Vocation Director: Sister Concepcion Santiago, H.F.S.J.

FRANCISCAN SISTERS OF (W340)
ST. JOSEPH (F.S.S.J.), 5286 S. Park Ave., Hamburg, NY 14075
Web: www.franciscansisters hamburg.org
Members: 106 Sisters
Apostolic Work: Education on elementary and secondary levels, health care service, pastoral ministry and social services
Representation: Archdioceses of Baltimore, Detroit, Milwaukee and Washington, DC and Dioceses of Buffalo, Harrisburg, Springfield, and Trenton.
Vocation Director: Contact: (716) 649-1205

FRANCISCAN SISTERS OF (W341)
ST. PAUL, MN (O.S.F.)
Franciscan Regional Center, 1388 Prior Ave. S., St. Paul, MN 55116
Web: www.askmotherrose.org
Email: spfranci@askmotherrose.org
Members: 450 worldwide; 11 Sisters in US
Apostolic Work: We are committed to live the Gospel plainly and simply among the people, to serve each other in community, and be open to God's challenge, whatever the time and place, in actively relieving human suffering. We serve in multiple ministries abroad, and in the U.S. We minister in health care, education, and social services, especially among the poor. Prayer is the substance of our choice of life. We invite any woman between the ages of 21 and 40 who wishes to make this choice of life to accompany us on our journey.
Representation: Archdiocese of Minneapolis/St. Paul. Also in Germany, the Netherlands, and Brazil

Vocation Director: Vocation Directress, (651) 690-1501, fax: (651) 690-2509

SISTERS OF ST. FRANCIS (W342)
OF SAVANNAH, MO (O.S.F.)
Provincial House, LaVerna Heights, PO Box 488, 104 East Park, Savannah, MO 64485
Web: www.sistersofstfrancis.org
Email: osf@stjoelive.com
Members: 12 Professed Sisters
Apostolic Work: Education, nursing, CCD ministry, pastoral care, supportive ministries, peace and justice
Representation: Diocese of Kansas City-St. Joseph.
Vocation Director: S. Kathleen Reichert, (816) 324-3179

SISTERS OF SAINT FRANCIS (W343)
(O.S.F.), Leadership Office, 2500 Grant Blvd., Syracuse, NY 13208
Rooted in the gospel and energized by the spirit of St. Francis and St. Clare, we seek to be Women of Vision living in right relationship with God, one another, and all creation. Come, join us in our ministry to the People of God. Become a vowed Franciscan woman who spreads the good news of God's Love through ministry and message
Web: www.sosf.org
www.millvalefranciscans.org
Email: yesGodislove@juno.com, guidance@nauticom.net
Members: Over 500
Apostolic Work: Education (Infant to Post Graduate), Religious Education, Health Care, Child Care, Music Ministry, Art Ministry, Technology, Elder Care, Care of the Dying, Care of the Homeless, Care for the Earth, Peace and Justice, Clinical Psychology, Law, Theology, Pastoral Care, Spiritual Care, Retreat Ministry, Prayer Ministry, Social Ministry, Doctors
Representation: 28 dioceses including the Hawaiian Islands, Kenya, Peru, Puerto Rico, Canada
Vocation Director: Sister Jeanne F. Karp, OSF, (315) 727-3284; Sister Kathy Adamski, OSF, (412) 215-7708

FRANCISCAN SISTERS, (W345)
DAUGHTERS OF THE SACRED HEARTS OF JESUS AND MARY (Wheaton Franciscans) (O.S.F.)
Our Lady of the Angels Motherhouse PO Box 667, 26 W. 171 Roosevelt Rd., Wheaton, IL 60189-0667
Web: http://wheatonfranciscan.org/
Email: jford@wheatonfranciscan.org
Apostolic Work: The Sisters respond to the needs of our times, ministering in mutuality and partnership, and collaborating with other religious communities and lay partners in health, shelter and other human service ministries. Individual ministries are as diverse as the gifts that each Sister brings to community life
Representation: Archdioceses of Chicago, Denver, Dubuque, Milwaukee and St. Louis and in the Dioceses of Gary, Green Bay, Joliet, La Crosse, Rockford and Springfield-Cape Girardeau. Also in Brazil, Rome, France, Germany, Holland, Indonesia and Romania
Vocation Director: Sr. Jean Ford, OSF

SISTERS OF ST. FRANCIS (W346)
OF ASSISI (O.S.F.)
Motherhouse: St. Francis Convent 3221 South Lake Dr., Milwaukee, WI 53235-3799
Web: www.lakeofs.org
Email: vocdir@lakeofs.org
Members: 290 Sisters
Apostolic Work: Our Franciscan congregation is committed to bringing the teaching, healing, reconciling and liberating power of Jesus to every life we touch. We stand in solidarity with women, and those who are poor, oppressed and disenfranchised, promoting social justice and working for the preservation of the earth, harmony and world peace while seeking to deepen our Franciscan identity.Diverse ministries include: administrators; teachers; health care providers; social workers and counselors; campus, prison and parish ministers; childcare workers; artists and musicians.
Representation: Dioceses across the US and Taiwan
Vocation Director: (414) 744-1160

SCHOOL SISTERS OF THE (W348)
THIRD ORDER OF ST. FRANCIS, UNITED STATES PROVINCE (O.S.F.)
Provincial Office: Mount Assisi Convent, Pittsburgh, PA, 934 Forest Ave., Pittsburgh, PA 15202
Web: www.franciscansisters-pa.org
Email: vocationsosf@gmail.com
Members: 98 Sisters in US Province
Apostolic Work: Pastoral ministry, teaching (early childhood, elementary, secondary, adult education), prayer and retreat ministry, nursing, youth ministry, religious education, parish social services, home for the aged, counseling, clerical work, missionary work, ministry to Hispanics and Native Americans in Southwest, other works corresponding to the gifts of the members
Representation: Archdioceses of Newark, Philadelphia, and San Antonio and the Dioceses of Allentown, Erie, Greensburg, Manchester, Metuchen, Paterson, Pittsburgh, Phoenix, San Angelo, Springfield, Trenton, and Tucson. Also missions in Chile and South Africa. Delegation of sisters in Trichur, India, and Central Asia. Generalate in Rome, Italy; Provinces in Slovak Republic, Czech Republic, Italy and United States
Vocation Director: Sister Frances Marie Duncan, OSF, 934 Forest Ave., Pittsburgh,PA 15202, (412) 761-6004

(W349)
SCHOOL SISTERS OF ST. FRANCIS (The Panhandle Franciscans) (O.S.F.)
Motherhouse: Vienna
North American Region
Third Region: Argentina
Sancta Maria Convent, PO Box 906, Panhandle, TX 79068
Web: www.panhandlefranciscans.org
Email: schsrs@gmail.com
Members: 24 Sisters
Apostolic Work: Catholic schools, faith formation, youth groups, nursing home
Representation: Diocese of Amarillo
Vocation Director: Sister Mary Michael Huseman, O.S.F., (806) 537-3182

SCHOOL SISTERS OF (W350)
ST. FRANCIS (OSF)
US Province, 1515 S. Layton Blvd., Milwaukee, WI 53215
Web: usp.sssf.org
Email: vocations@sssf.org
Members: 650 Sisters (US Province)
Apostolic Work: Education, health care, pastoral ministry, social service, the arts, sponsorship of institutions
Representation: An international community of Franciscan sisters in service to the people of God in dioceses throughout the United States, Latin America, Europe and India
Vocation Director: Vocation Ministers, (414) 385-5253 or 384-1515, fax: (414) 384-1950

SISTERS OF ST. FRANCIS (W351)
(O.S.F.), 6832 Convent Blvd., Sylvania, OH 43560-2897
Web: www.sistersosf.org
Email: gnowak@sistersosf.org
Members: 205 Professed Sisters
Apostolic Work: Religious and academic education at all levels (elementary through college), health care, parish ministries, retreat work, social services, missions (Haiti)
Representation: Archdioceses of Cincinnati, Detroit, New Orleans, St. Paul-Minneapolis and the Dioceses

of Austin, Biloxi, Cleveland, Columbus, Fort Wayne, Gallup, Lansing, Raleigh, Richmond, St. Cloud, Steubenville, Toledo and Wheeling
Vocation Director: Sr. Geraldine Nowak, OSF, (419) 824-3914

SISTERS OF ST. FRANCIS (W352)
OF THE HOLY EUCHARIST (O.S.F.)
2100 N. Noland Rd., Independence, MO 64050
Web: www.osfholyeucharist.org
Email: stfran2100@aol.com
Members: 16 Sisters
Apostolic Work: Spiritual direction, retreat work, teaching on Scripture/New Catechism; academic education - all levels; social service, collaboration with the laity, outreach to the poor including shipments of relief goods to foreign countries.
Representation: Dioceses of Kansas City-St. Joseph, MO
Vocation Director: Sister Andrea Kantner, O.S.F, 816-252-1673

SISTERS OF ST. FRANCIS (W353)
OF PENANCE AND CHRISTIAN CHARITY (OSF), Holy Name Province, 4421 Lower River Rd., Stella Niagara, NY 14144-1001, (716) 754-4312, Ext. 9701
Web: www.franciscans-stella-niagara.org
Email: annmcd@miamiarch.org
Members: 192 Sisters, 65 Associates
Apostolic Work: Education (all levels), health care, foreign/home missions, parish ministry, retreat work, social work, homeless ministry, Hispanic ministry, small Christian communities, lay ministry formation, rural ministry, L'Arche community, refugee ministry, spiritual companionship
Representation: (Arch)dioceses of Buffalo, Chicago, Cincinnati, Columbus, Louisville, Miami, Orlando, Paterson, St. Petersburg, Sante Fe, Trenton and Wheeling-Charleston. Also in Chiapas (Mexico) and Tanzania.
Vocation Director: Sister Ann McDermott, osf, 1238 Funston St., Hollywood, FL 33019, (954) 925-5875

SISTERS OF ST. FRANCIS (W354)
OF PENANCE AND CHRISTIAN CHARITY (O.S.F.), Sacred Heart Province, 2851 W. 52nd Ave., Denver, CO 80221
Web: www.marycrest.org
Email: patty@marycrest.org
Members: 53 Sisters
Conduct: 2 assisted living facilities: 1 for the elderly and 1 for younger persons with physical disabilities and/or AIDS; 1 foster home on Pine

Ridge Reservation; Wisdom Center
Apostolic Work: Education, parish work, pastoral care, work among Native Americans on one reservation; social ministries with very young, the aging and prisoners; Hispanic outreach, artistry, spiritual formation/direction; outreach to Vietnam
Representation: Archdioceses of Denver, Omaha and Kansas City and the Dioceses of Grand Island, Rapid City. Also in Chiapas, Mexico and Tanzania
Vocation Director: Sr. Patty Podhaisky, osf, New Membership Director, (303) 458-6270, ext. 122 and Sr. Colleen Mahony, osf, (303) 458-6270, ext. 131

SISTERS OF ST. FRANCIS (W355)
OF PENANCE AND CHRISTIAN CHARITY, Redwood City Franciscans, 1330 Brewster Ave., Redwood City, CA 94062
Members: 105 Sisters
Apostolic Work: Elementary and secondary education, pastoral ministry in parishes, administration, Catholic social services, residence for retired women and men, marriage tribunal ministry, religious education; Reiki, massage, Qigong and Shiatsu practitioners; bilingual education, Hispanic ministry, psychological counseling, peace and justice ministry, refugee ministry, health care ministry, teaching English as a Second Language (ESL), work with indigenous women
Representation: Archdioceses of Los Angeles, Portland, San Francisco and Seattle and the Dioceses of Oakland, Phoenix, Reno-Las Vegas and Sacramento. Also in Chiapas (Mexico) and Tanzania
Vocation Director: Sr. Carole Snyder, OSF, (650) 369-1725

SISTERS OF ST. FRANCIS, (W356-1)
TIFFIN, OHIO (O.S.F.)
St. Francis Convent, 200 St. Francis Ave., Tiffin, OH 44883-3458
Web: www.tiffinfranciscans.org
Email: osftiffin@tiffinfranciscans.org
Members: 110 Sisters, 56 Associates
Apostolic Work: Education, health care, pastoral work, parish ministry, child care, care of elderly, social work, earth literacy, retreat and renewal programs, diocesan offices, ministry to the people of Appalachia and to Hispanics
Representation: (Arch)dioceses of Charlotte, Columbus, Lansing, Lexington, Milwaukee, Owensboro, Santa Fe, Toledo, Wheeling-Charleston and in the Diocese of San Cristobal (Mexico) and

Cuernavaca (Mexico).
Vocation Director: Director of Vocation Ministry, (419) 447-0435

SISTERS OF THE THIRD (W357-1)
ORDER OF ST. FRANCIS (O.S.F.)
1175 St. Francis Ln., East Peoria, IL 61611-1299
Web: www.franciscansisters peoria.org
Email: vocation.info@osfhealth care.org
Apostolic Work: Health care and education
Representation: Dioceses of Peoria and Rockford, IL and Marquette, MI
Vocation Director: Sister Agnes Joseph, O.S.F., 740 NE Glen Oak Ave., Peoria, IL 61603 (309) 655-4840

THE LITTLE PORTION (W357-2)
FRANCISCAN SISTERS (O.S.F.)
645 Assisi Way, Republic, MO 65738
Web: www.littleportionfranciscan sisters.org
Email: lportion@juno.com
Members: 3 Sisters
Apostolic Work: We strive to be a healing presence to the poor through our ministry at the Kitchen Inc, where we provide shelter, transitional housing, case management, free medical and dental care, emergency care to prevent homelessness, educational programs for GED and life skill classes. At our Little Portion Retreat Center we provide solitude and reflection for individuals and groups.
Representation: Diocese of Springfield-Cape Girardeau
Vocation Director: Contact: (417) 732-6684

GLENMARY SISTERS (W358)
(G.H.M.S.), The Glenmary Center 405 W. Parrish Ave., PO Box 22264, Owensboro, KY 42304-2264
Web: www.glenmarysisters.org
Email: srsharon@glenmary sisters.org
Apostolic Work: Founded in 1941, the Glenmary Sisters work in the rural areas of the deep South and Appalachia. They are radically involved with the issue of injustice, spiritual and material poverty and the rights of the downtrodden. The Sisters let the people know that they and their Catholic Christian communities do care
Representation: Dioceses of Owensboro, Lexington, Savannah, and Springfield-Cape Girardeau
Vocation Director: Sr. Sharon Miller, G.H.M.S., PO Box 22264, Owensboro, KY 42304 (270) 686-8401

GOOD SHEPHERD SISTERS (W361)
160 Conover Road,
Wickatunk, NJ 07765
Web: www.goodshepherdsisters.org
Email: gsvocny@optonline.net
Apostolic Work: We, the Good
Shepherd Sisters, are an international apostolic and contemplative
congregation, numbering around
5,000, with communities in 71
countries throughout the world. Our
mission is one of reconciliation. We
believe that, "One person is of more
value than a world." Through our
prayer and ministry, we strive to
model our lives after the heart of
Jesus, the Good Shepherd, who left
the 99 to respond to the one in
special need. Our apostolic work
includes a variety of human
services, primarily social work and
social justice advocacy, with a
particular focus on women and
children. Our contemplative prayer
strives to bring the liberating love of
Jesus, the Good Shepherd, to all of
God's people.
Representation: Throughout
numerous states and provinces in
the United States and Canada, as
well as located on 5 continents in 71
countries
Vocation Director: Vocation Contacts:
Sr. Adrienne F. Baker, 5100
Hodgson Rd., St. Paul, MN 55126,
651-482-5245, abake@hgsmn.net

Sr. Barbara Beasley, 1819 Newburg
Rd., Louisville, KY 40205, 502-742-
3744, b.beasley@earthlink.net

Christine Alvarez, 160 Conover Rd.,
Wickatunk, NJ 07765, 732-946-
0515, gsvocny@optonline.net

Sr. Gilda Fernando, 25 Good
Shepherd Court, Toronto, Ont., M6B
4E7, 416-787-4285,
gildafernando@hotmail.com

Sr. Claudia Palacio, 1114 W. Grace
St., Chicago, IL 60613, 773-935-
3434, palacioc@comcast.net

Sr. Frances Marie Ellul, 4140 Maple
Ave., Baltimore, MD 21227, 410-
247-1485 ell4franc@aol.com

GREY NUNS OF MONTREAL (W362)
See "C" - Charity of Montreal, Sisters
of

GREY NUNS OF THE (W363)
SACRED HEART (G.N.S.H.)
(Motherhouse), 1750 Quarry Rd.,
Yardley, PA 19067-3998,
(215) 968-4236
Web: www.greynun.org
Email: jdaly@greynun.org
Members: 128 Vowed Members
Apostolic Work: Education, health

care, social work, pastoral ministry,
spiritual direction, religious educa-
tion, ministry on behalf of the poor
Representation: Archdioceses of
Anchorage, Atlanta, Baltimore, NY,
and Philadelphia and the Dioceses
of Brooklyn, Buffalo, Camden,
Ogdensburg, Port-Au-Prince, Haiti,
Rochester, Rockville Centre, and
Trenton.
Vocation Director: Sr. Joan Daly,
GNSH, Grey Nuns Motherhouse,
1750 Quarry Rd., Yardley, PA
19067, (215) 968-4236

GUANELLIAN SISTERS (W364)
See "D" - Daughters of St. Mary of
Providence

SISTERS OF THE GUARDIAN (W365)
ANGEL (S.A.C.), Motherhouse: Madrid
US Foundation, 4529 New York St.,
Los Angeles, CA 90022
Web: www.planalfa.es/confer
Email: hilfranca@hotmail.com
Members: 559 Sisters worldwide
Apostolic Work: Social/pastoral work,
helping the sick and elderly,
education and the missions
Representation: Archdiocese of Los
Angeles. Also in Bolivia, Colombia,
Ecuador, El Salvador, France,
Germany, Guinea, Italy, Ivory Coast,
Japan, Mali, Mexico, Nicaragua, the
Philippines, Spain and Venezuela
Vocation Director: (323) 266-4431

HANDMAIDS OF THE (W367)
PRECIOUS BLOOD (HPB)
Motherhouse, Cor Jesu Monastery,
PO Box 90, Jemez Springs, NM
87025
Members: 23 Professed Sisters, 1
Sister in First Vows
Apostolic Work: Contemplative life of
Perpetual Eucharistic Adoration for
the sanctification of priests and
needs of the entire world
Representation: Archdioceses of
Santa Fe and Chicago.
Vocation Director: Rev. Mother
Marietta, HPB, Mother Prioress,
(505) 829-3906

HANDMAIDS OF REPARATION (W368)
OF THE SACRED HEART OF JESUS
(A.R), Sacred Heart Villa, 36 Villa Dr.,
Steubenville, OH 43953
Members: 6 Sisters in US, 230
worldwide
Apostolic Work: Education - all levels,
parish and diocesan ministry, CCD,
orphanages and missionary work in
Africa, Brazil, Poland and Ukraine
Representation: Dioceses of Arlington
and Steubenville
Vocation Director: Sister Mary
Ernestine Vitello, A.R., Superior,
740-282-3801

HANDMAIDS OF THE (W369)
SACRED HEART OF JESUS (a.c.j.)
US Provincial Residence, 616
Coopertown Rd., Haverford, PA 30345
Web: www.be-a-nun.org
Email: acjoasis@gmail.com
Members: 30 Sisters in US; 1,400
Sisters in 24 countries
Apostolic Work: The Sisters are
called to minister as agents of
reconciliation building bridges of
understanding, appreciation and
love among cultures, faith traditions,
social status and God, fostering
wholeness and holiness through
nurturing spiritual growth and human
development. They serve in schools
parishes, social work agencies,
hospitals, retreat centers, immigrant
outreach centers, etc.
Representation: (Arch)dioceses of
Philadelphia, Atlanta, and Miami as
well as Latin America, Africa, Asia,
India, Ireland, Great Britain, Europe
and the Philippines.
Vocation Director: Sr. Margarita
Martin, acj, Pine Wood Estates
North, 1465 Hwy. 29N, Lot G-21,
Athens, GA 30601, (706) 714-6624.

HERMANAS CATEQUISTAS (W370)
GUADALUPANAS (H.C.G.)
Mexican Foundation
Motherhouse: Mexico
American Regional Delegation, 4110
S. Flores St., San Antonio, TX 78214
Members: 17 Sisters in US
Apostolic Work: Missions, evangeli-
zation, catechesis. Pastoral work in
parishes, rural areas, schools
Representation: Archdioceses of
Oklahoma City and San Antonio and
the Diocese of Fort Worth
Vocation Director: Sister Virginia
Clara Ruiz, HCG

HERMANAS JOSEFINAS (W371-1)
(H.J.), Motherhouse: Mexico
Seminario de La Asuncion
US Foundation, 3203 W. Ashby
Place, San Antonio, TX 78228
Email: cdsamagu@sbcglobal.com
Members: 4 Sisters, Comunidad
Seminario de La Asuncion
10 Sisters, Comunidad Casa
Delegacion,"Santa Maria de
Guadalupe", 2622 W. Summit Ave.,
San Antonio, TX, 78228
13 Sisters, Comunidad Casa de
Oracion San Jose, 402 John Adams
Dr., San Antonio, TX, 78228
Representation: Archdioceses of
Chicago and San Antonio

HERMITAGE OF THE (W371-2)
ADVENT, 215 Highland St.,
Marshfield, MA 02050
Web: www.hermitage-ofthe-
advent.org

Email: hermitage@verizon.net
Apostolic Work: Contemplative monastic community in formation
Vocation Director: Contact: (781) 319-6688

HERMIT SISTER OF (W371-3)
ST. ROMUALD
Prayer Mountain Hermitage
Contact: Sr. Mary Vogel, H.S.S.R. 10089 ACR 404, Palestine, TX 75803
Apostolic Work: Contemplative prayer

SOCIETY OF THE HOLY (W372)
CHILD JESUS (S.H.C.J.)
(American Province) Provincial House, 460 Shadeland Ave., Drexel Hill, PA 19026-2312
Web: www.vocations.shcj.org
Email: ctorres@shcj.org
Members: 196 Sisters
Apostolic Work: Founded in 1846, we are an international community of women religious. Our mission is "to help others to believe God lives and acts in them and in our world, and to rejoice in God's presence." Our life of prayer and community strengthens us for a variety of spiritual, educational, pastoral, social service, legal, and healthcare ministries. We sponsor 15 schools, one college, and several social service ministries. Cornelia Connelly, our foundress, exhorted her sisters "to meet the wants of the age."
Representation: Europe, South America, Chile, Dominican Republic, and the United States:California, Colorado, Connecticut, District of Columbia, Florida, Illinois, Louisiana, Maryland, Massachusetts, Nevada, New Jersey, New York, North Carolina, Oregon, Pennsylvania, and Wisconsin
Vocation Director: Carmen Torres, SHCJ, (610) 626-1400, ext. 304

HOLY CROSS SISTERS (W373)
1400 O'Day Street, Merrill, WI 54452
Web: www.holycrosssisters.org
Email: kwiesneski@holycross
sisters.org
Members: 40 Sisters, 43 Associates (US); over 4,400 worldwide
Apostolic Work: All the Works of Mercy inspired by the motto: "The need of the times is the will of God".
Representation: Archdiocese of Cincinnati, Detroit, Milwaukee, Minneapolis-St. Paul, New Orleans, Washington D.C. and in Diocese of Gaylord, La Crosse, Lansing, Owensboro, Steubenville and Superior. Also in Switzerland
Vocation Director: Sister Kathy Wiesneski, (715) 539-1460

Co-Directors of Associate Program: Sr. Helen Huss and Carol Mancl, (715) 539-1460

SISTERS OF THE HOLY (W374)
CROSS (CSC), Generalate
Saint Mary's, 103 Center Bldg., Notre Dame, IN 46556
Web: www.cscsisters.org
Email: pwelch@cscsisters.org, vocations@cscsisters.org
Members: 549 Sisters, 21 Temporarily Professed, 14 Novices, 13 Candidates
Apostolic Work: Education, health care, parish, retreats, social service, work for justice
Representation: in the United States, Mexico, Brazil, Peru, Ghana, Uganda, Bangladesh and India
Vocation Director: Sister Pam Welch, CSC, 574-284-5560

SISTERS OF HOLY (W375)
CROSS (C.S.C.), US Regional Office
377 Island Pond Rd., Manchester, NH 03109-4811
Web: www.sistersofholycross.org
Email: paulette3087@comcast.net
Members: 168 Sisters in US; 895 worldwide (international congregation)
Apostolic Work: Educators for Liberation: teachers, principals, librarians, pastoral ministry, directors of religious education, hospital ministry; prison ministry, AIDS ministry, private adoption agency and more
Representation: Dioceses of Manchester, Burlington, and St. Petersburg. Also in Canada, Bangladesh, Chile, Mali, Peru and Haiti
Vocation Director: Sr. Fran (Francoise) DeMers, CSC, (603) 622-9504, fax: (603) 622-9782

CONGREGATION OF THE (W376)
SISTERS OF THE HOLY FAITH
(C.H.F.), US Region, 12322 Paramount Blvd., Downey, CA 90242, (562) 869-6092
Web: www.holyfaithsisters.net
Email: shfaith@aol.com
Members: 35 Sisters
Conduct: 9 grammar schools, 2 high schools, religious education directors, pastoral associates, social work, R.C.I.A. directors, ministry directors, parish sisters, spiritual directors, counselors, Margaret Aylward Center for the Poor
Representation: Archdioceses of Los Angeles, New Orleans and San Francisco and the Diocese of Sacramento. Also in Ireland, Trinidad, New Zealand, and Australia
Vocation Director: New Membership: Sr. Liz Curtis, 1053 N. Texas St., Fairfield, CA 94533, (707) 425-3572

Corporate Ministry of Sisters of the Holy Faith: Margaret Aylward Center, 4270 Acacia Ave., Pico Rivera, CA 90660

CONGREGATION OF THE (W378)
SISTERS OF THE HOLY FAMILY OF NAZARETH (C.S.F.N.), 310 N. River Road, Des Plaines, IL 60016
Web: www.nazarethfamily.org
Email: Voc4Naz@aol.com
Members: 1500 internationally
Apostolic Work: Ministry to families in all levels of education, healthcare, child care, retirement and nursing homes, parish ministry, youth ministry, religious education, retreat ministry, inner-city ministries, prison ministry
Representation: Illinois, Massachusetts, Michigan, New York, New Jersey, Pennsylvania, Puerto Rico, Texas
Vocation Director: Sister Michele Vincent Fisher, CSFN, 2723 Holme Ave., Philadelphia, PA 19152, (215) 335-6387

CONGREGATION OF THE (W382)
SISTERS OF THE HOLY FAMILY
(S.S.F.), 6901 Chef Menteur Hwy., New Orleans, LA 70126
Web: www.sistersoftheholyfamily.org
Email: sylviathib@aol.com
Members: 140 Sisters
Apostolic Work: Education at elementary and secondary levels, nursing home, apartments for the elderly/disabled/handicapped, day care centers, pastoral/social service
Representation: Archdioceses of New Orleans and Washington (DC) and the Dioceses of Galveston-Houston, and Lafayette (LA) . Also in Belize, Central America
Vocation Director: Sr. Theresa Sue Joseph, S.S.F., Vocation Director; Sr. Eva Regina Martin, Congregational Leader, (504) 256-0036

SISTERS OF THE HOLY (W383)
FAMILY (S.H.F.), PO Box 3248, Fremont, CA 94539
Web: www.holyfamilysisters.org
Email: vocations@holyfamily
sisters.org
Members: 97 Sisters, 64 Associates
Apostolic Work: Religious education classes, teacher training for laity, parish home visiting, parent education, family programs, youth ministry programs, pastoral care (hospital chaplains, bereaved and infirm), parish pastoral administrators, social service/social workers, home health care, child and family counselors, director of worship, religious education classes for developmentally disabled children, diocesan religious education

directors and coordinators, and day care for pre-school children
Representation: (Sisters) Archdioceses of Anchorage, Los Angeles, San Francisco and San Antonio, and in the Dioceses of Honolulu, Fresno, Monterey, Oakland, Reno, Sacramento, San Diego, San Jose, Las Vegas, and Stockton (Associates – Men and women who, in the midst of their ordinary lives, feel drawn to the mission of Jesus in the spirit and charism of the Sisters of the Holy Family) Arizona, California, Florida, Missouri, New Mexico, South Dakota and Utah
Vocation Director: Sr. Gladys Guenther, S.H.F., (510) 624-4595

SISTERS OF THE HOLY (W385)
NAMES OF JESUS AND MARY (S.N.J.M.), US-Ontario Province Administrative Center, Portland, OR 97212
Web: www.snjm.org
Email: everettsnjm@earthlink.net
Members: 683 Sisters; 381 Associates
Conduct: Ministries: Education in pre-school through college; religious education; parish ministry; pastoral care in hospitals; counseling; retreat work; campus ministry; healthcare; migrant ministry; social work; various ministries to the disadvantaged; community organizers; social justice advocacy. Ministry in CA, OR, WA, NY and Ontario; missionary work in Central and South America, and Southern Africa. Associate and volunteer opportunities for women and men.
Apostolic Work: Education in pre-school through college; religious education; parish ministry; pastoral care in hospitals; counseling; retreat work; campus ministry; healthcare; migrant ministry; social work; various ministries to the disadvantaged; community organizers; social justice advocacy. Ministry in CA, OR, WA, NY and Canada; missionary work in Central and South America, Southern Africa. Associate and volunteer opportunities for women and men.
Representation: Represented in the (Arch)dioceses of Los Angeles, San Francisco, Oakland, San Jose, Orange, Monterey, San Bernardino in CA; Seattle, Spokane, and Yakima in WA; Portland and Baker in OR; Albany, New York; Orlando, St. Petersburg, Venice, and Palm Beach in FL; S. Paul-Minneapolis; Baltimore, MD; Bland, VA; Jackson, MS; Washington, D.C.; Detroit, and London ,Ontario.
Vocation Director: Sister Rosemary Everett, SNJM, 10364 B Vista Dr., Cupertino, CA 95014-2039

SISTERS OF THE HOLY (W388)
REDEEMER (CSR), American Province, 521 Moredon Rd., Huntingdon Valley, PA 19006
Web: www.SistersHoly Redeemer.org
Email: vocations@holyredeemer .com
Members: 31 Sisters in US, 600 worldwide
Apostolic Work: Over 150 years ago, Mother Alphonse Maria Eppinger desired to bring the healing presence and compassion of the Redeemer to those who suffer in body, mind and spirit. Today, her vision is realized in Germany, Tanzania and in the US. Our sisters deeply value community life, embodied through sharing our lives, our prayer and our ministry. Sponsors of Holy Redeemer Health System, we serve Jesus as advocates of the poor, the sick, the elderly and homeless women and children through health care, social services and pastoral care. Discernment opportunities: Long Distance Contact Program for women living at a distance and unable to visit regularly; Affiliate Program provides a deeper connection with community and an experience of religious spirituality for women continuing the discernment process.
Vocation Director: Vocation Ministry Office, (215) 914-4114, 914-4109

SISTERS OF THE MOST (W389)
HOLY SACRAMENT (M.H.S.)
See "M" - Most Holy Sacrament, Sisters of the

HOLY SPIRIT ADORATION (W390)
SISTERS (Sister Servants of the Holy Spirit of Perpetual Adoration) S.Sp.S.A.P., Mount Grace Convent 1438 E. Warne Ave., St. Louis, MO 63107
Web: www.mountgraceconvent.org
Email: mountgrace@sbcglobal.net
Members: 67 Sisters in US
Conduct: Contemplative life
Apostolic Work: Perpetual Adoration of the Most Blessed Sacrament exposed in the monstrance day and night
Representation: Archdiocese of Philadelphia and in the Dioceses of Corpus Christi and Lincoln. Also, in the Philippine Islands, Argentina, Germany, Holland, India, Brazil, Poland, Togo, Indonesia, Chile, and Slovakia
Vocation Director: Sr. Mary Gemma, (314) 381-2654

HOLY SPIRIT MISSIONARY (W391)
SISTERS (S.Sp.S.), (Provincial House) Convent of the Holy Spirit

PO Box 6026, Techny, IL 60082-6026 An international community of 3,600 women called to witness to the presence and power of the Holy Spirit, and to continue the saving mission of Jesus Christ.
Web: www.ssps-usa.org
Email: sspsovm@aol.com
Members: 90 Sisters in the US
Apostolic Work: In schools from preschool through university; in technical and professional schools; in hospitals as administrators, physicians, nurses, technicians, dietitians, and chaplains; involved with the elderly and the marginalized; in parishes in religious education and youth ministry; in spiritual direction, retreat work, counseling and social work
Representation: 46 countries: Angola, Antigua (West Indies), Argentina, Australia, Austria, Benin, Bolivia, Botswana, Brazil, Chile, China, Cuba, Czech Republic, England, Ethiopia, Germany, Ghana, India, Indonesia, Ireland, Italy, Japan, Korea, Mexico, Mondovia, Mozambique, Netherlands, Papua New Guinea, Paraguay, Philippines, Poland, Portugal, Romania, Russia, Slovakia, South Africa, South Korea, Spain, St. Kitts, Switzerland, Taiwan, Togo, Ukraine, USA, Vietnam, Zambia
Vocation Director: Vocation Ministry: Sr. Agathe Bramkamp, SSpS, Office of Vocation Ministry, 319 Waukegan Rd., Northfield, IL 60093, (847) 441-0126, ext. 704

MISSION SISTERS OF THE (W392)
HOLY SPIRIT (MSSp), Motherhouse, 1030 N. River Rd., Saginaw, MI 48609
Members: 7 Professed Sisters
Apostolic Work: Religious education, social work, pastoral ministry, pastoral administrators
Representation: Diocese of Saginaw
Vocation Director: Sr. Mary Lou Owczarzak, MSSp, President, (989) 781-0934

SISTERS OF THE HOLY (W393)
SPIRIT (S.H.S.), 5246 Clarwin Ave., Pittsburgh, PA 15229
Web: www.sistersoftheholyspirit.com
Email: mjuras2003@libcom.com
Members: 50 Sisters
Apostolic Work: Teaching, retreat ministry, geriatric care, nursing and nursing education, administration, business, social services, pastoral ministry, formation ministry, youth ministry, ministry to the poor, the arts. Open to emerging needs
Representation: Diocese of Pittsburgh
Vocation Director: Sister Marita Juras, SHS, 4736 Friendship Ave., Pittsburgh, PA 15224, (412) 683-2044

SISTERS OF THE HOLY (W394)
SPIRIT (C.S.Sp.), 10102 Granger Rd., Garfield Heights, OH 44125
Email: sisterpatricia.raelene@jenningscenter.org
Members: 12 Sisters
Apostolic Work: Elementary and secondary education; nursing, nursing home administration, dietary supervision, medical records, physical therapy, occupational therapy, related health care services, pastoral ministry, other service areas according to the needs of the Church and the particular talents of the community
Representation: Diocese of Cleveland
Vocation Director: Sr. Patricia Raelene, C.S.Sp., (216) 581-2941 or (216) 978-1110

SISTERS OF THE HOLY (W395)
SPIRIT AND MARY IMMACULATE (S.H.Sp.), Motherhouse Holy Spirit Convent, 301 Yucca St., San Antonio, TX 78203
Web: www.shsp.org
Email: sghession@hotmail.com
Members: 98 Sisters
Apostolic Work: Minister with the poor and marginated in schools, catechetical centers, social services, parish ministry, health care, home for the aged
Representation: (Arch)dioceses of San Antonio, Dallas, Fort Worth, Brownsville, Galveston-Houston, New Orleans, Houma-Thibodaux, Lafayette, Biloxi, Jackson and Shreveport. Also in Nayarit and Oaxaca (Mexico) and Zambia (Africa)
Vocation Director: Sister Gabriel Hession, SHSp, (210) 533-5140 or 5149, fax: (210) 533-3434

HOLY UNION SISTERS (W396)
(SUSC) (US PROVINCE)
US Province, PO Box 410, Milton, MA 02186-0006, 617-696-8765, fax: 617-696-8571
Web: www.holyunionsisters.org
Email: huvocations@juno.com
Members: 145 Sisters
Apostolic Work: Education, pastoral ministry, social services, spiritual development, health care
Representation: Florida, Kentucky, Maryland, Massachusetts, Michigan, New York, Pennsylvania, Rhode Island Tennessee and Virginia. Also in Argentina, Belgium, Cameroon, Chile, England, France, Haiti, Ireland, Italy, Scotland, Tanzania and Wales
Vocation Director: Coordinator of Vocations/Formation, 14 Main St., Groton, MA 01450-1450

SISTERS, HOME VISITORS (W398-1)
OF MARY (H.V.M.), 121 East Boston Blvd., Detroit, MI 48202-1318
Email: homevisitors@att.net
Members: 21 Sisters
Apostolic Work: A religious community founded in 1949, and dedicated to the mission of serving Christ among people in the heart of the city. Pastoral ministry, evangelization, lay leadership development, retreat work, small Christian community development, human relations seminars, Life Streams Spirituality Center; nurturing body, mind, and spirit; aids counseling.
Representation: Archdiocese of Detroit and Abuja, Nigeria, West Africa
Vocation Director: Sr. Laura Marie Kendrick, HVM, (313) 869-2160, (313) 297-6550

FRANCISCAN HOSPITAL (W398-2)
SISTERS (OSF) (Hospital Sisters of the Third Order of St. Francis)
American Province: St. Francis Convent, 4849 LaVerna Rd., PO Box 19431, Springfield, IL 62794
Web: www.franciscansatspfld.org
Email: joschulte@hsosf-usa.org
Members: 118 Sisters in the American Province, 1,132 Sisters Worldwide
Conduct: 13 hospitals, retreat and conference center in Illinois and Wisconsin. Mission Outreach (recycles medical equipment from US hospitals to send to developing countries)
Apostolic Work: Healing ministries including nursing, social work, home healthcare, therapy, parish ministry pastoral care and administration
Representation: International congregation with sisters in Poland, Germany, Japan, and India. Missions in Haiti and Tanzania.
Vocation Director: Membership Invitation Ministers: Sisters Mary Jo Schulte and Marguerite Cook

CONGREGATION OF THE (W400)
HUMILITY OF MARY (C.H.M.)
820 W. Central Park, Davenport, IA 52804-1900
Web: www.chmiowa.org
Email: ramonak1@juno.com
Members: 140 Sisters, 86 Associates
Apostolic Work: Education: teaching and administration; pastoral ministry/religious education; social services: homeless and abused persons, substance abuse rehabilitation; other individual ministries: law, communications, artist, health services, ministry to the elderly,

retreat and prayer ministry, multi-cultural ministries, music ministry, prison ministry, neighborhood ministries
Vocation Director: Sister Ramona Kaalberg, C.H.M., Coordinator of Formation, (515) 282-3521

SISTERS OF THE HUMILITY (W401)
OF MARY (H.M.), Motherhouse, Villa Maria Community Center, PO Box 522, Villa Maria, PA 16155-0522, (724) 964-8861
Web: www.humilityofmary.org
Email: tlardie@hmministry.org, crose@hmministry.org
Members: 183 Sisters, 65 Associates
Apostolic Work: Diversified ministries, including education at all levels, health care, parish ministry, retreat ministry, spiritual direction, evangelization, social services, work for justice and peace, and prayer
Representation: Primarily in the dioceses of Cleveland, Pittsburgh and Youngstown. Also minister in smaller numbers in the Archdiocese of Cincinnati and in the Dioceses of Arlington, Erie, Grand Island, Lansing, Lexington, Palm Beach, Richmond, Toledo, Tucson, and Wheeling-Charleston. Also in Haiti.
Vocation Director: Sr. Toby Lardie, HM and Sr. Cheryl Rose, HM, 20015 Detroit Rd., Rocky River, OH, 44116-2418, (440) 356-5711

I.C.M. MISSIONARY (W402-1)
SISTERS (I.C.M.) (Missionary Sisters of the Immaculate Heart of Mary)
238 E. 15th St., Apt. 5, New York, NY 10003-3901
Email: icmusdist@juno.com
Members: 17 Sisters in US, 897 worldwide
Apostolic Work: Sisters involved in various forms of educational, pastoral, social, health care ministries and ecology. Similar ministries in foreign missions
Representation: 11 mission posts in the US Archdioceses of Los Angeles and New York and the Diocese of Brownsville, 121 communities overseas in 14 different countries of Africa, Asia, Europe and Latin America
Vocation Director: Sr. Tellie Lape, ICM, (212) 677-2959

IDENTE MISSIONARIES (W402-2)
OF CHRIST THE REDEEMER (Foundation of Christ the Redeemer) (M.Id.), 143-48 84th Dr., Briarwood, NY 11435-2232
Email: elaine.schenk@verizon.net
Members: 400 Sisters

Apostolic Work: Spiritual direction, campus ministry, catechesis, parish work, youth ministry
Representation: New York. Also in Europe, the Far East, Cameroon, Chad and in most South American countries
Vocation Director: Sr. Elaine Schenk, M.Id., (718) 526-3595, fax: (718) 526-9632

SISTERS OF THE (W404)
IMMACULATE CONCEPTION (R.C.M.) Delegation House, 2230 Franklin St., San Francisco, CA 94109
Web: www.rc.net/conception
Email: delesf@yahoo.com
Members: 13 Sisters in US (550 around the world)
Conduct: Education-parochial schools, missionary work, social and parish work, catechesis, orphanages, youth ministry
Representation: Archdiocese of San Francisco and the Diocese of Fresno. Also in Spain, Italy, Brazil, Venezuela, Cameroon, Dominican Republic, Japan, Zaire, Equatorial Guinea, S. Korea, Philippines, India and Mexico
Vocation Director: Sr. Angeles Marin, RCM, (415) 474-0159

SISTERS OF THE (W405)
IMMACULATE CONCEPTION OF THE BLESSED VIRGIN MARY (**Lithuanian**), Immaculate Conception Convent and Novitiate, 600 Liberty Hwy., Putnam, CT 06260-2503
Web: www.immaculateconception site.org
Email: sbernadette@ct.metro cast.net
Members: 76 Sisters worldwide
Apostolic Work: Committed to Christ through a life of dedicated service and prayer: Catechetics and religious instruction, spiritual renewal programs, education, camping, health care ministry of the sick and elderly, social service, social work with abused children, pastoral and parish ministries, communications and hospitality
Representation: Archdiocese of Chicago and the Dioceses of Norwich, CT and Burlington, VT. Also in Toronto, Canada. Generalate and 5 dioceses in Lithuania
Vocation Director: Sr. M. Bernadette Matukas, MVS, (860) 928-7955

SISTERS OF THE (W406)
IMMACULATE HEART OF MARY (**I.H.M.**), Motherhouse: Gerona, Spain US Province, 3820 N. Sabino Canyon Rd., Tucson, AZ 85750
Email: abmartinez@theriver.com

Members: 20 Sisters in US
Apostolic Work: Academic and religious education
Representation: Diocese of Tucson
Vocation Director: Sister Alice Martinez, I.H.M., Provincial Superior, 520-886-4273

SISTERS OF THE (W406-2)
IMMACULATE HEART OF MARY, MOTHER OF CHRIST (I.H.M.) Immaculate Heart Convent, 1209 South Walnut Avenue, Freeport, IL 61032
Web: www.ihmmc.org
Email: mail@ihmmc.org
Members: 38 Sisters in the US; 700+ worldwide
Apostolic Work: Medical, teaching, pastoral, social and ecclesiastical works (all talents are welcome)
Representation: Diocese of Rockford, Diocese of Syracuse, Archdiocese of Minneapolis, Diocese of Gallup and in Nigeria, Ghana, Kenya, Tchad, Sierra Leone, Italy, Britain, Germany, Canada, Caribbean, and Ireland.
Vocation Director: (815) 297-8287

SISTERS OF THE (W407-1)
IMMACULATE HEART OF MARY OF WICHITA (I.H.M.), 145 S. Millwood St., Wichita, KS 67213
Web: www.sistersihmofwichita.org
Email: vocations@sistersihmof wichita.org
Members: 18 Sisters
Apostolic Work: Education and retreat work
Representation: Diocese of Wichita
Vocation Director: Sr. Maria Jacinta, IHM, (316) 722-9316

SISTERS OF THE INCARNATE (W408)
WORD AND BLESSED SACRAMENT (**S.I.W.**), Motherhouse House of Formation, 6618 Pearl Rd., Parma Heights, OH 44130-3808
Web: www.incarnatewordorder.org
Email: smrksiw@yahoo.com
Members: 27 Vowed Members, 48 Associate Members
Apostolic Work: Education, pastoral care, hospital chaplaincy, social work, retreats and spiritual direction
Vocation Director: Sister Mary Rose Kocab, SIW, (440) 886-6440, ext.1102

CONGREGATION OF THE (W409)
INCARNATE WORD AND BLESSED SACRAMENT (C.V.I.), Motherhouse and Novitiate: Incarnate Word Convent, 3400 Bradford Pl, Houston, TX 77025-1398
Web: www.incarnatewordsisters houston.org
Members: 45 Sisters, 1 Sister in Formation

Apostolic Work: 2 elementary schools, 1 high school, religious education, pastoral ministry, nursing
Representation: Dioceses of Beaumont and Galveston-Houston
Vocation Director: Contact: Sister Rosalia Purcell, C.V.I., Superior (713) 668-0423

CONGREGATION OF THE (W410)
INCARNATE WORD AND BLESSED SACRAMENT (IWBS), Incarnate Word Convent, 1101 N.E. Water St., Victoria, TX 77901
Web: www.iwbsvictoria.org
Email: iwbsvoc@yahoo.com, srjacintab@yahoo.com
Members: 90 Sisters
Apostolic Work: Education, CCD centers, hospitals, parishes
Representation: Archdiocese of San Antonio and in the Dioceses of Corpus Christi, Dallas, Galveston-Houston and Victoria. Also in Africa.
Vocation Director: Sister M. Mildred Truchard, IWBS and Sister M. Jacinta Benavidez, IWBS, (361) 575-7111

CONGREGATION OF THE (W411)
INCARNATE WORD AND BLESSED SACRAMENT (I.W.B.S.) (Sisters of the Incarnate Word and Blessed Sacrament of Corpus Christi) Motherhouse and Novitiate 2930 S. Alameda St., Corpus Christi, TX 78404-2798
Web: www.iwbscc.org
Email: srmortiz27@yahoo.com
Members: 60 Sisters
Conduct: 1 private high school, 2 private middle schools, 2 private grade schools, 2 kindergartens, 1 Montessori, 1 parochial grade school, 1 language school, 6 parish ministry, 4 diocesan offices, 3 hospital chaplains, co-sponsor free" ;Nativity School" for the poor
Representation: Dioceses of Beaumont, Brownsville, Corpus Christi and Houston
Vocation Director: Sister Rosa Maria Ortiz, IWBS (361) 882-5413, Fax (361) 880-4152

CONGREGATION OF THE (W412)
INFANT JESUS (C.I.J.) (Nursing Sisters of the Sick Poor) Motherhouse: Villa St. Joseph 984 North Village Ave, Rockville Centre, NY 11570
Web: www.cijnssp.org
Email: info@cijnssp.org
Members: 53 Sisters
Apostolic Work: Healing ministry. Engaged in nursing, administration, social services, physical therapy, pastoral care, parish outreach, home health care and hospice care

B-91

and other works related to health services
Representation: Dioceses of Brooklyn, Rockville Centre, Portland (ME) and Lexington, Kentucky
Vocation Director: (516) 823-3800, Fax (516) 594-0412

INSTITUTE OF THE BLESSED (W413) **VIRGIN MARY (I.B.V.M.) (Loretto Sisters) Loreto Branch,** Loretto Convent, PO Box 508, Wheaton, IL 60187
Web: www.ibvm.us
Email: cvandborg@ibvm.org
Members: 83 in the US; 1,100 worldwide
Apostolic Work: Education in its broadest sense; spiritual, pastoral and social ministry.
Representation: Arizona, California, Illinois, Michigan, Wisconsin, and 18 countries
Vocation Director: Sr. Claire Vandborg, IBVM, (630) 868-2904

CONGREGATION OF THE (W416) **BENEDICTINES OF JESUS CRUCIFIED (O.S.B.)**
See "B" - Benedictine Sisters

POOR SISTERS OF JESUS (W417-1) **CRUCIFIED AND THE SORROWFUL MOTHER (C.J.C.),** Our Lady of Sorrows Convent, 261 Thatcher St., Brockton, MA 02302-3997
Web: www.cjcbrockton.org
Email: sgfn@cjcbrockton.org
Members: 25 Sisters
Apostolic Work: Nursing homes
Representation: Archdiocese of Boston
Vocation Director: Sister Geraldine Nevaras, CJC (508) 588-5070, ext. 35 Fax (508) 580-6770

SISTERS IN JESUS THE (W417-2) **LORD (C.J.D.) (Canonissae in Jesu Domino),** Formation House: St. Paul, Minnesota, 525 Thomas Ave., St. Paul, MN 55103-1691
Web: www.cjd.cc
Email: info@cjd.cc
Members: 3 Sisters, 1 Novice
Apostolic Work: Private association of missionaries, contemplatives in action. The Sisters, consecrated under the three vows, are dedicated to going out to the nations (especially to those nations who have not known the faith or have had it crushed out) and reviving the faith in Jesus the Lord through evangelization and many different kinds of work.
Representation: Archdiocese of St. Paul/Minneapolis
Vocation Director: Sister Julia Mary, MM, (651) 291-7777

THE SISTERS OF JESUS (W417-3) **OUR HOPE (SJH),** 376 Bellis Road, Bloomsbury, NJ 08804-2009
Web: www.sistersofjesusourhope.org
Email: sisterjudith@sistersofjesusourhope.org
Members: 14 Sisters
Apostolic Work: Proclaiming Jesus Christ through evangelization, catechetical instruction and faith formation of adults, youth and children according to Pope John Paul II's vision for the New Evangelization which urges us to lead God's people into a deeper relationship with the Risen Lord. By the witness of our vibrant community life, and through our apostolate in the Church, we proclaim Jesus Christ – His life, His teachings, His promises – and the great truth of His merciful love which is the source of hope for the world.
Representation: Serving in 5 parishes in the Diocese of Metuchen, NJ as Directors of Religious Education, as teachers, as pastoral assistants and in youth ministry.
Vocation Director: Sr. Judith Andrews, SJH, (908) 995-7261, Fax: (908) 995-7262

SISTERS OF THE LAMB OF (W418) **GOD (A.D.),** Motherhouse in Brest, France, 2063 Wyandotte, Owensboro, KY 42301-2301
Web: www.sistersofthelambofgod.org
Email: lambaudrey@gmail.com
Members: 90 Sisters in Congregation; 11 in the US
Apostolic Work: Offers to the healthy as well as to those with physical disabilities the opportunity to fulfill their vocation, witnessing to the love of God and serving in diverse apostolates, according to their interests and abilities
Representation: Diocese of Owensboro. Missions in Mexico and Africa
Vocation Director: Sr. Audrey, A.D., (270) 926-8656

SISTERS OF LIFE (Sorores (W419) **Vitae) (S.V.),** Motherhouse: St. Paul the Apostle Convent, 586 McLean Ave, Yonkers, NY 10705, (914) 968-8094, Fax: (914) 968-0462
Web: www.sistersoflife.org
Members: 43 Professed, 16 Novices, 7 Postulants
Apostolic Work: Contemplative-apostolic. The Community's charism is the protection and enhancement of the sacredness of every human life
Representation: Archdioceses of New York and Toronto, Canada. Also in the Diocese of Bridgeport.

Vocation Director: Sr. Mary Gabriel, S.V., St. Frances de Chantal Convent, 198 Hollywood Ave., Bronx, NY 10465-0465, (718) 863-2264, Fax (718) 792-9645

LITTLE COMPANY OF MARY (W420) **SISTERS (L.C.M.),** American Provincial House, 9350 S. California Ave., Evergreen Park, IL 60805-2521
Web: www.lcmh.org
www.lcmglobal.org
Email: vocations@lcmh.org
Members: 400 Sisters Worldwide
Apostolic Work: Compassionate presence in health care ministries in hospitals and extended care facilities; parishes (pastoral ministry) and outreach programs
Representation: Archdioceses of Chicago and Los Angeles and in the Dioceses of Orange, CA and Evansville, IN. Also in England, Ireland, Scotland, Wales, Italy, South Africa, Zimbabwe, Korea, Australia, New Zealand and Tonga
Vocation Director: Suzanne Petrouski, Vocation Minister, (708) 229-5095
Sr. Jean Stickney, LCM, Vocation Director, (708) 229-5797

LITTLE FRANCISCANS OF (W421) **MARY (P.F.M.),** Regional House, 55 Moore Ave., Worcester, MA 01602
Email: rmgpfm@yahoo.com
Members: Total membership 195
Apostolic Work: Nursing, teaching, pastoral work, care of the aged, catechetical work, foreign mission in Madagascar
Representation: Dioceses of Portland and Worcester. Also in Quebec Province. Foreign Missions
Vocation Director: Sister Rena Mae Gagnon, pfm, (508) 755-0878

LITTLE SERVANT SISTERS (W424) **OF THE IMMACULATE CONCEPTION (L.S.I.C.),** Motherhouse: Poland Immaculate Conception Convent, Provincialate/Novitiate, 1000 Cropwell Rd., Cherry Hill, NJ 08003
Web: www.geocities.com/lsic2006
Email: lsic.prov@verizon.net
Members: 73 Sisters, 1 Novice, 2 Postulants; 1,371 Sisters worldwide
Apostolic Work: 1 provincialate, 1 novitiate, 2 retreat houses, 3 nursery schools, 1 elementary school, 1 home nursing service, 2 senior residences, 1 assisted living, 2 nursing homes, religious education, prayer cenacles, hospital pastoral care, social services, youth ministry
Representation: Archdioceses of Newark and Philadelphia and in the Dioceses of Camden and Metuchen.

B-92

Motherhouse: Poland. Also represented in Italy, Austria, England, Germany, Moldova, Ukraine, Russia (including Eastern Siberia), South Africa, Zambia, Malawi, and Tanzania
Vocation Director: Sister M. Philomena Nowicka, LSIC, (856) 424-1962, Fax (856) 424-5333

LITTLE SISTERS OF THE (W425)
ASSUMPTION (L.S.A.)
Motherhouse in Paris, France
1100 Sisters in 24 Countries
US Provincial Office: 100 Gladstone Ave., Walden, NY 12586
39 sisters
Web: www.littlesisters.org
Email: srjanet@littlesisters.org
Conduct: Nursing, Social Work, Advocacy, Pastoral Ministry, Early Childhood, Parenting Education, 1 Family Shelter, 2 Family Health and Social Service Agencies, 1 Hospitality Center. Any skill which enhances the quality of Family Life.
Apostolic Work: Live and work among the poor. Focus on the family through inner-city center and home-based services. Holistic concern for health at all levels: economic, spiritual, physical, social and emotional. Strive to create a more just and loving environment for families struggling against the odds of poverty. Committed to the work of Peace, Justice and the Integrity of Creation
Representation: Archdioceses of Boston, New York and Philadelphia and in the Diocese of Worcester, MA.
Vocation Director: Vocation Minister, Little Sisters of the Assumption, 475 E. 115th St., 1st Floor, New York, NY 10029, (212) 369-4406, Fax: (845) 672-0434

LITTLE SISTERS OF THE (W426)
GOSPEL OF CHARLES DE FOUCAULD, PO Box 305, Mott Haven Station, Bronx, NY 10454-0454
Members: 3 Sisters in the US; 74 Sisters worldwide
Apostolic Work: Fostering the growth of Christian community among the poor. Apostolate springs from a deep contemplative spirit, prayer and community life
Representation: Archdiocese of New York and in Europe, Africa, Central and South America and the Caribbean
Vocation Director: Sister Simone Ponnet

LITTLE SISTERS OF JESUS (W428)
(L.S.J.), Regional House, 400 N. Streeper St., Baltimore, MD 21224

Web: www.rc.net/org/littlesisters
Email: littlesrs.chg@juno.com
Members: 26 Sisters in US; 1,300 worldwide
Apostolic Work: Contemplative life in the midst of the world, sharing the life and work of those who are poor and marginalized; a ministry of presence and friendship
Representation: Archdioceses of Anchorage, Baltimore, and Chicago and in the Dioceses of Altoona, Fairbanks, and Paterson.
Vocation Director: Sister Lynn Flear, L.S.J., (410) 327-7863

LITTLE SISTERS OF JESUS (W429)
AND MARY (L.S.J.M.), Joseph House PO Box 1755, Salisbury, MD 21802
Web: www.thejosephhouse.org
Email: lsjm@ezy.net
Members: 5 Sisters, 2 Postulants
Apostolic Work: Active contemplatives called to cry the Gospel with their lives, particularly in the midst of the poor. Prime purpose is to help stabilize family life. Through crisis centers in poverty-ridden areas, provide direct service to the poor by addressing their social, spiritual and economic problems. Also conduct a religious art and book store, and a residential program for homeless men.
Representation: Diocese of Wilmington
Vocation Director: Sr. Pat Lennon, (410) 543-1645

LITTLE SISTERS OF THE (W430)
POOR (l.s.p.), Motherhouse: France (Brooklyn Province) Provincialate: Queen of Peace Residence, 110-30 221st St., Queens Village, NY 11429 (Baltimore Province) Provincialate: Saint Martin's Home, 601 Maiden Choice Ln., Baltimore, MD 21228 (Chicago Province) Provincialate: 80 W. Northwest Hwy., Palatine, IL 60067-3580
Web: www.littlesistersofthepoor.org
Email: serenity@littlesistersofthe poor.org
Members: 3,000 Sisters in 32 countries
Apostolic Work: Welcoming the needy aged to 32 homes in the United States and Canada. Also present in France, Belgium, Spain, Peru, Portugal, Malta, Italy, Algeria, Benin, Congo, Nigeria, Kenya, Turkey, England, Ireland, Scotland, Jersey (Channel Islands), Philippines, Colombia, Chile, Argentina, India, Sri Lanka, South Korea, Hong Kong, Malaysia, Taiwan, Western Samoa, New Zealand, Australia, and New Caledonia
Representation: Archdioceses of

New York, Boston, Hartford, Philadelphia, Baltimore, Cincinnati, Louisville, Indianapolis, Washington, Chicago, Los Angeles, Mobile, San Francisco, Denver, Saint Paul and Saint Louis, and in 14 other dioceses in the US
Vocation Director: Sr. Rosemary, l.s.p., Little Sisters of the Poor, 601 Maiden Choice Lane, Baltimore, MD 21228, (410) 744-9367

LITTLE WORKERS OF THE (W431)
SACRED HEARTS (P.O.S.C.)
Motherhouse: Rome
Regional House, 645 Glenbrook Rd., Stamford, CT 06906-1409
Web: www.ourladyofgraceschool.net
Email: littleworkerposc@aol.com
Members: 23 Sisters in the US; 400 Sisters worldwide
Apostolic Work: Ministry in the fields of academic and religious education especially catechesis, parish ministry, social work, and care of aged and infirm
Representation: Diocese of Bridgeport and in the Archdioceses of Philadelphia and Washington, DC.; also in Italy, Argentina, India and Albania
Vocation Director: Sister Gesuina Gencarelli, P.O.S.C., (203) 348-5531, fax: (203) 324-9638

SISTERS OF THE LIVING (W432)
WORD (SLW), Living Word Center 800 N. Fernandez Ave.-B, Arlington Heights, IL 60004
Web: www.slw.org
Email: connect@slw.org
Members: 70 Sisters
Apostolic Work: Our Mission is to reflect and affirm the Word, Jesus, who frees the oppressed and gives new life. Our ministries include youth and adult education, parish, campus and diocesan ministry, health care, retreat and spiritual direction, counseling, healing ministries, environmental advocacy, and outreach to new immigrants as well as to victims of violence, hunger, unemployment and homelessness.
Representation: 9 states in the Archdioceses of Chicago, Detroit, New Orleans and St. Paul/ Minneapolis and in the Dioceses of Alexandria, Cleveland, Jackson, Joliet in Illinois, Lansing, Memphis, Rapid City, and Sioux City
Vocation Director: Vocation Team: Office of New Membership, (Sponsoring weekend vocation retreats), (847) 577-5972
Sister Kathleen Heer, SLW, kathleen_slw@yahoo.com
Sister Lisa Polega, lisa_slw@yahoo.com

SISTERS OF LORETTO (S.L.) (W433-1)
(Sisters of Loretto at the Foot of the Cross) LORETTO COMMUNITY
Loretto Staff Offices, 4000 S. Wadsworth Blvd., Lakewood, CO 80123
Web: www.lorettocommunity.org
Email: marykay@loretto community.org
Members: 294 Sisters, 212 Co-Members (an ecumenical partnership of women and men who share community and ministry) located in 32 states and 8 foreign countries
Apostolic Work: A community of faith and service, working for justice and acting for peace. Ministries are determined by needs and personal talents and include education, advocacy on behalf of women and other minorities, efforts to change unjust systems, health care and social work. Sister communities in Africa and Guatemala. Beginning a foundation in Pakistan. The volunteer program welcomes others to mission.
Vocation Director: Mary Kay Brannan, SL, (303) 986-1541 (Colorado) Fax (303) 986-8453 (877) LORETTO (toll-free, outside Colorado);

(W433-2)
SISTERS OF LORETTO (I.B.V.M.)
See "I" - Institute of the Blessed Virgin Mary

LOVERS OF THE HOLY (W434)
CROSS SISTERS (LHC) (Los Angeles)
Holy Cross Convent, 14700 S. Van Ness Ave., Gardena, CA 90249
Email: graceducle@aol.com or lhcla@yahoo.com
Members: 57 Sisters
Apostolic Work: Parish ministry, teaching, nursing and social work
Representation: Archdiocese of Los Angeles and in the Diocese of Orange and San Bernardino.
Vocation Director: Sr. Grace Duc T. Le, Vocation Director, 1401 S. Sycamore St., Santa Ana, CA 92707
Sr. Anne Lanh Tran, Superior General, Holy Cross Convent, 14700 S. Van Ness Ave., Gardena, CA 90249, (310) 768-1906 or (310) 516-0271

MANTELLATE SISTERS (W435)
See "S" - Servants of Mary

MARIAN SISTERS (M.S.) (W436)
Marycrest Motherhouse, 6765 N. 112th St., Waverly, NE 68462-8462
Web: www.mariansisters.org
Email: marian-vocations@ cdolinc.net
Members: 35 Sisters

Apostolic Work: Education, health care, social work, and other forms of service to Diocese
Representation: Diocese of Lincoln
Vocation Director: Sister Melissa Moxley, M.S. (402) 786-2750 Fax (402) 786-7256

MARIANIST SISTERS (F.M.I.) (W437)
US Foundation, 251 W. Ligustrum Dr., San Antonio, TX 78228
Web: www.marianistsisters.org
Email: gtrautman@sm-usa.org
Members: 19 Sisters in US Province
Apostolic Work: Faith community formation, campus ministry, educational, social and pastoral ministry. Novitiate in San Antonio
Representation: Archdioceses of Cincinnati and San Antonio
Vocation Director: Sr. Gretchen Trautman, FMI, (210) 431-2193; Sr. Laura Leming, FMI, 30 Sawmill Rd., Dayton, OH 45420-2522, (937) 224-5896

MARIANITES OF HOLY (W438)
CROSS (MSC), (North American Continent), 1011 Gallier St, New Orleans, LA 70117, (504) 945-1620
Web: www.marianites.org
Email: reneemsc@marianites.org
Members: 200 Sisters
Apostolic Work: Education-primary through adult, pastoral ministry in parishes and hospitals, campus ministry, health care, social ministries, counseling, foreign missions
Representation: in the Archdioceses of New Orleans and New York and in the Dioceses of Alexandria, Austin, Baton Rouge, Biloxi, Camden, Dallas, Houma-Thibodaux, Houston, Jackson, Lafayette, Lake Charles, Manchester, Paterson and Trenton. Also in the Dioceses of Mt. Laurier and Sherbrooke in Canada. Foreign missions in Bangladesh and Haiti
Vocation Director: Sr. Renee Daigle, MSC, 409 W. Dakota St., Hammond, LA 70401, (985) 345-7206

MARIST MISSIONARY (W439)
SISTERS (S.M.S.M.), Provincialate 349 Grove St, Waltham, MA 02453
Web: www.maristmissionary smsm.org
Email: smsmvoc@aol.com
Members: 600 Sisters worldwide
Apostolic Work: To proclaim Jesus to the world, SMSMs participate in pastoral ministries, education, health, social services, administration, etc. In respect and dialogue, SMSMs try to be bonds of communion between peoples, races and cultures and witnesses to God's universal love

Representation: (Arch)dioceses of Boston, Memphis, Oakland, and St. Petersburg. Also in Asia, Africa, Caribbean, Europe, South Pacific and Latin America
Vocation Director: Sr. Claiare Rheaume, smsm,(781) 893-0149 Fax (781) 899-6838

MARIST SISTERS (S.M.) (W440)
(US Sector), 326 Logan St., McMechen, WV 26040
Web: www.marists.org
Email: lindasevcik@yahoo.com
Members: 14 Sisters in US, 400 worldwide
Apostolic Work: Missionaries, teachers, social workers, counsellors, pastoral ministers.
Representation: Archdiocese of Detroit and in the Dioceses of Laredo and Wheeling-Charleston
Vocation Director: Sr. Linda Sevcik, S.M., (304) 233-5579

SISTERS OF MARY (W441)
IMMACULATE (S.M.I.)
US Foundation, 118 Park Rd., Leechburg, PA 15656
Email: lbgsmi@alltel.net
Members: 6 Sisters in the US
Vocation Director: (724) 845-2828

SISTERS OF MARY OF THE (W442)
PRESENTATION (S.M.P.)
Maryvale Novitiate, 11550 River Rd., Valley City, ND 58072-8072
Web: www.sistersofmaryofthe presentation.com
Email: dorothy.bunce@fargo diocese.org
Members: 39 Sisters
Conduct: 1 elementary schools, 4 hospitals, parish ministry, home health agency, spirituality center
Representation: Dioceses of Crookston, Fargo and Peoria
Vocation Director: Sister Dorothy Bunce, SMP, (701) 845-2864

SISTERS OF MARY (W443-1)
REPARATRIX (S.M.R.), Society of Mary Reparatrix, American Province 17320 Grange Rd., Riverview, MI 48193
Web: www.smr.org
Email: joanpricoli@comcast.net
Members: 24 Sisters
Apostolic Work: Retreats, spiritual direction, religious education, parish ministry, eco-spirituality ministries, pastoral care for the hospitalized and elderly, programs for the poor and needy
Representation: Archdioceses of Detroit and New York and in the Diocese of Brooklyn. Foreign Missions: Africa, South America, Panama

Vocation Director: Sister Joan Pricoli, S.M.R., Coordinator, (734) 285-4510, Fax: (734) 285-8147

MARYKNOLL SISTERS OF (W443-3) **ST. DOMINIC (M.M.)**, PO Box 311, Maryknoll, NY 10545-0311
Web: http://maryknollsisters.org
   www.maryknoll.org
Email: vocation@mksisters.org
Members: 535 Sisters
Apostolic Work: The charism of the Maryknoll Sisters is to participate in the Church's universal mission. Missionary life in cross-cultural context is what enriches and enlivens them. They find God's presence outside of their own cultural, economic and social boundaries. They walk with the poor, the oppressed and deprived peoples of many lands, as pastoral or social workers, catechists, doctors, nurses, artists, advocates of justice, peace and integrity of creation, farmers, teachers, and theologians. They seek the empowerment of those whom they serve. Multicultural in membership, they appreciate diversity. Finding God's presence in diverse cultures, races and situations is the spirituality that unites and nourishes these women missionaries.
Representation: Africa, Asia, Pacific Islands, Central and South Americas and the US
Vocation Director: Sr. Leonila V. Bermisa, M.M., (914) 941-7575, Ext. 5676

MARYVALE SISTERS (CLHC) (W444) **(Congregation of Our Lady Help of the Clergy)**, Motherhouse: Maryvale Motherhouse, 2522 June Bug Rd, Vale, NC 28168-8168
Email: mvsrs2522@hughes.net
Members: 5 Sisters
Apostolic Work: Home visitation to the sick, elderly, shut-ins, hospital visitations, pastoral assistance in areas of counseling, youth ministry, day care, evangelization ministry, spiritual direction and retreat ministry; retreat residence available for private or directed individual/group retreats
Vocation Director: Sister Mary Norman, C.L.H.C., (704) 276-2626

MEDICAL MISSION SISTERS (W445) **(MMS)**, 8400 Pine Rd., Philadelphia, PA 19111-1312
Web: www.medicalmission sisters.org
Email: mms8400@aol.com
Members: 650 Sisters
Apostolic Work: At the heart of their common call to mission is the deep belief that they are called to be an active presence of Christ, the Healer. Together with the poor, the oppressed, the broken, the Sisters seek to struggle for wholeness, forgiveness, justice, healing and peace. Their ministry encompasses a wide variety of healing activities in Africa, Asia, South America, North America and Europe
Vocation Director: Sister Marguerite Papineau, M.M.S., Membership Advisor, (215) 742-6100, ext. 159; cell: (215) 205-8979

MEDICAL MISSIONARIES (W446) **OF MARY**, Motherhouse: Ireland 179 Highland Ave., Somerville, MA 02143-1515
Web: www.mmmusa.org
Email: madeleinemmm@yahoo.com
Members: 400 Sisters worldwide
Apostolic Work: Inspired by our Blessed Mother's visit to her cousin Elizabeth, the MMMs follow her example, bringing Christ's healing love to those most in need. Sustained by prayer and community life, each sister, in self-surrender, seeks God through a life-long commitment of poverty, celibacy and obedience in service to the sick, poor, marginalized and most neglected of our world. MMM is particularyly drawn to those services that heal and empower women. MMM presently serve in nine African countries, Brazil, and Honduras, ministering in a variety of professional capacities such as midwives, nurses, doctors, social services, administrators, and various pastoral ministries. The sisters strive to identify, respect and affirm cultural differences and wisdom with particular regards to health and healing. Primary Health Care, in continuous dialogue with the local people, is a MMM priority.
Representation: Archdioceses of Boston, Chicago and New York and in the Dioceses of Richmond and San Diego
Vocation Director: Sister Madeleine LeBlanc, MMM, (617) 666-3223

MEDICAL SISTERS OF (W447) **ST. JOSEPH (MSJ)**, Motherhouse: India 3435 E. Funston St., Wichita, KS 67218-7218
Email: msjkansas@aol.com
Members: 700 Sisters (worldwide)
Apostolic Work: Health care
Representation: in the Diocese of Wichita and 10 dioceses in India
Vocation Director: (316) 686-4746

MERCEDARIAN (W448-1) **MISSIONARIES OF BERRIZ (M.M.B.)** Generalate: Rome
Motherhouse: Spain
2115 Maturana Dr., 101B, Liberty, MO 64068-7985
Web: www.ourladyofmercy.net/ ourstory.html
   www.mercedariasmisioneras deberriz.net (Spanish speaking)
   www.mmberriz.com/usa.php (English speaking)
Email: mmbus@sbcglobal.com
Members: 15 Sisters in US, 500 Sisters worldwide
Apostolic Work: International missionary congregation; teachers, social workers, nurses, catechists, co-pastors, youth leaders
Representation: Diocese of Kansas City-St. Joseph. Foreign Missions: Micronesia: Mariana and Caroline Islands; Mexico; Guam; Guatemala; Nicaragua; Peru; Equador; Japan; Taiwan; Philippines; Democratic Republic of the Congo; Zambia, Africa
Vocation Director: Sister Betty Preston, MMB, (816) 781-8202, Fax (816) 781-8205

MERCEDARIAN SISTERS (W448-2) **OF THE BLESSED SACRAMENT (HMSS)**, Motherhouse: Mexico City Local House: 227 Keller St., San Antonio, TX 78204
Regional House, 234 W. Cevallos St., San Antonio, TX 78204-8204
Email: teresitap@sbcglobal.net
Members: 32 Sisters in the US; over 800 worldwide
Apostolic Work: Education: preschools, elementary, secondary and junior college; parish and diocesan ministry to Hispanics; sick and aged and imprisoned.
Representation: (Arch)dioceses of San Antonio, Cleveland, Corpus Christi, Baton Rouge, and San Diego. Also in Mexico, Italy, Spain, Colombia, El Salvador, Chile, Venezuela, Guatemala and Costa Rica.
Vocation Director: Sister Teresa Gomez, HMSS, 8171 Lemon Grove Way, Lemon Grove, CA 91945 (619) 460-4271 cell: (619) 415-3912
Email: sistermusict@yahoo.com

MERCEDARIANS (W448-3) See "O" - Our Lady of Mercy, Sisters of

SISTERS OF MERCY OF (W452) **THE AMERICAS (R.S.M.)**
Institute New Membership Office 2039 N. Geyer Road, St. Louis, MO 63131
Web: www.sistersofmercy.org/ vocations
Email: newmembership@sistersof mercy.org
Members: 4,395 Sisters, 41 New

Members, 2,980 Associates, 6 Companions in Mercy, 24 U.S. current Mercy Corps Volunteers and 1 serving Internationally, and 850 Alumni of Mercy Corp Volunteers.

Conduct: Universities/colleges, hospitals, clinics, social service centers, retreat centers, elementary and secondary schools.

Apostolic Work: We are an international community of women religious vowed to serve people who suffer from poverty, sickness, and lack of education, with a special concern for women and children. In innovative and traditional ways, Sisters of Mercy address human needs through collaborative efforts in education, health care, housing, and pastoral and social services. Among Sisters of Mercy one can find doctors, lawyers and paralegals, theologians, missionaries, justice advocates, peace activists and foster mothers.

Representation: North, South and Central America, the Caribbean, Guam, and the Philippines geographically organized in six Communities.

Sisters of Mercy of the Americas - CCASA Community Includes Argentina, Belize, Chili, Guyana, Guatemala, Honduras, Panama, Peru

Sisters of Mercy of the Americas - Mid-Atlantic Community Includes Delaware, New Jersey, Philadelphia, and Scranton areas of Pennsylvania, Southeast New York and Brooklyn

Sisters of Mercy of the Americas - Northeast Community Includes Connecticut, Maine, Massachusetts, New Hampshire, Rhode Island, Vermont, and the Albany, NY area

Sisters of Mercy of the Americas - New York Pennsylvania Pacific West Community Includes Rochester, Buffalo, and Western New York areas; Erie, Pittsburgh and Western Pennsylvania, Ft. Lauderdale and all Eastern cities of the State of Florida; and the Philippines.

Sisters of Mercy of the Americas - South Central Community Includes Maryland, Washington, D.C., Mississippi, Alabama, Georgia, North and Western parts of Florida, West Virginia, Ohio, Kentucky, Tennessee, North and South Carolina, Virginia, Eastern Missouri, Arkansas, Oklahoma, Eastern Kansas, Texas, Guam, and Jamaica

Sisters of Mercy of the Americas -

West Midwest Community Includes Michigan, Indiana, Illinois, Wisconsin, Iowa, Minnesota, Idaho, Oregon, South and North Dakota, Colorado, Montana, Nevada, Utah, Arizona, California, Western Kansas, Washington, Western Missiour and New Mexico, Hawaii and Alaska

Vocation Director: Sisters Patricia Donlin, RSM and Carol Mucha, RSM - Co-ministers in the Institute New Membership Office. Toll free number: 1-877-50-MERCY.

DIOCESAN SISTERS OF (W469-2)
MERCY OF PORTLAND (R.S.M.)
Our Lady of Mercy Convent
265 Cottage Rd., South Portland,
ME 04106
Web: www.cmswr.org/member_
  communities/DSMPortland.htm
Email: dsmvocation@gmail.com
Members: 7 Sisters
Apostolic Work: Education, social work, pastoral ministry
Representation: Diocese of Portland (ME)
Vocation Director: Contact: (207) 796-2359

MERCY SISTERS (R.S.M.) (W474)
Generalate: Dublin, Ireland
US Province: Sisters of Mercy
1075 Bermuda Dr., Redlands, CA
92374-2374
Email: mgallagher_sm@
  sbdiocese.org
Members: 100 Sisters
Apostolic Work: Pastoral and health care, education, social work, ministry to women, the poor and the immigrant
Representation: 12 Dioceses in the US
Vocation Director: (909) 798-4747
Fax (909) 798-5300

MERCY SISTERS (R.S.M.) (W475)
St. Joan of Arc, 500 S.W. Fourth
Ave., Boca Raton, FL 33432
Members: 4 Sisters
Representation: in the Diocese of Palm Beach.
Vocation Director: (561) 368-6655

(IRISH) SISTERS OF MERCY (W476)
US PROVINCE, Holy Infant Convent
239 Nancy Pl., Ballwin, MO 63021
Members: 2 Sisters
Apostolic Work: Education, pastoral ministries
Representation: Archdiocese of St. Louis
Vocation Director: Sister Laurentia Cusack, Facilitator, (636) 391-1528

SISTERS OF MERCY- (W480)
Elphin Community (S.M.)
Sisters of Mercy, St. John's Convent
2960 Mendoza Dr., Costa Mesa, CA
92626
Email: mvianney@sjbschool.net
Members: 1 Sister
Representation: Dioceses of Orange, San Bernardino and San Diego
Vocation Director: (714) 545-2116

(IRISH) SISTERS OF MERCY (W481)
US PROVINCE (S.M.)
Sacred Heart Convent, 6240 105th
St., Jacksonville, FL 32244
Members: 5 Sisters
Representation: in the Diocese of St. Augustine
Vocation Director: Sister Patricia O'Hea, S.M., (904) 771-3858

(W482)
MERCY SISTERS (Galway)
(R.S.M.), Provincialate: Sisters of Mercy, 1075 Bermuda Dr, Redlands, CA 92374
Email: mbanersm@gmail.com
Members: 2 Sisters
Apostolic Work: Education (works of mercy)
Representation: Diocese of Orlando
Vocation Director: Mary Divilly, RSM, Divine Mercy Convent, 1930 N. Courtenay Pkwy., Merritt Island, FL 32953 (321) 452-1279/5955

SISTERS OF MERCY OF THE (W486)
BLESSED SACRAMENT (H.M.S.S.)
See "M" - Mercedarian Sisters of the Blessed Sacrament

(W487)
METROPOLITAN ASSOCIATION OF CONTEMPLATIVE COMMUNITIES (MACC), See member communities' individual listings:
SISTERS ADORERS OF THE PRECIOUS BLOOD (Brooklyn, NY)
SISTERS ADORERS OF THE PRECIOUS BLOOD (Watertown, NY)
CONGREGATION OF THE BENEDICTINES OF JESUS CRUCIFIED (Branford, CT)
CAMALDOLESE NUNS (Windsor, NY)
CARMELITE NUNS, DISCALCED (O.C.D.) (Beacon, NY)
CARMELITE NUNS, DISCALCED (O.C.D.) (Elysburg, PA)
DOMINICAN NUNS, CLOISTERED (O.P.) (Bronx, NY)
GOOD SHEPHERD SISTERS (Dix Hills, NY)
GOOD SHEPHERD SISTERS (Trenton, NJ)
PASSIONIST NUNS (C.P.) (The Nuns of The Most Holy Cross and Passion of Our Lord Jesus Christ)
POOR CLARE NUNS (O.S.C.) (Wappinger Falls, NY)

REDEMPTORISTINE NUNS
(Esopus)
VISITATION NUNS (Brooklyn, NY)
Carmelite Monastery, 89
Hiddenbrooke Dr., Beacon, NY
12508-2230
Web: macc.catholic.org
Vocation Director: Sr. Rita Donahue, OCD

MILL HILL SISTERS (F.M.S.J.) (W488)
(Franciscan Missionaries of St. Joseph), 703 Derzee Court, Delmar, NY 12054
Email: kerleyjl@lemoyne.edu
Members: 2 Sisters in US; 150 worldwide
Apostolic Work: Parish ministry, foreign missions, social work, teaching, nursing
Representation: Dioceses of Albany and Syracuse. Also in Kenya, East Africa, Ecuador, South America
Vocation Director: Sister Joan Kerley, (518) 482-1991

MINIM DAUGHTERS OF (W490)
MARY IMMACULATE (C.F.M.M.)
General Motherhouse: Mexico
US: Regional/Retirement House, Our Lady of Lourdes Elementary/High School, PO Box 1865, Nogales, AZ 85628-1865
Email: lmvaldez@lourdescatholic school.org
Members: 23 Sisters in the US; 395 worldwide
Apostolic Work: Elementary/high school
Representation: Diocese of Tucson
Vocation Director: Sr. Luise Marie Valdez, CFMM, 555 Patagonia Hwy., Nogales, AZ 85628-1865, (520) 287-3377

SISTERS MINOR OF MARY (W491)
IMMACULATE (S.M.M.I.)
Central Motherhouse and Novitiate-Rome, Italy. St. Francis Villa, 138 Brushy Hill Rd., Danbury, CT 06810
Members: 80 Sisters
Apostolic Work: Active-contemplative Franciscan Religious Congregation following the spirituality of St. Maximilian Kolbe and St. Therese of Lisieux. Ministry in the field of Academic and Religious Education; health care; pastoral care; care to the elderly, youths, widows, and immigrants. (Accepting candidates late teens to early 40's).
Representation: (Arch)dioceses of Bridgeport, Hartford, and Newark. Also in Africa, France, Italy, Poland, Slovania, and Turkey
Vocation Director: Sr. Theresa M. Kovacs, S.M.M.I., (203) 744-8041

MISERICORDIA SISTERS (W492)
(S.M.), Generalate: 12435 Ave. de la Misericorde, Montreal, Canada H4J 2G3. 225 Carol Ave., Pelham, NY 10803-0803, (514) 332-0550
Email: rosaliehal@aol.com
Members: 3 Sisters in US
Apostolic Work: 1 maternity home for unwed mothers
Representation: 3 Canadian Provinces and the Archdiocese of New York. Also in Ecuador
Vocation Director: Sister Ellen Hunt, S.M., 225 Carol Ave., Pelham, NY 10803

MISSION HELPERS OF THE (W493)
SACRED HEART (M.H.S.H.)
1001 W. Joppa Rd., Towson, MD 21204-1204
Web: www.missionhelpers.org
Email: olsand@comcast.net
Members: 94 Sisters, 1 Lay Minister in US, 3 in Venezuela
Apostolic Work: Visiting poor families in their homes to inquire about their needs, advocates for the handicapped and hearing impaired, feeding the homeless in cities, reaching out to the Hispanic community in the US, Puerto Rico and Venezuela, counseling and challenging young people, comforting families of the terminally ill, including those with AIDS, counseling families dealing with social, economic or psychological pressures, and proclaiming the Gospel through spirituality programs and formal religious education. Becoming aware of an existing need, a Mission Helper responds.
Representation: 14 states, Puerto Rico and Venezuela, South America, (States: Alabama, Arizona, California, Delaware, Florida, Indiana, Maryland, Massachusetts, New York, Ohio, Pennsylvania, Washington)
Vocation Director: Sr. Onellys Viegas, M.H.S.H., (301) 681-3556

MISSIONARIES OF CHARITY (W494)
(M.C.), (North America Province) 335 E. 145th St., Bronx, NY 10451-0451
Email: mtc@motherteresa.org
Members: 4,000 Sisters in the whole congregation
Apostolic Work: Giving wholehearted and free service to the poorest of the poor
Representation: (Arch)dioceses of Atlanta, Baltimore, Baton Rouge, Boston, Bridgeport, Charlotte, Chicago, Dallas, Denver, Detroit, Gallup, Gary, Houston, Indianapolis, Jenkins, Lafayette, Little Rock, Los Angeles, Memphis, Miami, Minneapolis, Newark, New Bedford, New

York, Peoria, Philadelphia, Phoenix, St. Louis, Sacramento, San Francisco, Spokane, Trenton and Washington (DC). Foreign missions in Albania, Algeria, Argentina, Armenia, Australia, Austria, Bangladesh, Belgium, Benin, Bolivia, Brazil, Burundi, Cairo, Cambodia, Cameroon, Canada, Central Africa, Chile, Columbia, Congo, Costa Rica, Cuba, Czechoslovakia, Denmark, Dominican Republic, Durban, East Africa, El Salvador, Estonia, Ethiopia, Egypt, Equador, Finland, France, Germany, Ghana, Greece, Grenada, Guatemala, Guinea, Guyana, Haiti, Holland, Honduras, Hong Kong, Hungary, Iceland, India, Iraq, Ireland, Israel, Italy, Ivory Coast, Japan, Johannesburg, Jordan, Kadjikoston, Kazakhstan, Kenya, Lebanon, Liberia, Libya, Lithuania, Macau, Macedonia, Madagascar, Malta, Mauritius, Mexico, Mongolia, Mozambique, Nepal, New Zealand, Nicaragua, Nigeria, Pakistan, Palestine, Panama, Papua New Guinea, Paraguay, Peru, Philippines, Poland, Portugal, Puerto Rico, Romania, Russia, Rwanda, Senegal, Seychelles, Sierra Leone, Singapore, Skopje, South Korea, Spain, Sri Lanka, Stockholm, Sudan, Sweden, Syria, Taiwan, Tanzania, Trinidad, Tunisia, Uganda, Ukraine, United Kingdom, Uruguay, Uzbekistan, Venezuela, West Africa, Yemen, Yugoslavia, Zaire, Zambia, Zimbabwe
Vocation Director: Sr. M. Leticia, MC, (718) 292-0019

MISSIONARIES OF THE (W495-1)
SACRED HEART OF JESUS (M.S.C.)
(Cabrini Sisters), Province Office, 222 E. 19th St, Apt. 5B, New York, NY 10003, (212) 375-0752
The Cabrini Family: MSC Vowed Religious Sisters; Lay Missionaries; Volunteers; Collaborators
Cabrini Mission Corps (CMC): 610 King of Prussia Rd., Mansion 2nd Floor, Radnor, PA 19087 (610) 971-0821. E-mail: cmcorps@aol.com
Web: www.mothercabrini.org
Email: mscvoc@aol.com
Apostolic Work: Way of Life: "To be Bearers of the Love of Christ in the world" through our missionary outreach, community, prayer, and works which include: evangelization; health care and education; youth and family ministry; pastoral outreach through parishes, in shrines, retreat houses and prisons; advocacy and work for justice on behalf of immigrants, refugees, women and children and those marginalized by society

Representation: New York, Pennsylvania, New Orleans, Chicago, Denver and Seattle. Also in the Philippines, Swaziland, Ethiopia, Australia, Europe, Central America, Argentina, Brazil and Russia
Vocation Director: Sr. Diane Olmstead, MSC, (se habla Espanol), 139 Henry St., New York, NY 10002 (212) 233-0233

MISSIONARIES OF THE (W495-2) **SACRED HEART OF JESUS AND OUR LADY OF GUADALUPE (M.S.C.Gpe.),** 1212 E. Euclid Ave., Arlington Heights, IL 60004
Apostolic Work: Schools, nursing homes, seminaries, foreign missions.
Representation: Archdioceses of Boston, Chicago, San Francisco and Washington
Vocation Director: (847) 255-5616

MISSIONARY BENEDICTINE (W496) **SISTERS (O.S.B.) (Congregation of Missionary Benedictine Sisters)** Immaculata Monastery & Spirituality Center, 300 N. 18th St., Norfolk, NE 68701-3687
Web: www.norfolkmbs.org
Email: srcacosb@yahoo.com
Members: 39 Sisters, 2 in Formation
Apostolic Work: Education, health care, catechetics, domestic and pastoral ministry, special apostolates among Hispanics and Native Americans, retreats, and spiritual direction
Representation: Dioceses of New Ulm and Omaha. Also in Angola, Argentina, Australia, Brazil, Bulgaria, China, Germany, India, Italy, Kenya, Namibia, the Philippines, Portugal, South Korea, Spain, Switzerland, Tanzania and Uganda
Vocation Director: Sr. Carole Ann Clark, OSB, (402) 371-3438, fax: (403) 379-2877

MISSIONARY CATECHISTS (W497) **OF DIVINE PROVIDENCE (M.C.D.P.)** St. Andrew's Convent, 2318 Castroville Rd., San Antonio, TX 78237
Web: www.mcdp.org
Email: mcdpvocation@sbcglobal.net
Members: 52 Sisters, 1 Candidate
Apostolic Work: Working with children, youth, young adults, adults in religious education within a parish setting. Also counselors, teachers, social work, consultants at the diocesan, state and local level. Special emphasis in Hispanic ministry
Representation: Archdioceses of Anchorage, Omaha and San Antonio and in the Dioceses of Austin, Brownsville, Corpus Christi,

Dallas, Fort Worth, Fresno, Galveston-Houston, Laredo and Tucson
Vocation Director: Sister Sylvia Garcia, MCDP, Vocation Office (210) 438-0052

MISSIONARY CATECHISTS (W498) **OF THE SACRED HEARTS OF JESUS AND MARY (M.C.S.H.)** Provincial Office, 203 E. Sabine St., Victoria, TX 77901
Email: misionera@suddenlink.net; mcofthesacredhearts@yahoo.com
Members: 40
Apostolic Work: Pastoral assistants, family orientation and formation, religious education ministry (C.C.D.), evangelization and catechesis in ministries, home visiting ministry, pastoral and liturgical activities at parish and diocesan levels
Representation: (Arch)dioceses Galveston-Houston, Sante Fe, Victoria, Ft. Worth, Lubbock and Metuchen. Also in Mexico, Africa and Spain
Vocation Director: Sister Midory Wu Sister Miriam Perez, Provincial Superior, (361) 570-3332, Fax (361) 570-3377

MISSIONARY DAUGHTERS (W499) **OF THE MOST PURE VIRGIN MARY (M.D.P.V.M.),** 919 N. 9th St., Kingsville, TX 78363-8363
Members: 35 Sisters in US; 500 Sisters worldwide
Apostolic Work: Education, social work, missions in Africa, Mexico and Peru, pastoral work, novitiate in Mexico
Representation: Dioceses of Corpus Christi, Yakima and Camden
Vocation Director: (361) 595-1087

MISSIONARY FRANCISCAN (W500) **SISTERS OF THE IMMACULATE CONCEPTION (MFIC)** Provincial House, 790 Centre St., Newton, MA 02458, Sr. Suzanne Fondini, MFIC, Provincial (617) 527-1004, Fax (617) 527-2528
Web: www.mficusa.org
Members: 150 Sisters in US, 270 Sisters worldwide
Apostolic Work: Varied, include education, pastoral care (especially among the poor), health care, social services, foreign missions
Representation: 12 dioceses in the US (East Coast) and 10 countries worldwide including Australia, Boliva, Canada, Egypt, England, Ireland, Italy, Papua New Guinea, Peru
Vocation Director: E-mail: mfic@mficusa.org

MISSIONARY SERVANTS OF (W501) **THE MOST BLESSED TRINITY (MSBT),** 3501 Solly Ave., Philadelphia, PA 19136
Web: www.msbt.org
Email: voc@msbt.org
Members: 170 Sisters, 6 in Formation
Apostolic Work: Missionary work, mostly through parishes and social service agencies, but also through young adult ministry, retreat centers, health care, etc. The Sisters look for abandoned but necessary works of the Church, especially in remote parishes or economically deprived neighborhoods; many of their missions serve immigrant families, especially Hispanic.
Representation: Dioceses throughout the US, Puerto Rico and Mexico
Vocation Director: Sr. Mary Kay McDonald, MSBT and Sr. Olivia Montejano, MSBT, Co-Directors (215) 335-7534

MISSIONARY SERVANTS (W502-1) **OF ST. ANTHONY (M.S.S.A.)** 100 Peter Baque Rd., San Antonio, TX 78209
Members: 4 Sisters
Apostolic Work: Ministering to children in learning centers, caring for retired priests
Representation: in the Archdiocese of San Antonio
Vocation Director: Sr. Mary Ann Domagalski, M.S.S.A., Superior General, (210) 824-4553

MISSIONARY SISTERS OF (W502-2) **THE BLESSED SACRAMENT AND MARY IMMACULATE (M.SS.MI.)** Convent of Mary Immaculate, 1111 Wordin Ave., Bridgeport, CT 06605
Email: misamieucaristia@sbc global.net
Representation: Archdioceses of Boston and Newark and in the Dioceses of Bridgeport and Oakland
Vocation Director: Sr. Nexaida Soto, M.SS.MI.(203) 334-5681 Fax (203) 333-1590

MISSIONARY SISTERS OF (W503) **THE HOLY ROSARY,** 741 Polo Road, Bryn Mawr, PA 19010-9010
Web: www.holyrosarymissionary sisters.org
Email: enechufn@yahoo.com
Members: 385
Apostolic Work: Teaching, medical work, pastoral work, social work, counseling, community development, refuge work, AIDS ministry
Representation: Archdiocese of Philadelphia. Also in Nigeria, Sierra Leone, Cameroon, Ghana, Kenya, Liberia, Zambia, Ethiopia, South

Africa, Brazil, Mexico, Ireland, England and Scotland
Vocation Director: Sr. Florence Enechukwu, MSHR (610) 520-1974
Fax (610) 520-2002

MISSIONARY SISTERS OF (W504-1)
THE IMMACULATE CONCEPTION OF THE MOTHER OF GOD (S.M.I.C.)
Franciscan Sisters, 779 Broadway, Paterson, NJ 07509-7509
Web: www.smic-missionary sisters.com
Email: vocationssmic@aol.com
Members: 40 Sisters in US; 350 worldwide
Apostolic Work: Health care, education, social services, parish, retreats and art (any talent is utilized)
Representation: Dioceses of Paterson, Portland, Austin, Galveston-Houston, Gallup, and San Bernadino. Also in Brazil, Germany, Taiwan, Angola, Africa and Manila, Philippines
Vocation Director: Sr. Andrea Westkamp, (973) 279-3790

MISSIONARY SISTERS OF (W504-2)
THE IMMACULATE HEART OF MARY
See "I" - I.C.M. Missionary Sisters

MISSIONARY SISTERS OF (W505)
JESUS, MARY AND JOSEPH (M.J.M.J.)
Motherhouse: Spain, US Formation House, 12940 Leopard St., Corpus Christi, TX 78410
Email: vallarta@elp.rr.com
Members: 25 Sisters
Apostolic Work: Among Hispanic poor, social work, early childhood education with children of working parents, pastoral ministry, provide an emergency shelter for abused children, religious education, and religious formation for pastoral leadership
Representation: Dioceses of Corpus Christi, El Paso and San Antonio. Also in Mexico. Diocese of Morelia, Michoacan and Matamoros, Tamaulipas as well as Spain, Chile
Vocation Director: Sister Raquel Vallarta, MJMJ, (915) 778-3407, 7681 Barton St., El Paso, TX 79915

MISSIONARY SISTERS OF (W506)
THE MOST SACRED HEART OF JESUS (M.S.C.) U.S.A.
US Province Center, 2811 Moyers Lane, Reading, PA 19605
Web: www.mscreading.org
Email: mscvocdir@aol.com
Members: 900 Missionary Sisters worldwide
Apostolic Work: Making God's love present to everyone through evangelization, social work, health care,

education, pastoral ministries, counseling, parish ministry, religious education and foreign missions
Representation: 8 dioceses in the US and in 17 other countries
Vocation Director: 610-929-0695

MISSIONARY SISTERS OF (W507)
MOTHER OF GOD
See Eastern Catholic Religious Communities for Women

MISSIONARY SISTERS OF (W508)
OUR LADY OF AFRICA (M.S.O.L.A.)
47 West Spring St, Winooski, VT 05404, (802) 655-4003
Web: http://www.smnda.org/ and http://soeurs-blanches.cef.fr/bis.htm
Email: msoladol@aol.com and msola1usa@aol.com
Members: 15 Sisters in US, 889 Sisters Worldwide, 129 Communities
Apostolic Work: Working in 14 African countries for the development of a local African Church: primary evangelization, parish leadership training, social development of women, youth retreats, media, primary health care and other forms of medical work, programs for AIDS victims and their children, teaching, counseling, development projects together with the local people, formation of small Christian communities and local Sisterhoods.
Representation: Archdiocese of Washington, DC and in the Dioceses of Burlington and Springfield (MA)
Vocation Director: Contact Person: Sr. Dolores Fortier, msola, Providence Place, 5 Gamelin Road, Apt. #328, Holyoke, MA 01040-4080 (413) 534-6741

MISSIONARY SISTERS (W509-1)
OF OUR LADY OF MERCY (M.O.M.)
Motherhouse: Brazil
Rainbow K, 388 Franklin St., Buffalo, NY 14202
Members: 4 Sisters
Representation: in the Diocese of Buffalo
Vocation Director: Sr. Therese Marie, M.O.M., (716) 854-5198

CONGREGATION OF (W509-2)
MISSIONARY SISTERS OF OUR LADY OF PERPETUAL HELP
(M.P.S.), Regional House in US: 427 Rigsby St., San Antonio, TX 78210, (210) 532-3546 (tel, fax)
Members: 14 Sisters in US; 350 Sisters worldwide
Apostolic Work: Proclaiming the evangelical message of salvation by catechetical instruction of children, youth and adults, permanent and

itinerant missions, home visitation, giving communion to the sick, parish work, campus ministry, prison ministry, orphanages
Representation: Diocese of San Antonio. Foreign missions: Mexico, Guatemala, Honduras, El Salvador, Venezuela, Argentina, Philippines, Macao China and India

MISSIONARY SISTERS OF (W510-1)
THE PRECIOUS BLOOD (C.P.S.)
Regional House and Novitiate: Precious Blood Convent
PO Box 97, Reading, PA 19607
Web: www.preciousblood-cps.org
Email: vocationscps@hotmail.com
Members: 65 Sisters in North American Province, 1,000 worldwide
Apostolic Work: AIDS ministry, art/crafts, care for the aged, catechetics, education at all levels, liturgical ministry, medical work, pastoral ministry, ministry to persons who are physically or mentally challenged, retreat ministry, social work, youth ministry
Representation: Dioceses of Allentown, Brooklyn, and Lexington. Also in Austria, Congo, Denmark, Germany, Italy, Kenya, Mozambique, Netherlands, Ontario (Canada), Papua New Guinea, Portugal, Romania, South Africa, South Korea, Sudan, Tanzania, Zambia and Zimbabwe
Vocation Director: (610) 777-1624

MISSIONARY SISTERS OF (W510-2)
THE SACRO COSTATO AND OF THE SORROWFUL MOTHER
Motherhouse: Rome
also: Sacro Costato House, 230 E. Atlee St, Stockton, CA 95204, (209) 462-6533
Sacro Costato House, 1300 Bayswater Ave., Burlingame, CA 94010
Email: mscstcat@pacbell.net, mscstockton@aol.com
Members: 8 Sisters in US
Apostolic Work: Education of children and youth, catechetical instruction and parish work, retreats and Apostleship of Prayer, spiritual and material assistance to the poor, and foreign missions
Representation: Dioceses of San Francisco and Stockton and in Albania, Brazil, Ecuador, Italy, the Philippines, Taiwan, Indonesia, Vietnam, and China
Vocation Director: (650) 342-4780

MISSIONARY SISTERS OF (W511)
ST. CHARLES BORROMEO (SCALABRINIANS) (MSCS)
Provincial House, 1414 N. 37th Ave., Melrose Park, IL 60160

Web: www.scalabriniane.org
Email: secretarymscs@global.net
Members: 65 Sisters in North American Province; 745 Sisters worldwide in 25 countries
Apostolic Work: The congregation's charism is the Pastoral Care for Migrants and it carries out the mission through Catechesis, Christian Education, Health and Pastoral Care of the Sick, Social-Pastoral Care of Migrants; and Center of Studies. We are ministering in: schools, hospital, parishes, orphanages, prisons, nursing homes, diocesan and archdiocesan migration centers
Representation: (Arch)dioceses of Boston, Chicago, New York, Springfield and Washington, DC. Also present in Albania, Angelo, Argentina, Bolivia, Brazil, Canada, Colombia, Congo, Dominican Republic, Ecuador, France, Germany, Honduras, Italy, Mexico, Mozambique, Paraguay, Philippines, Poland, Portugal, South Africa, Spain, and Switzerland
Vocation Director: Sister Elizabeth V. Pedernal, MSCS, (708) 343-2162, fax (708) 343-6452

MISSIONARY SISTERS OF (W512)
ST. COLUMBAN (S.S.C.), 73 Mapleton St., Brighton, MA 02315
Web: www.columbansisters.org
Email: columbanbrighton@verizon.net
Members: 201 Sisters
Apostolic Work: Pastoral, chaplaincy, indigenous people, elderly, education, medical, migrant workers, developmentally disabled, ecumenism, organic farming, hospice, people with AIDS
Representation: Archdioceses of Boston and Los Angeles and in the Diocese of Buffalo. Also in Hong Kong, China, Myanmar, Korea, the Philippines, Chile, Peru, Pakistan, England, Scotland and Ireland
Vocation Director: Sr. Margaret Devine, (617) 325-3916

MISSIONARY SISTERS OF (W513)
ST. PETER CLAVER (S.S.P.C.), 265 Century Ave. So, Woodbury, MN 55125
Web: www.clavermissionary sisters.org
Email: sspcdelegateoffice@usfamily.net
Members: 230 World Wide
Apostolic Work: Mission animation: to increase the awareness of the needs of missionaries and to support them spiritually and financially
Representation: Archdioceses of St.

Louis, St. Paul and Chicago
Vocation Director: Sr. Genevieve Kudlik, S.S.P.C., (651)738-9704

MONASTIC FAMILY OF (W514-1)
BETHLEHEM AND OF THE ASSUMPTION OF THE VIRGIN
Our Lady of Lourdes Camp, Livingston Manor, NY 12758-2758
Members: 15 Nuns in US; 500 total
Apostolic Work: A life of contemplative prayer
Representation: Archdiocese of New York and in France, Austria, Belgium, Spain, Israel, Italy, Germany, Argentina, Canada, Lithuania, Chile and Cyprus
Vocation Director: Sister Amena, Prioress, (845) 439-4300

SISTERS OF THE MOST (W514-2)
HOLY SACRAMENT (M.H.S.)
PO Box 90037, Lafayette, LA 70509
Email: 105241.1405@compuserv.com
Members: 32 Sisters
Apostolic Work: Teaching, CCD, pastoral work, social work, health care, home missions and parish ministry.
Representation: Archdiocese of New Orleans and in the Dioceses of Baton Rouge and Lafayette
Vocation Director: Sister Hilda Mallet, MHS, Sister Judine Theriot, MHS (337) 989-9817 or (337) 981-8475, sjtmhs@eatel.net

SISTERS OF THE MOST (W514-3)
HOLY SOUL OF CHRIST (S.S.C.H.)
Motherhouse: Poland
1042 SE 9th St., Stuart, FL 34996
Web: www.sistersofthemostholy soulofchrist.com
Email: sschusa@yahoo.com
Members: 101 Sisters, 1 Postulant (worldwide)
Apostolic Work: Active contemplative: teaching, healthcare, catechesis, parish ministry, propagating devotion to the Most Holy Soul of Christ and the sanctification of humanity
Representation: Diocese of Palm Beach. Also in Poland and Africa
Vocation Director: Sister Martina, SSCH, (772) 286-5720

SISTERS OF THE MOST (W515)
HOLY TRINITY (O.SS.T.)
21281 Chardon Rd., Euclid, OH 44117-1591
Web: www.srstrinity.com
Email: osst@srstrinity.com
Members: 23 Sisters
Apostolic Work: Teaching, National Shrine of Our Lady of Lourdes
Representation: Archdiocese of Philadelphia and in the Diocese of

Cleveland, OH. Foreign missions in Madagascar and the Philippines. Generalate house in Rome, with about 20 houses spread throughout Italy
Vocation Director: Vocation Directress, (216) 481-8232

SISTERS OF THE MOST (W516)
PRECIOUS BLOOD (C.PP.S.)
204 N. Main St., O'Fallon, MO 63366-2299
Web: www.cpps-ofallon.org
Email: vocationdir@cpps-ofallon.org
Members: 180 Sisters
Conduct: The Sisters, an apostolic community, are rooted in the Eucharist and personal prayer, and strive to be and experience Christ's redeeming presence as they affirm and empower one another and those they serve, especially the poor
Apostolic Work: Education, parish ministry, geriatrics, special education, foreign missions, ecclesiastical art (the making of vestments), residential care, nursing, hospital ministry, health care services and social work
Representation: 6 states in the US. Foreign missions in Bolivia, Finland, Italy, Peru and Estonia.
Vocation Director: Sr. Maria Orf, C.PP.S. and Leah Wand, (636) 240-6010

MOTHERS OF THE (W517-1)
HELPLESS (M.D.),
Motherhouse: Spain
US: Sacred Heart Residence , 432 W. 20th St., New York, NY 10011-2902
Email: sacredheartresidence@hotmail.com
Members: 7 Sisters
Apostolic Work: in New York: 1 day nursery and 1 residence for young women. Worldwide: Houses in Spain (Motherhouse); Puerto Rico; Mexico; Chile; Argentina and Rome, Italy; Novitiates in Spain and Colombia. Foreign missions in Guatemala and Colombia. Home for the aged and orphaned children; schools, retreat house, residence and day care centers.
Representation: in the Archdiocese of New York and 8 foreign countries.
Vocation Director: Mother Esperanza Fernandez, (212) 929-5790, 0839

SISTERS OF NAZARETH (W517-2)
(C.S.N.), (Regional House and Novitiate) Nazareth House Los Angeles, 3333 Manning Ave., Los Angeles, CA 90064
Web: www.nazarethhouse.org

B-100

Email: vocations_naz@yahoo.com
Apostolic Work: The Sisters of Nazareth are a dynamic, prayerful community of consecrated religious serving the Lord through loving care given to seniors and the needy elderly at Nazareth House residential and skilled-nursing facilities throughout the globe, and to all children through quality religious and academic education offered at the Nazareth Schools
Representation: 6 US Nazareth Houses located in the California Archdioceses of Los Angeles and San Francisco, the Dioceses of San Diego and Fresno, and also Madison (WI) and Pago Pago (American Samoa) plus 50 locations worldwide
Vocation Director: Sr. Fintan, CSN, Vocation Coordinator, 310-839-2361

SISTERS OF THE NEW (W518)
COVENANT (S.N.C.), Private Association of the Christian Faithful 16440 Grays Way, Broomfield, CO 80023
Web: www.sncweb.org and www.vocations-snc.org
Email: cetc@sncweb.org
Apostolic Work: Following Jesus in the style of St. Francis. Evangelization, spreading the Good News of Jesus Christ
Representation: Archdiocese of Denver
Vocation Director: Sister Brigid Meierotto, S.N.C. (303) 451-8677

OUR LADY OF SION (N.D.S.) (W520)
(Sisters of Sion)
Generalate: Rome, Via Garibaldi 28, 00153, Roma
6322 North Wayne Ave., Chicago, IL 60660-1334
Web: www.sistersofsion.net
Email: sschmidts@sbcglobal.net
Members: 8 Sisters in US; 400 Sisters worldwide
Apostolic Work: Called to witness to God's faithful love for the Jewish people and to God's fidelity to the promises of justice, peace and love, which were revealed by the prophets of Israel for all humanity.
Representation: Archdiocese of Chicago and in the Dioceses of Brooklyn and Boston, South Orange, NJ and St. Paul, MN
Vocation Director: Membership Coordinator: Sr. Stephanie Schmidts, (773) 973-7543

NOTRE DAME SISTERS (ND) (W521)
Provincial Motherhouse, 3501 State St., Omaha, NE 68112-1799
Web: www.notredamesisters.org
Email: nd.voc@juno.com

Members: 52 Sisters
Apostolic Work: Teaching, pastoral ministry, religious education, counseling, nursing, home care, day care, chaplaincy, campus ministry, spiritual direction, family ministry, mission work in Honduras
Representation: Archdioceses of Omaha, Denver, Dubuque and Kansas City and in the Dioceses of Lincoln and Pueblo
Vocation Director: Sr. Dorothy Rolf, ND, (402) 455-2994 Fax (402) 455-3974

SISTERS OF NOTRE DAME (W525)
(S.N.D.), US Provinces: Ohio, Kentucky and California

Chardon Province: 13000 Auburn Rd., Chardon, OH 44024. (440) 286-7101
Vocation Director: Sr. Kathleen Mary Hine, SND, (440) 279-1194.
E-mail: khine@ndec.org, sndvocation@ndec.org; www.sndchardon.org

Covington Province: St. Joseph Heights, 1601 Dixie Hwy., Covington, KY 41011. (859) 291-2040
Vocation Director: Sister Jean Marie Hoffman, SND E-mail: vocations@sndky.org, www.sndky.org

Toledo Province: 3837 Secor Rd., Toledo, OH 43623
Vocation Director: Sister Mary Delores Gatliff, SND, (419) 474-5485
E-mail: dgatliff@toledosnd.org, www.sndtoledo.org

Thousand Oaks Province: 1776 Hendrix Ave., Thousand Oaks, CA 91360. (805) 496-3243
Vocation Director: Sister Valerie Marie Roxburgh, SND. E-mail: sistervalsnd@gmail.com www.sndca.org

Web: www.snd1.org
Members: 2,600 Sisters and Associates worldwide on 6 continents
Apostolic Work: Education: preschool through college, parish work, health care, social services, missionary and other ministries
Representation: Represented in United States, Brazil, South Korea, Great Britain, Germany, Holland, Italy, India, Indonesia, Kenya, Mozambique, Tanzania, Uganda, The Philippines, Papua New Guinea.

SISTERS OF NOTRE DAME (W526)
DE NAMUR (SNDdeN)
For information, call the vocation contact in your area or call toll free: (1-888) 827-1724. E-mail: Angele.Lewis@SNDdeN.org;

Web: http://ASKanSND.org or www.SNDdeN.org

Sister Josita Colbert, SNDdeN, 468 Poquonock Ave., Windsor, CT 06095-2473, (860) 285-0038, E-mail: Josita.Colbert@SNDdeN.org

Sister Angele Lewis, SNDdeN, 30 Jeffreys Neck Rd., Ipswich, MA 01938, (978) 380-1571, Angele.Lewis@SNDdeN.org

Sister Jacinta Martinez, SNDdeN*
Habla espanol, 43 Elm Street, San Carlos, CA 94070-2231
(650) 722-1040. E-mail: Jacinta.Martinez@SNDdeN.org

Sister Stephanie Thompson, SNDdeN, 701 E. Columbia Ave., Cincinnati, OH 45215, (513) 679-8111, E-mail:Stephanie.Thompson@SNDdeN.org

Web: www.SNDdeN.org
Members: Internationally we are over 1,600 professed Sisters with 38 novices/affiliates and 602 Associates. In the United States, we number over 900 with 7 novices/affiliates and 339 Associates
Conduct: Sisters of Notre Dame de Namur, women with hearts as wide as the world, make known God's goodness and love of the poor through a Gospel way of life, community and prayer. Julie Billiart and Francois Blin de Bourdon began the congregation in France in 1804 in the midst of the religious, social and political upheaval of the French Revolution. Because of their friendship, and mutual vision, the mission "to the poor in the most abandoned places" endures today. This global vision has been realized as we strive to serve the good God on five continents: Africa (Congo, Kenya, Nigeria, South Africa and Zimbabwe), Europe (Belgium, France, Great Britain, and Italy), Japan, Latin America (Brazil, Mexico, Nicaragua, and Peru) and North America (United States).
Apostolic Work: Religious education, formal education at all levels, health ministries, hospital chaplaincies, pastoral ministry, youth ministries, retreats and spiritual direction, ministry of prayer, social services, counseling, community development, legal services, service to immigrants and refugees, peace and justice work, prison ministry, missionary work and other developing ministries which respond to the needs in today's Church and world.
Representation: The Sisters of Notre Dame de Namur serve in 14 Archdioceses and 37 Dioceses within

the United States: (AZ) Phoenix; (CA) Los Angeles, San Francisco, Monterey, Oakland, Sacramento, San Jose, Stockton; (CT) Hartford, Bridgeport, Norwich; (DC) Washington, DC; (DE) Wilmington; (FL) Jacksonville, Miami, Orlando, Palm Beach; (IL) Chicago, Joliet; (IN) Lafayette; (KY) Covington, Lexington, Louisville; (MA) Boston, Springfield, Worcester; (MD) Baltimore; (ME) Portland; (MI) Saginaw; (NC) Charlotte, Raleigh; (NJ) Newark; (NY) New York, Brooklyn, Buffalo, Rockville Centre; (OH) Cincinnati, Columbus; (OR) Portland; (PA) Philadelphia, Harrisburg; (RI) Providence; (SC) Charleston; (SD) Sioux Falls; (TX) Austin; (VA) Arlington, Richmond; (VT) Burlington; (WA) Seattle; and (WV) Wheeling-Charleston

SCHOOL SISTERS OF (W532)
NOTRE DAME (SSND)
Atlantic-Midwest Province
Vocation Director: Maria Iannuccillo, SSND, 345 Belden Hill Rd., Wilton, CT 06897, (203) 762-4152, E-mail:imiannucillo@amssnd.org

Vocation Director: Kathy Jager, SSND, 6401 N. Charles St., Baltimore, MD 21212-1099, (410) 377-5179, Fax (410) 377-6945 E-mail: k-jager@juno.com

Vocation Director: Carolyn Jost, SSND, 9535 S. Loomis, Chicago, IL 60643, (708) 899-3971, E-mail: scarjost@aol.com

Milwaukee Province: Milwaukee, WI Vocation Director: Barbara Linke, SSND, 13105 Watertown Plank Rd., Elm Grove, WI 53122-2291, (262) 782-9850, ext. 716 Fax (262) 782-5725, E-mail:blinke@ssnd-milw.org

Mankato Province: Mankato, MNVocation Director: Julie Brandt, SSND, 170 Good Counsel Drive, Mankato, MN 56001-3138, (507) 389-4296, E-mail: jbrandt@ssndmankato.org

St. Louis Province: St. Louis, MO Vocation Director: Jean Greenwald, SSND, 320 East Ripa St., St. Louis, MO 63125-2897 (314) 633-7016 (Tel., Fax), E-mail: jeangreen@ssnd-sl.org

Dallas Province: Dallas, TX Vocation Director: Christine Garcia, SSND, 11106 Whisper Hollow, San Antonio, TX 78230, (210) 479-1734, E-mail: christinegarciassnd@yahoo.com

Canadian Province: Waterdown, Ontario
Vocation Director: Martha Fauteux, SSND, 1921 Snake Rd., Waterdown, Ontario, Canada L0R 2H0, (905) 689-6344, ext. 609 Fax (905) 689-9418, E-mail: mjfauteux@yahoo.ca

Web: www.ssnd.org
Email: sisters@ssnd.org
Conduct: We, the School Sisters of Notre Dame, are an international congregation, committed to serving God and God's people in order to bring Jesus' message of love and unity to our world. We work toward the transformation of persons through education. As women religious, we value prayer, faith sharing, and a community life that calls us to be of "one mind and one heart." Today approximately 4,000 School Sisters of Notre Dame serve in over 30 countries on five continents. We believe that our international network gives us a unique global perspective as we address, through various ministries, the urgent needs of our times, particularly the needs of women, youth and persons who are poor. You are invited to share this joy-filled life with us.
Apostolic Work: Education in colleges, high schools, elementary schools, preschools, day care, religious education, adult education, missionary work (domestic and oversees), social services, justice ministry and direct service to the poor, health and legal professions, parish and diocesan administration, pastoral ministry, prison ministry, retreat work and spiritual direction
Representation: We minister in over 30 states and in 36 countries: Argentina, Albania, Austria, Belarus, Bolivia, Brazil, Canada, Chile, Czech Republic, El Salvador, England, Germany, Ghana, Guam, Guatemala, Honduras, Hungary, Italy, Japan, Kenya, Korea, Marshall Islands, Micronesia, Nepal, Nigeria, Paraguay, Peru, Poland, Puerto Rico, Romania, Serbia, Sierra Leone, Slovenia, Sweden, The Gambia, USA
Vocation Director: SSND vocation ministers are located in eight regions throughout North America.

NUNS OF THE PERPETUAL (W539)
ADORATION OF THE BLESSED SACRAMENT (A.P.)
(San Francisco Province) Monastery of Perpetual Adoration, 771 Ashbury St., San Francisco, CA 94117-4013
Email: mpador@aol.com
Members: 15 Sisters

Representation: (Arch)dioceses of El Paso, San Francisco and Sioux Falls and in Alaska. Also in Africa, Chile, Italy, Mexico and Spain
Vocation Director: Sr. Alma Ruth Vargas, (415) 566-2743

NUNS OF THE PERPETUAL (W540-1)
ADORATION OF THE BLESSED SACRAMENT (A.P.) (Autonomous Monasteries), Monastery of Perpetual Adoration, 145 N. Cotton Ave., El Paso, TX 79901-9901
Email: mary.guadalupe@att.net
Members: 14 Sisters
Representation: Archdioceses of Anchorage and San Francisco, and in the Diocese of El Paso and Sioux Falls, SD
Vocation Director: (915) 533-5323

NUNS OF SAINT BASIL (W540-2)
THE GREAT
See Eastern Catholic Religious Communities for Women

SISTERS OBLATES TO THE (W541)
BLESSED TRINITY (O.B.T.)
St. Aloysius Novitiate
306 Beekman Rd., PO Box 98, Hopewell Junction, NY 12533
Web: www.Staloysius-ny.org
Email: jstab35097@aol.com
Apostolic Work: Teaching in parish schools, care of elderly and sick, catechetics and retreats
Representation: Archdiocese of New York and in the Dioceses of Madison, WI, San Juan and Ponce, Puerto Rico. Also Milan, Italy and El Salvador, Central America
Vocation Director: Superior General: Mother Gloria Castro, (845) 226-5671 or (845) 226-1917

OBLATE SISTERS OF (W542)
JESUS THE PRIEST (O.J.S.)
General Motherhouse: Mexico, Saint Patrick's Seminary, 320 Middlefield Rd., Menlo Park, CA 94025
Web: www.ojsoblates.org,
www.oblatasdejesus.org.mx
Email: oblates@sbcglobal.net
Members: 28 Sisters in US, 135 Sisters in Mexico
Representation: Archdioceses of Chicago, New York and San Francisco.
Vocation Director: (650) 322-4611, 322-5518

OBLATE SISTERS OF THE (W543)
BLESSED SACRAMENT (O.S.B.S.)
St. Sylvester Convent, 103 Church Drive, PO Box 217, Marty, SD 57361-0217
Email: osbs@cme.com
Members: 6 Sisters
Apostolic Work: American Indian Apostolate

Representation: Dioceses of Rapid City and Sioux Falls, SD
Vocation Director: St. Sylvester Convent, (605) 384-3305 Fax (605) 384-3575

OBLATE SISTERS OF (W545)
PROVIDENCE (O.S.P.)
Motherhouse and Novitiate: Our Lady of Mount Providence Convent 701 Gun Rd., Baltimore, MD 21227
Web: www.oblatesisters.com
Email: annette-beecham@ yahoo.com or srannette@oblatesisters.com
Members: 75 Sisters (multi-cultural)
Apostolic Work: Pastoral ministers/ associates, reading center, day care center, teaching, counseling, Hispanic/migrant ministry and retreat ministry
Representation: Archdiocese of Baltimore, and the Dioceses of Buffalo and Miami Beach, FL and also in Costa Rica
Vocation Director: Sr. Marcia L. Hall, OSP, (410) 242-8500, ext. 147

OBLATE SISTERS OF THE (W546)
SACRED HEART OF JESUS (O.S.H.J.)
Villa Maria Teresa, 50 Warner Rd., Hubbard, OH 44425
Web: www.oblatesistersofshj.com
Email: jcoblate@aol.com
Members: 17 Sisters in the States, 200 in the Congregation
Apostolic Work: Minister with, and to, diocesan priests as Directors of Religious Education, care for elderly priests, pastoral ministry, primary and elementary education, mission work
Vocation Director: Sister Teresina Rosa, (330) 759-9329 or 8468

OBLATE SISTERS OF (W547)
ST. FRANCIS de SALES (O.S.F.S.)
399 Childs Rd., Childs, MD 21916
Web: www.oblatesisters.org
Email: oblatesisters@ mountaviat.org
Members: 16 Sisters
Apostolic Work: Teaching and social work
Representation: Archdiocese of Philadelphia and in the Dioceses of Arlington and Wilmington
Vocation Director: Sister John Elizabeth, OSFS, (410) 398-3699

ORDER OF THE MOST (W548)
HOLY REDEEMER
See "R" - Redemptoristine Nuns

SISTERS OF OUR LADY (W549-1)
OF CHARITY (O.L.C.), (North American Union of the Sisters of Our Lady of Charity), PO Box 340, Carrollton, OH 44615-0340
Web: www.nauolc.org

Email: naucenter@hotmail.com
Members: 90 Sisters
Apostolic Work: "girls and women", day care for children, social work, teaching in schools, working with people with AIDS, Spanish and English speaking parishes, CCD programs, retreats, nursing, human trafficking, migrants, domestic violence
Representation: (Arch)dioceses of New York, Buffalo, NY; Erie/ Pittsburgh, PA; El Paso, TX; Steubenville, OH; Green Bay, WI; Wheeling, WV; San Diego, CA and Venice, FL. Also in Canada and Mexico
Vocation Director: Sister Carol Pregno, Superior General, (330) 627-1641 Fax (330) 627-1935

SISTERS OF OUR LADY OF (W549-2)
CHARITY (O.L.C.), Mt. St. Michael Convent, 4500 W. Davis St., Dallas, TX 75211
Members: 7 Sisters
Vocation Director: Sr. Therese Blanchette, O.L.C., Major Superior (214) 331-1754

SISTERS OF OUR LADY OF (W550)
CHRISTIAN DOCTRINE (R.C.D.)
Visitation House, 629 N. Midland Ave., Nyack, NY 10960
Web: www.sistersrcd.org
Members: 25 Sisters
Apostolic Work: Religious education, nursing, counseling, spiritual direction and retreat work, pastoral ministry, social work
Representation: New York and New Jersey
Vocation Director: Contact: Sr. Angela Palermo, (845) 358-7733, fax: (845) 358-7663

SISTERS OF OUR LADY OF (W551)
THE GARDEN (O.L.G.), 67 Round Hill Rd., Middletown, CT 06457
Members: 12 Sisters in US; 1,050 Sisters worldwide
Apostolic Work: Teaching, nursing, social work, foreign missions, parish work
Representation: Archdiocese of Hartford and the Diocese of Norwich
Vocation Director: Sr. Donna Beauregard, O.L.G., (860) 346-5765

THE CONGREGATION OF THE (W552)
SISTERS OF OUR LADY OF MERCY (O.L.M.) (Divine Mercy), General Motherhouse: Warsaw, Poland 241 Neponset Ave., Dorchester, MA 02122-2122
Web: www.sisterfaustina.org
Email: vocation@sisterfaustina.org
Members: 9 Sisters in US; about 400 Professed Sisters, 25 Novices,

16 Postulants worldwide
Apostolic Work: Saint Faustina Kowalska belonged to this active-contemplative congregation. The Sisters cooperate with the infinite mercy of God by proclaiming the message of Divine Mercy to the men and women of our time and by imploring God's mercy for the world through prayer and sacrifice. They faithfully seek to fulfill its mission in the Church which Pope John Paul II confirmed when visiting the Congregation's shrine in Cracow: "Choosing from among you Sister Faustina, Christ…has called you to a particular apostolate, that of His Mercy…The people of today need your proclamation of mercy; they need your works of mercy and they need your prayer to obtain mercy." If you feel called to make the merciful Jesus known and loved, contact the Sisters. Age limit: 35
Representation: Archdiocese of Boston. Also in Rome, Jerusalem, Poland, Czech Republic, Belarus, Slovakia, and Kazakhstan
Vocation Director: Sr. M. Caterina Esselen, O.L.M., (617) 288-5323 Fax (617) 288-1177

SISTERS OF OUR LADY OF (W553)
THE HOLY ROSARY (R.S.R.)
Motherhouse: Rimouski, P.Q., Canada G5L 3E3, Regional House, 25 Portland Ave., Old Orchard Beach, ME 04064, (207) 934-0592
Email: rsr@maine.rr.com
Members: 8 Sisters in US; 503 Sisters worldwide
Apostolic Work: Christian education
Representation: Diocese of Portland, ME; in the Provinces of Quebec and New Brunswick in Canada and also in Honduras, Peru, Guatemala, and North Labrador
Vocation Director: Sr. Juliette Michaud, R.S.R., 20 Thomas St., Portland, ME 04102-3638, (207) 774-3756

SISTERS OF OUR LADY OF (W554)
SORROWS (O.L.S.), Motherhouse: Italy, US Headquarters: Our Lady of Sorrows Convent, 9894 Norris Ferry Rd., Shreveport, LA 71106
Web: www.ols.org
Email: vocations@ols.org
Members: 27 Sisters in US; 317 worldwide
Apostolic Work: Education, work with people with mental retardation, outreach to poor, pastoral ministry, CCD, adult education.
Representation: Dioceses of Alexandria, Lafayette, LA, and Shreveport, LA
Vocation Director: Sr. Fatima Aphiri, OLS

B-103

OUR LADY OF VICTORY (W555)
MISSIONARY SISTERS (OLVM)
PO Box 109, Huntington, IN 46750
Web: www.olvm.org
Email: voc@olvm.org
Members: 140 Sisters
Apostolic Work: Pastoral ministry,
religious education, social services
and health care. Prophetic ministry,
promoting justice for the poor and
oppressed, with emphasis on women
Representation: 16 states
Vocation Director: Sr. Rose Ann
Kaiser, Vocation Minister and Asso-
ciate Coordinator, (260) 356-0628,
fax: (260) 358-1504

PALLOTTINE SISTERS (W557)
**(C.S.A.C.) (Sisters of the Catholic
Apostolate), (**Immaculate Conception
Province) Provincialate, (845) 492-
5080, Queen of Apostles Center, PO
Box 118, Harriman, NY 10926
Web: www.pallottinesisters.org
Email: newapostle98@yahoo.com
Members: 45 Sisters; 700 worldwide
Apostolic Work: Schools, parish/
pastoral work, formation and
education of lay groups, collabora-
tion in communication, youth and
young adult work, hispanic ministry
Representation: Archdioceses of
Newark and New York. Also in
Europe, South America, India and
Mozambique
Vocation Director: Sr. Carmel
Therese Favazzo, PO Box 767,
Harriman, NY 10926, (845) 492-
5076

PALLOTTINE MISSIONARY (W558)
**SISTERS (S.A.C.) Society of the
Catholic Apostolate**
Generalate: Rome
Queen of Apostles Province
15270 Old Halls Ferry Rd.,
Florissant, MO 63034-1611
Web: www.pallottinespirit.org
Email: vocations@pallottinespirit.org
Members: 40 Sisters in US, 650
Worldwide
Apostolic Work: Education, health
care, retreat ministry, prison min-
istry, administrative, visual arts,
parish ministry, pastoral ministry,
spiritual direction and prayer.
Mission: As apostles of Jesus, in
collaboration with the laity, we
joyfully and generously commit
ourselves to respect, nurture, and
celebrate all life and to rekindle love
for God through prayer and works
of mercy.
Representation: Archdioceses of St.
Louis and Washington D. C. and
the Diocese of Wheeling-
Charleston
Vocation Director: Sr. Lena May,
SAC, (314) 830-9814

PARISH VISITORS OF MARY (W559)
IMMACULATE (P.V.M.I.)
Marycrest Convent, Box 658,
Monroe, NY 10949-0658
Web: www.parishvisitorsisters.org
Email: tallon@pocketmail.com
Members: 62 Sisters (including
Postulants)
Apostolic Work: Contemplative-
missionary community serving the
Church in visitation/evangelization,
through person-to-person contact
by visiting families, individuals or
groups; religious education for the
total parish; spiritual counseling;
social service; in all of this seeking
out the spiritually, morally or
materially impoverished, the
rejected and neglected
Representation: Archdiocese of New
York and in the Dioceses of
Brooklyn, Syracuse and Scranton.
Also in the Archdiocese of Manila,
Philippines and Dioceses of Abuja
and Okigwe, Nigeria.
Vocation Director: Sister Dolores
Marie, P.V.M.I., (845) 783-2251

SISTERS OF THE PASSION (W559-1)
**AND CROSS (Traditional Franciscan
Contemplatives),** Monastery of the
Blessed Sacrament, PO Box 366,
New Middletown, OH 44442-0366
Web: www.adorationmonastery.org
Email: JesuMaria@aol.com
Apostolic Work: Contemplation,
Intercessory Prayer, Eucharistic
Adoration

PASSIONIST NUNS (C.P.) (W560)
**(The Nuns of The Most Holy Cross
and Passion of Our Lord Jesus
Christ),** 1151 Donaldson Hwy.,
Erlanger, KY 41018
Represented in five independent
monasteries in the US:
Our Lady of Sorrows Monastery of
the Passionist Nuns, 2715 Church-
view Ave., Pittsburgh, PA 15227-
2141, (412) 881-1155 9 Nuns, 1
Novice
St. Gabriel's Monastery, 631 Griffin
Pond Rd., Clarks Summit, S.
Abington Twp., PA 18411, (570) 586-
2791 8 Nuns
St. Joseph's Monastery, 8564 Crisp
Rd., Whitesville, KY 42378-9729,
(270) 233-4571 15 Nuns, 2 Novices
Monastery of the Sacred Passion,
1151 Donaldson Hwy., Erlanger, KY
41018, (859) 371-8568 8 Nuns
Immaculate Conception Monastery,
1032 Clayton Rd., Ellisville, MO
63011, (636) 227-3550 13 Nuns, 1
Novice
Web: www.passionistnunscls.org
Email: passionistnunscls@
yahoo.com
Apostolic Work: Contemplation

Vocation Director: Sr. Helen, C.P., St.
Gabriel's Monastery, 631 Griffin
Pond Rd., Clarks Summit, S.
Abington Twp., PA 18411-8899,
(570) 586-2791

PASSIONIST SISTERS (C.P.) (W561)
(Sisters of the Cross and Passion)
Holy Family Convent, 1 Wright Ln.,
North Kingstown, RI 02852
Web: www.passionistsisters.org
Email: theresinascully@aol.com
Members: 39 Sisters in US
Apostolic Work: Education, retreats,
pastoral care, social work, cate-
chetics, foreign missions.
Representation: Archdiocese of
Hartford, New York and Washington
(DC) and in the Dioceses of
Memphis, Providence and Rockville
Centre. Also in Jamaica, West
Indies.
Vocation Director: Sr. Theresina
Scully, CP, (401) 294-3554

SISTERS OF PERPETUAL (W562)
ADORATION (A.P.G.)
US Foundation
2403 West Travis Street, San
Antonio, TX 78207-8207
Members: 9 Sisters
Vocation Director: Sr. Maria del
Carmen Sanchez Obregon,
Superior, (210) 227-5546

SISTERS OF THE PIOUS (W563)
**SCHOOLS (Sch.P.) (Madres
Escolapias),** Motherhouse: Rome
US Headquarters, Province of
California-Mexico, 17601 Nordhoff
St., Northridge, CA 91325
Web: www.escolapias.org
Email: camexschp@sbcglobal.net
Members: 46 Sisters, 10 Junior
Professed, 2 Novices, 2 Postulants,
3 Aspirantes
Conduct: Schools, religious
education
Representation: Archdiocese of Los
Angeles. Also missions in Mexico,
Latin America, India, Japan, Africa,
Philippines, Spain, Poland, Italy
and Vietnam
Vocation Director: Sr. Guadalupe
Gonzalez, Sch.P., (818) 885-6265
Fax (818) 718-6752

POOR CLARE COLETTINE (W565)
NUNS (P.C.C.), Corpus Christi
Monastery, 2111 S. Main St.,
Rockford, IL 61102
Web: www.rockfordpoorclares.org
Members: 21 Sisters, 1 Novice, 3
Postulants
Vocation Director: Mother Mary
Regina, P.C.C., Abbess,
(815) 963-7343

POOR CLARE MISSIONARY (W566) **SISTERS (M.C.),** Regional House and Novitiate,1019 N. Newhope, Santa Ana, CA 92703-2703
Email: clarisas@netzero.net
Members: 45 Sisters; approx. 600 worldwide
Apostolic Work: Education, nursing, catechesis, retreat houses, pastoral work
Representation: Archdiocese of Los Angeles and in the Diocese of Orange. Also in Mexico, Costa Rica, Japan, Indonesia, Ireland, Spain, Italy, India, Russia, Sierra Leone, Nigeria, Korea and Germany
Vocation Director: Sr. Celia Martinez, M.C., (714) 554-8850 Fax (714) 554-5886

POOR CLARE NUNS (O.S.C.) (W567) **or (P.C.C.),** The Poor Clare Nuns are a contemplative Order of over 1,000 independent monasteries worldwide. The nuns do not engage in any direct apostolate outside of their monasteries.,

POOR CLARE NUNS (P.C.C.) (W569) St. Joseph's Monastery Poor Clare Colettines, 1671 Pleasant Valley Rd., PO Box 160, Aptos, CA 95001-0160
Web: www.poorclaresofaptos.org
Email: st.josephmonastery@ sbcglobal.net
Members: 10 Solemn Vows, 2 in Perpetual Vows
Vocation Director: Mother Francis Maria, P.C.C., Abbess, (831) 761-9659

POOR CLARE NUNS (W570) Immaculate Heart Monastery 28210 Natoma Rd., Los Altos Hills, CA 94022-4022
Members: 16 Sisters
Vocation Director: (650) 948-2947

POOR CLARE NUNS (P.C.C.) (W571) Monastery of Poor Clares, 215 E. Los Olivos St., Santa Barbara, CA 93105-3605
Web: www.poorclaressanta barbara.org
Members: 13 Professed, 1 in Formation
Vocation Director: Mother M. Clare, PCC, Abbess, (805) 682-7670

POOR CLARE NUNS (O.S.C.) (W573-1) Christ the King Monastery, 3900 Sherwood Blvd., Delray Beach, FL 33445-5699
Web: http://poorclares.delray.google pages.com
Email: ctkmdelray@aol.com
Members: 8 Sisters
Apostolic Work: Franciscan Contemplative Nuns

Vocation Director: Sr. Frances Vass, O.S.C., (561) 498-3294

POOR CLARE COLETTINE (W573-2) **NUNS (P.C.C.),** Annunciation Monastery, 6200 East Minooka Rd., Minooka, IL 60447
Web: www.poorclaresjoliet.org
Email: paxbonum@aol.com
Members: Poor Clares - 11 Sisters, 1 Junior, 7 Novices, 2 Postulants
Apostolic Work: Prayer and contemplation
Representation: Diocese of Joliet
Vocation Director: Mother Mary Dorothy, P.C.C., Poor Clare Nuns, (815) 467-0032

POOR CLARE NUNS (O.S.C.) (W574) Monastery of St. Clare, 6825 Nurrenbern Rd., Evansville, IN 47712-8518
Web: poorclare.org/evansville
Email: janemdelevin@juno.com
Members: 11 Sisters
Vocation Director: Sr. Jane Marie De Land, Abbess, (812) 425-4396

POOR CLARE NUNS (P.C.C.) (W575) Maria Regina Mater Monastery, 1175 N. 300 W, Kokomo, IN 46901-1799
Web: www.thepoorclares.org
Members: 9 Sisters, 1 Postulant
Apostolic Work: Prayer and penance
Vocation Director: Mother Miriam, P.C.C., Abbess, (765) 457-5743

POOR CLARE NUNS (O.S.C.) (W576) Order of St. Clare, St. Clare Monastery, 720 Henry Clay Ave., New Orleans, LA 70118-0118
Web: poorclarenuns.com
Email: srrmh@juno.com
Members: 8 Solemnly Professed, 1 Simply Professed
Apostolic Work: Gospel-living women in the Franciscan tradition, devoted to the contemplative life, the liturgical life of the Church and the Church's mission in the world
Vocation Director: Sister Rita Marie Hickey, OSC, (504) 895-2019

POOR CLARE NUNS (O.S.C.) (W577) Monastery of St. Clare, 445 River Rd, Andover, MA 01810-4213, (978) 683-7599
Email: poorclares445@aol.com
Members: 14 Sisters
Vocation Director: Contact: Sr. Emily Marie Silveira, osc, Formation Director

POOR CLARE NUNS (O.S.C.) (W578-1) Franciscan Monastery of St. Clare 920 Centre St., Jamaica Plain, MA 02130
Web: www.st.anthonyshrine.org/ poorclares

Email: bostonpoorclares@ worldnet.att.net
Members: 20 Final Professed, 3 in Formation
Apostolic Work: Strictly contemplative cloistered order.
Representation: Archdiocese of Boston
Vocation Director: Sister Clare Frances McAvoy, osc, Abbess

POOR CLARE NUNS (O.S.C.) (W578-2) **(Sisters of St. Clare),** 4875 Shattuck Rd., Saginaw, MI 48603-2962
Web: www.rc.net/saginaw/srsclare
Email: srsclare@sbcglobal.net
Members: 4 Sisters
Apostolic Work: Contemplative life style in community
Representation: Diocese of Saginaw
Vocation Director: Sr. Dianne Doughty, O.S.C., (989) 797-0593

POOR CLARE NUNS (O.S.C.) (W578-3) St. Clare Monastery, 8650 Russell Ave. S., Minneapolis, MN 55431-1998
Web: www.poorclares minneapolis.org
Email: jocasey1@juno.com
Members: 13 Sisters
Apostolic Work: Prayer and welcoming others to pray with us
Representation: Franciscan contemplative community
Vocation Director: Sister M. Jo Casey, osc (952) 881-4766

POOR CLARE NUNS (O.S.C.) (W579) St. Clare's Monastery, 421 South 4th St., Sauk Rapids, MN 56379-1898
Members: 17 Perpetually Professed, 2 Junior Professed, 1 Novice, 2 Externs
Apostolic Work: Contemplatives with Papal Enclosure
Vocation Director: (320) 251-3556 fax: (320) 203-7052
POOR CLARE NUNS (O.S.C.) (W580-1) Monastery of St. Clare, 200 Marycrest Dr., St. Louis, MO 63129-4813
Members: 10 Nuns in Solemn Vows
Apostolic Work: Cloistered contemplatives

POOR CLARE NUNS (O.S.C.) (W580-2) 3020 18th Avenue S, Great Falls, MT 59405-5167
Web: www.poorclaresmt.org
Email: sisters@poorclaresmt.org
Members: 4 Sisters
Apostolic Work: Enclosed contemplative community established in 1999 living the Form of Life written by St. Clare of Assisi. Members of the Holy Name Federation of Poor Clare Nuns
Vocation Director: Sister Catherine Cook, osc, (406) 453-7891 Fax 406-453-8689

B-105

POOR CLARE NUNS (O.S.C.) (W581)
Monastery of St. Clare, 3626 N. 65th
Ave., Omaha, NE 68104-3299
Web: www.omahapoorclare.com
Email: stjpoorclare@yahoo.com;
theresina@omahapoorclare.org
Members: 7 Sisters of solemn vows,
1 candidate
Vocation Director: Sister Theresina
R. Santiago, OSC, (402) 558-4916,
(402) 350-6335

POOR CLARE NUNS (W582)
(Cloistered), Monastery of St. Clare
150 White Pine Rd., Chesterfield,
NJ 08515
Web: www.poorclaresnj.org
Email: mvarleyosc@verizon.net
Members: 15 Sisters
Apostolic Work: Contemplative
Community
Vocation Director: Sister Miriam
Varley, OSC, Abbess, (609) 324-
2638

POOR CLARE NUNS (P.C.C.) (W583)
Monastery of Our Lady of
Guadalupe, 809 E. 19th St.,
Roswell, NM 88201-7599
Web: www.poorclaresroswell.com
Members: 23 Sisters
Apostolic Work: Cloistered contem-
plative community
Vocation Director: Mother Mary
Angela, P.C.C., Abbess, (505) 622-
0868, Fax (505) 627-2184

POOR CLARE NUNS (O.S.C.) (W584-1)
Monastery of Saint Clare, 70 Nelson
Ave., Wappingers Falls, NY 12590
Web: www.poorclaresny.org
Email: clarelight@gmail.com or
claresny@gmail.com
Members: 13 Sisters
Vocation Director: Sister Mary C.
Keyser, OSC, 845-297-1685, fax:
845-297-7657

POOR CLARE NUNS (O.S.C.) (W585-1)
Monastery of St. Clare, 1505 Miles
Rd., Cincinnati, OH 45231-2427
Web: www.poorclarescincinnati.org
Email: dianneshort@fuse.net
Members: 8 Sisters
Apostolic Work: Contemplative
Representation: Archdiocese of
Cincinnati
Vocation Director: Sr. Dianne Short,
O.S.C., (513) 825-7177 Fax (513)
825-4071

POOR CLARE COLETTINE (W585-2)
NUNS (P.C.C.), Monastery of the
Blessed Sacrament, 3501 Rocky
River Dr., Cleveland, OH 44111-2998
Web: www.poorclarecolettines-
cleveland.org
Members: 15 Solemnly Professed
Nuns, 2 Extern Sisters, 1 Novice

Apostolic Work: Dedicated to contemplative prayer and the Divine
Office, living in joyous penance,
poverty and simplicity and in Papal
Enclosure. Perpetual Adoration of
the Blessed Sacrament
Vocation Director: Reverend Mother
Mary Jude, P.C.C., Abbess, (216)
941-2820

POOR CLARE NUNS (O.S.C.) (W586-1)
(Contemplative Life Style)
Monastery of Saint Clare, 1271
Langhorne-Newtown Rd.,
Langhorne, PA 19047-1297
Web: www.poorclarepa.org
Email: stclare@poorclarepa.org
Members: 13 Sisters
Vocation Director: Sr. Evelyn, O.S.C,
(215) 968-5775

POOR CLARE NUNS (O.S.C.) (W586-2)
Monastery of St. Clare, 37
McCauley Rd., Travelers Rest, SC
29690-9244
Web: www.poorclaresc.com
Email: jenkinsosc@juno.com
Members: 17 Sisters
Apostolic Work: Contemplative
Vocation Director: Sister Mary Ann
Jenkins, osc, (864) 834-8015 Fax:
(864) 834-5402

POOR CLARE NUNS (O.S.C.) (W586-3)
Monastery of St. Clare, 1310 Dell-
wood Ave., Memphis, TN 38127-8127
Web: www.poorclare.org/memphis
Email: memphisclares@yahoo.com
Members: 6 Sisters
Conduct: Contemplative community
Vocation Director: Sr. Mary John,
osc, (901) 357-6662 Fax (901) 353-
3783

POOR CLARE NUNS (P.C.C.) (W586-5)
Monastery of Poor Clares Collettine
P.C.C., 5500 Holly Fork Rd,
Barhamsville, VA 23011
Web: www.poor-clares.org
Email: mtstfrancis@megasurf.net
Members: 13 Nuns
Vocation Director: Mother Mary
Clare, P.C.C., (757) 566-1684

POOR CLARE NUNS (O.S.C.) (W586-6)
Franciscan Monastery of St. Clare
4419 N. Hawthorne St., Spokane,
WA 99205-1399
Web: www.calledbyjoy.com or
www.poorclare.org
Email: stclare@icehouse.net
Members: 5 Solemnly Professed
Sisters
Apostolic Work: Cloistered, contem-
plative prayer; 24 hour Catholic
Radio station; Web ministry with
Catholic card site; publishing
Vocation Director: Sr. Marcia Kay
LaCour, OSC, (509) 327-4479

POOR CLARES NUNS OF (W587)
PERPETUAL ADORATION (P.C.P.A.)
Sancta Clara Monastery, 4200 N.
Market Ave., Canton, OH 44714
Web: www.poorclares.org
Email: sismomzelt@yahoo.com
Members: 11 Sisters
Apostolic Work: Eucharistic Adora-
tion and contemplative prayer,
environment for private retreats,
prayer and sacrifices for the world
Representation: Diocese of
Youngstown
Vocation Director: Sr. Magdalen
Colson, PCPA, (330) 492-1171

POOR CLARES OF (W588-1)
PERPETUAL ADORATION (P.C.P.A.)
Our Lady of the Angels Monastery
3222 County Rd #548, Hanceville,
AL 35077
Web: www.olamshrine.com
Members: 40 Nuns
Apostolic Work: Perpetual adoration
of the Most Blessed Sacrament
Vocation Director: Sr. Mary Catherine,
PCPA, Vicar, (205) 271-2917

POOR CLARES OF (W588-2)
PERPETUAL ADORATION (P.C.P.A.)
3900 13th St, NE, Washington, DC
20017-2699
Web: www.poorclareswdc.org
Email: ourpreciousgift@poorclares
wdc.org
Members: 6 Sisters
Apostolic Work: Perpetual Adoration
of the Most Blessed Sacrament;
Enclosed Contemplative Order
Vocation Director: Sr. Mary Rita,
PCPA, (202) 526-6808 Fax (202)
526-0678

POOR CLARES OF (W589)
PERPETUAL ADORATION (P.C.P.A.)
Adoration Monastery, Autonomous,
Contemplative Community, 4108
Euclid Ave., Cleveland, OH 44103
Web: www.thepoorclares.com
Email: angelspcpa@sbcglobal.net
Members: 20 Sisters
Apostolic Work: Perpetual
Eucharistic Adoration
Representation: (Arch)dioceses of
Cleveland, Washington, DC,
Youngstown, OH; Columbus, OH
and Birmingham, AL. Also in India,
Poland, France, Germany and
Austria
Vocation Director: Mother Mary
James, P.C.P.A., (216) 361-0783

POOR CLARES OF (W590)
PERPETUAL ADORATION (P.C.P.A.)
St. Joseph Adoration Monastery
2311 Stockham Lane, Portsmouth,
OH 45662-3049
Web: www.stjosephmonastery.com
Email: nuns@stjoseph
monastery.com

Members: 9 Cloistered Nuns
Apostolic Work: Contemplative prayer, Perpetual Adoration of the Blessed Sacrament
Vocation Director: Sr. Imelda Marie, P.C.P.A., (740) 353-4713

POOR HANDMAIDS OF (W595)
JESUS CHRIST (PHJC)
PO Box 1, Donaldson, IN 46513
Web: www.poorhandmaids.org
Email: skathyh@poorhandmaids.org
Apostolic Work: Focused on partnering in the work of the Spirit, PHJC ministries include various facets of education, pastoral work, social/neighborhood-based health ministries, child-care, spiritual guidance and care for the environment
Representation: (Arch)dioceses of Belleville, Chicago, Cincinnati, Detroit, Fort Wayne-South Bend, Gary, Joliet, Lafayette, Savannah, Springfield (IL) and Providence, RI. Also in Germany, Kenya, Nigeria, the Netherlands, England, India, Mexico and Brazil
Vocation Director: Sister Kathy Haas, PO Box 1, Donaldson, IN 46513, (574) 936-9936

POOR SERVANTS OF THE (W596)
MOTHER OF GOD (S.M.G.)
Motherhouse: England, Emmaus House, 101 Center St., Perth Amboy, NJ 08861-8861
Web: www.poorservants.com
Email: sisterlucy@pbmccrc.com
Members: 13 Sisters in the USA
Apostolic Work: Health care, education, retreats, social concerns, catechetics
Representation: (Arch)dioceses of Charlotte, Camden, Gallup, and Metuchen. Also in Africa, England, France, Ireland, Rome, Scotland, and South America
Vocation Director: Sr. Lucy Hennessy, S.M.G., 1315 Greensboro Rd., High Point, NC 27260 (336) 454-3014 Fax (336) 886-2350

(W597)
POOR SISTERS OF NAZARETH
See "N" - Nazareth, Sisters of

POOR SISTERS OF (W598)
ST. JOSEPH, US Foundations in Alexandria, VA, Bethlehem, PA, and Reading, PA, 4319 Sano Street, Alexandria, VA 22312
Email: hnassangabriel@aol.com
Members: 11 Sisters in US
Apostolic Work: Schools, hospitals, nursing homes, (parish) pastoral work
Vocation Director: Mother Maria D. Gonzalez, (703) 354-0395

SISTERS OF THE PRECIOUS (W599)
BLOOD (C.PP.S.), Generalate, 4000 Denlinger Rd., Dayton, OH 45426-2399, (937) 837-3302
Web: www.preciousbloodsisters dayton.org
Email: vocations@preciousblood sistersdayton.org
Members: 189 Sisters
Apostolic Work: Pastoral ministry, religious education, retreat work, food service, healthcare, social services, teaching (elementary, secondary, university), and Chilean and Guatemalan foreign missions
Representation: Archdioceses of Cincinnati, Denver and Detroit and in the Dioceses of Cleveland, Columbus, Lafayette, Lansing, Lexington, Phoenix, Richmond, San Bernardino, San Diego, Toledo, and Tucson
Vocation Director: Sister Carolyn Hoying, C.PP.S., Coordinator of Vocation Ministry, 4960 Salem Ave., Dayton, OH 45416, (937) 278-0871, ext. 1303

UNION OF SISTERS OF THE (W600)
PRESENTATION OF THE BLESSED
VIRGIN MARY (P.B.V.M.) - UNITED
STATES PROVINCE, Provincialate, 5151 Evergreen Ave., Cypress, CA 90630, (714) 527-4844
Web: www.pbvmunion.org
Email: juliecielito2@aol.com
Members: 73 Sisters
Apostolic Work: Teaching, religious education, adult education, nursing, social work, parish ministries, retreat work
Representation: Archdioceses of Los Angeles, Mobile, New Orleans, San Antonio and San Francisco and in the Dioceses of Biloxi, Birmingham, Oakland, Orange, Phoenix, San Bernardino and Tucson. Sisters in Africa, England, India, Ireland, New Zealand, Pakistan, Philippines and South America
Vocation Director: Sr. Julie Hurtado, PBVM, (714) 737-0812

PRESENTATION SISTERS (W601)
OF ABERDEEN (P.B.V.M.)
Motherhouse: Presentation Heights 1500 N. Second, Aberdeen, SD 57401-1238
Web: www.presentationsisters.org
Email: vocoff@presentation sisters.org
Members: 100 Sisters
Apostolic Work: Education, hospital, nursing homes, parish and youth ministries and social services, ministry with Native American, Hispanic and rural people, retreat work, campus ministry
Representation: Primarily in South

Dakota. Also in Minnesota, California, Iowa, Nebraska, New York, and Africa.
Vocation Director: Sister Phyllis Gill, P.B.V.M., (605) 229-8414

PRESENTATION SISTERS (W602)
OF DUBUQUE (P.B.V.M.)
Motherhouse and Novitiate, 2360 Carter Rd., Dubuque, IA 52001-2997
Web:
www.dubuquepresentations.org
Email: vocations@dubuque presentations.org
Members: 138
Apostolic Work: College, high schools, elementary schools, religious education, pastoral ministry, campus ministry, youth ministry, home and foreign missions, spiritual direction, housing, vocation ministry, retreat work, prison ministry, social justice lobbying, massage therapy, food service, spirituality and art workshops, tutoring, Hispanic ministry, immigrant ministry
Representation: Archdioceses of Dubuque, Chicago, Louisville, New Orleans, Omaha, St. Paul-Minneapolis and Washington, D.C. and in the Dioceses of Arizona, Davenport, Jackson, LaCrosse, Orlando, Sioux City, South Bend, Texas and Winona. Also in Entre Rios, Tarija, Bolivia
Vocation Director: Sr. Carla Popes, PBVM, (563) 588-2008

SISTERS OF THE (W603)
PRESENTATION OF THE BLESSED
VIRGIN MARY (P.B.V.M.)
Motherhouse and Novitiate: 1101 32 Ave. S., Fargo, ND 58103-6036, (701) 237-4857
Web: www.presentationsisters fargo.com
Email: srshawna@hotmail.com
Members: 49 Professed Sisters
Apostolic Work: Education, pastoral ministry, health care, domestic services, social work, spirituality centers, home and foreign missions
Representation: (Arch)dioceses of Columbus, Fargo, and New Ulm, Jackson. Also in Peru
Vocation Director: Sr. Shawna Foley, PBVM, Presentation Ministries, 3001 11th St. S., Fargo, ND 58103, (701) 235-8246, (701) 552-1083 (cell)

SISTERS OF THE (W604)
PRESENTATION OF BVM-NEW
WINDSOR, NY (P.B.V.M.)
Mt. St. Joseph, Administration Center, 880 Jackson Ave, New Windsor, NY 12553, (845) 564-0513 Fax (845) 567-0219

B-107

Web: www.sistersofthe
presentation.org
Email: mcredmond13@aol.com
Members: 140 Sisters
Apostolic Work: High schools, elementary schools, social/pastoral ministry, health care and religious education.
Representation: Archdioceses of Boston, Los Angeles, Newark, New York and Washington and in the Dioceses of Brooklyn, Manchester, Metuchen, Norwich, Paterson, Providence, Rockville Center, Trenton and Worcester. Also in Tarija (Bolivia)
Vocation Director: Sr. Mary Catherine Redmond, PBVM, 4504 Richardson Ave., Bronx, NY 10470, (718) 325-5172

SISTERS OF THE   (W606)
PRESENTATION OF THE BLESSED VIRGIN MARY (P.B.V.M.), SAN FRANCISCO, Congregational Offices 281 Masonic Ave., San Francisco, CA 94118
Web: www.presentationsisterssf.org
Email: sstill@pbvmsf.org
Members: 100 Sisters
Apostolic Work: Presentation women are committed to fulfilling the mission of their foundress, Nano Nagle, by continuing to serve the poor in the ministries of education, parish ministry, community organizing, pastoral care in hospitals, literacy programs, foreign missions, immigration work, spiritual direction, retreat work, personal care facility for the poor, and SafeHouse for women wanting to escape prostitution.
Representation: Archdioceses of San Francisco and Los Angeles and in the Dioceses of Oakland, San Jose and Orange with missionaries in Guatemala and Nicaragua. Find out more about our history, charism, and current life on our Website, presentationsisterssf.org
Vocation Director: Sr. Stephanie Still, PBVM, (415) 422-5020

PRESENTATION SISTERS   (W607)
OF STATEN ISLAND (P.B.V.M.)
Motherhouse: Our Lady of the Presentation, 419 Woodrow Rd., Annadale, SI, NY 10312-1351
Email: rosemarypssi@aol.com
Members: 16 Sisters (members of an international organization of women)
Apostolic Work: Elementary schools, high school, university, pastoral ministry in parish, hospital and university.
Representation: (Arch)dioceses of New York, Newark, Philadelphia and Sioux Falls

Vocation Director: Sr. Rosemary Ward, PBVM, Congregation Leader, (718) 356-2121, Fax (718) 966-2365

PRESENTATION SISTERS   (W608)
OF WATERVLIET (P.B.V.M.),
St. Colman's Presentation Convent 11 Haswell Road, Watervliet, NY 12189-2189
Web: www.stcolmans.com
Email: pbvm@stcolmans.com
Apostolic Work: Founded in Ireland in 1775 by Mother Nano Nagle, the Presentation Sisters came to Watervliet, New York in 1881 to establish a home for orphan children. Today, our Sisters continue to minister to the needs of children in their residential programs for the emotionally handicapped, the autistic, and the special needs child. Day care programs for the preschooler, teaching in diocesan schools and parish ministry are also part of our apostolate. A Habit, daily Mass and prayer schedule, as well as convent living are important factors in the life of a Presenation Sister.
Representation: Diocese of Albany
Vocation Director: Sr. Mary Michael, P.B.V.M., (518) 273-4911

SISTERS OF THE   (W609)
PRESENTATION OF MARY (P.M.)
Manchester Province: 495 Mammoth Rd., Manchester, NH 03104
Methuen Province: 209 Lawrence Street, Methuen, MA 01844
Web: www.presentationofmary.com or www.presmarymethuen.org
Email: provincialhouse@ presmarynh.org or prov.methuen@verizon.net
Members: 260 Sisters in the USA; 1,288 Sisters worldwide in 20 countries
Apostolic Work: Teaching and School Administration Pre-K to College levels, Campus Ministry, Pastoral Ministry, Faith Formation all levels, Youth Ministry, Retreat Ministry, Spiritual Direction, House of Discernment, Ministry to the poor.
Representation: Maine, Massachusetts, New Hampshire, Rhode Island, and 19 other countries
Vocation Director: Sr. Lorraine Aucoin, pm, 495 Mammoth Rd., Manchester, NH 03104 (603) 668-1791, srlorrainea@yahoo.com
Sr. Linda Mae Plourde, pm, 10 Evans Rd., Biddeford, ME 04005, (207) 284-5671
pmvocations@yahoo.com

SISTERS OF PROVIDENCE   (W611)
(S.P.) (Western US), (Mother Joseph Province),1801 Lind Ave. SW #9016, Renton, WA 98057-9016, (425) 525-3355, fax: (425) 525-3984
Web: www.sistersofprovidence.net
Email: vocations@providence.org
Members:163 Professed Sisters, 3 in Temporary Vows, 2 Candidates, 1 Transfer
Apostolic Work: Ministries: Varied according to the needs of the people and the gifts and creativity of each Sister. Many Sisters minister in health care, education, parish/ diocesan ministries, low-income housing, shelters, prisons, pastoral care, administration, and elderly and multicultural ministries. Opportunities for foreign mission ministry.
Sponsor/Manage: A high school, university, Montessori school, child care center; many health-care facilities from Anchorage to Burbank, Seattle to Great Falls; shelters/ housing for women and children, women in transition, those with AIDS, the elderly and handicapped
Representation: (Arch)dioceses of Anchorage, Boise, Great Falls, Helena, Los Angeles, Oakland, Portland (OR), Seattle, Spokane and Yakima. Also in El Salvador
Vocation Director: Sr. Judy George, SP, Manager, Vocation Office, 9 East Ninth Ave., Spokane, WA 99202-1209, (509) 474-2323

SISTERS OF PROVIDENCE   (W612)
OF HOLYOKE (SP), 5 Gamelin St, Holyoke, MA 01040-4080
Web: www.sisofprov.org
Email: ahorgan@sisofprov.org
Members: 71 Members
Apostolic Work: Through lives of prayer, community and service, the Sisters are called to reveal the loving care of God's Providence through ministries of hope and healing with particular emphasis on women, the earth and those who are poor. Sponsored ministries include soup kitchens/shelters, healthcare facilities and a spiritual life center
Representation: Dioceses of Springfield and Worcester (MA) and Raleigh (NC)
Vocation Director: Sister Ann Horgan, SP, (413) 536-7511, ext. 558

SISTERS OF PROVIDENCE OF   (W614)
SAINT MARY-OF-THE-WOODS (S.P.)
Motherhouse: 1 Sisters of Providence, St. Mary-of-the-Woods, IN 47876-1007, (800) 860-1840, ext. 2897 or (812) 535-2897
Web: www.sistersofprovidence.org

Email: moreinfo@spsmw.org
Members: 420 Sisters
Apostolic Work: Education ministries in colleges, universities, high schools, grade schools, parishes, adult learning centers; pastoral ministry in parishes, colleges, prisons, retirement and health-care facilities, retreat centers; health-care ministries; social service ministries including counseling, administration, justice work, eco-justice center; administrative ministries in arch/diocesan and parish offices, congregation service, national organizations; foreign missions
Representation: (Arch)dioceses of Belleville, Boston, Charlotte, Chicago, Cincinnati, Cleveland, Corpus Christi, Duluth, Evansville, Fort Wayne/South Bend, Gary, Indianapolis, Joliet, Los Angeles, Lafayette (IN), Lafayette (LA), Lexington, Louisville, Manchester, Oklahoma City, Omaha, Orange, Peoria, Portland, Raleigh, San Antonio, San Bernardino, San Francisco, Santa Fe, Springfield, St. Paul, St. Petersburg, Trenton, Venice, and Washington, DC. Also in China and Taiwan
Vocation Director: Sister Jenny Howard, SP, Owens Hall, (800) 860-1840, ext. 2897 or (812) 535-2897

REDEMPTORISTINE NUNS (W615)
(O.Ss.R.) (Order of the Most Holy Redeemer), Mother of Perpetual Help Monastery, PO Box 220, Esopus, NY 12429-0220
Web: www.RedemptoristineNunsof NewYork.org
Email: ContemplativeCall@ hotmail.com
Members: 9 Professed Sisters in this monastery; 550 members in approx. 45 monasteries worldwide
Apostolic Work: Contemplative Prayer
Representation: Archdiocese of New York and St. Louis
Vocation Director: Sr. Hildegard Magdalen Pleva, O.Ss.R
(845) 384-6533

(W617)
RELIGIOUS OF THE ASSUMPTION
See "A" - Assumption, Religious of the

RELIGIOUS OF THE (W618)
INCARNATE WORD (C.V.I.)
Motherhouse: Mexico City
US Vice Provincial, 153 Rainier Court, Chula Vista, CA 91911-1911
Email: ccrabbe@hotmail.com
Members: 10 Members in US; 475 Sisters
Apostolic Work: Teaching, residence

for students, campus ministry, catechetics, pastoral ministry, Third Order, home for aged and missions
Representation: Diocese of San Diego. Also in Mexico, Spain, France, Guatemala, Argentina and Africa.
Vocation Director: Sr. Camille Crabbe, C.V.I., (619) 420-0231

RELIGIOUS OF JESUS AND (W619)
MARY (R.J.M.), (US Province)
Provincial Offices,125 Michigan Ave., 4th Floor, Washington, DC 20017, (202) 884-9795, Fax: (202) 884-9794
Web: www.rjm-us.org
Email: srfarnham@yahoo.com
Members: 100 Sisters; 1,300 worldwide
Apostolic Work: Teaching at all levels, pastoral team work, cate-chetical instruction, health care, counseling, community social action, retreat work, nursing. Summer and long-term QUEST, lay volunteer program experiences with the poor and minority groups. Lay Associates: The Family of Jesus and Mary. Missions in seven foreign countries
Representation: Archdioceses of Boston, New York, Los Angeles and Washington, DC and in the Dio-ceses of Providence, El Paso, Manchester, Fall River and San Diego; in Haiti, Diocese of Gonaives
Vocation Director: Sr. Janice Farnham, RJM, Sophia House, 24 Everett St., Arlington, MA 02474-6902, (781) 643-5430 Fax: (781) 643-6515

RELIGIOUS OF MARY (W620)
IMMACULATE (R.M.I.), Villa Maria, TX, 719 Augusta St., San Antonio, TX 78215, (210) 226-0025, Fax (210) 226-3305
Centro Maria, 539 W. 54th St., New York, NY 10019-5017, (212) 581-5273, Fax (212) 307-5687
650 Jackson St. N.E., Washington, DC 20017-1424, (202) 635-1697, Fax (202) 635-7246
Web: www.religiosasdemaria inmaculada.org
Email: cenmariany@ mindspring..com
Members: 28 Sisters in US; 1,700 Sisters in 21 countries
Apostolic Work: Residences for young girls of good moral conduct, away from home for work, study or both. Age 17-29 normally, of any age, creed or nationality
Representation: Archdioceses of New York, Washington, DC and San Antonio
Vocation Director: Sr. Hilda Ramirez, Local Superior, Centro Maria, 539 W. 54th St., New York, NY 10019-5017, (212) 581-5273, Fax (212) 307-5687

RELIGIOUS MISSIONARIES (W621)
OF ST. DOMINIC (O.P.)
See "C" - Congregation of the Religious Missionaries of St. Dominic

RELIGIOUS OF THE SACRED (W622)
HEART OF MARY (R.S.H.M.)
An international Apostolic Institute of women religious in North and South America, Europe and Africa.
Eastern Province: 50 Wilson Park Dr., Tarrytown, NY 10591-3037
Western Province: 441 N. Garfield Ave., Montebello, CA 90640-2901
Provincial Center, 441 North Garfield Ave., Montebello, CA 90640-2901
Web: www.rshm.org
Members: (Eastern American Province) 207 Sisters
(Western American Province) 75 Sisters
900 worldwide
Apostolic Work: Education at all levels, diverse pastoral ministries, retreat and spiritual direction, health care, social work, refugee services, elder care, prisons, peace and justice advocacy, creative and fine arts, campus ministry, and other ways of promoting life, especially in those situations where it is denied, devalued or diminished.
Representation: (Arch)dioceses of Arlington, Baltimore, Brooklyn, Hartford, Los Angeles, Monterey, New York, Norwich, Oakland, Palm Beach, Richmond, Rockville Centre, San Bernardino, San Diego, San Francisco, St. Louis, Trenton, Venice (FL) and Winona. Also in Africa, Europe, and Mexico.
Vocation Director: Eastern American Province: Sr. Ines Gizzarelli, RSHM, (914) 631-8872, inesrshm@aol.com
Western American Province:
Sr. Virginia Garza, 011-52-(751) 348-0149, Amacuzac, Mexico 62640, intercorazon@prodigy .net.mx
Sr. Miriam Tiburcio, (323) 887-8821, ext. 215, Los Angeles, CA, vocations@rshm.org

RELIGIOUS SISTERS OF (W624)
CHARITY (R.S.C.)
Motherhouse: Ireland
US Headquarters: Caritas
10668 St. James Dr., Culver City, CA 90230, (310) 559-0176, 559-1654
Fax (213) 559-3530
Web: www.rsccaritas.org
Email: marshamoon.la@gmail.com
Members: 31 Sisters in California
Apostolic Work: Education, health care, parish ministry, juvenile hall, counseling, religious education, retreat and spirituality work, special outreach to marginalized in all settings

Representation: Archdiocese of Los Angeles. Also in Venezuela, Ireland, England, Zambia and Nigeria
Vocation Director: Sr. Eva Bryan, RSC, 1608 Eighth St., San Fernando, CA 91340, (818) 365-7926, evabryrsc@msn.com

RELIGIOUS SISTERS OF (W624-2)
MERCY OF ALMA (R.S.M.)
1965 Michigan Ave., Alma, MI 48801
Web: www.rsmofalma.org
Email: vocation@rsmofalma.org
Apostolic Work: Education: teach at the elementary/ high school/seminaries, academic administration; health care: physicians, nurses, social worker and psychologists
Representation: (Arch)Dioceses of Boston, Bridgeport, Denver, Lansing, Washington, Winona, Portland, Saginaw and Tulsa. Also in Italy, Germany, and Australia
Vocation Director: Contact: (989) 388-2063

RELIGIOUS TEACHERS (W625)
FILIPPINI, M.P.F. (Filippini Sisters)
(St. Lucy Province) Motherhouse, Novitiate and Provincial House Villa Walsh, 455 Western Ave, Morristown, NJ 07960-4928
Web: www.filippiniusa.org
Email: srmelloyd@gmail.com
Members: 1 Sister
Apostolic Work: Elementary and secondary education, parish ministry, retreat ministry, and foreign missions
Representation: Foundations in the United States, Italy, Brazil, Eritrea, Ethiopia, India, England, Ireland and Albania. Another province in Connecticut
Vocation Director: Contact: (973) 538-2886, ext. 124

RELIGIOUS VENERINI (W626)
SISTERS (M.P.V.), Generalate: Rome Provincialate: Worcester, 23 Edward St., Worcester, MA 01605-1605
Web: www.venerinisisters.com
Email: mpv31@aol.com
Members: 26 Sisters in the USA; 405 worldwide
Apostolic Work: Teaching, religious education, parish work, social work, nursing, pastoral associate and missionary work
Representation: Dioceses of Albany and Worcester. Also in Albania, Brazil, Cameroon, Chile, India, Italy, Nigeria, Romania
Vocation Director: Mary Rose Zaccari, MPV, Provincial, (508) 754-1020

SISTERS OF REPARATION (W627-1)
OF THE CONGREGATION OF MARY
(S.R.C.M.), Motherhouse: St. Zita Villa, 50 Saddle River Rd. N., Monsey, NY 10952-0952
Members: 3 Sisters
Apostolic Work: 1 home for adult women, 1 novitiate
Representation: Archdiocese of New York
Vocation Director: Sr. Maureen Frances, Superior, (845) 356-2011

SISTERS OF REPARATION (W627-2)
OF THE SACRED WOUNDS OF JESUS
(S.R.), 2120 S.E. 24th Ave., Portland, OR 97214-5504
Web: www.ReparationSisters.org
Email: repsrs@comcast.net
Members: 3 Sisters, 6 Priest Associates, 200 Lay Donnes
Apostolic Work: Nursing, teaching, liturgy and worship, healing ministries, counseling, catechesis, music ministries, spiritual enrichment, ministering to the homebound and hospital visitation
Representation: Archdiocese of Portland (OR) and in the state of Washington
Vocation Director: Sister Mary Immaculate, SR, (503) 236-4207 Fax (503) 236-3400

SISTERS OF THE (W628)
RESURRECTION (C.R.)
(New York Eastern Province) Provincial House, 35 Boltwood Ave., Castleton-on-Hudson, NY 12033
Web: www.resurrectionsisters.org
Email: vocation@resurrection sisters.org
Apostolic Work: Education (primary and secondary), health care (nursing homes), pastoral care, campus ministry, catechetical programs
Representation: Archdiocese of New York and in the Dioceses of Albany and Trenton
Vocation Director: Sister Teresa Grace, C.R., (518) 732-2226

SISTERS OF THE (W629)
RESURRECTION (C.R.)
(Chicago Western Province) 7432 W. Talcott Ave., Chicago, IL 60631-3743
Web: www.resurrectionsisters.org
Email: callres@hotmail.com
Members: 49 Sisters
Apostolic Work: Teaching and administration, nursing and health care, day care centers, retirement center, hospital pastoral care, parish pastoral ministry
Representation: (Arch)dioceses of

Chicago and Mobile
Vocation Director: Sister Kathleen Ann, C.R., (773) 792-6363

SACRAMENTINE NUNS (W630)
(O.S.S.), Blessed Sacrament Monastery, 86 Dromore Rd., Scarsdale, NY 10583-1706
Web: macc.catholic.org
Email: obsny@optonline.net.
Members: 12 Sisters
Apostolic Work: Cloistered contemplatives. Perpetual Adoration
Representation: Archdiocese of New York and in the Diocese of Gaylord, MI
Vocation Director: Sr. Mary Sygne Dyda, OSS, (914) 722-1657, fax (914) 722-1665

SACRAMENTINE NUNS (W631)
(O.S.S.), Sacramentine Monastery of Perpetual Adoration, 2798 US 31 N., PO Box 86, Conway, MI 49722-0086
Members: 2 Sisters
Representation: Archdiocese of New York and in the Diocese of Gaylord.
Vocation Director: Sister Rosalie, O.S.S., Prioress, (231) 347-0447

SISTERS OF THE SACRED (W632)
HEART OF JESUS (S.S.C.J.)
Generalate/Motherhouse: France (Sacred Heart Province) Provincialate Offices, 11931 Radium St., San Antonio, TX 78216, (210) 344-7203
Web: www.texas.net/~square1/ vocation/sscj.html
Email: sisterfrancisca.aleman@ gmail.com
Members: 51 Sisters in Texas, 790 Sisters worldwide in 11 countries
Conduct: Work in education, pastoral work, nursing, social services in Texas in US, 1 Mexican mission
Representation: Archdioceses of San Antonio and Galveston-Houston and in the Diocese of Brownsville. Also in Mexico City
Vocation Director: Sr. Francisca O. Alemán, 7112 Hagy Circle, San Antonio, TX 78216, (210) 340-0249

SISTERS OF THE SACRED (W633)
HEART OF JESUS OF RAGUSA
(S.S.H.J.), Motherhouse Sacred Heart Villa, 5269 Lewiston Rd., Lewiston, NY 14092
Web: www.shvilla.org
Email: sshj_vocation@yahoo.com, sacredhrtv@yahoo.com
Members: 650 Sisters
Apostolic Work: All areas of education, rest homes and hospitals, social service, catechetical and parish ministry and missions

Representation: In New York and Connecticut. Also in Italy, Canada, Madagascar, India, Philippines, Nigeria, Romania, Panama, and France
Vocation Director: Sister Grace Dike, (716) 284-8273 (tel., fax-call first to fax our Vocation Director), 94 Chapel Hill Rd., North Haven, CT 06473, (203) 239-8012, E-mail: st_frances_cabrini@sbcglobal.net or sshj_vocation@yahoo.com

SOCIETY OF THE SACRED (W634)
HEART (R.S.C.J.) (Religious of the Sacred Heart) Provincial House, 4100 Forest Park Ave., Suite A, St. Louis, MO 63108, (314) 652-1500
Web: www.rscj.org
www.rscjinternational.org
Email: ecollesano@rscj.org
Members: Approximately 2,800 Sisters in 45 countries, including 400 in the United States
Apostolic Work: Contemplatives in action, the Sisters are committed to making God's love visible in the heart of the world. Ministries include teaching and educational administration on every level, work with the poor, health care, social work, counseling; pastoral ministry in hospitals, parishes and prisions; communication; spiritual direction and retreats; law and art
Representation: Archdioceses of Baltimore, Boston, Chicago, Detroit, Miami, New Orleans, New York, Omaha, St. Louis, San Francisco, Seattle and Washington, DC and in the Dioceses of Albany, Bridgeport, Lafayette, Galveston-Houston, San Jose, San Diego and Trenton
Vocation Director: Ellen Collesano, RSCJ, 888-844-7725

SACRED HEARTS (W635)
COMMUNITY - SISTERS OF SACRED HEARTS OF JESUS AND MARY (SS.CC.), Generalate: Italy Pacific Province: 1120 5th Ave., Honolulu, HI 96816, 808-737-5822; East Coast Region: Fairhaven, MA 35 Huttleston Ave., Fairhaven, MA 02719
Web: www.sscc.org
Email: 105135.1656@compu serve.com
Members: 47 Sisters in US
Apostolic Work: A variety of parish ministries, religious education, schools, hospital chaplaincy, visiting and bringing Eucharist to the elderly and the homebound, visiting prisoners, working in shelters for the homeless, education for justice and peace, intercessory prayer, home and foreign missions
Representation: Dioceses of Fall River and Honolulu. Also in 15 foreign countries

Vocation Director: Sr. Dolores Paveo, SS.CC., East Coast Regional Superior, (508) 994-9341

SISTERS OF THE SACRED (W636)
HEARTS OF JESUS AND MARY (S.H.J.M.), 2150 Lakeshore Ave., Oakland, CA 94606-1123
Email: klavertyshjm@juno.com
Members: 11 Sisters US, 230 Sisters worldwide
Conduct: Pastoral care of the sick and shut-ins, campus ministry, education, nursing, refugee ministry; caring ministries to AIDS sufferers, people with special needs, women and children
Representation: Dioceses of Oakland and Stockton. Also in England, Scotland, Ireland and Wales. Foreign missions in Zambia, El Salvador, Colombia, Uganda and the Philippines
Vocation Director: Contact Person: Sr. Kathleen Laverty, SHJM, (510) 839-5213

CONGREGATION OF (W637-1)
ST. AGNES (C.S.A.), St. Agnes Convent, 320 County Rd. K, Fond du Lac, WI 54935, 920-907-2300
Web: www.csasisters.org
Email: vocations@csasisters.org
Members: 336 Sisters
Apostolic Work: Work in fields of education, health care, pastoral ministry, social services, art, law and spiritual direction
Representation: Archdioceses of Chicago, New York, Milwaukee and St. Paul as well as 24 dioceses. Also in Nicaragua and Honduras
Vocation Director: Sister Jean Hinderer, CSA, (920) 907-2310

SISTERS OF SAINT ANN (W637-2)
(S.S.A.), Headquarters: Rome Motherhouse in US: Mt. St. Ann PO Box 328, Ebensburg, PA 15931 (814) 472-9354 (tel., fax)
Email: sister_lucia78411@ yahoo.com
Members: 8 Sisters in US, 1,500 worldwide
Apostolic Work: Education, retreat ministry, foreign mission, pastoral ministry
Representation: Dioceses of Altoona-Johnstown and Corpus Christi
Vocation Director: Sr. Lucia D'Cunha, SSA, 2100 Morris St., Corpus Christi, TX 78405, (361) 888-4027

SISTERS OF ST. ANNE (W638)
(S.S.A.), St. Marie Province 720 Boston Post Rd., East, Marlborough, MA 01752
Email: spg102@hotmail.com
Apostolic Work: Education, parish ministry, spiritual direction, retreats,

elderly care, religious education, secretarial work, healthcare and chaplaincy
Representation: in the Archdiocese of Boston and in several other dioceses. Also in Africa, Canada, Chile and Haiti
Vocation Director: (508) 485-3791

SISTERS OF ST. ANNE (W639)
(SSA), Province Administration 1550 Begbie St., Victoria, B.C., Canada, V8R-1K8, (250) 592-3133
Web: www.ssacong.org
Email: gscott@ssabc.ca
Members: 600 Sisters
Apostolic Work: Education, health care and pastoral ministry.
Representation: Ministering in Canada, US, Haiti, Chile, Cameroon, DR of Congo
Vocation Director: Gertrude Scott, SSA

SISTERS OF ST. BASIL (W640-1)
THE GREAT (Byzantine Rite)
See Eastern Catholic Religious Communities for Women

SISTERS OF THE ORDER (W640-2)
OF ST. BASIL THE GREAT (Ukrainian Byzantine Rite)
See Eastern Catholic Religious Communities for Women

CONGREGATION OF (W641)
ST. BRIGID (C.S.B.)
Motherhouse: Ireland
US Foundation: St. Brigid's Convent, 5118 Loma Linda Dr., San Antonio, TX 78201
Web: www.brigidine.org.au
Email: brigidines@sbcglobal.net or annedrea08@yahoo.com
Members: 15 Sisters
Apostolic Work: Education-all levels, pastoral ministry, campus ministry, detention ministry, ministry to migrants and immigrants, health care ministry and music ministry.
Representation: Archdioceses of Boston and San Antonio and in the Diocese of Wilmington
Vocation Director: Sr. Imelda Phelan, CSB; Sr. Anne Drea, CSB, Regional Coordinator, (210) 738-1721 or (210) 733-0701

SISTERS OF ST. CASIMIR (W642-1)
(S.S.C.), Motherhouse
Vocation Ministry Office, 2601 West Marquette Rd., Chicago, IL 60629
Web: www.ssc2601.com
Email: prayers@ssc2601.com
Apostolic Work: Education in 2 high schools, 3 parishes, health care in 1 hospital, 2 missions in Argentina
Representation: Archdioceses of Chicago, Philadelphia and in the Diocese of Kalamazoo
Vocation Director: (773) 776-1324

SISTERS OF (W642-2)
ST. CHRETIENNE (S.S.Ch.)
Provincial House, 297 Arnold St.,
Wrentham, MA 02093-2093
Web: www.sistersofstchretienne.org
Email: ssch@tiac.net
Members: 51 Sisters in US
Apostolic Work: Teaching, nursing,
pastoral ministry, foreign missions,
retreats, spiritual direction
Representation: Archdiocese of
Boston and in the Dioceses of
Providence, St. Petersburg and
Portland, ME. Also, in Canada,
France, Austria, Africa and Hungary
Vocation Director: Sister Lisette
Michaud, SSCh, Provincial Superior,
(508) 384-8066, Fax (508) 384-3170

SISTERS OF ST. CLARE (W643)
(O.S.C.), Generalate: Ireland
Regional Residence: St. Clare's
Convent, 446 South Poplar Ave.,
Brea, CA 92821-6649,
(714) 256-1278
Email: sr.eflood@rcbo.org
Conduct: Religious education, adult
faith formation, diocesan
administration, secretarial.
Representation: Dioceses of Orange,
San Diego, St. Petersburg and
Wilmington. Also in Australia, El
Salvador, England, Ireland and
Wales
Vocation Director: Sister Eymard
Flood, OSC, Marywood Center,
2811 East Villa Real Dr., Orange,
CA 92867, (714) 282-3114

SISTERS OF ST. CLARE (W644-1)
**(OSC) (Franciscan Spirituality within
the Order of St. Clare)**, 446 South
Popular Ave., Brea, CA 92621
Apostolic Work: Prayer-retreat
ministry; education in all its forms;
care of deprived children and the
elderly; social and pastoral work in
the local church, and evangelization
in the Third World. Efforts to match
the gifts of the Sister with the needs
of the local community
Representation: in Great Britain,
North and Central America and
Albania
Vocation Director: Contact:
Sr. Eymard Flood, OSC,
(714) 579-6605

ST. COLUMBAN SISTERS (W644-2)
See "M" - Missionary Sisters of St.
Columban

SISTERS OF SAINTS CYRIL (W645)
AND METHODIUS (SS.C.M.)
Villa Sacred Heart, Danville, PA
17821-1698
Web: www.sscm.org
Email: debbiesscm@hotmail.com
Members: 105 Sisters, 100

Associates
Apostolic Work: Educational
apostolate in Catholic schools from
preschool/kindergarten level
through university, religious education, parish and campus ministry,
music conservatory, pastoral care,
hearing impaired, spiritual direction,
retreat ministry, ecumenism and
evangelization. Elder Care apostolate in hospital chaplaincy, hospice
care, Continuing Care Retirement
Community and home for the aged
Representation: (Arch)dioceses of
Bridgeport, Charleston, Chicago,
Gary, Harrisburg, San Antonio,
Scranton, and Syracuse
Vocation Director: Sister Deborah
Marie, SS.C.M., (570) 275-1093
Fax (570) 275-5997

CONGREGATION OF THE (W646)
SISTERS OF ST. DOROTHY (S.S.D.)
(North American Province) Provincial
House: Mt. St. Joseph, 13 Monkey
wrench Ln., Bristol, RI 02809-2809
Email: sistersards@hotmail.com
Members: 45 Sisters in US, 1,200
worldwide
Apostolic Work: Education at all
levels, catechetical work, summer
camps, pastoral ministry, hospital
ministry, social work
Representation: Archdiocese of New
York and in the Dioceses of
Brownsville, Fall River and
Providence. Also in 18 foreign lands
Vocation Director: Sister Mary
Sardinha, S.S.D., PO Box 147,
Progreso, TX 78579,
(956) 565-9430
Mt. St. Joseph, 13 Monkeywrench
Ln., Bristol, RI 02809, (401) 253-
5434 (June-Sept)

SISTERS OF SAINT FRANCIS (W648)
(O.S.F.), 588 N. Bluff Blvd., Clinton,
IA 52732-3953
Web: www.clintonfranciscans.com
Email: sisters@clinton
franciscans.com
Members: 73 Sisters, 2 Novices, 1
Candidate, 3 Sojourners, 73
Associates
Conduct: 1 retirement home/health
care facility, 1 speech & hearing
center
Representation: Archdioceses of
Chicago, Dubuque and St. Louis
and in the Dioceses of Belleville,
Davenport, Des Moines, Joliet,
Lexington, Phoenix, Portland,
Rockford (Illinois), San Bernardino,
San Diego, and Sioux City. Also in
Chulucanas, Peru, South America
Vocation Director: Sister Gael
Gensler, OSF, (563) 242-7611
Fax (563) 243-0007

ST. JOAN OF ARC SISTERS (W649)
(S.J.A.), Motherhouse
1505 Avenue de l'Assomption,
Quebec, Canada G1S - 4T3
Members: 105 Sisters in 5 convents
Apostolic Work: Twofold: uniting
contemplation with action – through
prayer and by performing ordinary
household tasks in rectories,
bishops' residences, homes for
retired priests, etc. Also in areas of
parish ministries
Representation: Diocese of Fall
River. Also in Canada
Vocation Director: Sr. Yolanda Roy,
s.j.a., (418) 681-4870, 527-2589

SISTERS OF ST. JOHN THE (W650)
BAPTIST (C.S.JB.)
General House: Rome, Italy, (US
Province), Provincial Residence,
3308 Campbell Dr, Bronx, NY 10465
(718) 518-7820
Web: http://baptistines.home.att.net
Email: lvw111b@aol.com
Members: 110 Sisters
Apostolic Work: Education, health
care for aged men and women,
religious education, social work and
any ministry connected with the
poor and abandoned especially
youth
Representation: Archdiocese of New
York and the Diocese of Paterson.
Also, missions in Zambia, India,
Canada, Chile, Brazil, Argentina,
the Philippines, Poland, Korea,
Italy, Mexico, Moldavia, South
Africa, Cameroon, Malawi and
Madagascar
Vocation Director: Sr. Anne Dolores
Van Wagenen, C.S.JB., 26 Landis
Ave., Staten Island, NY 10305,
(718) 442-6240

SISTERS OF ST. JOSEPH (W651-2)
OF BADEN, PA (C.S.J.)
St. Joseph's Convent, 1020 State St,
Baden, PA 15005
Web: www.stjoseph-baden.org
Email: dpashuta@stjoseph-
baden.org
Members: 224 Sisters
Apostolic Work: Education, health
care, social services, and spiritual
development.
Representation: (Arch)dioceses of
Altoona-Johnstown, Arlington,
Boston, Buffalo, Cheyenne, Detroit,
Erie, Fresno, Gallup, Greensburg,
Harrisburg, Hartford, Miami, New
York, Pittsburgh, Richmond, Sioux
Falls, Tucson, Washington (DC)
and Wheeling/Charleston.
Vocation Director: Sr. Dorothy
Pashuta, C.S.J., (412) 661-2528

B-112

SISTERS OF ST. JOSEPH (W652)
OF BOSTON (C.S.J.), Motherhouse
637 Cambridge St., Brighton, MA
02135-2135
Web: www.csjboston.org
Email: marytheresa.o'reilly@
csjboston.org
Members: 455 Sisters
Apostolic Work: Various ministries:
education, health care, social
services, pastoral ministry, coun-
selling and retreat work
Representation: Archdioceses of
Boston and New Mexico
Vocation Director: Contact:
Coordinator (617) 746-2045

SISTERS OF ST. JOSEPH (W653)
OF BRENTWOOD (C.S.J.)
Motherhouse and Novitiate:
St. Joseph Convent, 631-273-4531
1725 Brentwood Rd., Brentwood,
NY 11717
Web: www.sistersofstjoseph
brentwoodny.org
Email: vocationcsj@aol.com
Members: 990 Sisters
Apostolic Work: Primary, secondary
and higher education; health care,
campus ministry; religious
education, social service, pastoral
care, special education, prison
ministry, counseling, spiritual
direction, retreat work, shelters for
women
Representation: Archdiocese of New
York and in the Dioceses of
Brooklyn and Rockville Centre. Also
in Puerto Rico, Santo Domingo and
Brazil
Vocation Director: Mary R. Walsh,
CSJ, 95 Fulton Ave., Hempstead,
NY 11550, (516) 483-6799

SISTERS OF ST. JOSEPH (W654)
OF BUFFALO (S.S.J.)
10324 Main St., Clarence, NY 14031
Web: www.ssjbuffalo.org
Email: voc@ssjbuffalo.org
Members: 103 Sisters
Apostolic Work: The Sisters live out
their call to be women of unity and
reconciliation through a wide range
of apostolic works, with special
concern for the needy. They minister in the fields of education (at all
levels), health care, pastoral
services, retreats, spirituality and
counseling
Representation: in the (Arch)dio-
ceses of Buffalo, Cincinnati, Detroit
and Pensacola-Tallahassee
Vocation Director: (716) 759-6454,
ext. 14

SISTERS OF ST. JOSEPH (W655)
OF CARONDELET (C.S.J.)
Congregational Center, 2311 S.
Lindbergh Blvd, St. Louis, MO 63131
(314) 966-4048

St. Louis Province, St. Joseph
Provincial House, 6400 Minnesota
Ave, St. Louis, MO 63111
E-mail: membership@csjsl.org;
Web: www.csjsl.org 425 Sisters, 1
Novice

St. Paul Province, St. Joseph
Administration Center, 1884
Randolph Ave, St. Paul, MN 55105,
Web: www.csjstpaul.org; email:
sisterweb@csjstpaul.org
322 Sisters, 1 Novice

Albany Province, St.Joseph
Provincial House, 385 Watervliet-
Shaker Rd, Latham, NY 12110,
Web: www.csjalbany.org
437 Sisters, 1 Novice

Los Angeles Province, Carondelet
Center, 11999 Chalon Rd, Los
Angeles, CA 90049,
E-mail: vocations@csjla.org;
Web: www.csjla.org
374 Sisters, 1 Novice

Hawaii Vice Province, Carondelet
Convent, 5311 Apo Dr, Honolulu,
Oahu, HI 96821-1829, (808) 373-
3850
22 Sisters

Web: www.csjcarondelet.org
Email: congctroffice@
csjcarondelet.org
Apostolic Work: Teaching, nursing,
pastoral care, parish work, foreign
missions, campus ministry, educat-
ing the deaf, social services
Representation: 182 dioceses in the
US. Also in Peru, Japan and Chile
Vocation Director: Contact the
Director of Applicants for Province
closest to you

SISTERS OF ST. JOSEPH (W656)
OF CHAMBERY/WEST HARTFORD
(C.S.J.), (US Province)
Provincial House: Convent of Mary
Immaculate, 27 Park Rd., West
Hartford, CT 06119
Web: www.sistersofsaintjoseph.org
Email: sebcsj@hotmail.com
vocation@sistersofsaintjoseph.org
Members: 120 Sisters in US; 2,000
worldwide
Apostolic Work: Higher education,
religious education, special
education, health care, day shelter,
social services, pastoral ministry,
soup kitchen, spiritual direction,
retreat ministry, counseling,
overseas missions, AIDS ministry,
ministry to the elderly, hospice.
Representation: Archdioceses of
Hartford, Miami and in the Dioceses
of Bridgeport, El Paso, Fairbanks,
Lexington, Oakland, and Springfield
(MA)
Vocation Director: Sr. Elaine
Betoncourt, CSJ, (860) 233-5126,
Ext. 217

CONGREGATION OF (W657)
ST. JOSEPH (CSJ)
Congregational Center
3430 Rocky River Drive, Cleveland,
OH 44111-2997, (216) 252-0440
Web: www.csjoseph.org
Email: vocations@csjoseph.org
Members: Over 800
Apostolic Work: The Congregation of
St. Joseph is a community of vowed
women religious and associates
who in the following of Christ Jesus,
live and work that all may be one.
Rooted in God and this mission of
unity, we believe that relationship is
at the heart of who we are and who
we are becoming. We desire to
move toward greater inclusivity that
reflects the interconnectedness of
all creation, reverences diverse
cultures and religions, and directs
our choices in ministry, community
living, and corporate decisions. We
are pastoral ministers, artists,
musicians, teachers, social workers,
spiritual counselors, nurses, and
advocates for peace, justice, reconciliation, and sustainable development of Earth. Who does your
following of Christ lead you to
become?
Representation: Throughout dioceses
in the United States and in Japan
and Nicaragua
Vocation Director: Sister Ileana
Fernandez, CSJ, 2263 Stonehenge
Ave., Baton Rouge, LA, 70820,
(225) 388-2262
Sister Judith Minear, SSJ, 110 15th
St., Wheeling, WV, 26003, (304)
232-7733
Sister Karen Salsbery, CSJ, 3700
E. Lincoln, Wichita, KS 67218-2099,
(316) 689-4029

SISTERS OF ST. JOSEPH (W658)
OF CLUNY (S.J.C.)
(American Novitiate) Mary
Immaculate Queen Novitiate
20955 Halldale Ave., Torrance, CA
91754-1754
Web: www.sjcluny.org
Email: clunyvocation@hotmail.com
Members: 29 Sisters USA, 3,000
worldwide
Apostolic Work: Ministry: Engaged in
every corporal work of mercy on
five continents, but especially
concentrated in the Third World
Representation: Archdioceses of Los
Angeles and Newark and in the
Dioceses of Providence and Little
Rock. Also in Canada
Vocation Director: Sister Genevieve
Vigil, S.J.C., Mary Immaculate
Queen Community, 943 Lagoon
Ave., Wilmington, CA 90744

B-113

SISTERS OF ST. JOSEPH (W659)
OF CONCORDIA (C.S.J.)
215 Court St, Box 279, Concordia,
KS 66901, (785) 243-2149
Web: www.csjkansas.org
Email: annacsj@idir.net
Members: 156 Sisters
Apostolic Work: Making visible the
love of God in our midst through
communal life and all ministry
efforts to live in unity and
reconciliation with God and the "the
dear neighbor." The Sisters serve in
health care institutions, schools,
parish ministries, centers of spirituality and social justice, domestic
violence shelters and prisons
Representation: Diocese of Salina
and in 13 other dioceses throughout the US. Also mission in Brazil
Vocation Director: Sr. Anna Marie
Broxterman, C.S.J.

SISTERS OF ST. JOSEPH OF (W660)
NORTHWESTERN PENNSLYVANIA
(S.S.J.), 5031 W. Ridge Rd., Erie, PA
16506-1249
Web: www.ssjerie.org
Email: s.lfusco@ssjerie.org
Members: 135 Members
Apostolic Work: All levels of
education - preschool through
college; health care, social
ministries, social justice and
advocacy, voice for the voiceless,
care of the elderly, poor, shelter for
women, pastoral ministry, liturgical
ministry, spiritual directors, directors
of religious education, fine arts/art,
writing plus others
Representation: Archdioceses of
Chicago, Miami, and Washington
(DC) and in the Dioceses of Buffalo,
Cleveland, Memphis. Also France
Vocation Director: Linda Fusco, SSJ,
(814) 836-4127

SISTERS OF ST. JOSEPH OF (W663)
ORANGE (C.S.J.), 480 S. Batavia St,
Orange, CA 92868
Web: www.csjorange.org
Email: vocationcsj@csjorange.org
Members: 164 Sisters
Apostolic Work: Education at all
levels, education network with 22
grammar schools, health system
with 10 hospitals and clinics, Center
for Spiritual Development, social
justice center, foreign missions,
pastoral ministries, spiritual
direction, campus ministry, prison
ministry, social justice ministries,
Hispanic ministries and ministry
with the poor
Representation: Archdioceses of Los
Angeles and San Francisco and in
the Dioceses of Colorado Springs,
Oakland, Orange, San Bernardino,
Santa Rosa and San Diego.
Foreign missions in: Tijuana
(Mexico), El Salvador and Australia

Vocation Director: Sr. Mary Elizabeth
Nelsen, CSJ, (714) 633-8121, Fax:
(714) 744-3135

SISTERS OF ST. JOSEPH (W664)
Lyon, France (C.S.J.) USA Province
(207) 873-4512 Fax (207) 873-1976
93 Halifax St, Winslow, ME 04901
Web: www.csjwinslowmaine.org
Email: csjwinme@adelphia.net
Members: 940 Sisters ministering in
14 countries, 40 Sisters in the US,
24 CSJ Associates in the US
Apostolic Work: Spiritual direction,
retreat ministry, holistic care,
pastoral care, ecology, education,
social work, Canon law, community
organizing, social justice/peace,
parish ministry, ministry to the
mentally challenged, school
nursing, work with
immigrants/refugees and prison
ministry.
Representation: (Arch)dioceses of
Manchester (NH), New York, San
Francisco (CA) and Portland (ME).
Vocation Director: Sr. Claire Lepage
c.s.j., 121 Webber Ave., Lewiston,
ME 04240 E-mail:
cblepage@gwi.net

SISTERS OF ST. JOSEPH OF (W666)
PEACE (C.S.J.P.), (St. Joseph
Province) Shalom Center, 399
Hudson Terr., Englewood Cliffs, NJ
07632-7632
Web: www.csjp.org/sjp
Email: mjklingcsjp@verizon.net
Members: 111 Sisters, 57
Associates, and 1 Novice
Conduct: The Sisters are an
international community built on a
rich heritage of promoting social
justice as a way of peace. In accord
with their tradition, they commit
themselves to promote peace in
family life, in the Church and in
society. They minister in education,
health and hospital services, social
services, religious education, parish
ministry, social justice, spiritual
direction and peace ministry
Representation: Archdioceses of
Newark and Washington, DC and in
the Dioceses of Camden, Orlando,
Paterson, Trenton, and Metuchen
Vocation Director: Sister Margaret
Jane Kling, Director of
Ministry/Formation,
(201) 568-6348, ext. 13

CONGREGATION OF THE (W667)
SISTERS OF ST. JOSEPH OF
PEACE (C.S.J.P.), Western U.S.
1663 Killarney Way, PO Box 248,
Bellevue, WA 98009-0248
Web: www.csjp.org/olp
Email: jmiller@csjp-olp.org,
vocations@csjp-olp.org

Members: 300 Sisters, 100
Associates
Apostolic Work: Education, health
and hospital services, social
services, religious education, parish
ministry, retreat ministry, social
justice and peace ministry
Representation: Archdioceses of
Anchorage, Los Angeles, Portland,
San Francisco and Seattle and in
the Dioceses of Juneau, San
Diego, Yakima and Spokane. Also
in El Salvador
Vocation Director: Jo-Anne Miller,
CSJP, (425) 451-1770, ext. 118

SISTERS OF ST. JOSEPH OF (W668)
PHILADELPHIA (S.S.J.)
Mount Saint Joseph Convent
9701 Germantown Ave,
Philadelphia, PA 19118-2694
Web: www.ssjphila.org
Email: kclaflin@ssjphila.org
Members: 977 Sisters
Apostolic Work: The Sisters meet
the needs of "our dear neighbor"
through ministry in education at all
levels from preschool to university,
offering daycare and after school
care, special education, and
through a variety of social, pastoral
and spiritual services in parishes,
institutions and dioceses, serving
the elderly, the homeless and
persons with AIDS. Works include 1
college, 4 academies, 1 retreat
house, 1 spirituality center, 1
welcome center, 1 hospitality
house, 4 housing projects for senior
citizens, and 1
healthcare/retirement facility
Representation: Archdioceses of
Baltimore, Chicago, Miami, Newark,
New York, Philadelphia, Washington and and in the Dioceses of
Allentown, Altoona-Johnstown,
Arlington, Brooklyn, Camden,
Charlotte, Fairbanks, Fort Wayne-
South Bend, Harrisburg, Jackson,
Metuchen, Paterson, Raleigh, San
Antonio, Savannah, St. Petersburg,
Trenton, Venice, Wheeling-Charles-
ton, and Wilmington. Also in Canada,
Peru, and France
Vocation Director: Sister Kathy
Claflin, SSJ (215) 248-7236

SISTERS OF ST. JOSEPH OF (W670)
ROCHESTER (S.S.J.), 150 French
Rd., Rochester, NY 14618-3822
Web: www.ssjrochester.org
Email: vocations@ssjrochester.org
Members: 295 Sisters, 110
Associate Members
Apostolic Work: We are a commun-
ity of women committed to the
radical message of the gospel and
the reconciling love of Jesus. We
define our lives through prayer,

community, and service to those in need. We meet those needs by using our individual and collective gifts in a variety of ways. We are hospital administrators, principals, teachers, social workers, artists, nurses and nurse practitioners, drug and alcohol counselors, pastoral counselors, community organizers, spiritual directors, parish administrators, pastoral associates, outreach workers, lawyers, realtors, doctors, secretaries, musicians, college professors, missionaries in Brazil and Alabama, directors of soup kitchens, chaplains in prisons, youth workers, and much, much, more... We are pray-ers for unity and reconciliation in a struggling and hope-filled world.
Representation: Dioceses of Rochester, NY and Birmingham, AL. Missions in Brazil. We also offer the SSJ Volunteer Corps in Rochester, NY and Pine Apple, AL, where a person can serve in one of our ministries as a volunteer and live with us in community.
Vocation Director: Sr. Donna Del Santo, SSJ (585) 641-8122
Cell: (585) 733-4422

SISTERS OF ST. JOSEPH OF (W672)
ST. AUGUSTINE, FLORIDA (S.S.J.)
St. Joseph's Convent , 241 St. George St., St. Augustine, FL 32084
Web: www.ssjfl.org
Email: ssjflvocations@bellsouth.net
Members: 99 Sisters
Apostolic Work: Ministries of "unity and reconciliation" in parishes, schools, hospitals, prisons, with the poor, AIDS patients, the elderly, persons with disabilities, retreatants and those seeking spiritual direction. Social work, liturgical design, counseling and any needed ministry for which we are prepared.
Representation: Throughout the Dioceses of Florida
Vocation Director: Sister Kathleen Power, SSJ, (904) 610-9228, (407) 246-4928

SISTERS OF ST. JOSEPH (W673)
OF ST. MARK (S.J.S.M.)
(Cleveland Generalate, 21800 Chardon Rd., Euclid, OH 44117
Members: 9 Sisters in US
Apostolic Work: Nursing, care of the aged, technicians, social service, administrative, clerical and dietetic work
Representation: Diocese of Cleveland
Vocation Director: Sr. M. Raphael Gregg
Mother M. Therese Trunk, Superior General, (216) 531-7426

SISTERS OF ST. JOSEPH (W674)
OF SPRINGFIELD (S.S.J.)
Mont Marie, 34 Lower Westfield Rd., Ste. 1, Holyoke, MA 01040-2739
Web: www.ssjspringfield.org
Email: ncain@ssjspringfield.com
Members: 310 Sisters, 88 Associates
Apostolic Work: Members of the congregation are encouraged to discern individual gifts and ministries within the framework of community goal, to live simply and to work toward alleviating unjust structures. Ministries include educational ministry in elementary schools, high schools, college; religious education, special education, pastoral ministry, health care, social services, spiritual direction, counseling, prison ministry, campus ministry and hospital chaplaincy
Representation: (Arch)dioceses of Baltimore, Bridgeport, Fall River, Lake Charles, Maine, Providence, Rutland, Springfield (MA), and Worcester. Also in Kenya and Tanzania
Vocation Director: Natalie Cain, ssj, (413) 536-0853, ext. 249

SISTERS OF ST. JOSEPH (W676)
OF WATERTOWN (S.S.J.)
Motherhouse, 1425 Washington St., Watertown, NY 13601, (315) 788-6574
Web: www.ssjwatertown.org
Email: smgssj@yahoo.com
Members: 55 Members
Apostolic Work: Education-all levels, parish/diocesan administration, social work.
Representation: Diocese of Ogdensburg
Vocation Director: Sr. Mary Gregory Munger, SSJ, 1425 Washington St., Watertown, NY 13601

SISTERS OF ST. JOSEPH (W679)
OF THE THIRD ORDER OF ST. FRANCIS (SSJ-TOSF)
Central Office, PO Box 305, 1300 Maria Dr., Stevens Point, WI 54481
Web: www.ssj-tosf.org
Email: vocation@ssj-tosf.org
Members: 325 Perpetually Professed Sisters, 4 Temporary Professed, 109 Associates
Apostolic Work: Members of the Congregation serve in a variety of ministries with the ultimate desire to promote the spiritual and material development of the human family including all aspects of education, parish ministry, social work, health care, diocesan services/administration and community services
Representation: Numerous states including Arizona, California, Connecticut, DC, Florida, Illinois, Indiana, Michigan, Minnesota, Nebraska, Ohio, Pennsylvania,

Tennessee, Washington and Wisconsin. Also in Brazil, Puerto Rico, and Peru
Vocation Director: Sr. Debra Weina, SSJ-TOSF, (715) 341-8457, fax: (715) 341-8830

SISTERS OF ST. JOSEPH (W680)
THE WORKER (S.J.W.)
General Motherhouse: Saint William Convent, 1 Saint Joseph Lane, Walton, KY 41094
Web: www.saintjosephacademy.net/ssjw/index.htm
Email: stjoseph0@insightbb.com
Members: 16 Sisters
Apostolic Work: Catholic education, care of the elderly, secretarial and domestic work
Representation: Dioceses of Covington and Lexington
Vocation Director: Mother Celeste Marie Downes, S.J.W., Superior

CONGREGATION OF THE (W681)
SISTERS OF ST. LOUIS (S.S.L.)
Regional House in US: Louisville Convent, 22300 Mulholland Dr., Woodland Hills, CA 91364-4933
Web: www.stlouissisters.org
Email: sslca4@attglobal.net
Members: 70 Sisters in the US
Conduct: Several grammar schools, high schools, college, parish ministry, hospital ministry, prison ministry and social services
Representation: Archdiocese of Los Angeles, in several other locations in California and North Carolina. Also in Ireland, England, France, Nigeria, Ghana and Brasil, Antigua
Vocation Director: Sr. Rita McCormack, S.S.L., (818) 883-5148

SISTERS OF ST. MARY OF (W682)
NAMUR (S.S.M.N.), Eastern Province
241 Lafayette Ave, Buffalo, NY 14213
Web: www.ssmn.us
Email: carolinessmn@yahoo.com
Members: 90 Sisters (Eastern Province), 600 worldwide
Apostolic Work: Diversified; Primary emphasis to stand with the poor and marginalized of the earth. Commitment to missions; to refugees; to women and youth
Representation: (Arch)dioceses of Boston, Buffalo, Charleston and Savannah. Also in Texas, Canada, Belgium, Great Britain, Africa, Brazil and the Dominican Republic
Vocation Director: Sister Caroline Smith, SSMN, (716) 884-8221

SISTERS OF ST. MARY OF (W683)
NAMUR (S.S.M.N.), (Western Province)
909 West Shaw St., Fort Worth, TX 76110-4057
Web: www.web2.airmail.net/ssmn/ and www.ssmn-e.com

Email: smargm@airmail.net
Members: 41 Sisters, 3 Sisters transferring from other Congregations, 2 Candidates, 4 pre-candidates, 6 Oblates, 82 Associates
Apostolic Work: In teaching, health care, evangelization, and spiritual formation, social service, care of the aged, and foreign missionaries, the Sisters read the signs of the times to denounce evil by standing as beacons of hope and non-violence.
Representation: Dioceses of Dallas and Fort Worth. Also in Canada, England, Belgium, Brazil, Democratic Republic of the Congo and poor, Cameroon, Rwanda, Dominican Republic and Tanzania
Vocation Director: Vocation Contact: (817) 923-8393, Fax (817) 923-1511

SISTERS OF ST. MARY OF (W684)
OREGON (S.S.M.O.)
Motherhouse: St. Mary of the Valley 4440 S.W. 148th Ave., Beaverton, OR 97007-7007
Web: www.ssmo.org
Email: srcharleneh@ssmo.org
Members: 73 Sisters
Apostolic Work: Education: day care, kindergarten, high school, grammar schools; health care: 1 nursing home. Also parish ministry, religious education, Hispanic ministry, chaplaincy
Representation: (Arch)dioceses of Portland (OR), Helena, and Los Angeles
Vocation Director: Sister Charlene Herinckx, SSMO, (503) 906-1131

SISTERS OF ST. PAUL OF (W686)
CHARTRES (S.P.C.)
General House: 193 Via della Vignaccia, Rome, 1-00163 Italy US Province, 1300 County Road 492, Marquette, MI 49855
Web: www.sistersofstpaulusa.org
Email: martha_ngan@yahoo.com
Members: 16 Sisters in US; 4,000 worldwide
Apostolic Work: Academic and religious education, pastoral associates, ministry to the aged, hospital chaplaincy
Representation: Archdiocese of Washington, DC and in the Diocese of Marquette
Vocation Director: Sr. Martha Trinh, S.P.C.

SISTERS OF ST. PHILIP NERI (W687)
MISSIONARY TEACHERS (R.F.)
Motherhouse: Spain
135 Pascus Pl., Sparks, NV 89431-3340, also at: 2525 S.W. 9th Ave., Fort Lauderdale, FL 33315 (954) 525-3533
Web: www3.planalfa.es-filipensesm.
Email: sistersreno@sbcglobal.net

Apostolic Work: Teaching, social work, retreat houses
Representation: Archdiocese of Miami and in the Diocese of Reno
Vocation Director: Sr. Ofelia Roibas, R.F., (775) 331-0708

SISTERS OF ST. RITA (W688)
(O.S.A.), Motherhouse: Germany
St. Rita's Convent, 4014 N. Green Bay Rd, Racine, WI 53404-3404
Web: www.sistersofstrita.org
Email: sr.angelica@sbcglobal.net
Members: 118 Sisters
Apostolic Work: Spiritual - social family care, health care, care of the aged and poor, pastoral ministry, C.C.D., education, hospice, prison ministry, retreat, and spiritual direction
Representation: Archdiocese of Milwaukee. Also in Germany and Switzerland
Vocation Director: Sr. Angelica Summer, O.S.A., (262) 639-1766; 5050

SOCIETY OF ST. TERESA (W689)
OF JESUS (S.T.J.), Provincial House, 18080 St. Joseph's Way, Covington, LA 70435-5624, (985) 893-1470
Web: www.teresians.org
Email: teresianvocations@ yahoo.com
Members: 50 Sisters in US, 1,800 worldwide
Apostolic Work: Elementary and secondary education, catechetical work, youth groups, youth retreats, prayer groups, Hispanic ministry and foreign missions
Representation: New Orleans, Covington (LA); Miami (FL); and San Antonio, Uvalde (TX). Also in Mexico, Nicaragua, Colombia, Guatemala, Venezuela, Brazil, Uruguay, Paraguay, Argentina, Chile, Cuba, Portugal, Spain, France, Italy, Angola, Sao Tome, Bolivia, Ivory Coast, Burkina Fasso and Philippines
Vocation Director: Sr. Clarice Suchy, STJ, 18158 St. Joseph Way, Covington, LA 70435, (985) 893 - 1557

CONGREGATION OF (W690)
SISTERS OF ST. THOMAS OF VILLANOVA (S.S.T.V.), 76 West Rocks Rd., Norwalk, CT 06851
Web: www.sistersofsaintthomasof villanova.com
Email: vocationdirectorsstv@ juno.com
Members: 4 Sisters in US; 330 worldwide
Conduct: 1 convalescent home
Representation: Diocese of Bridgeport
Vocation Director: Sister Marie Lucie Monast, S.S.T.V., 203-847-2885, fax: 203-847-3740

SISTERS OF ST. URSULA (W691)
(S.U.), Motherhouse, 50 Linwood Rd, Rhinebeck, NY 12572-2572
Web: www.societyofstursula.org
Email: mlezonsu@aol.com
Members: 30 Sisters
Apostolic Work: Teaching, religious education, retreats, African missions, ministry to aged, social work, parish ministry, campus ministry, nursing, financial and secretarial service
Representation: Archdiocese of New York and in the Dioceses of Providence and Raleigh. Also in France and the Democratic Republic of the Congo
Vocation Director: Sr. Michelle Lezon, (845) 876-2341

SALESIAN MONASTIC (W692-1)
COMMUNITY (SMC), Salesian Monastery, HC#1, Box 455, Frantz Rd., Brodheadsville, PA 18322-9630, (570) 992-0230
Web: www.gentlestrength.org
Email: monk@epix.net
Members: 1 Solemnly Professed Monk (perpetual private vows), 1 Solemnly Professed Nun (perpetual private vows), 8 Monastic Associates (through an understanding of our charism), 381 Affiliates (through attendance at retreats, workshops, and/or prayerful connection).
Apostolic Work: Monastic life, Liturgy of the Hours, use of any gift/talent compatible with monastic life, e.g., pastoral care, retreat work, nursing, medicine, manual labor
Representation: Diocese of Scranton
Vocation Director: Abbot: Brother Bernard Seif, SMC, (570) 992-3448

SALESIAN SISTERS OF (W692-2)
ST. JOHN BOSCO (F.M.A)
(Daughters of Mary Help of Christians), Eastern Province, 20 Old Swartswood Rd., Newton, NJ 07860
Web: www.salesianvocations.org
Email: fmavoc@aol.com
Apostolic Work: We, Salesian Sisters of St. John Bosco, are an international congregation of more than 14,000 Sisters ministering to, and with, youth in 89 countries around the world. A deep prayer life, a strong community life and a youth-centered ministry give us the strength and energy we need to face the challenges of daily life. Our ministry is one: reaching out to the young through formal education, youth groups, catechesis, youth centers, summer camps, retreat centers and missionary work. We walk with the young making a difference in the world!
Representation: Archdioceses of Los

Angeles, Miami, Newark, New York, New Orleans, San Antonio and San Francisco and in the Dioceses of Austin, Corpus Christi, Monterey, Paterson, Phoenix and St. Petersburg
Vocation Director: Sr. Colleen Clair, FMA, (973) 579-2419

SALESIAN SISTERS OF (W692-3)
ST. JOHN BOSCO (F.M.A.)
(Daughters of Mary Help of Christians), Western Province, 6019 Buena Vista St., San Antonio, TX 78237, 210-432-0090
9758 Foster Rd., Bellflower, CA 90706
Web: www.salesiansisterswest.org
Email: fmasuovoc@aol.com
Apostolic Work: We, Salesian Sisters of St. John Bosco, are an international congregation of more than 14,000 Sisters ministering to and with, youth in 89 countries around the world. A deep prayer life, a strong community life and a youth-centered ministry give us the strength and energy we need to face the challenges of daily life. Our ministry is one: reaching out to the young through formal education, youth groups, catechesis, youth centers, summer camps, retreat centers and missionary work. We walk with the young making a difference in the world!
Representation: Archdioceses of Los Angeles, Miami, Newark, New York, New Orleans, San Antonio and San Francisco and in the Dioceses of Austin, Corpus Christi, Monterey, Paterson, Phoenix and St. Petersburg
Vocation Director: Sr. Carmen Botello, FMA, 562-866-0675

SALVATORIANS (W693-1)
(Sisters of the Divine Savior) (S.D.S.)
4311 N. 100 St., Milwaukee, WI 53222-1393
Web: www.sistersofthedivine savior.org
Email: czais@salvatoriansisters.org
Members: 90 Sisters in US, 1,200 Sisters worldwide
Apostolic Work: The Salvatorians are an international religious community of sisters, priests, brothers and laity. We were founded by Fr. Francis Jordan and Blessed Mary of the Apostles in Rome in the 1880's. Our mission is to make Jesus, our Savior, known so that all may experience the fullness of life. Our apostolic works include parish ministry, social work, nursing, teaching, art, secretarial, law, and retreat ministry - wherever there is a need. Come and See weekends are scheduled for those interested, and

visits can be arranged any time. Preferred age is 19-45, with the equivalency of a high-school education
Representation: (Arch)dioceses of Birmingham, AL; Phoenix, Tucson, AZ; Monterey, CA; Nashville, TN; Green Bay, La Crosse, Madison, and Milwaukee, WI. Also in 29 countries worldwide
Vocation Director: Sister Karlyn Cauley, SDS, Sister Mary Lee Grady, SDS, Sister Carol Jean Zais, SDS, New Membership Team, Vocation Office, 414-466-0810, ext. 229

SCALABRINIANS (W693-2)
See "M" - Missionary Sisters of St. Charles Borromeo

SERVANTS OF GOD'S (W693-3)
LOVE (S.G.L.), 4399 Ford Rd., Ann Arbor, MI 48105-8105
Web: www.servantsofgodslove@ catholicweb.com
Email: mfoggin@dioceseof lansing.org
Members: 17 Sisters, 3 Postulants
Apostolic Work: Foster care home for medically fragile babies, 2 homes for the elderly (Emmanuel Houses), teaching, nursing, evangelization
Representation: Diocese of Lansing
Vocation Director: Sr. Mary Ann Foggin, SGL, (517) 342-2506
Fax (734) 663-6128

SERVANTS OF THE HOLY (W694)
HEART OF MARY (S.S.C.M.)
15 Elmwood Dr., Kankakee, IL 60901-3631
717 N. Batavia Ave., Batavia, IL 60510-1228
Web: www.sscm-usa.org
Email: sscm.vocations@yahoo.com
Members: 44 Sisters in US, 587 Sisters worldwide
Apostolic Work: Health care, education, pastoral ministry in hospitals, parishes and campuses as well as counseling and opportunities to use business expertise in a human service system
Representation: Dioceses of Bellville, Joliet, Rockford and Peoria and in the Archdiocese of Chicago
Vocation Director: Sister Marie Mason, SSCM, 815-370-7228

SERVANTS OF THE (W695)
IMMACULATE HEART OF MARY (S.C.I.M.) (also known as Good Shepherd Sisters of Quebec)
Provincial Residence, 313 Seaside Ave, Saco, ME 04072
Web: www.scimsisters.org
Email: elachance@gwi.net
Members: 72 Sisters in US

Apostolic Work: Social work: group homes for single moms and mother and child, adoption agency; transitional housing for women, prison ministry; education: parish and public schools; pastoral work, faith formation; and foreign missions in South Africa, Brazil, Haiti, Lesotho and Rwanda
Representation: Archdiocese of Boston and in the Diocese of Portland, ME
Vocation Director: Sister Elaine Lachance, s.c.i.m., Director of Vocation Ministry, SCIM Vocation Office, 11 Aspen Ave., South Portand, ME 04106, (207) 775-1128

SERVANTS OF JESUS (S.J.) (W696-1)
8080 Kinmore St., Dearborn Heights, MI 48127
Members: 19 Sisters
Representation: Archdiocese of Detroit and in the Dioceses of Gaylord, Grand Rapids and Saginaw
Vocation Director: Sr. Virginia Skurski, SJ, (313) 562-6156; fax: (313) 562-7769

SERVANTS OF THE LORD (W696-2)
AND THE VIRGIN OF MATARA (S.S.V.M.), Provincial House, 226 E. 113th St., New York, NY 10035
Province of the Immaculate Conception, (US, Canada, Guyana)
Our Lady Queen of Angels Convent/ Provincial House
Blessed Kateri Tekakwitha Novitiate, 1714 Craine Highway, Upper Marlboro, MD 20715
Web: www.ssvmusa.org, www.servidoras.org
Email: m.lumen@servidoras.org
Members: 67 Sisters, 13 Novices, 10 postulants
Apostolic Work: Parish work, education, missions, works of charity (orphanages, homes for the elderly, handicapped children, etc.)
Charism: Evangelization of the culture
Representation: Archdioceses of New York, Philadelphia, California and Washington, DC and in the Diocese of Brooklyn, Bridgeport, Toronto and Georgetown, Guyana.
Vocation Director: Mother Lumen Christi Fitzharris, SSVM, (917)-492-3668

SERVANTS OF MARY (W697)
(O.S.M.) (Servite Sisters)
1000 College Ave. West, Ladysmith, WI 54848, (715) 532-3364
Web: www.servitesisters.org
Email: balho@chibardun.net
Members: 60 Sisters, 47 Secular Servites

Apostolic Work: Worship, education, healing, social service and justice, health care, pastoral work, community organizing, law, counseling, and ministry to youth and elderly
Representation: Arizona, Florida, Illinois, Massachusetts, Minnesota, and Wisconsin
Vocation Director: Membership Director: Sr. Bonnie Alho, OSM, 334 N. Wilson Ave., Rice Lake, WI 54868, (715) 234-2032 (w), (715) 234-4732 (h)

SERVANTS OF MARY (W698)
(O.S.M.) (Servites)
US Province: Our Lady of Sorrows
7400 Military Ave., Omaha, NE 68134
Web: www.osms.org
Email: sam@osms.org
Members: 98 Servite Sisters and 72 Associate Members
Apostolic Work: Prayer, spirituality, liturgy, education, pastoral ministry, counseling, social justice advocacy, health care, hospital chaplaincy, cancer and life threatening illnesses, St. Peregrine ministry to those with life threatening illnesses. Missions: Jamaica, West Indies and the Republic of the Congo
Representation: (Arch)dioceses of Omaha and Grand Island, NE; Des Moines, Iowa; Tucson, AR; Detroit, MI; Ogdensburg, NY; and Portland, OR. Also in France, England, Belgium, Austria, Canada and Congo
Vocation Director: Sr. Ann Marie Petrylka, OSM (402) 571-2547
Fax (402) 573-6055

SERVANTS OF MARY (W699-1)
(M.S.M.) (Mantellate Sisters)
Provincialate: Mother of Sorrows
Convent, 13811 S. Western Ave.,
Blue Island, IL 60406,
(708) 385-2103
Web: www.mantellatesisters
msm.org
Email: srmaria@prodigy.net
Members: 19 Sisters
Apostolic Work: Teaching: elementary, kindergarten, C.C.D., foreign mission in South Africa
Representation: in the Archdiocese of Chicago
Vocation Director: Sr. Maria Teresa Musto, M.S.M.Villa Santa Maria Convent, 5901 Oak Forest Ave., Tinley Park, IL 60477, (708) 532-2241 Fax: (708) 532-8433

SERVANTS OF MARY (W699-2)
(O.S.M.) (Mantellate Sisters)
Marian Lake Convent, 16949 S.
Drauden Rd., Plainfield, IL 60544
Web: www.mantellatesisters
msm.org
Email: smaosm@aol.com

Members: 8 Sisters
Apostolic Work: Pastoral ministry, retreat work, counseling, St. Peregrine ministry
Representation: Diocese of Joliet in Illinois
Vocation Director: Sr. Gesuina Bongiorno, O.S.M., (815) 436-5796

SERVANTS OF THE MOST (W700)
SACRED HEART OF JESUS
(S.S.C.J.), Sacred Heart Province-USA, 866 Cambria St., Cresson, PA 16630-1713
Web: www.sacredheartsisters.org
Email: sscjusa@pngusa.net
Members: 33 Sisters, 4 Novices, 2 Postulants in US; 700 Sisters worldwide
Apostolic Work: Teaching, nursing, parish work, mission, social service
Representation: Archdiocese of Philadelphia and in the Dioceses of Altoona-Johnstown and Metuchen
Vocation Director: Sister Amabilis, S.S.C.J., (814) 886-4223

SERVANTS OF THE (W701-1)
SACRED HEART OF JESUS AND
OF THE POOR (S.S.H.J.P.)
US Regional House: Sacred Heart Children's Home Convent, 3310 S. Zapata Hwy., Laredo, TX 78046-8046
Members: 41 Sisters in US; 661 Sisters worldwide
Apostolic Work: Education/religious education - all levels, Children's Home.Conduct: Elementary schools, high schools, colleges, boarding schools, children's homes, hospitals, nursing homes, dispensaries, mobile clinics
Representation: Dioceses of El Paso and Laredo. Also in Chile, Colombia, Guatemala, Italy, Kenya (E. Africa), Mexico, Nicaragua, Cuba and Venezuela.
Vocation Director: Sr. Maria Yolanda Fernandez, S.S.H.J.P., Regional Superior, (956) 723-3343, Fax: (956) 723-3409

SISTERS ADORERS OF (W701-2)
THE PRECIOUS BLOOD (A.P.B.)
See "A"

CONGREGATION, SERVANTS (W702)
OF CHRIST THE KING (S.S.C.K.)
Villa Loretto, N8114 Calvary St., Mt. Calvary, WI 53057-3057
Web: www.villalorettonh.org
Email: sisterss@netscape.net
Members: 7 Sisters
Conduct: Nursing homes, residential home, assisted living facility (inquiries to Sr. M. Stephon) Cristo Rey Ranch (weekend respite care for children)

Representation: Archdiocese of Milwaukee and in the Diocese of Fargo, North Dakota
Vocation Director: Sr. M. Stephen Blosel, Superior

SISTERS, SERVANTS OF (W703)
THE IMMACULATE HEART OF
MARY (I.H.M.), Villa Maria House of Studies, 1140 King Rd., PO Box 200, Immaculata, PA 19345-0200
Web: www.ihmimmaculata.org
Email: ihmvoc@aol.com
Members: 950 Sisters
Apostolic Work: We are committed to serving Christ and the Church through the public profession of vows, supported and energized by prayer and Eucharistic devotion. Hospitality, simplicity, joyful service, and devoted charity characterize our life in common. With missions in North and South America, we embrace a corporate commitment to Catholic education from preschool through college, day care, adult education, CCD, and sacramental preparation. Our desire to witness Gospel values and to foster faith formation is also expressed in pastoral work, nursing, and spiritual direction. In the spirit of St. Alphonsus, we promote peace and justice and in addressing the needs of the most abandoned poor
Representation: (Arch)dioceses of Allentown, Arlington, Camden, Harrisburg, Hartford, Metuchen, Miami, Philadelphia, Raleigh, Savannah, and Trenton. Also Lawrence (MA) and in two countries in South America
Vocation Director: Sister Carmen Teresa Fernandez or Sr. Rose Bernadette Mulligan, (610) 889-1553, fax: (610) 889-4874

SISTERS, SERVANTS OF (W704)
THE IMMACULATE HEART OF
MARY (IHM), IHM Center, 2300 Adams Ave., Scranton, PA 18509
Web: www.sistersofihm.org
Email: harkir@sistersofihm.org
Members: 485 Sisters
Apostolic Work: We are an apostolic community of approximately 450 women religious. In the passionate spirit of Saint Alphonsus Liguori, we joyfully participate in the redeeming mission of Jesus, which impels us to proclaim the Good News of God's unconditional love for all. We embrace Mary, the first disciple, as our model of a life rooted in God. We reclaim and confirm the core values of ROOTEDNESS IN GOD, COMMUNITY, JUSTICE, RESPECT FOR DIVERSITY AND WHOLENESS, that impel and permeate our participation in the mission of Jesus

B-118

Christ. While currently serving in the United States and Latin America, we live our mission by engaging in and sponsoring ministries that meet contemporary needs and foster the full development of human potential in the fields of education, health-care, social service and pastoral service.
Representation: 36 (Arch)dioceses including Baltimore, Bridgeport, Brooklyn, Harrisburg, New York, Philadelphia, Pittsburgh, Raleigh, Rockville Centre, St. Augustine, St. Petersburg, Scranton, Syracuse, Trenton, Washington, Wheeling-Charleston and Wilmington. Also in Peru and Guatamala
Vocation Director: If you are interested in experiencing our joyful spirit of hospitality or for more information contact Sister Ruth Harkins, IHM, (570) 346-5413 or above address and email

SISTERS, SERVANTS OF (W705)
THE IMMACULATE HEART OF MARY (I.H.M.), Membership Office, IHM Motherhouse, (734) 240-9821 610 W. Elm, Monroe, MI 48162
Web: www.ihmsisters.org
Email: membership@ihmsisters.org
Members: 488 Sisters, 120 Associates
Apostolic Work: We are a progressive, visionary faith community of 488 sisters, 120 associates and volunteers, who understand our God quest leads us along many pathways. Our mission has evolved and grown in response to the pressing global, social and ecological injustices in the world. Those needs offer us various opportunites in ministry, including traditional and nontraditional education, justice advocacy, spirituality and sustainability. We build community that sustains us as individuals, as sisters and as interdependent members of the entire community of life. We are willing to take risks for the sake of the future and trust in divine providence.
Representation: 48 Dioceses in the US and in 8 Dioceses outside of the US including Puerto Rico, Canada, South Africa, Uganda, Italy, and Mexico
Vocation Director: Contact us at our Membership Office by e-mail listed above, by phone (734) 240-9821, and by mail at address listed above; or visit our website.

SERVANTS OF MARY, (W706)
MINISTERS TO THE SICK (S.de M.)
(US Province) Provincial House 800 N. 18th St., Kansas City, KS 66102

Web: www.sisterservantsofmary.org
Email: servantsmaryny@optonline.net
Members: 260 Sisters in US; 2,000 worldwide
Apostolic Work: Nursing-private and visiting nursing in patients' homes and hospitals
Representation: Archdioceses of Kansas City, Los Angeles, New Orleans and New York and in France, Spain, England, Italy, Portugal, U.R. of Cameroon, Mexico, Columbia, Ecuador, Brazil, Argentina, Bolivia, Cuba, Dominican Republic, Puerto Rico, Belgium, Panama, Peru, the Philippines and Uruguay
Vocation Director: Sister Victoria Soto, S. de M., 3305 Country Club Rd., Bronx, NY 10465-1296, (718) 829-0428, Fax (718) 829-2346

SISTERS SERVANTS OF (W707)
MARY IMMACULATE (S.S.M.I.)
See Eastern Catholic Religious Communities for Women

SISTERS, SERVANTS OF (W708-1)
MARY IMMACULATE (S.S.M.I.)
(Provincialate and Novitiate) 1220 Tugwell Drive, Catonsville, MD 21228
Members: 32 Sisters in American Province; 900 worldwide
Apostolic Work: Primarily social and charitable ministry to the aged and health care
Representation: Dioceses of Baltimore, Cleveland and Washington, DC. General Motherhouse in Poland. Also in Rome, Africa and Lithuania
Vocation Director: Sister Ce Ann Sambor, S.S.M.I., 285 Panorama Dr., Seven Hills, OH 44131 (216) 441-5402

SERVITES (W708-2)
See Servants of Mary

SISTERS OF OUR LADY OF (W708-3)
MERCY (MERCEDARIAN SISTERS)
See "O" - Our Lady of Mercy, Sisters of

SISTERS OF SOCIAL (W709-2)
SERVICE OF BUFFALO (S.S.S.)
US Residence No institutions by Constitution (Members are free to work for Church-related and secular agencies)
296 Summit Ave, Buffalo, NY 14214
Web: www.sistersofsocialservice buffalo.org
Email: sssbuf@verizon.net
Members: 14 Sisters in US
Apostolic Work: Social work, health care ministry, inner-city work, parish

ministry, retreat work, political ministry and education for social justice
Representation: (Arch)dioceses of Buffalo, Miami, and Ponce, P.R.
Vocation Director: Sr. Teresina Joo, 716-834-0197, E-mail: jteresina@ verizon.net

SISTERS OF SOCIAL (W710)
SERVICE (S.S.S.)
4316 Lanai Road, Encino, CA 91436
Web: www.sistersofsocialservice .com/home.html
Email: ssocialser@aol.com
Members: 100 Sisters
Apostolic Work: Primarily social workers: pastoral ministry and social work in parish settings, neighborhood centers in low-income communities, drop-in center for homeless teens, foster care, parent education for inner-city mothers, therapeutic counseling, lobby for social justice at the legislative level, summer camps for inner-city children, retreat center. Similar programs at international locations
Representation: Archdioceses of Boston, Los Angeles, Portland (OR), San Francisco and Seattle and in the Dioceses of Oakland, Sacramento and San Diego, Taiwan, Mexico, Philippines
Vocation Director: Sr. Catherine Connell and Sr. Deborah Lorentz, (818) 285-3355

SISTERS OF THE SOCIETY (W711)
DEVOTED TO THE SACRED HEART (S.D.S.H.), Motherhouse, 9814 Sylvia Ave., Northridge, CA 91324
Web: www.sacredheartsisters.com
Email: webmaster@sacredheart sisters.com
Members: 52 Sisters
Apostolic Work: Religious education, family retreats, catechetical/sacramental retreats for children, youth retreats, catechist formation, worldwide video catechesis, girls' summer camps and music; members of the International Council for Catechetics.
Representation: Archdioceses of Los Angeles and St. Louis and in the Dioceses of San Bernardino and Orange. Also in Taiwan and Hungary.
Vocation Director: Sister Paula Sawhill, S.D.S.H., (805) 688-6158

SOCIETY OF HELPERS (W712-1)
(S.H.), Generalate: Paris 4721 J South Woodlawn, Chicago, IL 60615
Web: www.helpers.org
Members: 31 Sisters in US, 900 worldwide
Conduct: The Helpers, an international society, are engaged in the

B-119

pastoral work of the Church, especially with those who are suffering in any way
Representation: Archdioceses of Chicago, New York, St. Louis and San Francisco and in the Diocese of San Juan.
Vocation Director: Sr. Mary Ellen Moore, Provincial Superior, (773) 548-5026

SOCIETY OF THE HOLY (W712-2)
CHILD JESUS
See "H" - Holy Child of Jesus, Society of the

SOCIETY OF OUR (W713-1)
MOTHER OF PEACE (SMP)
Mary the Font Solitude, 6150 Antire Rd, High Ridge, MO 63049-6225 (636) 677-3235 Fax (636) 677-5284
Web: www.cmswr.org/member_communities/SMP.htm
Email: smpconvent@yahoo.com
Members: 17 Sisters in the US
Apostolic Work: Contemplative-apostolic balance of life in the context of simplicity and poverty; emphasis on solitary prayer; apostolates of retreat work and spiritual direction; direct evangelization especially within the African-American community and among the poor
Representation: Archdiocese of St. Louis and in the Diocese of Springfield-Cape Girardeau. Also in the Philippines and in Nigeria
Vocation Director: Sister Maryjoy, SMP, Our Mother of Peace Convent, 8307 Madison Ave., Vinita Park, MO 63114-6225, (314) 426-7725

SOCIETY OF OUR LADY (W713-2)
OF THE MOST HOLY TRINITY
(S.O.L.T.), Motherhouse, Bosque, NM 87006
Web: www.solt3.org
Email: soltsistersvocations@gmail.com
Members: 98 Professed Sisters, 20 in Formation
Apostolic Work: Disciples of Jesus and Mary serving on Ecclesial Teams, made up of Priests, Sisters and Laity, in areas of deepest apostolic need
Representation: (Arch)dioceses of Corpus Christi, Fargo, Kansas City-St. Joseph, Laredo, Pueblo and Santa Fe.
Vocation Director: Sr. Mary Emmanuel Schmidt, SOLT, Vocations Servant, (701) 244-2449, Our Lady of Guadalupe Convent, PO Box 1089, Dunseith, ND 58329

SISTERS OF THE (W714)
SORROWFUL MOTHER (Third Order Regular of St. Francis of Assisi)
(SSM), SSM Emmaus House of Formation, 40 Morris Ave., Denville, NJ 07834
Web: www.ssmfranciscans.org
Email: ssmvoc@aol.com
Members: 400 Sisters Internationally
Apostolic Work: Teaching and healing the unserved through literacy and advocacy programs, retreat ministry, education, Native American and Hispanic ministry, nursing, art therapy, administration, hospice, accounting, social work, counseling, outreach clinics, clerical work, archives, patient advocacy, House of Discernment, hospital chaplain
Representation: (Arch)dioceses of Galveston-Houston, Green Bay, La Crosse, Las Cruces, Los Angeles, Milwaukee, Paterson, Superior, Tulsa, Wichita and Winona. In the Caribbean: Castries, St. Lucia; St. George, Grenada; Santiago, Dominican Republic; Port of Spain, Trinidad. Also minister in Austria, Brazil, Germany, Italy, and Tanzania, Africa
Vocation Director: (973) 627-0424

TRAPPISTINES (O.C.S.O.) (W716-1)
(Cistercian Nuns of the Strict Observance), Santa Rita Abbey HC1 Box 929, Sonoita, AZ 85637
Web: www.santaritabbey.org
Email: sracommty@wildblue.net
Members: 10 Sisters
Representation: Diocese of Tuscon, AZ
Vocation Director: Sr. Victoria Murray, O.C.S.O. (520) 455-5595 Fax (520) 455-5770

TRAPPISTINES (O.C.S.O.) (W716-2)
(Cistercian Nuns of the Strict Observance), Redwoods Monastery 18104 Briceland Thorn Rd, Whitethorn, CA 95589-5589
Web: www.redwoodsabbey.org
Email: novicedirector@redwoodsabbey.org
Members: 9 Sisters
Representation: Diocese of Santa Rosa
Vocation Director: Contact Person: Sr. Claire Bouttin, OCSO, (707) 986-7419

TRAPPISTINES (O.C.S.O.) (W717)
(Cistercian Nuns of the Strict Observance), Our Lady of the Mississippi Abbey, 8400 Abbey Hill, Dubuque, IA 52003-2003
Web: www.mississippiabbey.org
Email: vocations@olmabbey.org
Members: 22 Solemnly Professed Sisters, 3 Novices

Conduct: Contemplative monastic community
Representation: Archdiocese of Dubuque
Vocation Director: Sr. Martha Juskewycz, O.C.S.O., (563) 582-2595, ext. 21

TRAPPISTINES (O.C.S.O.) (W718)
(Cistercian Nuns of the Strict Observance), Mount Saint Mary's Abbey, 300 Arnold St., Wrentham, MA 02093-1799
Web: www.msmabbey.org
Email: sisters@msmabbey.org or tintern@msmabbey.org
Members: 50 Sisters, 3 Junior Professed, 5 Novices, 1 Postulant
Apostolic Work: Contemplative Monastic Order
Representation: Archdiocese of Boston
Vocation Director: Sr. Elizabeth LaSalle, OCSO, (508) 528-1282, E-mail: s.elizabeth@msmabbey.org

TRAPPISTINES (O.C.S.O.) (W719-1)
(Cistercian Nuns of the Strict Observance), Monastery of Our Lady of the Angels, 3365 Monastery Dr., Crozet, VA 22932-2932
Web: www.olamonastery.org
Email: vocations@olamonastery.org
Members: 10 Professed, 1 Junior Professed
Apostolic Work: Contemplative monastic
Representation: Diocese of Richmond
Vocation Director: Sister Barbara Smickel, O.C.S.O., (434) 823-1452

TRINITY MISSIONS (W719-2)
(M.S.B.T.) (Missionary Servants of the Most Blessed Trinity)
See "M" - Missionary Servants of the Most Blessed Trinity

URSULINE SISTERS (O.S.U.) (W720)
(Roman Union) (Western Province) 639 Angela Dr., Santa Rosa, CA 95403-1793
Web: www.ursulinewest.com
Email: cvs535@aol.com
Members: 34 Sisters
Apostolic Work: Spiritual development through education: preschool, elementary and secondary; parish ministries, retreat and conference centers; spiritual assistance for women and children, the poor, the elderly, spiritual direction
Representation: Archdioceses of Anchorage, Los Angeles and San Francisco and in the Dioceses of Boise, Fairbanks, Great Falls/Billings, Juneau, San Jose and Santa Rosa.

Vocation Director: Sr. Margaret Johnson, O.S.U., Provincial Prioress, (707) 545-6811

URSULINE SISTERS (O.S.U.) (W723) (Congregation of Paris), 3105 Lexington Rd., Louisville, KY 40206
Web: www.ursulineslou.org
Email: rdressman@ursulineslou.org
Members: 127 Sisters, 1 Novice
Apostolic Work: Teachers and administrators in Montessori pre-school, elementary schools, secondary schools, colleges and adult and religious education, music, special education, among Hispanics, administrators of health and social services. Also in pastoral ministry, deaf ministry, retreat ministry and spiritual direction, ministry to the sick and elderly. Foreign mission in Peru.
Representation: Archdioceses of Louisville, Baltimore, Cincinnati, Philadelphia and in the Dioceses of Grand Island, Lexington, Wheeling-Charleston, Callao and Cajamarca, Peru
Vocation Director: Sister Rita Dressman, O.S.U., (502) 896-3948

URSULINE SISTERS OF (W724) MOUNT SAINT JOSEPH (O.S.U.)
Mount Saint Joseph, 8001 Cummings Rd., Maple Mount, KY 42356
Web: www.ursulinesmsj.org
Email: vocations@maplemount.org
Members: 186 Sisters
Apostolic Work: Through a ministry of education and Christian formation in the spirit of Saint Angela Merici, our founder, we commit to simplicity, hospitality, justice and service
Representation: Archdioceses of Louisville, Santa Fe, St. Paul, Minneapolis, and Washington (DC) and in the Dioceses of Belleville, Gallup, Kansas City-St. Joseph, Memphis, Owensboro, Shreveport, Springfield, IL, and Springfield-Cape Girardeau. Also in Chile and Jamaica.
Vocation Director: Contact: (270) 229-4103

URSULINE NUNS (O.S.U.) (W725)
(Roman Union) (Northeastern Province, 45 Lowder St., Dedham, MA 02026-4200
Email: provosu@verizon.net
Members: 31 Sisters
Apostolic Work: 1 high school, 1 elementary school
Representation: Archdiocese of Boston and in the Diocese of Portland (ME)
Vocation Director: Sr. Angela Krippendorf, o.s.u., Provincial, (781) 326-7296

URSULINE SISTERS (O.S.U.) (W726)
(Roman Union, Central Province) Ursuline Provincialate, 353 S. Sappington Rd., Kirkwood, MO 63122, (314) 821-6884
Web: www.osucentral.org
Email: srsusan@osucentral.org
Members: 145 Sisters
Apostolic Work: Education for evangelization in schools, parishes, diocesan offices, ministry to the poor, foreign mission, retreat work, counseling, pastoral care in hospitals, social work
Representation: (Arch)dioceses of Minneapolis-St. Paul, St. Louis, Springfield (IL), Springfield-Cape Girardeau, Dallas, San Antonio, Galveston-Houston, Laredo, New Orleans, Cincinnati, and Anchorage. Also in Europe, Asia, Africa, Latin America, the Caribbean, Australia and the Middle East
Vocation Director: Sr. Susan Kienzler, OSU, PO Box 8, Cape Girardeau, MO 63702-0008, (573) 332-1804

URSULINE SISTERS (O.S.U.) (W727)
(Roman Union) (Eastern Province of the U.S.), 1338 North Avenue, New Rochelle, NY 10804-2121
Web: www.osueast.org
Email: patsosu@aol.com
Apostolic Work: Education-pre-primary through university, diverse pastoral/social services
Representation: Archdioceses of New York and Washington (DC) and in the Dioceses of Ogdensburg and Wilmington
Vocation Director: Sr. Pat Schifini, O.S.U., (914) 712-0060, Ext. 113

URSULINE SISTERS OF (W728) TILDONK (O.S.U.), 81-15 Utopia Pkwy., Jamaica, NY 11432
Web: www.members.tripod.com/~tressy
Email: mbarrett@tildonkursuline.org
Members: 58 Sisters in the USA
Apostolic Work: Grammar schools, pastoral ministry, religious education, hospital chaplaincy, social work, spirituality
Representation: Archdioceses of New York and Hartford and in the Dioceses of Bridgeport, Brooklyn, Rockville Centre, and Burlington. Provinces in Belgium, Canada and India, District in Democratic Republic of the Congo, Africa
Vocation Director: Contact: Sister Mairead Barrett, O.S.U., (718) 591-0681, ext. 3202

URSULINES OF CINCINNATI (W729) (O.S.U.) (Congregation of Paris)
St. Ursula Convent, 1339 E. McMillan St, Cincinnati, OH 45206
Email: mefkeman.osu@fuse.net

Members: 16 Sisters
Apostolic Work: Teaching, adult education, parish ministry, neighborhood community services, counseling, Catholic communications
Representation: Archdiocese of Cincinnati
Vocation Director: Sr. Eileen Connelly, O.S.U., 3006 Beaver Ave., Cincinnati, OH 45213, (513) 351-9574

URSULINE SISTERS OF (W730) CLEVELAND (O.S.U.)
Motherhouse, 2600 Lander Rd., Pepper Pike (Cleveland), OH 44124
Web: www.ursulinesisters.org
Email: jbeck@ursulinesisters.org
Members: 225 Sisters
Apostolic Work: Education and pastoral ministry, but also includes nursing, social service, El Salvador mission and retreat ministry
Representation: Primarily in the Diocese of Cleveland with individual sisters also serving in several other states and El Salvador
Vocation Director: Sister Juliana Beck, OSU, (440) 449-1200, ext. 138

URSULINE SISTERS (O.S.U.) (W731) (Congregation of Paris)
Ursulines of Brown County Ursuline Center, 20860 State Rte. 251, St. Martin, OH 45118, (513) 875-2020
Web: www.ursulinesofbc.net
Email: phoman@tds.net
Members: 33 Sisters
Apostolic Work: Academic education-all levels, catechetical instruction, administration, retreats, counseling, parish ministry, organization consultation, social-inner city and rural ministry, nursing, spiritual direction
Representation: (Arch)dioceses of Cincinnati and Toledo
Vocation Director: Contact: Sr. Patricia Homan, OSU, (513) 875-2020, ext. 27

URSULINE SISTERS (O.S.U.) (W732)
Ursuline Convent of the Sacred Heart, 4045 Indian Rd., Toledo, OH 43606-3606
Web: toledoursulines.org
Email: sanjea_43606@yahoo.com
Members: 57 Sisters
Apostolic Work: Teaching, administration, hospital chaplain, D.R.E.; pastoral asssociate, spiritual direction, home health care, missionary work, available for any work of charity
Representation: (Arch)dioceses of Toledo, Fresno and Washington, DC. Foreign mission in Peru.
Vocation Director: Sister Sandy Sherman, OSU, (419) 536-9587

URSULINE SISTERS OF (W733-1)
YOUNGSTOWN (O.S.U.)
(Congregation of Paris)
Motherhouse, 4250 Shields Rd.,
Canfield, OH 44406
Web: www.theursulines.org
Email: theursulines@yahoo.com
Members: 59 Sisters and 39
Associates; also Companions in
Mission (lay volunteer ministry),
Company of Angela (lay prayer
associates)
Apostolic Work: Religious/academic
education-all levels, parish ministry,
social services, hospital services,
single parenting, AIDS ministry, and
music.
Representation: Dioceses of
Brownsville, Cleveland, and
Youngstown.
Vocation Director: Sr. Kathleen
McCarragher, 745 Bryson St.,
Youngstown, OH 44502, (330) 743-
2152

VERONA MISSIONARY (W733-2)
SISTERS, See "C" - Comboni
Missionary Sisterson

VINCENTIAN SISTERS OF (W734)
CHARITY (V.S.C.), 8200 McKnight
Rd., Pittsburgh, PA 15237-5237
Web: www.vincentiansrspgh.org
Email: vmiller@vincentiansrspgh.org
Members: 110 Sisters
Apostolic Work: Education: day care,
kindergarten, elementary, high
schools; health care: nursing
homes, disabled children's home,
clinic, interpreter for deaf; religious
education; social services; hospital
chaplaincy; parish, pastoral and
youth ministry
Representation: PA, OH, FL, AL, WI
and Canada
Vocation Director: Sr. Valerie Miller,
V.S.C.,
(412) 364-6201 Fax (412) 364-9055

VISITATION NUNS (V.H.M.) (W736)
Monastery of the Visitation of
Georgetown, 1500 Thirty-fifth St.,
N.W., Washington, DC 20007-0007
Web: www.georgetownvisitation.org
Email: visitationsister@yahoo.com
Members: 16 Sisters, 1 Postulant
Apostolic Work: Prayer and educa-
tion (girls' high school)
Vocation Director: Sr. Anne E. Fiore,
VHM, (202) 337-0305, Fax (202)
965-3845

VISITATION NUNS (V.H.M.) (W738-1)
Monastery of the Visitation
2455 Visitation Dr., Mendota
Heights, MN 55120
Web: www.visitationmonastery.com
or www.visitationmonastery.net
Email: denvil@vischool.org

Members: 9 Sisters
Apostolic Work: Prayer and
educational ministries of various
forms with a variety of people
Vocation Director: For information
call: (651) 683-1700

VISITATION NUNS (V.H.M.) (W738-2)
Visitation Monastery, 1527 Fremont
Ave North, Minneapolis, MN 55411
Web: www.visitationmonastery
minneapolis.com
Email: mullinkf@aol.com
Apostolic Work: Contemplative/
monastic prayer, living in the midst
of our inner-city neighbors offering
hospitality and hope.
Representation: Archdiocese of St.
Paul and Minneapolis
Vocation Director: Sister Katherine
Mullin, V.H.M., (612) 521-6113 Fax
(612) 521-4020

VISITATION NUNS (V.H.M.) (W739)
Visitation Monastery, 3020 N. Ballas
Rd, St. Louis, MO 63131
Web: www.visitationmonastery.org/
stlouis
Email: srcbrady@visitation
academy.org
Members: 20 Sisters
Apostolic Work: Seeking union with
God in contemplation; community
life creates family bonds among the
members and also with those
entrusted to the sisters' apostolates
of prayer, spiritual direction, and
teaching (preschool through 12th
grade)
Vocation Director: Sr. Catherine
Brady, V.H.M., (314) 625-9213

VISITATION NUNS (V.H.M.) (W740)
Visitation Monastery, 8902 Ridge
Blvd., Brooklyn, NY 11209-5716
Web: www.visitationsisters.org/
mona/ bro_main.asp
Email: vamonastery@aol.com
Members: 23 Sisters, 7 in
Formation, 2 Associates
Apostolic Work: Primary mission:
ministry of prayer in the monastic
contemplative tradition. Retreatants
and those discerning vocations are
invited to experience monastic life
with the Sisters. Religious instruc-
tion in the Sisters' private academy
for girls (N-8)
Representation: Diocese of Brooklyn
Vocation Director: Sr. Pauline Baulis,
V.H.M., (718) 745-5151, fax: (718)
745-3680

VISITATION NUNS (V.H.M.) (W742)
(Cloistered), (First Federation of
North America) Monastery of the
Visitation, 12221 Bienvenue Rd.,
Rockville, VA 23146-3146

Monasteries:
2300 Springhill Ave., Mobile, AL
36607
5820 City Ave., Philadelphia, PA
19131
12221 Bienvenue Rd., Rockville, VA
23146
1745 Parkside Blvd., Toledo, OH
43607
14 Beach Rd., P.O. 432, Tyringham,
MA 01264
2055 Ridgedale Dr., Snellville, GA
30278
Web: www.visitmontemaria.com
Email: info@visitmontemaria.com
Members: 14
Apostolic Work: Prayer is primary,
limited retreats
Vocation Director: Mother Mary
Emmanuel Stahl, VHM,
Philadelphia Cloistered Monastery
vocation contact: Mother Frances
deSales Paganelli, VHM, 5820 City
Ave., Philadelphia, PA 19131, (804)
749-4885, viznunphil@aol.com,
www.religiouslife.com/w_visphila01.
phtml

VISITATION NUNS (V.H.M.) (W743)
Monastery of the Visitation, 410
Washington Ave., Wheeling, WV
26003
Web: www.visitationsisters.org or
www.mountdechantal.org
Members: 6 Sisters
Apostolic Work: Education, spiritual
direction, retreats
Vocation Director: Sr. Jo Anne
Gonter, (304) 232-1283

SISTERS OF THE (W743-1)
VISITATION, Monastery of the
Visitation, 1745 Parkside Blvd.,
Toledo, OH 43607-1599
Web: www.toledovisitation.org
Email: toledovisitation@
email.toast.net
Members: 16 Professed, 3 Tempor-
ary Professed, 2 Novices
Apostolic Work: Prayer and
contemplation
Representation: Diocese of Toledo
Vocation Director: Contact Vocation
Directress, (419) 536-1343

SISTERS OF VISITATION OF (W744)
THE CONGREGATION OF THE
IMMACULATE HEART OF MARY
(S.V.M.), 2950 Kaufmann Ave.,
Dubuque, IA 52001-1655
Email: bcuroe@loras.edu
Members: 6 Sisters
Apostolic Work: Also engaged in
adult education, college counseling
Representation: Archdiocese of
Dubuque
Vocation Director: Sister Bernadine
Curoe, President, (563) 556-2440,
ext. 3

VOCATIONIST SISTERS (W745) **(S.D.V.) (Sisters of Divine Vocations)** Sister Joanna Formation House, 88 Brooklake Rd., Florham Park, NJ 07932
US Foundation: Perpetual Help Day Nursery, 172 Broad St., Newark, NJ 07104, (973) 484-3535
Vocationist Sisters, 223 14th Street, Palisades Park, NJ 07650
Web: www.vocationist.org/sisters
Email: vocationist@yahoo.com
Apostolic Work: To guide and foster vocations to priesthood and religious life; teaching, parish ministry and missionary work; special emphasis is given to work with the poor and underprivileged
Representation: Dioceses of Newark and Paterson. Also in Italy, France, Brazil, Argentina, Philippines, India, Indonesia, Madagascar and Nigeria
Vocation Director: Sr. Joy Sabesaje, S.D.V., (973) 966-9762

XAVIER SISTERS (XS) (W746) **(Catholic Mission Sisters of St. Francis Xavier)**, 37179 Moravian Dr., Clinton Township, MI 48036-3600
Members: 1 Sister
Representation: Archdiocese of Detroit
Vocation Director: Sister Mary Agnes Malburg, XS, (586) 465-5082

XAVERIAN MISSIONARY (W747) **SISTERS OF MARY (X.M.M.)**
US Headquarters, 242 Salisbury St., Worcester, MA 01609-1609
Email: xavsistersusa@msn.com
Members: 8 Sisters in US
Apostolic Work: Evangelization among non-Christian peoples: catechetical, medical, educational, social work.
Representation: Italy (Motherhouse), R.D. Congo, Brazil, Cameroon, Chad, Mexico, Japan, Burundi, and Thailand. In US: Diocese of Worcester.
Vocation Director: Sister Superior, (508) 757-0514 (tel., fax)

EASTERN CATHOLIC COMMUNITIES FOR WOMEN

ANTONINE SISTERS (WE001) **(MARONITE) (A.S.)**, Headquarters, 2691 North Lipkey Rd., North Jackson, OH 44451
Web: www.antoninesisters.com
Email: anto9srs@aol.com
Conduct: 5 Sisters in US; 195 worldwide
Apostolic Work: Education, health care, pastoral ministry and social service
Vocation Director: Sr. Marie Madeleine Iskandar, AS, Superior, 330-538-9822 or 2567, fax: 330-538-9820

BASILIANS - (WE002) **CONTEMPLATIVE NUNS OF SAINT BASIL THE GREAT, OSBM**
Sacred Heart Monastery, 209 Keasel Rd., Middletown, NY 10940-6287
Web: www.basiliannuns.org.ar
Apostolic Work: Contemplative community
Vocation Director: Mother Georgianne Snihur, OSBM, (845) 343-1308

BASILIANS - SISTERS OF (WE003) **ST. BASIL THE GREAT (Byzantine Catholic Church) OSBM**
500 W. Main St., PO Box 878, Uniontown, PA 15401
Web: www.sistersofstbasil.org
Email: sbjm45@yahoo.com
Members: 74 Sisters; 41 Associates
Conduct: 2 grammar schools,1 nursing home, 1 retreat center, staff religious education offices, diocesan offices, pastoral and parochial ministry
Representation: Byzantine Catholic Archeparchy of Pittsburgh and in the Eparchies of Parma, Passaic and Van Nuys
Vocation Director: Sr. Barbara Jean Mihalchick, OSBM, (724) 438-7149

BASILIANS – SISTERS OF (WE004) **THE ORDER OF ST. BASIL THE GREAT (O.S.B.M.) (Ukrainian Byzantine Rite)**, 710 Fox Chase Rd., Fox Chase Manor, PA 19046-4198
Web: www.stbasils.com
Email: province@stbasils.com
Members: 60 Sisters
Apostolic Work: Education at all levels, pastoral ministry, chancery support, spiritual direction, retreats, liturgical arts
Vocation Director: Sr. Cecilila, OSBM, (215) 379-3998, ext. 524

BENEDICTINE SISTERS (WE005) **(BYZANTINE) (O.S.B.)**, Queen of Heaven Monastery, 8640 Squires Ln. N.E., Warren, OH 44484
Web: www.benedictinebyzantine.org
Email: agnes@netdotcom.com
Conduct: 7 members
Apostolic Work: Teaching, religious education, pastoral care, parish ministry, office work, retreat work, spiritual direction
Vocation Director: Sister Agnes Knapik, OSB, (330) 856-1813

BYZANTINE NUNS OF (WE006) **ST. CLARE (B.N.S.C.)**, Poor Clares in the Byzantine Rite in the Ruthenian Eparchy of Parma, OH Monastery of Holy Protection
6688 Cady Rd., N. Royalton, OH 44133
Members: 6 Professed
Apostolic Work: Contemplatives, Second Order of St. Francis, in

Eastern Monasticism
Vocation Director: (440) 237-6800

COMMUNITY OF THE (WE007) **MOTHER OF GOD OF TENDERNESS (C.M.G.T.)**, 79 Golden Hill Rd., Danbury, CT 06811
Conduct: 3 Sisters
Apostolic Work: Active/contemplative community
Vocation Director: (203) 794-1486

DISCALCED CARMELITE (WE008) **NUNS OF THE BYZANTINE RITE (O.C.D.)**, Holy Annunciation Monastery, 403 W. County Rd., Sugarloaf, PA 18249
Web: www.byzantinediscalced carmelites.com
Email: marija@ptd.net
Members: 14 Professed Nuns
Vocation Director: Mother Marija of the Holy Spirit, OCD, Prioress, (570) 788-1205, Fax: (570) 788-3329

MISSIONARY SISTERS OF (WE009) **MOTHER OF GOD (M.S.M.G.)**
Novitiate located at: 111 W. North St., Stamford, CT 06902, 203-323-1237
Motherhouse, 711 North Franklin St, Philadelphia, PA 19123
Web: www.msmg.ukrcathedral.com
Email: MSMG@ukrcathedral philadelphia.net
Members: 11 Sisters
Apostolic Work: Elementary education, catechetical instructions, kindergarten and nursery schools; liturgical art distribution
Representation: Ukrainian Archdiocese of Philadelphia and in the Ukrainian Diocese of Stamford
Vocation Director: Sister Yosephata, MSMG, (215) 627-7808 or (732) 826-9165

SISTERS SERVANTS OF (WE010) **MARY IMMACULATE (S.S.M.I.)** (Immaculate Conception Province) Provincialate
PO Box 9, Sisters Servants Lane, Sloatsburg, NY 10974-0009
Web: www.ssmi-us.org
Email: ssminy@aol.com
Apostolic Work: Serves the Eastern Catholic Church (Ukrainian and Byzantine). Teaching, nursing, senior citizens, youth ministry, pilgrimages, catechizing, sewing vestments, retreats, pastoral ministries, arts, domestics, administration
Representation: Foreign Countries: Canada, Brazil, Argentina, Italy, Poland, Slovakia (Serbia), France, England, Germany, Ukraine
Vocation Director: Sr. Michele Yakymovitch, SSMI, Provincial Superior, (845) 753-2840, fax: (845) 753-1956

Lay Associates Share in Mission of Religious Communities

Associate relationship is a way in which women and men outside of the vowed membership can share in the mission and goals of a religious congregation. The relationship is mutually creative; it enriches, supports and challenges both associates and vowed members to a deeper living of the Gospel commitment. The essential element of association is to widen and strengthen bonds with others who affirm the goals and mission of a religious community. Associates do this while maintaining their independent life style.

Associates often go through an official formation or orientation period to learn about the community's charism and mission. Although associates do not take formal vows as religious do, they commit to living the mission and charism of the religious institute within their independent lay life style as married, single, or widowed folk. They strive to balance family life, work, prayer and leisure in a way that puts "first things first." The associate relationship is fostered by regular contact with vowed religious and other associates.

Associates have been a presence in the Church community since the 1970's; today, they number over 27,000 in the United States. Because nearly 50 percent of male associate groups did not begin until the 1990's, women associates outnumber men associates by about seven to one.

Associates say that they are encouraged to participate more often in the prayer life and social activities of the institute than in institute committees, chapters or financial meetings. As they gain familiarity with the religious institute, many associates report a growing desire to serve others and to become involved in various forms of ministry.

The majority of vowed religious support the associate relationship, with age being a variable as to the extent of the support. Older vowed religious are less likely to have relationships with associates in their communities and to be less familiar with the formation and orientation process for associates. Younger vowed religious are much more likely to interact with associates in prayer and faith-sharing, and to be aware of the commitment of associates to live the charism and mission of the institute.

Women and men become associates for varied reasons. Associates in men's communities are greatly attracted by the ministries of the institute and a desire to work with vowed members. There is also a desire for community that draws them. In institutes of women religious, associates are more attracted by a desire for deeper spirituality, especially the spirituality of the institute. They seek opportunities for prayer and faith sharing with other association members and associates. Both men and women associates agree on the main focus of association as living the mission, charism and spiritual tradition of the institute.

The majority of associates make - and renew - a formal commitment to live the mission of the religious institute as associates. This commitment is a strengthening and a mutual support for both associates and the religious community, as well as being a support for the Church as a whole.

Printed with permission of the North American Conference of Associates and Religious (NACAR). All rights reserved. For more information about the goals of NACAR, membership, workshops and its annual convention, contact NACAR at 20011 9B Road, Plymouth, IN 46563-9416, (574) 935-1712, E-mail: nacar96@juno.com, Web: www.nacar96.org

Vocation Discernment

Making **any** decision can be a time of special graces and a vehicle for the Holy Spirit to manifest guidance if approached prayerfully. Considering a life in service to Our Lord, and to our brothers and sisters in Christ, as a professed priest, brother or sister is a significant deliberation. But, it's really no more complex than any vocation choice. After all, decisions have consequences.

St. Ignatius of Loyola offers very wise and practical counsel and spiritual direction for those trying to discern a life choice. He encourages one to project ahead to the time of death, and to look back to this present moment and the current decision to be made. Essentially, St. Ignatius suggests envisioning your deathbed scene. Will you regret making this decision, or not making this decision, from that retrospective? It's an interesting spiritual exercise.

If you find yourself in discernment about a religious vocation to the priesthood, brotherhood or sisterhood, you are on a very special journey. Travelers set a course and gather provisions. Trust that you can rely on the Lord as your compass. As your fare, include the reception of the Holy Eucharist, an active prayer life, and spiritual direction. Visit the tabernacle daily for quiet prayer. Make a directed or non-directed retreat. Stay close to the Lord because God, indeed, is close to you.

The writings of St. Gaspar Bertoni, founder of the Stigmatine community, include this pithy advice, "When things are not very clear, then we must await enlightenment with (full) confidence. Before asking men's opinions, let us put our problems and even the order and manner of solving them, before the Lord."

St. Gaspar himself felt unworthy to respond to the inner prompting he experienced to the call of priesthood, but he determined that the Holy Spirit affirmed his vocation when his parish priest chided him, "Get on with it, Bertoni! You know that you have been called to be a priest!"

Our Lord operates on a "need to know" basis. He will make your discernment clear. Let Him, and on His timetable! Sometimes just "showing up" allows Him to do the rest. Like everything else in this life, discernment unfolds "one day at a time."

Volunteer Lay Ministries

The laity has a significant role in our Church today, being identified as the principle bearers of the Church's social message to civil society.

We are all called to social ministry to fulfill our baptismal responsibility.

As John Paul II stated, "The call is addressed to everyone." Lay people are called by the Lord to a mission on behalf of the Church and the world. "You go into my vineyard too!"

This represents the unity within our Church. The union between Christ and the disciples who were called to bear their own fruit in the world continues in the modern-day disciples called lay volunteers.

Many of our laity – young, old, married and single – fully respond to their call as Catholics. This growing number of people are leaving their jobs, money, security, and material possessions to serve for one, two or three years as lay missioners to our needy world. Daily, they are putting their faith into action.

These lay mission volunteers can be found across our own country in parishes, schools, social agencies, and hospitals. They are working with those in need in our nation's rural and urban areas. They can be found in soup kitchens and child-care centers. No area is without their presence.

They can be found in churches in Africa, Asia, Oceania, Europe, Latin and Central America. Whether teachers, construction workers, home-care aides, or accountants (and the list goes on), these lay people in mission are apostles of hope.

Challenged by Our Holy Father, these lay volunteers know that to say "CHURCH" is to say "MISSION!"

Information about volunteer mission work may be obtained by contacting one or more organizations listed in the section that follows or by contacting:

Catholic Network of Volunteer Service (CNVS)
6930 Carroll Ave., Suite 820
Takoma Park, MD 20912-4423
(800) 543-5046
(301) 270-0900
Fax: (301) 270-0901
E-mail: cnvsinfo@cnvs.org
Web: www.cnvs.org

St. Vincent Pallotti Center
415 Michigan Ave., NE, Washington, DC 20017
(877) VOL-LINK (877-865-5465)
(202) 529-3330, Fax: (202) 529-0911
E-mail: pallotti@pallotticenter.org
Web: www.pallotticenter.org

Lay Person
(Church-Related Career)

Examples of this vocation would include service as a director of religious education, campus minister, hospital chaplain, prison minister, pastoral associate, pastoral administrator or teacher. Such a person might be married or single. Someone specifically interested in these kinds of ministries should contact the local diocesan chancery and ask for the diocesan official responsible for the given area of interest. One also might contact Catholic colleges or schools of theology where there are programs in ministry.

Lay Person
(Volunteer Service)

Usually this service extends for a year or two in a mission of the Church either in the U.S. or overseas. In this ever-expanding group, opportunities are available for people to render service in numerous areas of Church activity. Religious communities affirm that lay extensions actually intensify their charism of service. People representing every type of service are incorporating positions for lay volunteers into the work they give in the Church. Young, old, married and single are responding to this challenge. The benefits often include stipend, room and board, health insurance and some travel allotment. The personal rewards for a lay volunteer begin with the immeasurable gratitude expressed by those who are served. The blessings continue in ways bestowed by the Spirit and unique to each person.

Turn to the **Lay Missionary** section of this book to discover which volunteer mission work holds the most promise for you. And/or contact:

Catholic Network of Volunteer Service (CNVS)
Jim Lindsay, Executive Director
6930 Carroll Ave., Ste. 820, Takoma Park, MD 20912-4423
(800) 543-5046, (301) 270-0900, ext. 18, Fax: (301) 270-0901
E-mail: cnvsinfo@cnvs.org, jlindsay@cnvs.org; Web: www.cnvs.org

Lay Person
(Associates)

Associates are men and women who want to enrich their Christian life by an affiliation with a religious community of priests, brothers or sisters. Their occupations vary – each continues to carry out the usual duties of their state of life in whatever their chosen job or profession. Associates may be married, single or widowed. Solemn promises (vows) – usually of commitment – are made with some religious communities.

Associates, also known as co-members, oblates, co-disciples, agregés (companions on the road), etc., choose a particular religious community based on their identification with that community's unique charism, values and mission. By sharing in the spiritual life, prayers and apostolic works of the religious community, associates have the opportunity for personal growth, the sharing of their own gifts and the mutual support of a faith community.

Turn to the **Associates, Oblates, Secular Institutes and Other Communities** section of this book to find a religious community with which to affiliate. And/or contact:

North American Conference of Associates and Religious (NACAR)
Sr. Catherine Schwemer, PHJC, Executive Director
20011 9B Road, Plymouth, IN 46563-9416
Phone and Fax: (574) 935-1712
E-mail: nacar96@juno.com, Web: www.nacar96.org

NACAR is the clearinghouse for all US and Canadian Associates and provides identification and exploration of issues concerning Associate life; assistance in policy and guideline development for Associate groups; networking, mutual support, workshops, annual conferences; and visioning for the future.

Secular Institutes

Over 60,000 Catholic lay men, lay women and secular clergy belong to over 160 canonically erected secular institutes throughout the world. The vocation of a single consecrated secular is a vocation in, and of, the world. Members take vows of poverty, celibacy and obedience, but do not wear distinctive attire or live in community as do members of religious orders. Generally, members live alone or with their families and hold regular jobs. They come together for periodic meetings, retreats and spiritual renewal. For information about secular institutes, contact one or more of the institutes listed elsewhere in this book or write to:

United States Conference of Secular Institutes
Rev. George F. Hazler, President
2104 Eagle Pointe, Bloomfield Hills, MI 48304
E-mail: director@voluntasdeiusa.org; Web: www.secularinstitutes.org

USA Council of Serra International

The mission of the USA Council of Serra International is to foster vocations to the ministerial priesthood and vowed religious life in the United States through prayer, awareness, affirmation and support and through this ministry enrich and develop its members' common Catholic faith.

The USA Council of Serra International
65 E. Wacker Place, Suite 802, Chicago, IL 60601-7203
(888) 777-6681, Fax: (888) 777-6803
E-mail: serraus@serraus.org; Web: www.serraus.org

B-128

ALASKA RADIO MISSION - KNOM (L001)
107 West Third, PO Box 988
Nome, AK 99762-0988
Contact: Ric Schmidt, (907) 443-5221
Mission Areas: Nome, Alaska
Type of Service: radio announcers, news reporter, producers
Term of Service: 1 year (renewable)
Basic Benefits: rt air transportation; room/board; stipend; medical insurance; Alaska Radio Mission Fellowship
Basic Requirements: M/F; 21 and up; single; college degree preferred; able to read and speak aloud in unaccented English (prior broadcasting experience not necessary - training provided)
Affiliation: Diocese of Fairbanks
Email: knomgeneralmanager@gmail.com
Web: www.knom.org

ALIVE (A Lay Invitation to a Visitation Experience) (L002)
7325 N. Claremont Ave.
Chicago, IL 60645
Contact: Sr. Marilyn Medinger CND (708) 359-9299
Mission Areas: US, Canada
Type of Service: ministry to poor in educational or parish settings
Term of Service: 1 year
Basic Benefits: room/board, monthly stipend, health insurance, local transportation
Basic Requirements: Single women; 21-30; Catholic orientation
Affiliation: Congregation of Notre Dame
Email: ALIVEwithCNDS@aol.com
Web: www.cnd-m.com

AMATE HOUSE (L003)
3600 South Seeley Ave.
Chicago, IL 60609
Contacts: Annie Devine, John Lucas, (773) 376-2445 fax: (773) 376-3445
Mission Area: Chicago
Type of Service: teaching, community work, health care, legal, social services
Term of Service: 1 year
Basic Benefits: room/board; stipend; health insurance; transportation to/from mission site
Basic Requirements: M/F; single; between 21 and 29; college graduate
Affiliation: Archdiocese of Chicago
Email: jlucas@amatehouse.org
Web: www.amatehouse.org

AMERICAN SAMOA APOSTOLIC WORKERS (L004)
PO Box 596
Pago Pago, AS 96799-0596
Contact: Superintendent of Catholic Schools 011-684-699-1238 or 5023
Mission Area: American Samoa
Type of Service: education, accounting, counseling
Term of Service: 2 years minimum
Basic Benefits: room; stipend; travel to/from American Samoa
Basic Requirements: M/F; four-year college degree; experience in field a plus
Affiliation: Roman Catholic Diocese of Samoa Pago Pago and Catholic Education System

ANDRÉ HOUSE OF ARIZONA (L005)
PO Box 2014, Phoenix, AZ 85001
Contact: Fr. Bill Wack, CSC (602) 255-0580
Mission Area: Phoenix
Type of Service: services to poor and homeless in houses of hospitality
Term of Service: 1 year preferred
Basic Benefits: room/board; medical insurance; stipend
Basic Requirements: M/F; 21 and up; Catholic; willing to live in community
Affiliation: Holy Cross Priests (Indiana Province), Catholic Worker
Email: director@andrehouse.org
Web: www.andrehouse.org

ANNUNCIATION HOUSE (L006)
815 Myrtle Ave., El Paso, TX 79901
Contacts: Ruben Garcia, Director; Amy Joyce, Volunteer Coordinator (915) 533-4675
Mission Areas: El Paso, TX; Juarez, Mexico
Type of Service: hospitality shelter staff, community/social services, work with Hispanics, immigration/refugee services, basic health care, border education/research, office/computer work, building maintenance and construction and Christian Based Communities
Term of Service: 1 year; shorter term for special skills available; 10-week summer internship
Basic Benefits: room/board; health insurance (yearlong term); transportation allowance home after year of service
Basic Requirements: M/F; single/married without dependents; 20 or older; Christian; college education and Spanish extremely helpful
Email: volunteercoordinator@annunciationhouse.org
Web: www.annunciationhouse.org

ST. ANTHONY FAMILY SHELTER-CATHOLIC CHARITIES (L008)
256 N. Ohio, Wichita, KS 67214
Contact: Kate McPheeters, Program Director, (316) 264-7233
Mission Area: Wichita, KS
Type of Service: homeless shelter
Term of Service: 30 days
Basic Requirements: M/F; 21 and up; married with or without children; or single parent with children
Web: www.wkscatholiccharities.org

ASSOCIATE MISSIONARIES OF THE ASSUMPTION (L009)
16 Vineyard St., Worcester, MA 01603
Contacts: Beth Fleming, Sr. Mary Ann Azanza, RA, (508) 767-1356
Mission Areas: US, Ireland, Bolivia, England, Guatemala, Italy, France, Rwanda, Philippines, Tanzania, Madagascar, Mexico, Canada, Ecuador, Chile
Type of Service: catechetics, community work, education, health care, office work, youth ministry, cooperation with L'Arche communities, parish ministry, Hispanic ministry
Term of Service: 1 to 2 years (renewable)
Basic Benefits: room/board; stipend; medical expenses/insurance
Basic Requirements: M/F; single; between 22 and 40; Catholic
Affiliation: Religious of the Assumption (Provincial House: Worcester, MA)
Email: ama-usa@juno.com
Web: www.assumptionvolunteers.org

AUGUSTINIAN VOLUNTEERS (L011)
259 N. Lawrence Street
Philadelphia, PA 19106
Contact: April L. Gagne (215) 627-1316
Mission Areas: Bronx, NY; Lawrence, MA; Chicago, IL; San Diego, CA; Chulucanas, Peru; Durban, South Africa
Type of Service: teaching on various levels, youth ministry, work with the elderly, day care and services for children, outreach to immigrants, food pantry, soup kitchen
Term of Service: 10 months (late August through June)
Basic Benefits: room/board; health insurance; monthly stipend; transportation to/from site
Basic Requirements: M/F; 21-29 years of age; college degree or equivalent work experience
Affiliation: The Augustinians
Email: av@osavol.org
Web: www.osavol.org

BEND VOLUNTEER CORPS (L012)
61545 Orion Dr., Bend, OR 97702
Contact: Charlotte Roe, Director of Recruiting, (541) 318-4636

Mission Areas: Bend and surrounding areas in Central Oregon
Type of Service: various placements with local nonprofit agencies directly serving the poor/marginalized
Term of Service: 1 full year: Aug. 1-Aug. 1
Basic Benefits: room/board; stipend; health insurance; to/from relocation expenses
Basic Requirements: college graduate or adequate work experience, Catholic
Email: info@bendvolunteercorps.org
Web: www.bendvolunteercorps.org

BENEDICTINE APPALACHIAN (L013)
VOLUNTEERS
150 Mt. Tabor Rd., Martin, KY 41649
Contact: Sr. Kathleen Weigand, O.S.B., (606) 886-9624
Mission Areas: Appalachian region of Eastern Kentucky
Type of Service: catechetics, community work, education, health care, office work, gardening, home repairs
Term of Service: 2 weeks to 3 months
Basic Benefits: room/board
Basic Requirements: M/F w/o dependents; 21 years and up
Affiliation: Mt. Tabor Benedictines
Email: skrw@hotmail.com
Web: www.mtabor.com

BENEDICTINE ASSOCIATE (L014)
PROGRAM
St. Scholastica Monastery, 1001 Kenwood Ave., Duluth, MN 55811
Contact: Sister Grace Marie Braun, OSB, (218) 723-5984
Mission Area: Duluth
Type of Service: clerical or computer work, household tasks, gardening, music ministries, reading mentor for elementary school children, parish/pastoral, reading to and companionship to the elderly.
Term of Service: 6 months to one year or longer
Basic Benefits: room/board; shared prayers with Sisters, spiritual growth opportunities, cultural and academic opportunities, experience of living in a monastic community, live/work/dine/pray/play with the Sisters, participation in Benedictine mission
Basic Requirements: F; 21 years of age or college junior; in good health
Email: gmbraun@duluthosb.org
Web: www.DuluthBenedictines.org

BENEDICTINE LAY (L015)
VOLUNTEERS
110 S.E. 28th Ave., SE #302
Watertown, SD 57201
Mother of God Monastery

Contact: Sister Rose Palm, Director (605) 882-6651
Mission Area: South Dakota
Type of Service: community service work, ministries within the monastery, gardening, ESL teaching
Term of Service: 2 weeks to 1 year
Basic Benefits: room/board; experience Benedictine community life
Basic Requirements: F; 21-60 (year long); F; 18 and up (summer program)
Affiliation: Benedictine Sisters (Watertown) at Mother of God Monastery
Email: benedictinevolunteers@dailypost.com
Web: www.watertownbenedictine.org

BENEDICTINE SISTERS OF (L016)
THE BYZANTINE RITE VOLUNTEER PROGRAM
Queen of Heaven Monastery, 8640 Squires Ln., N.E., Warren, OH 44484
Contact: Sr. Margaret Mary Schima, OSB, (330) 856-1813
Mission Area: Warren (OH) and neighboring cities
Type of Service: clerical, library work, outreach to the elderly, gardening, cooking, housekeeping, driver, computer work
Term of Service: 2 weeks - 1 year
Basic Benefits: room/board; experience Byzantine Benedictine spirituality, community life and ministry
Basic Requirements: F; 18 and up
Affiliation: Benedictine Sisters (Byzantine)
Email: smm@netdotcom.com
Web: www.benedictinebyzantine.org

BENEDICTINE SISTERS OF (L017)
FLORIDA VOLUNTEER PROGRAM
Holy Name Monastery, PO Box 2450
St. Leo, FL 33574-2450
Contact: Sister Mary David Hydro, OSB, (352) 588-8320
Mission Area: Holy Name Monastery, St. Leo, FL
Type of Service: Housekeeping, gardening, cooking, hospitality, care/companionship for elderly Sisters, driving, computer work, clerical, development
Basic Benefits: room/board; shared prayer with Sisters; spiritual growth opportunities; experience of living in community
Basic Requirements: F; 25-70; no dependents; good health
Affiliation: Benedictine Sisters of Florida
Email: mary.david.hydro@saintleo.edu
Web: www.floridabenedictines.com

BENEDICTINE SISTERS (L018)
VOLUNTEER PROGRAM
840 S. Main St.
Mt. Angel, OR 97362-9527
Contact: Sister Marietta Schindler, OSB, (503) 845-6141
Mission Areas: rural Mt. Angel, OR
Type of Service: community work, nurse, gardening, receptionist, computer, library, homeless shelter
Term of Service: varies - 1 week to 1 year
Basic Benefits: room/board
Basic Requirements: M/F; single/married w/o dependents; 18-65
Affiliation: Benedictine Sisters (Mt. Angel, OR)
Email: smarietta@juno.com
Web: www.benedictine-srs.org

BENEDICTINE VOLUNTEER (L022)
PROGRAM (Rapid City, SD)
St. Martin Monastery, 2110-C St. Martin Dr., Rapid City, SD 57702
Contact: Sr. Yvette Mallow, OSB, Director, (605) 343-8011
Mission Area: Rapid City
Type of Service: hospitality, housekeeping, gardening, dietary assistance, care of elderly
Term of Service: several weeks to one year
Basic Benefits: room/board
Basic Requirements: F; 18 years and older; no dependents
Affiliation: Benedictine Sisters (Rapid City, SD)
Email: fmartin620@aol.com
Web: www.blackhillsbenedictine.com

BENEDICTINE VOLUNTEERS (L023)
31970 State Highway P
Clyde, MO 64432-8100
Contact: Sr. Sarah Schwartzerg, Director of Volunteers
(918) 245-2734
Mission Areas: four monasteries of the Congregation: Clyde, MO; Tucson, AZ; and Dayton, WY
Type of Service: Type of Placement Cook, maintenance, housekeeper, groundskeeper/gardener; altar bread production and distribution.
Term of Service: 1 month to 1 year (renewable); possible short-term opportunities
Basic Benefits: room/board
Basic Requirements: M/F; 20 to 65; men in good health, non-addicted; commitment to celibacy during time of service; desirous of prayer and spiritual growth; ability to live generously in community
Affiliation: Benedictine Sisters of Perpetual Adoration
Email: volunteer@benedictinesisters.org

BETHANY VOLUNTEERS - (L024)
YOUNG PEOPLE WHO CARE (YPWC)
1031 Germania Rd., PO Box 129
Frenchville, PA 16836
Contact: Volunteer Coordinator
(814) 263-4855
Mission Area: Clearfield County in
western PA-rural Appalachia
Type of Service: hands-on service
work in the community with poor/
disadvantaged
Term of Service: 6 months to 1 year
and longer; summer program
Basic Benefits: room/board; monthly
stipend; medical insurance
Basic Requirements: M/F; single; 20
and over
Affiliation: Anawim Community of
Frenchville, PA; Diocese of Erie
Email: bethanyadult
@pennswoods.net
Web: www.anawimcommunity.org or
www.bethanyretreatcenter.org

BON SECOURS (L025)
VOLUNTEER MINISTRY PROGRAM
Bon Secours Spiritual Ctr.
1525 Marriottsville,
Marriottsville, MD 21104
Contact: Shannon Curran, Director
(410) 442-5519
Mission Areas: Baltimore, MD. Other
sites on the East Coast are being
developed.
Type of Service: health care, home
health care to people who are poor,
case management, outreach.
Term of Service: one year,
renewable
Basis Benefits: room/board; stipend;
health insurance
Basic Requirements: M/F; 21-65;
Christian
Affiliation: Sisters of Bon Secours
Email: volunteer@bshsi.org
Web: www.bonsecours.org/bsvm/

BOYS HOPE GIRLS HOPE (L026)
12120 Bridgeton Sq Dr.,
Bridgeton, MO 63044-2607
Contact: AmeriCorps Programs
Coordinator, 877-878-HOPE (4673)
Mission Areas: St. Louis, New York,
Chicago, New Orleans, Cincinnati,
Detroit, Cleveland/Akron, Phoenix,
Pittsburgh, Las Vegas, Orange
County, Denver, Baton Rouge, San
Francisco, Baltimore, Kansas City
Type of Service: Live and work with
academically motivated youth.
Support academic success,
community involvement and build
relationships while supporting our
staff in carrying out the mission of
Boys Hope Girls Hope.
Term of Service: 1 year or more
Basic Benefits: room/board; stipend;

medical insurance; transportation to
orientation program, opportunity for
full-time employment; possible
education award through
AmeriCorps
Basic Requirements: M/F; single; 21
and up, college degree or
experience working with youth
Affiliation: Jesuit traditions, private
Email: hope@bhgh.org
Web: www.BoysHopeGirlsHope.org

BROTHER BENNO'S (L027)
FOUNDATION
3260 Production Ave., PO Box 308,
Oceanside, CA 92054
Contact: Deacon Harold Kutler
(760) 439-1244, ext. 106
Mission Area: Oceanside, CA
Type of Service: day center, soup
kitchen, emergency shelter staff,
community work, ESL, after school
tutoring program, case management,
accounting, administration,
warehouse, alcohol/drug recovery
program
Term of Service: 1 year (or longer)
Basic Benefits: room/board (in ministry
house) stipend; transportation
Basic Requirements: M/F; single; 25-
70; self-sufficient
Affiliation: Benedictine Monks
(Prince of Peace Abbey)
Email: info@brotherbennos.org
Web: www.brotherbennos.org

CABRINI MISSION CORPS (L029)
610 King of Prussia Rd.
Radnor, PA 19087-3698
Contacts: Gina Pultorak
(610) 971-0821
Mission Areas: NY
Type of Service: a faith-based lay
mission organization serving in the
areas of education, health care,
pastoral ministry, youth ministry,
child care, elder care, and other
social services
Term of Service: 1 year
Basic Benefits: room/board; monthly
living allowance; medical insurance;
transportation to/from mission site
Basic Requirements: M/F; 21 and
up; single/married couples w/o
dependents; Christian; college or
work experience
Affiliation: Missionaries of the Sacred
Heart of Jesus (Cabrini Sisters)
Email: cmcorps@aol.com
Web: www.cabrini-missioncorps.org

CAMP GRAY (L030)
E10213 Shady Lane Rd.
Reedsburg, WI 53959
Contact: Jeff Hoeben, Camp Director
800-711-GRAY or (606) 356-8200

Mission Areas: Camp Gray
(camp/retreat center)
Type of Service: facilitate youth
retreats and environmental
stewardship programs for youth;
administrative/support functions
Term of Service: 9 months (Sept.
through May)
Basic Benefits: room/board; health
insurance; stipend; four weeks
vacation
Basic Requirements: M/F; at least 1
year of college (college graduates
preferred); active, practicing
Christians
Affiliation: Diocese of Madison
Email: bigfun@campgray.com
Web: www.campgray.com

CANOSSIAN INTERNATIONAL (L031)
VOLUNTARY SERVICE (VOICA)
5625 Isleta Blvd., SW
Albuquerque, NM 87105
Contact: Sr. Kay Taylor, FdCC
(505) 873-2059; cell: (505) 400-4324
Mission Areas: US, Canada, Mexico,
Albania, Brazil, Angola, Congo,
Malawi, Tanzania, Togo, some Asian
countries
Type of Service: health care,
teachers, pastoral ministry and more
Term of Service: long-term: doctors/
other health care specialists: 2
months to 2 years; teachers, all
other placements: 1-2 years; short-
term: varies
Basic Benefits: long-term:
room/board; stipend; medical
insurance; travel expenses to/from
overseas mission site from Rome;
short-term: room
Basic Requirements: F; married
couples; short-term: M/F; 19 to 30
Affiliation: Canossian Daughters of
Charity, Roman Catholic
Email: sbsvolunteers@aol.com or
voica@fdcc.org
Web: www.voica.org/en

CAPUCHIN FRANCISCAN (L032)
VOLUNTEER CORPS
4502 Park Heights Ave.
Baltimore, MD 21215
EAST: 4502 Park Heights Ave.,
Baltimore, MD 21215
Contact: Br. Dennis Klemash, OFM
Cap, (410) 367-0334
MIDWEST: 1927 North 4th St.,
Milwaukee, WI 53212
Contact: Michelle Roder,
(414) 375-8841
Mission Areas: East: Baltimore,
Washington, Pittsburgh, Papua New
Guinea; Midwest: Chicago, Detroit,
Milwaukee, Panama
Type of Service: advocacy,
education, community organizing,

B-131

health care, social service
Term of Service: 1 to 2 years (renewable)
Basic Benefits: room/board (in community with other volunteers); stipend; medical insurance; transportation to/from work site
Basic Requirements: M/F; single/married w/o dependents; 21 and up
Affiliation: Capuchin Franciscan Friars
Email: capcorps@thecapuchins.org or volunteers@capuchin.com
Web: www.capuchin.com

CAPUCHIN YOUTH AND (L033)
FAMILY MINISTRIES
781 Rte. 9D, PO Box 192
Garrison, NY 10524
Contact: Bro. Lake Herman, OFM Cap, Chaplain, (845) 424-3609
Mission Areas: New York, Connecticut
Type of Service: community work, retreat ministry, youth and family ministry, high school ministry
Term of Service: one year (beginning in Aug.)
Basic Benefits: room/board; stipend; medical insurance; education grant
Basic Requirements: M/F; Catholic, 21 and older; college graduate (preferred)
Affiliation: Capuchin Franciscan Friars
Email: cyfm@cyfm.org
Web: www.cyfm.org

CASA JUAN DIEGO (L034)
4818 Rose, PO Box 70113, Houston, TX 77270
Contacts: Mark or Louise Zwick, (713) 869-7376
Mission Area: Houston, TX
Type of Service: refugee work for men and women, Spanish speaking, battered and/or homeless women and children
Term of Service: No minimum
Basic Benefits: room/board (in community); stipend; medical insurance; transportation home after 1 year of service
Basic Requirements: M/F; single/married/widowed; 21 and up; functional Spanish; faith commitment
Affiliation: Catholic Worker
Email: info@cjd.org
Web: www.cjd.org

CATHOLIC CHARITIES - (L036)
PROJECT SERVE
725 Fallsway, Baltimore, MD 21202
Contact: Allison Stone, Coordinator, (443) 986-9029
Mission Area: greater Baltimore metro area
Type of Service: work with the poor,

homeless, emotionally abused children, adults with mental illness; nursing homes, volunteer coordination, advocacy
Term of Service: one year (August to August)
Basic Benefits: room/board; medical insurance; monthly stipends; AmeriCorps ed award (if applicable); student loan deferment
Basic Requirements: M/F; 21 years and older; single; college degree; ability to live in community
Affiliation: Catholic Charities, Baltimore
Email: astone@cc-md.org
Web: www.catholiccharities-md.org

CATHOLIC MEDICAL (L038)
MISSION BOARD
10 West 17th St.
New York, NY 10011-5765
Contact: Lizaura Javier
(212) 242-7757
Mission Areas: Africa, Latin America, the Caribbean, Asia
Type of Service: health care
Term of Service: 1-3 years (shorter term possibilities)
Basic Benefits: room/board; stipend; transportation; Visa; full health/individual medical evacuation/life/malpractice insurance
Basic Requirements: Licensed and registered to practice medicine, nursing; therapists, lab techs and most areas of health trained personnel in the United States and Canada
Affiliation: Catholic
Email: ljavier@cmmb.org
Web: www.cmmb.org

CATHOLIC NETWORK OF (L039)
VOLUNTEER SERVICE (CNVS)
6930 Carroll Ave., Suite 820
Takoma Park, MD 20912-4423
Contact: Jim Lindsay, Executive Director
800-543-5046 or (301) 270-0900
Type of Service: Connecting people, transforming lives. CNVS is a national association and network of Christian volunteer and mission programs serving those in need throughout the U.S. and worldwide. Annual publication: a directory of more than 200 full-time, faith-based volunteer/lay mission opportunities. To receive your FREE copy of the Response directory, call, write or email us. Volunteer opportunities also available at the CNVS office.
Basic Benefits: Room/board; stipend; medical insurance; transportation to/from mission site, retreats, AmeriCorps Education

Award (varies according to program chosen)
Affiliation: Catholic, private, nonprofit
Email: cnvsinfo@cnvs.org
Web: www.cnvs.org

CATHOLIC RELIEF SERVICES (L040)
Catholic Relief Services Volunteer Program, 228 W. Lexington St., Baltimore, MD 21201-3413
Contact: Gerard Lambert, Program Officer, (410) 951-7456
Mission Areas: Africa, Asia, Caribbean, Eastern Europe, Latin America, Middle East
Type of Service: Accounting/Finance, Agriculture, Business Administration, Communication, Computers, Education, Engineering, Health, HIV/AIDS, Legal, Medical, Monitoring and Evaluation, Organizational Development, Parish Ministry, Peace Building/Conflict Resolution, Research, Writing
Term of Service: 2 years (18 months served overseas and 6 months served in the United States
Basic Benefits: Housing, stipend, transportation to and from the country of placement, medical/dental/life benefits. Volunteers are given a fund-raising goal to help raise support.
Basic Requirements: Relevant experience, commitment to the poor, cross-cultural experience, Catholics active in a faith community, commitment to service, at least 25 years of age, single or married but without dependent children, where the primary language spoken in the country is French, Spanish or Portuguese, proficiency in that language is required
Affiliation: Conference of Catholic Bishops
Email: volunteer@crs.org
Web: www.crs.org/about/careers/volunteer/

CATHOLIC VOLUNTEERS (L044)
IN FLORIDA
PO Box 536476
Orlando, FL 32853-6476
Contact: Candace M. Thompson (407) 382-7071
Mission Area: Florida (urban, rural)
Type of Service: community work, education, health care, social work, legal, counseling, shelter and group homes, disaster recovery and relief
Term of Service: 1 year (renewable)
Basic Benefits: room/board; stipend; medical insurance; AmeriCorps ed award
Basic Requirements: M/F; single/married/no dependents; 21 and up;

Christian; degree or work experience; previous part-time volunteer experience; interest in social justice; emotional maturity; flexibility
Affiliation: Sisters of St. Joseph of St. Augustine, Florida; The Bishops of Florida
Email: volunteer@cvif.org
Web: www.cvif.org

CATHOLIC WORKER (L045)
HOUSES
36 East First St., New York, NY 10003
Online directory of all Catholic Worker houses
www.catholicworker.org/communities/commlistall.cfm or subscribe to The Catholic Worker, 36 East First St., New York, NY 10003, (212) 777-9617 (list of houses published in May edition)
Contact: the Catholic Worker house you are interested in (see above)
Mission Areas: 37 states in US
Type of Service: serve the poor/homeless; work for social justice
Web: www.catholicworker.org/
     communities/commlistall.cfm

CATHOLIC WORKER (L046)
HOUSES (Winona, MN)
PO Box 102, Winona, MN 55987
Contact: Eileen Hanson
(507) 454-8094 or 457-3451
Mission Area: Winona
Type of Service: temporary shelter to women/families at Dan Corcoran House and to single men at Bethany House, advocate for peace/justice issues
Term of Service: long term: 1+ year(s); short term: 2 summer months as an intern
Basic Benefits: room/meals; use of car; possible stipend for summer interns
Basic Requirements: M/F; 18+
Affiliation: Catholic Worker
Email: winonacatholicworker@
     gmail.com
Web: www.winonacatholicworker.org

CENTRAL CITY TEACHING (L048)
PARTNERSHIP (CCTP)
1515 S. 29th St.
Milwaukee, WI 53215
Contact: (414) 645-1060
Mission Areas: Milwaukee
Type of Service: Full-time teaching and after-school activity coordinator in Catholic elementary/middle schools. CCTP schools primarily serve low-income, Latino families
Term of Service: 1 year (renewable)
Basic Benefits: room/board; stipend; medical/dental insurance; AmeriCorps ed award; loan

forbearance, shared car; fitness center membership
Basic Requirements: M/F; 21-30; single: college degree; Spanish a plus
Affiliation: Jesuits (Wisconsin Province)
Web: www.njms.org

CHANGE A HEART (L049)
(Franciscan Volunteer Program)
146 Hawthorne Rd.
Pittsburgh, PA 15209
Contact: Kelly Caddy, (412) 821-0861
Mission Areas: Pittsburgh, Waynesburg (PA) and Ashtabula (OH)
Type of Service: education, health care, social services, parish ministry, Hispanic ministry
Term of Service: 1 to 2 years, renewable
Basic Benefits: room/board; medical insurance; stipend; transportation home at end of service; AmeriCorps ed award
Basic Requirements: M/F; 21-35 (negotiable); high-school graduate with 2 years work experience or college graduate
Affiliation: Millvale Franciscan Sisters
Email: volunteer@
     millvalefranciscans.org
Web: www.changeaheart
     volunteers.org

CHRIST HOUSE (L050)
1717 Columbia Rd. NW
Washington, DC 20009-2803
Contact: Lizzie Bebber, Director of Volunteers, (202) 328-1100
Mission Area: Washington, DC
Term of Service: Full-time volunteers for one year beginning around August 1. Shorter term volunteers for a minimum of one month are accepted as needed.
Basic Benefits: room/board (in community with other volunteers); 1 year or more service is eligible for stipend, transportation; health/life insurance
Basic Requirements: M/F; Short-term volunteers: 18 years or older; Year-long volunteers: 21 or older
Type of Service: Christ House is a 33 bed residential medical recovery facility for men and women who are homeless and sick. Volunteers serve as Nurses, Nursing Assistants, Case Management Assistants, Community Builders, Medical Unit Assistant, Food Service Assistants, Maintenance Assistants, and other general service assistants.
Email: volunteers@christhouse.org
Web: www.christhouse.org

CHRISTIAN APPALACHIAN (L054)
PROJECT, Volunteer Program,
4192 N. Wilderness Rd.
Mt. Vernon, KY 40456
Contact: Amy Schill
800-755-5322 or (606) 256-0973
Mission Areas: Appalachian region of eastern Kentucky
Type of Service: long-term: child/family development centers, adult education programs, elderly services, programs serving people with disabilities, housing and home repair, family advocacy, educational programming,etc.; short-term: summer camp opportunities: camp counselors, lifeguards, medical personnel, arts/crafts instructors; Christmas Baskets program-Nov./Dec; group opportunites available for one week of service
Term of Service: long-term: 9 months-1 year or longer; short-term: 3 weeks-9 months; summer camp: 2-9 weeks in June and July; group volunteers: 1 week
Basic Benefits: room/board; long-term: stipend, health insurance, college loan deferment, potential AmeriCorps Education Award
Basic Requirements: M/F; individuals; 18 and up; single/married (without dependent children); high school diploma; college degree for some positions; groups: 12 and up
Email: volunteer@chrisapp.org
Web: www.christianapp.org

CHRISTIAN BROTHERS LAY (L055)
VOLUNTEER PROGRAM
10001 South Pulaski Road
Suite 105, Chicago, IL 60655-3356
Affiliation: Edmund Rice Christian Brothers North American Province
Contact: Br. Bob Koppes, CFC, (773) 298-2520 fax: (773) 429-4381
Type of Service: Educational, Social Service, and Youth Ministry
Term of Service: long-term: United States, Canada and Grenada are 12 months. There is an 8-week summer opportunity in Florida.
Basic Benefits: long-term: medical insurance, room/board, monthly stipend; transportation at beginning and end of service, opportunity for language studies for those serving in Florida; short-term: room and board, transportation at beginning and end of service, stipend. AmeriCorps Education Awards are available for qualifying service.
Basic Requirements: long-term: a candidate must be single, have a bachelor's degree or equivalent work experience, be in good physical and mental health, have a desire to work

with the marginalized and those in need, be willing and able to live in and to participate fully in community life. For the summer program in Florida, a candidate need only have one year of college.
Mission Areas: Bonita Springs, Florida; New York City; Ontario, Canada for both men and women. British Columbia, Canada and Grenada British West Indies for men only.
Applications received by March 1 will be given first consideration.
Applications received after March 1 will be considered if placements are available
Email: christianbrosvp@ sbcglobal.net
Web: www.cbvp.org

CLARETIAN SUMMER (L057)
MINISTRY PROGRAM
205 W. Monroe St., 10th Fl.
Chicago, IL 60606-5013
Contact: Mario Delgado
(312) 236-7846
Mission Area: Chicago inner city
Type of Service: based on applicant's skills and interests and the needs of the communities, with opportunities including children, youth, adults, social justice, medical clinic, and legal clinic
Term of Service: Mid-June to August (one-week orientation, ongoing discernment and support)
Basic Benefits: an experience of ministry, community, and spirituality that helps deepen one's sense of vocation; an experience of a lifestyle of service. Live with other participants and Claretian Missionaries (priest, brothers, lay). Room/board; stipend; transportation to/from site
Basic Requirements: M/F; 18 or older; recommendation forms; telephone interview; app. deadline Apr. 30
Affiliation: Claretian Missionaries
Web: www.claretianvocations.org

CLARETIAN VOLUNTEERS (L058)
205 W. Monroe St.
Chicago, IL 60606-5013
Contact: Director, (312) 544-8176
Mission Areas: Atlanta, Chicago, Springfield (MO), Perth Amboy (NJ)
Type of Service: community organizing, housing, teaching, youth/young adult/elderly/senior outreach and ministry, immigration/refugee services, Hispanic ministries, campus ministry, food pantry, soup kitchen, homeless shelter, peace and justice, legal, religious education. Limited

international placements available after domestic service
Term of Service: 1 year (renewable)
Basic Benefits: room/board (with other volunteers); stipend; medical insurance; transportation
Basic Requirements: M/F; single/married/widowed w/o dependents; 21 to 35
Affiliation: Claretian Missionaries
Email: volunteers@claretians.org
Web: www.claretianvolunteers.org

COLORADO VINCENTIAN (L059)
VOLUNTEERS - Companions on the Journey
1732 Pearl St., Denver, CO 80203
Contacts: Bill Jaster, Mary Frances Jaster, Directors, (303) 863-8141
Mission Areas: downtown Denver
Type of Service: school/parish ministries, social services, health care; elderly/women/AIDS/homeless ministries
Term of Service: one year (August to August)
Basic Benefits: room/board; stipend; medical insurance; transportation
Basic Requirements: M/F; ages 22 to 30; college degree or equivalent work experience
Affiliation: The Vincentian Family of laity, religious and clergy
Email: cvv@covivo.org
Web: www.covivo.org

COMBONI LAY MISSIONARY (L063)
PROGRAM
1615 East 31st St.
La Grange Park, IL 60526-1377
Contacts: Paul Wheeler, JoAnne Harbert, (708) 588-1602
Mission Areas: Africa, Latin America
Type of Service: doctors, nurses, teachers (secondary, special education, religious education), clerical, accountants, social service workers
Term of Service: 4 months training in Chicago, 3 years of service in mission country
Basic Benefits: room/board; stipend; medical insurance; transportation to/from mission site
Basic Requirements: M/F; 24-55; single/married/widowed; active Catholic
Affiliation: Comboni Missionaries
Email: info@laymission-comboni.org
Web: www.laymission-comboni.org

(L064)
COMFORT HOUSE SERVICES, INC.
617 Dallas Ave, McAllen, TX 78501
Contact: Mary Rincones-Botello
(956) 687-7367

Mission Areas: McAllen, TX and entire Rio Grande Valley
Type of Service: caregivers for residential ministry to the terminally ill and their families
Term of Service: 1 year (flexible), 16 months, also
Basic Benefits: room/board; monthly stipend; health insurance
Basic Requirements: M/F; some college; maturity, judgment, physical capacity, commitment to care for the dying (college students who speak Spanish preferred)
Email: marychsi@att.net
Web: www.comforthouseservices.org

COMMUNITY LIVING AND (L065)
SERVICE PROJECTS - CLASP
7712 N. Paulina #2
Chicago, IL 60626
Contact: Sr. Cecilia Fandel, OSM
(773) 973-4812
Mission Areas: Ladysmith, WI, Chicago
Type of Service: tutor, ESL, homebound visits, outdoor work, hospitality, youth/child programs, clerical/receptionist, seniors, justice/peace advocacy
Term of Service: 1 week - 3 months (renewable)
Basic Benefits: room/board
Basic Requirements: M/F; 18 and older; married/single/couples
Affiliation: Servants of Mary (Ladysmith, WI)
Email: crf1229@sbcglobal.net
Web: www.servitesisters.org

CONWAY-EGAN CATHOLIC (L066)
HIGH SCHOOL
611 Wistar Rd.
Fairless Hills, PA 19030-4197
Contact: Edna Galloway
(215) 945-6200, ext. 214
Mission Area: Fairless Hills, PA (located outside Philadelphia)
Type of Service: technology/resources development; fundraising; public relations
Basic Requirements: M/F; college degree; good interpersonal, organizational, computer skills
Affiliation: Archdiocese of Philadelphia
Web: www.conwell-egan.org

COVENANT HOUSE FAITH (L067)
COMMUNITY
Administration, 5 Penn Plaza
New York, NY 10001
Full Time Volunteer Service with Homeless Youth
Contact: Paula Rote, Assistant Coordinator, (212) 727-4081
Mission Areas: Ft. Lauderdale, FL; Atlantic City, NJ; New York, NY

Type of Service: The majority of Faith Community members serve in direct care to youth at the shelter as Resident Advisors, Case Managers, or Youth Advisors; while others may serve indirectly in food services, health services, pastoral ministry, outreach, or administration. Volunteers receive training for their service placement, and serve a minimum of 40 hours per week in regularly scheduled shifts at Covenant House.
Term of Service: Faith Community is a full time volunteer program where individuals can spend 3 months, 6 months, or 12 months serving the youth of Covenant House.
Basic Benefits: Room and board (includes utilities, linens, basic hygiene stipend, transportation, and food), small weekly living stipend, severance stipend at end of service commitment, medical and dental insurance, community retreats in March and August, deferral of most student loans, and AmeriCorps Educational Award opportunity
Basic Requirements: 21 years of age or older, college degree or commensurate life experience, emotional maturity and good health (medical exam required), open, flexible, and joyful outlook on life, ready to serve at any site and in any position where there is the most need, applicants may be married or single (no dependents), and willingness to submit stories and/or photos about Faith Community experience to Covenant House
Affiliation: Covenant House (non-profit organization)
Email: faithmail@ covenanthouse.org
Web: www.covenanthouse.org/ faithcommunity

CRISPAZ VOLUNTEERS & SUMMER INTERNS (L068)
215 E. 14th Street
Cincinnati, OH 45202
Contact: Dennis O'Connor, Executive Director, (513) 381-4520
Mission Area: El Salvador
Type of Service: work with women's group, youth programs, education, rural communities, appropriate technology, peacemaking, cross-cultural understanding
Term of Service: 2 separate programs; 3 months or 15 months
Basic Requirements: long term: intermediate level Spanish and church or community sponsorship; short term: financial sponsorship
Email: dennis@crispaz.org
Web: www.crispaz.org

CRISTO REY JESUIT ALUMNI VOLUNTEERS (L069)
Cristo Rey Jesuit High School, 1852 W. 22nd Place, Chicago, IL 60608
Contact: Katherine Mitchell
(773) 890-7144
Mission Area: Chicago
Type of Service: social service, child care, education, tutoring, prison/youth/parish ministry, Latino/Hispanic outreach.
Term of Service: 2 years
Basic Benefits: room/board; transportation; stipend
Basic Requirements: M/F; 21 and older; single; college education or comparable experience
Affiliation: Jesuits (Chicago Province)
Email: kmitchell@cristorey.net
Web: www.cristorey.net

CSJ VOLUNTEER PROGRAM OF CONCORDIA, KS (L070)
1837 Grandview Ave.
El Paso, TX 79902
Contact: Christine Doman, CSJ
(915) 532-7452
Mission Areas: Southwest and Midwest
Type of Service: Work with Peace and Justice Center (better months are fall and spring); assisting with transportation, visiting, reading, writing for and with our elderly Sisters at our Motherhouse and Mt. Joseph Residence; Parish ministry at a K-6th school; spirituality center in Silver City, NM participating in building upkeep, yard work and retreat work in collaboration with the director; variety of activities in El Paso, TX
Term of Service: long-term: 6 months to 1 year; short-term: 1 to 3 months
Basic Benefits: room/board; $150.00 month stipends
Basic Requirements: Female only with exceptions, in some places, for couples. Must be 20 or over
Affiliation: Sisters of St. Joseph of Concordia
Email: cdoman56@aol.com
Web: www.csjkansas.org

CSJ VOLUNTEERS IN MISSION (L074)
27 Park Rd., West Hartford, CT 06119
Contact: Sr. Elaine Betoncourt, CSJ
(860) 233-5126, ext. 217
Mission Areas: long-term: Hartford (CT), Kentuck;. short-term: Hartford (CT) , Kentucky
Term of Service: long-term: 1 year minimum; short-term: college breaks, summer: 1 week-2 month
Basic Benefits: room/board; stipend; medical insurance; AmeriCorps ed award
Basic Requirements: F; single; 18 and up
Type of Service: teaching, medical clinic, tutoring, rural ministry, child care
Affiliation: Sisters of St. Joseph of Chambery
Email: sebcsj@hotmail.com
Web: www.sistersofsaintjoseph.org

CATHOLIC CHARITIES SERVICE CORPS (L077)
525 Washington St.
Buffalo, NY 14203
Contact: Amy Vukelic
(716) 853-4424, ext. 3028
Mission Area: Buffalo
Type of Service: live in an intentional, simple community with other volunteers, exploring how their faith can be more fully integrated while responding to their own special call to service through working among their marginalized brothers and sisters
Term of Service: 1 year (Sept. to Aug.)
Basic Benefits: rent; utilities; food/personal expenses stipend; transportation to/from work; deferment of educational loans; health insurance; retreat costs; relocation funds, AmeriCorps ed award
Basic Requirements: M/F; 21 and up; some college; demonstrated and desired commitment to service/social justice, community and simple living, and Christian spirituality
Affiliation: Catholic Charities of Buffalo
Email: avossvuk@ccwny.org
Web: www.ccservicecorps.org

DIOCESE OF CHARLESTON VOLUNTEERS (L078)
34 Wentworth St.
Charleston, SC 29401-1617
Contacts: Rev. Msgr. A .La Femina, Director, Jerome Remkiewicz, Volunteer Administrator
(843) 723-5758
Mission Areas: South Carolina
Type of Service: inner-city and rural ministries, ethnic ministries, shut-ins, elderly, youth ministry, parish ministry, soup kitchen/clothing center, tutoring, home repair
Term of Service: long term: 6 months to 1 year
Basic Benefits: room/board; stipend; car allowance, health insurance (long term)
Basic Requirements: M/F; 18 and up: physically/mentally/spiritually

sound; desirous of living Catholic commitment; able to participate in community living with other volunteers.
Email: volunteers@catholic-doc.org

(L079)
DOMINICAN VOLUNTEERS USA
PO Box 891121, Chicago, IL 60608
Contact: Anthony Butler, Executive Director, (708) 524-5985/4
Mission Areas: Throughout the US
Type of Service: community work, education, health care, social service, farming, parish ministry
Term of Service: 1 to 3 years
Basic Benefits: room/board; accident/medical insurance; monthly ($100) stipend; transportation
Basic Requirements: M/F; single/married; 21 or older
Affiliation: Dominican Priests, Brothers and Sisters
Email: dominicanvolunteers@gmail.com
Web: www.dvusa.org

EDUCATIONAL PARTNERS (L081)
IN CATHOLIC SCHOOLS - EPICS
Seton Hall U. - Kozlowski, 4th Fl., 400 S Orange Ave.
South Orange, NJ 07079
Contact: Fr. Kevin Hanbury, Director (973) 761-9390
Mission Areas: underserved elementary/secondary schools in NJ and surrounding areas
Type of Service: teaching Term of Service: 2 years
Basic Benefits: live in community; tuition reimbursement
Basic Requirements: M/F; college degree; able to pursue master's degree in educationAffiliation: Seton Hall University, Archdiocese of Newark
Email: hanburke@shu.edu
Web: http://education.shu.edu/epics/flash.html

OAKLAND ELIZABETH HOUSE (L082)
6423 Colby St., Oakland, CA 94618
Contact: Volunteer Coordinator (510) 658-1380
Mission Area: North Oakland
Type of Service: live in residence for women/children in transition: assist in daily activities, provide support/encouragement to families and administrative support
Term of Service: long-term: 1 year (flexible); short-term: 3 months or less (particularly summer)
Basic Benefits: room/board; stipend; long-term only: AmeriCorps ed award
Basic Requirements: good communication skills; respect for

diversity; strong work ethic; computer skills; experience with homelessness/addiction desirable
Email: volunteer@oakehouse.org
Web: www.oakehouse.org

FAMILY LIFELINE (L084)
VOLUNTEERS, INC.
100 Gladstone Ave.
Walden, NY 12586
Contact: Director, (845) 778-8529
Mission Areas: Massachusetts and New York
Term of Service: Ordinarily one year with option to renew. Open to other possibilities on an individual basis.
Basic Benefits: room/board; monthly stipend; health insurance; 2 weeks vacation for each full year of service; AmeriCorps Education Award Program participant.
Basic Requirements: M/F; 20 and up; single or married couple. Persons of various religions, ethnicities, cultures and experiences welcomed to apply.
Type of Service: Child care and youth workers, social workers, community health nurses, shelter staff, maintenance workers, advocacy counselors, teachers (ESL and GED), tutors, thrift shop workers, computer data entry, administrative/clerical help, van drivers, home attendants, organizers for food bank, etc.; summer youth programs seek recreational, organizational, creative talents
Affiliation: Little Sisters of the Assumption
Email: director@familylifeline volunteers.org
Web: www.familylifeline volunteers.org

FAMILY UNITY (L088)
INTERNATIONAL, INC.
Working Boys Center, 12750 Stephen Pl., Elm Grove, WI 53122
Contact: Patricia Parks, Volunteer Coordinator, (262) 797-8988
Mission Area: Quito, Ecuador
Type of Service: teaching and ministering to the needs of the people
Term of Service: Aug. 24 to Aug. 1
Basic Benefits: room/board
Basic Requirements: M/F; college graduate or equivalent experience; fluency in Spanish
Affiliation: Archdiocese of Milwaukee
Email: jparks@wi.rr.com
Web: www.workingboyscenter.org

FATHER BEITING (L088-1)
APPALACHIAN MISSION CENTER
PO Box 885, Louisa, KY 41230
Contacts: Fr. Ralph Beiting, Jim

Haragan, (606) 638-0219
Mission Areas: Appalachian counties of Lawrence, Martin, Floyd (Kentucky)
Type of Service: mobilizing rural communities, community resource centers, warehouses, rummage stores
Term of Service: long-term: 1 year (renewable); short-term: 3-8 months; 1 week for groups
Basic Benefits: long-term: room/board, stipend, medical insurance; short-term: room/board
Basic Requirements: long-term: M/F; single/married/widowed/divorced w/o dependents; 21 years and older; short-term: 18 years and older; groups: 7th grade and older
Affiliation: Diocese of Lexington
Email: jimh1@lycomonline.com

FATHER CARR'S PLACE 2B (L089)
1965 Oshkosh Ave.
Oshkosh, WI 54902-2600
Contact: Joseph Geniesse (920) 231-2378
Mission Area: Oshkosh and surrounding area
Type of Service: community work, health care, soup kitchen, food pantry, domestic violence shelter, mission
Term of Service: 3 weeks to 1 year (or more)
Basic Benefits: room/board; free walk-in clinic
Basic Requirements: faith-filled, open heart; team worker; good health; able to live out Matt. 25: 31-46 and follow Mother Teresa and St. Martin de Porres
Email: geniessejmj@aol.com

(L091)
FRANCISCAN COMMON VENTURE
3390 Windsor Ave.
Dubuque, IA 52001-1311
Contact: Sr. Marie Therese Kalb, OSF, (563) 583-9786
Mission Areas: southern US: Texas, Mississippi, Iowa, Omaha
Type of Service: educational programs, GED, TESL, general pastoral care, children's recreation, immigration, resale store
Term of Service: 6 weeks - 1 year or longer
Basic Benefits: room/board; medical insurance; stipend; transportation to/from site
Basic Requirements: F; 21 and older; 2/4 year college degree or skills
Affiliation: Sisters of St. Francis of the Holy Family
Email: goedkenr@osfdbq.org
Web: www.osfdbq.org

FRANCISCAN COMPANIONS (L092)
IN MISSION
Our Lady of Angels Convent, 609 S.
Convent Rd., Aston, PA 19014-1207
Contact: Kathy Boehm, Director
(610) 558-7756
Mission Areas: Delaware Valley Area
Term of Service: 1 to 2 years
(renewable)
Type of Service: education, health
care, social and pastoral work
Affiliation: Sisters of St. Francis of
Philadelphia
Email: kboehm@osfphila.org
Web: www.osfphila.org

FRANCISCAN COVENANT (L093)
PROGRAM
PO Box 970
San Juan Bautista, CA 95045
Contact: Paul Barnes & Phyllis
Becker, Directors, (831) 623-1119
Mission Areas: California, Arizona
Type of Service: primarily in retreat
centers in variety of capacities such
as administration, bookkeeping,
gardening, gift shop, hospitality,
housekeeping, maintenance/repairs,
marketing, general office
Term of Service: 1-6 years (renewable
annually, upon mutual agreement)
Basic Benefits: living allowance;
room & board; health insurance
Basic Requirements: single/divorced/
married couples w/o dependents;
mature Catholic; under 67; US citizen
Affiliation: Franciscan Friars
(Province of St. Barbara)
Email: covprg@yahoo.com
Web: www.franciscancovenant
volunteers.org,
www.sbfranciscans.org

FRANCISCAN MISSION (L095)
SERVICE OF NORTH AMERICA
PO Box 29034
Washington, DC 20017-0034
Contact: Don Clausen, Interim
Executive Director; Vicki Caparas,
Office Manager, (202) 832-1762
Type of Service: health care,
teachers, social workers,
counselors, community developers,
agriculturists, pastoral work
Term of Service: 3 months
orientation plus 3 years service and
3 weeks re-entry/integration
Basic Benefits: monthly stipend;
medical/life insurance; transportation
to/from site, room/board
Basic Requirements: M/F; single/
married; 23 to 65; Catholic
Mission Areas: Franciscan mission
sites in Latin America and Africa
Email: fms5@comcast.net
Web: www.franciscanmission
service.org

FRANCISCAN OUTREACH (L096)
ASSOCIATION
1645 West Le Moyne St.
Chicago, IL 60622-7120
Contacts: Danielle Simonetti and
Rev. Vaughn Fayle
(773) 278-6724, ext. 17
Mission Areas: greater Chicago
metropolitan area
Type of Service: overnight shelter,
dining room, showers/laundry
Term of Service: 1 year, 1-3 months
summer, interim/holidays program
Basic Benefits: room/board (in
community); modest stipend;
medical insurance
Basic Requirements: M/F;
single/married w/o dependents;
college age and up
Affiliation: nonprofit, associated with
Franciscan Friars (Sacred Heart
Franciscan Province)
Email: volunteer@franoutreach.org
Web: www.franoutreach.org

FRANCISCAN PARTNERS (L097)
PROGRAM
PO Box 12395
Albuquerque, NM 87195
Contact: Br. Bruce Michalek, OFM
(505) 452-3270
Mission Areas: Navajo Reservation
(AZ), New Mexico, Juarez (Mexico)
Type of Service: catechists, home
visitors, teachers, doctors, nurses,
office helpers, mechanics,
construction, musicians, etc.
Term of Service: 1 year (shorter
possible)
Basic Benefits: room; food
allowance; personal stipend;
commuting expenses; medical
insurance, if necessary
Basic Requirements: M/F; 20+
Affiliation: Franciscan Friars
(Province of Our Lady of Guadalupe)
Email: bruceofm@aol.com
Web: www.olgofm.org

FRANCISCAN VOLUNTEER (L098)
MINISTRY
PO Box 29276
Philadelphia, PA 19125
Contact: Katie B. Sullivan, Director
(215) 427-3070
Mission Areas: Camden (NJ),
Philadelphia (PA), Wilmington (DE)
Type of Service: ESL instructor,
parish assistant, youth and elderly
outreach, prison ministry, soup
kitchen, teacher/teacher's aide,
community organizer, HIV/AIDS
ministry, coach, tutor/mentor,
migrant ministry
Term of Service: 1 year
Basic Benefits: room/board; stipend;
medical insurance and copays;

educational loan assistance;
communal/ministerial/spiritual support
Basic Requirements: M/F; single;
Christian; 18 and up, generally not
older than 40
Affiliation: Franciscan Friars
(Province of the Most Holy Name)
Email: fvmpd@aol.com
Web: www.FranciscanVolunteer
Ministry.org

FRANCISCAN VOLUNTEER (L099)
PROGRAM (Chicago, IL)
110 W. Madison St.
Chicago, IL 60602
Contact: Sister Kathy McNulty,
Director, (312) 628-1254
Mission Areas: Chicago, St. Louis,
Michigan, Texas, Tennessee
Type of Service: parish work,
HIV/AIDS service agencies,
education/educational facilities, work
with the elderly, immigration, home
repair
Term of Service: 1 year – renewable
Basic Benefits: room/board; small
salary/stipend; medical insurance
Basic Requirements: M/F; 19 and
up; college graduate
Affiliation: Franciscan Friars (Sacred
Heart Province)
Email: franvol@aol.com
Web: www.thefriars.org/volunteers

FRANCISCAN VOLUNTEER (L107)
PROGRAM (Savannah, MO)
104 E. Park, PO Box 488
Savannah, MO 64485
Contact: Sr. Kathleen Reichert, OSF
Mission Areas: Missouri
Type of Service: Work with elderly,
social services, GED and pastoral
ministry
Term of Service: 1 month to 1 year
Basic Benefits: Room/board;
orientation/in-service training;
opportunities for daily participation in
prayer/Eucharist; generally no
salary, but payment for any
contracted services
Basic Requirements: Regular
volunteers: M/F; w/o dependents,
over 21. Others: F; under 21; serve
under a year (usually less than six
months) modified form of program
Affiliation: Sisters of St. Francis of
Savannah, MO (O.S.F.)
Email: osf@stjoelive.com
Web: www.sistersofstfrancis.org

FRANCISCAN WORKERS (L108)
715 Jefferson St. #1
Salinas, CA 93905
Contact: Michelle Smith, Youth
Ministries Coordinator
(831) 770-1264
Mission Areas: Salinas (central CA)

Type of Service: homeless, disadvantaged youth, migrant workers
Term of Service: long-term: 6 months or longer (no cap); short-term: available year round
Basic Benefits: long-term: housing; stipend; short-term: negotiated on individual basis
Basic Requirements: M/F
Email: imagineparadise9@ neteze.com or michelle_smith@csumb.edu

(L109)
FRANCISCANS FOR THE POOR
60 Compton Rd.
Cincinnati, OH 45215-5199
Contact: Christine Lemmon
(877) 761-9040 ext. 110
Mission Area: Midwest US
Type of Service: inner-city ministry community work and youth mission trips
Term of Service: 1-week mission trips for junior high and high school youth groups. Alternative winter, spring and fall breaks for campus ministries. Alternative family vacation/mission trips. 3-11 month Long-term Americorp volunteers
Basic Benefits: Communal living at Tau Community House. Medical insurance and stipend for long-term Americorp volunteers.
Basic Requirements: M/F; single/ married/widowed/divorced; 18 and up. Chaperones required for youth groups under age 18.
Affiliation: Franciscan Sisters of the Poor
Email: DirectorFranForThePoor@ fuse.net
Web: www.FranForThePoor.org

(L110)
FRANCISCORPS (A Franciscan Lay Volunteer Experience)
Assisi Center, 800 N. Salina St.
Syracuse, NY 13208
Contact: Bro. Jim Moore, OFM Conv., (315) 426-0481
Mission Area: Syracuse and San Jose, Costa Rica
Term of Service: 1 year, begin early August, renewable
Type of Service: teaching, child care, youth programs, drop-in centers, soup programs, elderly, women's shelter, L'Arche, refugee resettlement, free medical/legal clinic
Basic Benefits: room/board; medical insurance; stipend; transportation to-from site
Basic Requirements: M/F; single: college degree or equivalent
Affiliation: Franciscan Friars (Order of Friars Minor Conventual)

(Immaculate Conception Province)
Email: francorps@gmail.com
Web: www.franciscorps.org

GATEWAY VINCENTIAN (L111)
VOLUNTEERS
2912 Arsenal St.
St. Louis, MO 63118
Contact: Jim & Geri Ryan
(314) 771-1474 or 888-771-7220
Mission Area: St. Louis
Type of Service: social/community service, child care, criminal justice, health care assistance, parish ministry
Term of Service: 1 year, starting in August
Basic Benefits: room/board; medical insurance; stipend; transportation: AmeriCorps ed award (if available)
Basic Requirements: M/F; single; 22-30; college degree or equivalent experience
Affiliation: Vincentians (Midwest Province)
Email: gatevol@aol.com
Web: www.vincentianvols.org

GIMME A BREAK (L113)
7325 N. Claremont Ave.
Chicago, IL 60645
Congregation of Notre Dame
Contact: Sister Marilyn Medinger, CND, (708) 359-9299
Mission Areas: Many areas of the US and Canada
Type of Service: service to the poor, many in educational settings
Term of Service: one week during Christmas/spring break
Basic Benefits:room/board; community experience with sisters; possible financial aid for long distance travel
Basic Requirements: M/F; college students; $50 fee; adventurous spirit
Email: gimmeabreak1994@aol.com
Web: www.cnd-m.com

GLENMARY GROUP (L114)
VOLUNTEER PROGRAM
PO Box 7, Vanceburg, KY 41179
Contact: Joe Grosek, Volunteer Director, (606) 796-3421
Mission Area: Lewis County, KY (Appalachia)
Term of Service: 5-10 days (year-round)
Type of Service: home repair/renovation, manual labor, health care center
Basic Benefits: participants pay nominal fee to cover room/board, accident insurance
Basic Requirements: groups of 12-20 (college, parish, high schools, etc.); M/F: 17-45; single; Catholic

Affiliation: Glenmary Home Missioners
Email: jgrosek@glenmary.org
Web: www.glenmary.org

GLENMARY COWORKERS (L115)
IN MISSION
1312 Fifth Ave. North
Nashville, TN 37208
Contact: Jay Gilchrist, Coordinator
(615) 256-4384
Mission Areas: 10 states in Appalachia, the South and Southwest
Type of Service: Starting new Catholic Churches in counties in the rural South where there currently is no Catholic congregation, or pastoring churches under missionary development. Emphasis on ecumenism, evangelization, justice and intercultural understanding
Term of Service: long-term commitment desired
Basic Benefits: professional salary and benefits
Basic Requirements: master's degree in Theology; at least three years of missionary or parish experience (preferably in a rural and Southern setting).
Affiliation: Glenmary Home Missioners
Email: jgilchrist@glenmary.org
Web: www.glenmary.org

(L116)
GOOD SHEPHERD VOLUNTEERS
25-30 21st St., Astoria, NY 11105
Contact: Volunteer Director
(718) 943-7488
Mission Areas: New York City, New Jersey, Los Angeles, Paraguay, Peru
Type of Service: Good Shepherd Volunteers provides full-time volunteers with the opportunity to work in social service ministries serving women, adolescents, and children affected by poverty, violence, and neglect. Type of service includes family and youth services, education, shelter for battered women, community outreach, fair trade, economic empowerment and advocacy.
Term of Service: 1 year (domestic); 2 years (international)
Basic Benefits: room/board; modest stipend; medical insurance; student loan deferment
Basic Requirements: M/F; single/ married w/o dependents; over 21, college or 2 years work experience
Affiliation: Sisters of the Good Shepherd
Email: gsv@goodshepherds.org
Web: www.gsvolunteers.org

B-138

GOOD WORKS (L117)
9701 Germantown Ave.
Philadelphia, PA 19118-2694
Contact: Sr. Rose Loughery, SSJ,
Volunteer Coordinator
(215) 248-7239
Mission Areas: long-term/short-term:
Philadelphia
Type of Service: long-term:
elementary/secondary education,
immigration services, teacher's aide,
tutoring, literacy programs, office
work; short-term: varies each year,
same as above plus home repair
Term of Service: long-term: flexible;
short-term: 1 week, spring break
Basic Benefits: long-term: room/
board; medical insurance (one year
commitment); stipend; short-term:
room/board
Basic Requirements: long-term: F;
21+; college or work experience;
short-term: M/F; 18+
Affiliation: Sisters of Saint Joseph of
Philadelphia
Email: rloughery@ssjphila.org
Web: www.ssjphila.org

HEART'S HOME USA (L117-1)
108 St. Edward's Street
Brooklyn, NY 11205
Contact: Sister Regine Fohrer,
Servants of God's Presence
(718) 522-2121
Mission Areas: USA (Brooklyn),
France, Italy, Romania, Switzerland,
Syria, Ukraine, India, Thailand,
Philippines, Senegal, Argentina,
Brazil, Peru, Chile, Ecuador, El
Salvador, Honduras.
Type of Service: To bring a presence
of love and compassion to the most
wounded and abandoned people,
especially children. We visit care
centers, hospitals, jails, and
orphanages.
Term of Service: From 14 to 24
months.
Basic Benefits: room/board, medical
insurance; travel expenses to/from
overseas mission site
Basic Requirements: M/F, over 21,
single, in good physical and
psychological shape, as well as to be
ready to give fully of oneself, sharing
the daily life of the poor.
Affiliation: Heart's Home Organization
Email: srregine@heartshomeusa.org
Web: www.heartshomeusa.org

HOLY FAMILY SERVICES- (L120)
BIRTH CENTER
5819 North FM 88
Weslaco, TX 78596
Contact: Nancy Sandrock, CNM
(956) 969-2538
Mission Areas: Rio Grande Valley (4

south most counties of Texas)
Term of Service: 1 year or longer
Type of Service: certified nurse-
midwives, registered nurses;
housekeeping services; clerical
services; billing; social work
Basic Benefits: room/board; shared
car; health insurance; monthly
stipend; continuing education funds;
Americorps eligible education
payback funds
Basic Requirements: nurse-
midwives/registered nurses: Texas
State License; others: minimum high
school education
Email: hfsbc@msn.com
Web: www.holyfamilybirthcenter.com

HOLY TRINITY MONASTERY (L121)
Benedictine Associate Program
PO Box 298, St. David, AZ 85630
Contacts: John Strom, Marco
Svoboda, Volunteer Coordinators
(520) 720-4016
Mission Area: Holy Trinity Monastery
Type of Service: clerical,
housekeeping, cook, assistant cook,
bakery work, maintenance,
groundskeeping, library, storekeeping
Term of Service: 3-6 months,
renewable
Basic Benefits: room/board
Basic Requirements: M/F; 18-40 but
flexible; single/married w/o dependents
Affiliation: Benedictine
Email: guestmaster@theriver.com
Web: www.holytrinitymonastery.org

HOPE FAMILY RESOURCES (HFR) (L122)
1925A Hone Ave., Bronx, NY 10461
Contact: Dr. Denise Mari
(914) 793-9508
Mission Area: greater NY metro area
Term of Service: 1 year minimum
preferred (renewable)
Type of Service: public relations,
culinary arts, development,
fundraising, grant-writing, library
science, office maintenance,
accounting, administration/
management, computer
programming/data entry, family/
pastoral counseling, paraprofessional
work, visitation of the sick/
imprisoned, respect life activities,
parish ministry, mentoring/tutoring,
translation, communications media,
counseling researchBasic Benefits:
stipend for counselors/
paraprofessionals and some
administrative/communications
positions
Basic Requirements: M/F:18-45
(flexible); high school degree;
college/work experience preferred;
commitment to Gospel values

Email: HFRMissionTeam@
muchomail.com
Web: www.hopeforme.org

HUMILITY OF MARY SERVICE (L123-1)
20015 Detroit Rd.
Rocky River, OH 44116
Contact: Ellen Divers, Director
(440) 333-5373; fax: (440) 356-5714
Mission Areas: Arizona, Florida,
Ohio, Pennsylvania and Chile
Term of Service: Long-term: Two
months to two years; Short-term: one
week to one month
Type of Service: social work,
community outreach, legal aid to
Haitians, housing and homeless
services, literacy project, education,
inner city neighborhood ministry,
parish ministry/outreach
Basic Benefits: Long-term: Room
and board, transportation, medical
insurance if needed, small stipend;
Short-term: Room and board
Basic Requirements: Long-term:
College graduates and older; Short-
term: College students and older
Affiliation: Sisters of the Humility of
Mary
Email: edivers@hmministry.org
Web: www.hmvolunteers.org

SEEDS OF HOPE-CONGREGATION (L123-2)
OF THE HUMILITY OF MARY
820 W. Central Park Ave.
Davenport, IA 52804
Contact: Barbara Gross, Coordinator
(563) 323-9466, fax: (563) 323-5209
Mission Areas: Iowa, Kentucky,
Mississippi, and Montana
Term of Service: Long-term: 2
months to 1 year; Short-term: 1 week
to 1 month
Type of Service: social work,
community outreach, housing and
homeless services, inner-city
neighborhood ministry
Basic Benefits: Long-term: room and
board, transportation, medical
insurance if needed and a small
stipend; Short-term: room and board
only
Basic Requirements: Must be a
college student or older, or parish
youth ministry group
Affiliation: Congregation of the
Humility of Mary
Email: barbarajgross@gmail.com
Web: www.chmiowa.org

IDAHO MONASTIC LIVING (L124)
EXPERIENCE
465 Keuterville
Cottonwood, ID 83522
Monastery of St. Gertrude

Contact: Sr. Teresa Jackson, OSB
(208) 962-5024
Mission Area: rural Idaho
Type of Service: join in monastic life, particularly in aspects of community, prayer and outside work
Term of Service: July 1-12, other possible dates
Basic Benefits: room/board
Basic Requirements: F; single; 18-45
Email: volunteer@stgertrudes.org
Web: www.stgertrudes.org

(L125)
IGNATIAN VOLUNTEER CORPS
801 St. Paul St.
Baltimore, MD 21202
Contact: Suzanne Geaney, Executive Director
(410) 752-4686 or 888-831-4686
Mission Areas: metropolitan regions of Baltimore, Chicago, Cincinnati, Cleveland, Detroit, Los Angeles, Minneapolis/St. Paul, New England, New York Metro, Omaha, Philadelphia, San Diego, Washington, DC/Northern Virginia, Cincinnati, and St. Louis
Type of Service: serving the materially poor in homeless shelters, food distribution centers, medical facilities, job placement/counseling services, housing services, ESL/GED/other adult literacy programs, after school programs for children, AIDS/hospice ministries, prison ministry, refugee services and more
Term of Service: 10 months (Sept. through June); 2 days a week (or equivalent hours)
Basic Requirements: M/F; 50 +; retired
Affiliation: Society of Jesus (Jesuits)
Email: info@ivcusa.org
Web: www.ivcusa.org

IHM VOLUNTEER PROGRAM (L126)
(Monroe, MI), 610 West Elm Ave.
Monroe, MI 48162
Contact: Membership Coordinator
(734) 240-9820
Mission Area: varied sites
Type of Service: summer environmental experiences
Term of Service: summer; short-term experiences
Basic Benefits: room/board; stipend
Basic Requirements: M/F; single/married w/o dependents; 21 and up; college/work experience; some connection to IHM Congregation
Affiliation: Sisters, Servants of the Immaculate Heart of Mary
Email: membership@ihmsisters.org
Web: www.ihmsisters.org

(L127)
INCARNATE WORD MISSIONARIES
4503 Broadway
San Antonio, TX 78209
Contact: Tere Manon, Director
(210) 828-2224, ext. 228
Mission Areas: US, Mexico, Guatemala, Peru and Zambia, Africa
Type of Service: parish/pastoral ministry, rural life ministry, teaching, health care, human rights, clinic/hospice ministry, counseling services, work with indigenous peoples, leadership development, work with children, women, agronomists, and medical personnel
Term of Service: Long term: 1 yr. minimum in own country; 2 yr. minimum in abroad country
Basic Benefits: housing; medical insurance; stipend; transportation to/from mission site
Basic Requirements: M/F; 21+; single/married w/o dependents; college degree preferred
Affiliation: Sisters of Charity of the Incarnate Word, San Antonio
Email: tere.manon@amormeus.org, meghan.green@amormeus.org
Web: www.amormeus.org

(L128)
INNER-CITY TEACHING CORPS
300 N. Elizabeth, Suite 300C
Chicago, IL 60607
Contact: Bridget Hogan
(312) 491-9100, ext. 216
Mission Area: Chicago
Type of Service: teachers, inner-city elementary schools, community living
Term of Service: 2 years
Basic Benefits: room/board, stipend, medical insurance, transportation, alternative teacher certification, Americorps Education Awards, credits toward a Master of Science in Education from Northwestern University
Basic Requirements: M/F; single; 21-30; college degree
Affiliation: Catholic
Email: teach@ictc-chicago.org
Web: www.ictc-chicago.org

INTERNATIONAL MISSION (L130)
PROGRAM (Diocese of Orlando)
PO Box 1800, Orlando, FL 32802
Contact: Sr. Bernadette Mackay, Mission Director, (407) 246-4890
Mission Area: Dominican Republic
Type of Service: ministry that encourages and supports spiritual/personal/economic development of persons and community
Term of Service: 2 years
Basic Benefits: room/board; stipend;

health/life/disability insurance; travel expenses
Basic Requirements: M/F; single/widowed/priests/religious; college graduate; fluency in Spanish
Affiliation: Diocese of Orlando
Email: bmackay@orlandodiocese.org
Web: www.missiondr.org

JESUIT VOLUNTEER CORPS (L132)
801 St. Paul St.
Baltimore, MD 21202
Basic Requirements: M/F; single/married couples - no dependents; over 21; Christian
Basic Benefits: room/board; stipend; medical insurance; transportation home
Affiliation: Jesuits
Type of Service: Domestic ministry is in youth work, legal issues, AIDS ministry, emergency assistance, education, health care, housing issues, immigration advocacy, etc. International ministry is in education (including math and science), social services and pastoral ministry
Term of Service: 1 year (Aug. to Aug. domestic); 2 years (international)
Web: www.jesuitvolunteers.org

(L132-1)
JESUIT VOLUNTEER CORPS - EAST
801 St. Paul St.
Baltimore, MD 21202
EAST: Kate Haser, Executive Director, (410) 244-1744
Email: jvceast@jesuitvolunteers.org

JESUIT VOLUNTEER (L132-2)
CORPS - MIDWEST
7333 W. Seven Mile Rd.
Detroit, MI 48221
MIDWEST: Angie Moloney, Executive Director, (313) 345-3480
Email: jvcmw@jesuitvolunteers.org
Web: www.jesuitvolunteers.org

JESUIT VOLUNTEER (L132-3)
CORPS - NORTHWEST
3928 N. Williams Ave.
Portland, OR 97227
(503) 335-8202 fax: (503) 249-1118
Email: info@jvcnorthwest.org
Web: www.jvcnorthwest.org

JESUIT VOLUNTEER (L132-4)
CORPS - SOUTHWEST
PO Box 459, Santa Clara, CA 95052
SOUTHWEST: Michael Braun, Executive Director, (408) 241-4200
Email: jvcsw@jesuitvolunteers.org
Web: www.jesuitvolunteers.org

JESUIT VOLUNTEER CORPS - SOUTH (L132-5)
PO Box 3126, Houston, TX 77253
SOUTH: Pam Krinock, Executive Director, (713) 756-5095
Email: jvcsouth@
jesuitvolunteers.org,
pam@jesuitvolunteers.org
Web: www.jesuitvolunteers.org

JOSEPH HOUSE VOLUNTEERS (L133)
PO Box 1755, Salisbury, MD 21802
Contacts: Sr. Patricia Lennon, Sr. Connie Ladd (410) 543-1645
Mission Areas: MD, DE, VA
Type of Service: any gifts and skills are useful in serving the poor
Term of Service: 1 year (renewable)
Basic Benefits: room/board; stipend; medical insurance
Basic Requirements: M/F; single/ married/widowed/divorced/religious; 21 and up; Christian
Affiliation: Little Sisters of Jesus and Mary
Email: lsjm@ezy.net
Web: www.thejosephhouse.org

L'ARCHE COMMUNITIES (L139-1)
1130 SW Morrison Street, Suite 230
Portland, OR 97205
Main Office
Contact: Abbey Piner, Recruitment Coordinator (503) 282-6231
For Regional Offices see:
L'ARCHE US EASTERN REGION;
L'ARCHE US CENTRAL REGION;
L'ARCHE US WESTERN REGION
Mission Areas: Alabama, California, Florida, Illinois, Iowa, Massachusetts, Oregon, Pennsylvania, Ohio, Washington (DC), New York, Kansas, Virginia, State of Washington
Type of Service: living in communities, working and sharing life with adults with developmental disabilities
Term of Service: 1 year to long term (flexible); some summer programs -1 year preferred
Basic Benefits: room/board; generous stipend; health insurance
Basic Requirements: M/F; single/ married /religious; over 18; no experience required, but must be willing to commit to living in community
Affiliation: international, ecumenical, Christian
Email: abbey@larcheusa.org
Web: www.larcheusa.org

L'ARCHE US CENTRAL REGION (L139-2)
PO Box 0278, Clinton, IA 52732
L'ARCHE US CENTRAL REGION

1841 130th Ave.,
Wheatland, IA 52777
Contact: JoAnne Horstmann, Regional Coordinator
(563) 242-5624
THE ARCH - Central Region,
PO Box 0278, Clinton, IA 52732
E-mail: larchia@clinton.net
Contact: Keith Kalaukoa, Director
(319) 243-9035
L'ARCHE CHICAGO - Central Region, 1049 S. Austin Blvd., Chicago, IL 60644
E-mail: larchechicago@hotmail.com
Alexandra Conroy, Director
(773) 287-8249
L'ARCHE HARBOR HOUSE - Central Region, 700 Arlington Rd., Jacksonville, FL
E-mail larchfl@aol.com
Contact: Amy Finn-Schultz, Director
(904) 744-4435
L'ARCHE HEARTLAND - Central Region PO Box 40493, Shawnee, KS 66204-4493
E-mail: larchkc@juno.com
Sue Coyle, Director
(913) 341-2265
L'ARCHE MOBILE - Central Region, 151 S. Ann St., Mobile, AL 36604
E-mail: larchmob@hotmail.com
Barbara Gaddy, Director
(334) 438-2094
Email: jcenusa@msn.com

L'ARCHE US EASTERN REGION (L139-3)
see below, for location nearest you
L'ARCHE EASTERN US REGION
Contact: S. Anita Maroun, SC, Regional Coordinator
1099 Old Broadway, Bedford, OH 44146
E-mail: vsclaw@juno.com
L'ARCHE BLUE RIDGE MOUNTAINS
Box 2242, Lynchburg, VA 24501
(434) 384-6300
E-mail: larchebrm@ntelos.net
Contact: Mark Russell, Director
L'ARCHE CLEVELAND
Box 20450, Cleveland, OH 44120
(216) 721-2614
E-mail: office@larchecleveland.org
Contact: Becky Brady, Director
L'ARCHE ERIE - 3745 W. 12th St., Erie, PA 16505
(814) 452-2065
E-mail: office@larcheerie.org
Contact: Vicki Washek, Director
L'ARCHE IRENICON - PO Box 1177, Haverhill, MA 01831
(978) 374-6928
E-mail: office@larcheirenicon.org
Contact: Swanna Champlin, Director
L'ARCHE SYRACUSE - 1232 Teall Ave., Syracuse, NY 13206
(315) 479-8088
E-mail: larchesyracuse@cynmail.com
Contact: Peggy Harper, Director

L'ARCHE GREATER WASHINGTON, DC - PO Box 21471, Washington, DC 20009
(202) 232-4539
E-mail: community@ larchewashingtondc.org
Contact: John Cook, Director
Web: www.larcheusa.org

L'ARCHE US WESTERN REGION (L139-4)
6205 NE Milton St.
Portland, OR 97213
L'ARCHE US WESTERN REGION
Contact: Patty McNally, Regional Coordinator
(503) 288-8535
L'ARCHE NEHALEM - Western Region, 8501 SE Stephens, Portland, OR 97216
E-mail:mail@larche-portland.org
www.larcheportland.org
Contact: Susan Mitchell, Director
(503) 251-6901
L'ARCHE NOAH SEALTH - Western Region, PO Box 22023, Seattle, WA 98122-0023
E-mail: gerry@larcheseattle.org
www.larcheseattle.org
Contact: Gerry Scully, Director
(206) 325-9434
L'ARCHE SPOKANE - Western Region, 703 E. Nora, Spokane, WA 99207
E-mail: larchespokane@earthlink.net
www.larchespokane.org
Contact: Cathy Klaus, Director
(509) 483-0438
L'ARCHE TAHOMA HOPE - Western Region, 12303 36th Ave. E., Tacoma, WA 98446
E-mail: tahomahope@larchethc.org
www.larchethc.org
Contact: Stacy Cates-Carney, Director
(253) 535-3178
WAVECREST-FRIENDS OF L'ARCHE - Western Region, 1614 Peacock Lane, Fullerton, CA 92833
E-mail: wavecrest@adelphia.net
www.wavecrestonline.org
Contact: Karen Carr, Director
(714) 879-2989

LALANNE (L140)
300 College Park, Dayton, OH 45469
Contact: Jacinta Mergler, Director
(937) 229-3928
Mission Areas: Cleveland, Dayton, Indianapolis, San Antonio, TX
Type of Service: teaching in urban Catholic schools
Term of Service: 2 years
Basic Benefits: stipend; medical insurance; live in community with other teachers; professional/spiritual development; Lalanne teachers earn a Master's degree
Basic Requirements: M/F; completed

an undergraduate degree; have/be eligible for teacher certificate/license; for beginning teachers
Affiliation: University of Dayton
Email: lalanne@notes.udayton.edu
Web: www.udayton.edu/~lalanne

LAMP MINISTRIES (L141)
2704 Schurz Ave., Bronx, NY 10465
Contacts: Drs. Tom and Lyn Scheuring, Marybeth and Ed Greene, (718) 409-5062
Mission Areas: Metropolitan New York
Type of Service: ministries of Catholic evangelization, in materially poor parishes and with the homeless, sick and disabled
Term of Service: 1 year minimum, community living available
Basic Benefits: room/board; stipend; medical insurance; transportation to/from mission site
Basic Requirements: M/F; single/ married/religious; over 24; Catholic
Affiliation: private, Catholic
Email: tscheuring@ lampministries.org or mgreene@lampministries.org
Web: www.lampministries.org

LASALLIAN VOLUNTEERS (L142)
Hecker Center, 3025 Fourth St. NE, Suite 300, Washington, DC 20017
Contact: Alisa Macksey
(202) 529-0047; fax: (202) 529-0775
Mission Areas: California, Illinois, Maryland, Missouri, New Jersey, New York, Oklahoma, Oregon, Pennsylvania, Rhode Island, Tennessee, Washington, Wisconsin
Type of Service: education, social work, youth ministry, catholic worker
Term of Service: 1 year domestic (renewable)
Basic Benefits: room/board; small stipend; medical insurance; college loan deferment or forbearance; AmeriCorps ed awards; transportation to/from home/worksite/ orientation/in-service sessions; spiritual growth and reflection; meaningful career experience
Basic Requirements: M/F; 21 and up; college degree or comparable work experience
Affiliation: De La Salle Christian Brothers
Email: lv@cbconf.org
Web: www.lasallianvolunteers.org

THE LAY MISSION - (L144)
HELPERS ASSOCIATION (LMH)
3435 Wilshire Blvd., Ste. 1035
Los Angeles, CA 90010-1901
Contact: Janice England
(213) 368-1870

Mission Areas: Taiwan, Sierra Leone, Cameroon, Kenya, Central America, Marshall Islands, Uganda, Tanzania
Type of Service: education, engineering/construction, health care, office/computer work, finance/ administration, skilled trades, computer technicians
Term of Service: 3 years
Basic Benefits: room & board; monthly stipend
Basic Requirements: M/F; single/married; over 21, Catholic
Email: info@laymissionhelpers.org;
Web: www.laymissionhelpers.org

LORETTO VOLUNTEERS (L145)
Loretto Staff Office, 590 E. Lockwood Ave., St. Louis, MO 63119-3279
Contact: Barbara Mecker, Volunteer Coordinator, (314) 962-8112
Mission Areas: Denver, El Paso, Kentucky (rural areas), New York, St. Louis, Washington (DC)
Type of Service (determined on individual basis): programs for low-income women/children, court diversion project for women, medical clinic for homeless, emergency assistance centers, environmental education program, assisting Loretto's NGO representative at UN
Term of Service: summer, 6 months, 1 year
Basic Benefits: room/board; stipend; medical insurance
Basic Requirements: F; single; 20 or older
Affiliation: Sisters of Loretto
Email: bmecker@ lorettocommunity.org
Web: www.lorettovolunteers.org

LU - CHOICE (L146)
(Loyola University Chicago Opportunities In Catholic Education)
820 N. Michigan Avenue, Suite 601
Chicago, IL 60611
Contact: Lee Hubbell
(312) 915-7049
Mission Area: Chicago
Type of Service: teaching
Term of Service: 2 years
Basic Benefits: long-term: upon successful completion of studies, M.Ed. with certification at no cost, health insurance, pension plan, professional growth allowance, loan deferment; possible AmeriCorps ed award; modest stipend
Basic Requirements: bachelor's degree with a non-education major, ability to work well with children, desire to live in community
Affiliation: (Jesuit) Loyola University of Chicago

Email: lhubbel@luc.edu
Web: www.luc.edu/education/ luchoice.shtml

MAGGIE'S PLACE (L147)
PO Box 1102, Phoenix, AZ 85001
Contact: Becky Fair, (602) 262-5555
Mission Areas: Phoenix, Tempe, Glendale, AZ; Coeur D'Alene, ID
Type of Service: House positions (women only): living with and providing direct service to pregnant women, new moms and newborns in need; House Support positions (men and women): computer maintenance; facilities and vehicle maintenance; database maintenance; newsletter coordination; business operations; human resources; programs; fundraising.
Term of Service: 1 year+; summer (8-12 weeks); alternative break groups
Basic Benefits: room/board; $350/ month stipend; medical insurance (year+); AmeriCorps Ed Award (year+)
Basic Requirements: Catholic and/or willing to live in a Catholic community; committed to Church teaching; 21+ and college degree or equivalent life experience (year+); 18+ and high school diploma (summer)
Email: mpstaff@maggiesplace.org
Web: www.maggiesplace.org

MARIANIST VOLUNTEER (L148)
PROGRAM
4425 W. Pine Blvd.
St. Louis, MO 63108-2301
Contact: Dan Richter, MVP Coordinator, (314) 533-1207
Mission Areas: visit www.marianist.com/mvp for most current location listings
Type of Service: education, social services, youth and parish ministry, family services, peace and justice, service for the homeless and community organizing
Term of Service: 1 year, renewable, two years international assignment
Basic Benefits: room/board; stipend; medical insurance
Basic Requirements: M/F; 21 years and older; no dependents
Affiliation: Marianists, Society of Mary
Email: drichter@sm-usa.org
Web: www.marianist.com/mvp

MARYKNOLL CHINA (L150)
VOLUNTEER TEACHERS PROGRAM
29 Cadence Court
Morristown, NJ 07960
Contact: Director
Mission Areas: Northern/Southern Provinces of the People's Republic of China
Type of Service: ESL teachers

Term of Service: long-term: 1 year; short-term: 5 weeks intensive summer program
Basic Benefits: long-term: rt transportation from Hong Kong to teaching site in mainland China; emergency medical insurance; accommodations at teaching site and in Hong Kong; stipend; relocation stipend; Chinese teaching visa; orientation
Basic Requirements: M/F; Native English speaker; college degree (any major acceptable)
Affiliation: Maryknoll
Email: chinaserveusa@msn.com
Web: www.chinaserv.org

MARYKNOLL LAY MISSIONERS (L154)
Bethany Bldg., PO Box 307
Maryknoll, NY 10545-0307
Contact: Michelle Born, 800-818-5276 or (914) 762-6364, ext. 114
Mission Areas: Bolivia, Brazil, Cambodia, Chile, East Timor, Kenya, Mexico, Peru, El Salvador, Tanzania, Thailand, Vietnam, Zimbabwe, Nepal
Type of Service: agriculture, community organizing, education, health care, leadership training, social justice, women's rights, sustainable development, faith formation, youth ministry
Term of Service: 3-1/2 years
Basic Benefits: room/board; stipend; transportation to/from country of assignment; language school; healthcare
Basic Requirements: M/F; 23 to 65; single/married/families/priests/brothers/sisters; active Catholics; US citizens or permanent residents
Affiliation: Maryknoll Fathers, Brothers, Sisters
Email: mborn@mklm.org
Web: www.mklm.org

THE MATTHEW KELLY (L155)
FOUNDATION
2330 Kemper Lane
Cincinnati, OH 45206
Contact: Volunteer Coordinator
(513) 221-7700
Mission Area: Cincinnati
Type of Service: assist the Foundation in its works, including managing speaking engagements; distribution of Catholic books, videos and tapes; hosting retreat in Fatima (Portugal); and help with quarterly newsletter
Email: info@matthewkelly.org
Web: www.matthewkelly.org

MENTORING ACADEMIC (L156)
GIFTS IN SERVICE (MAGIS)
Ed Dept/Creighton University, 2500 California Plaza, Omaha, NE 68178

Contact: Molly Davies
(402) 280-3491, fax: (402) 280-1117
Mission Areas: Nebraska, inner city of Omaha
Type of Service: under-served Catholic secondary schools in Omaha Archdiocese, Lincoln Diocese, Grand Island Diocese
Basic Benefits: stipend; health insurance; student loan deferment
Basic Requirements: M/F; bachelor's degree
Email: mollydavies@creighton.edu
Web: www2.creighton.edu/magis

MERCY VOLUNTEER CORPS (L157)
1325 Sumneytown Pike, PO Box 901
Gwynedd Valley, PA 19437-0901
Contact: Marian H. Uba, Executive Director, (215) 641-5535
Mission Areas: throughout US; Guyana (South America)
Type of Service: community work, education, health care, social work
Term of Service: 1 year (US), 2 years (international)
Basic Requirements: M/F; 21 and older; single/marriedw/o dependents
Affiliation: Institute of the Sisters of Mercy of the Americas
Email: contactus@
    mercyvolunteers.org
Web: www.mercyvolunteers.org

MERCY WORKS (L158)
VOLUNTEER PROGRAM
Mercy Home for Boys & Girls, 1140 W. Jackson Blvd., Chicago, IL 60607
Contact: Katie Smith, (312) 738-6369
Mission Area: Chicago
Type of Service: residential youth care worker; case worker; admissions case manager; career resources coordinator; education coordinatorTerm of Service: 1 year, renewable
Basic Benefits: room/board; health insurance; stipend; transportation assistance; Americorps Education Award; retreats; vacation; professional supervision; spiritual direction; sign-on bonus for full-time employment after successful completion of volunteer service; post-service financial assistance for education
Basic Requirements: M/F; 21 and up; single, no dependents; good physical/mental health; college degree preferred or experience working with youth in professional setting; driver's license
Affiliation: Archdiocese of Chicago
Email: katkel@mercyhome.org
Web: www.mercyhome.org

MICHAELA FARM (L159)
PO Box 100, Oldenburg, IN 47036
Contact: Sr. Carolyn Hoff, OSF
(812) 933-0661
Mission Area: Oldenburg, Indiana
Type of Service: agricultural outreach, garden development, livestock care, environmental education, spiritual renewal
Term of Service: 1 day - 2 weeks (extendable)
Basic Benefits: room; hands on experience, resource library
Basic Requirements: 18 or over; single/married; interest in sustainable agriculture, good health
Affiliation: Franciscan Sisters of Oldenburg
Email: michaelafarm@seidata.com
Web: http://oldenburgfranciscans.org

MIDTOWN EDUCATIONAL (L160)
FOUNDATION
1819 N. Wood St., Chicago, IL 60622
Contacts: John Heybach
(773) 292-2660
Mission Area: Chicago
Type of Service: Teaching, administrative duties, community outreach efforts, tutoring/mentoring program
Terms of Service: 7-8 weeks (mid-June to early Aug.) to 1 year
Basic Benefits: Part-time paid teaching positions available, particularly in summer, as well as unpaid tutor/mentor volunteer opportunities
Basic Requirements: M/F; college age/recent college grads
Affiliation: Opus Dei
Email: jheybach@midtown-metro.org
Web: www.midtown-metro.org

MILFORD SPIRITUAL CENTER (L167)
YOUTH MINISTRY INTERNSHIP
5361 S. Milford Rd.
Milford, OH 45150-9744
Contacts: Stephen Poat
(513) 248-3500, ext. 11
Mission Area: Milford, OH (Cincinnati area)
Type of Service: youth retreat team
Term of Service: 12 months
Basic Benefits: contract
Basic Requirements: M/F; college graduate preferred; interest in working with adolescents (13 to 17 years old)
Affiliation: Jesuits (Chicago Province)
Email: poat@jesuitspiritual
    center.com
Web: www.jesuitspiritualcenter.com

MINISTRY FOR HOPE (L168)
(HOPE HOUSE MINISTRIES)
PO Box 358
Port Jefferson, NY 11777
Contact: Father Francis Pizzarelli,
smm, (631) 928-2377, ext. 31
Mission Areas: Port Jefferson (NY)
Type of Service: residential care of
16-21 year olds, nontraditional
junior/senior high school, homeless,
drug/alcohol treatment, family
counseling, homeless shelter
Term of Service: June, July, August
Basic Benefits: room/board; stipend
Basic Requirements: M; single; at
least a college senior
Affiliation: Montfort Missionaries
Email: frfritz@aol.com
Web: www.hhm.org or
   www.montfortmissionaries.com

(L169)
MISERICORDIA/HEART OF MERCY
6300 North Ridge, Chicago, IL 60660
Contact: Theresa Rooney, Director
of Volunteers, (773) 273-4161
Mission Area: Chicago (IL)
Type of Service: working with
people with mental and/or physical
disability in residential, vocational
and recreational environments
Term of Service: minimum 2 to 3
hours per week for 6 months - 1 year
Basic Requirements: at least 16;
desire to work with people with
mental disability
Email: theresar@misericordia.com
Web: www.misericordia.org

(L170)
MISSION DOCTORS ASSOCIATION
3435 Wilshire Blvd, Ste. 1035
Los Angeles, CA 90010
Contact: Mrs. Elise Frederick
(213) 368-1875
Mission Areas: Africa, Latin America
Type of Service: medical
Term of Service: 3 years plus training;
short-term program of 1-3 months
Basic Benefits: 3-year program; full
sponsorship for physician and family;
short-term program: support varies
Basic Requirements: Catholic,
physician, medical license in good
standing, completed 12-month
residency, families welcome
Email: missiondrs@earthlink.net
Web: www.missiondoctors.org

MISSION OF FRIENDSHIP (L171)
St. Mark Center, 429 E. Grandview
Blvd., PO Box 10397, Erie, PA 16514
Contact: Mrs. Pat Marshall
(814) 824-1231
Mission Areas: Merida, Yucatan,
Mexico and surrounding areas

Type of Service: shelter and day
care staff, public health promoter,
elementary teaching in unstructured
setting
Term of Service: 15 months or more
Basic Benefits: room/board; stipend;
health insurance; transportation
to/from mission site
Basic Requirements: M/F; 23 years
and up: single: ability to speak
Spanish
Affiliation: Diocese of Erie
Email: pmarshall@eriercd.org
Web: www.eriercd.org/missions4.asp

MISSIONARY CENACLE (L173)
VOLUNTEERS
PO Box 35105, Cleveland, OH 44135
Contacts: Ms. Maureen Masterson
(long-term and short-term)
(800) 221-5740, (216) 252-4727
Mission Areas: US, Mexico, Puerto
Rico, Costa Rica
Type of Service: elementary school
teachers, youth ministers,
catechists, social workers,
maintenance workers, retreat
ministers, parish ministers, ministers
to the homeless, youth in crisis,
Native Americans, and Hispanics
Term of Service: long-term: 1 year;
short-term: 1 week-3 months
Basic Benefits: long-term:
room/board; small monthly stipend;
medical insurance reimbursement;
short-term: room/board
Basic Requirements: M/F; 18 years
old for short-term, 21 years old for
long-term; fluency in Spanish for
long-term Hispanic ministry and
some of the short-term Hispanic
placements
Affiliation: Missionary Servants of
the Most Blessed Trinity, Missionary
Servants of the Most Holy Trinity
Email: cenaclevolunteer@aol.com
Web: www.TMC3.org

MOTHER CAROLINE (L174)
ACADEMY/EDUCATION CENTER
515 Blue Hill Ave.
Dorchester, MA 02121
Contacts: Shirley Grover
(617) 427-1177, ext. 201, 205
Mission Area: Boston
Type of Service: teachers
Term of Service: 1 year minimum (2
years preferred)
Basic Benefits: room/board; stipend;
health/dental insurance;
transportation; AmeriCorps ed award
Basic Requirements: M/F; college
degree
Email: info@mcaec.org
Web: www.mcaec.org

(L175)
MOUNT ST. BENEDICT MONASTERY
LIVE-IN VOLUNTEER PROGRAM
Mount St. Benedict Monastery
620 Summit Ave.
Crookston, MN 56716-2799
Contact: Volunteer Director
(218) 281-3441
Mission Area: Crookston, MN
Type of Service: community work,
education, health care, homeless,
care of children
Term of Service: 1 month to 1 year
(renewable)
Basic Benefits: room/board (in
Benedictine community)
Basic Requirements: F; no
dependents; 23 and up
Affiliation: Benedictine Sisters
(Crookston, MN)
Email: volunteer@msb.net
Web: msb.net

NATIONAL EVANGELIZATION (L176)
TEAMS MINISTRIES
110 Crusader Ave. W.
St. Paul, MN 55118
Contact: Matt Reiswig
(651) 450-6833
Mission Areas: 65 dioceses in US
Type of Service: teams of 12 (6 men
and 6 women) proclaim the Gospel
through fun, high-energy retreats
Term of Service: mid-Aug. through
mid-May
Basic Benefits: room/board;
stipend; medical insurance
Basic Requirements: M/F; 18-28;
Catholic; personal faith, physical
stamina; raise $3,400 in partnership
funds prior to the start of training
Email: recruit@NETusa.org
Web: www.NETusa.org

(L177)
NATIVITY PREPARATORY SCHOOL
39 Lamartine St.
Jamaica Plain, MA 02130
Contact: Fr. John Wronski, SJ
(857) 728-0031
Mission Area: Boston
Type of Service: middle school
teachers (inner-city boys school)
Term of Service: 1 year minimum,
renewable
Basic Benefits: room/board; medical
insurance; AmeriCorps ed award;
Boston College graduate credits
Basic Requirements: M/F; college
degree
Affiliation: Jesuits (New England
Province)
Email: jwronskisj@nativityboston.org
Web: www.nativityboston.org

NATIVITY PREPARATORY SCHOOL OF NEW BEDFORD (L178)

66 Spring St.
New Bedford, MA 02740-5957
Contact: John Rompf, (508) 994-3800
Mission Area: New Bedford
Type of Service: teaching in middle school for boys from low income families
Term of Service: 1 year
Basic Benefits: room, allowance for board; stipend; medical insurance; approximately $5,000 for two years in AmeriCorps credits toward student loans
Basic Requirements: M/F; college graduate (no teaching experience or education coursework necessary); strong character
Email: principal@nativitynb.org
Web: www.nativitynb.org

NAZARETH FARM (L180)

Rt.2, Box 194-3, Salem, WV 26426
Contact: Angie Moloney
(304) 782-2742
Mission Area: Doddridge County, West Virginia, Appalachia
Type of Service: Nazareth Farm provides service retreats for youth, young adults and adults while providing home repair and building relationships in North Central West Virginia. Service includes: community work, construction, youth ministry, home repair, and service retreats
Term of Service: 1 year, long-term; 1 week, short term
Basic Benefits: room/board; stipend; medical insurance
Basic Requirements: M/F; single/married/widowed/divorced/separated/religious; 21 years and up; short-term: (weeklong) at least 16 years or junior in high school
Affiliation: Diocese of Wheeling/Charleston
Email: nazarethfarm@gmail
Web: www.nazarethfarm.org

NETWORK (A National Catholic Social Justice Lobby) (L182)

25 E Street, NW, Suite 200
Washington, DC 20001
Contact: Executive Director
(202) 347-9797
Mission Area: Washington, DC
Type of Service: advocacy, lobbying for social justice
Term of Service: 11 months (September - July)
Basic Benefits: stipend; contribution to health plan
Basic Requirements: M/F; college through retiree age
Affiliation: Catholic, independent
Email: network@networklobby.org
Web: www.networklobby.org

NEWARK BENEDICTINE VOLUNTEER PROGRAM (L185)

520 Martin Luther King Blvd.
Newark, NJ 07102-1314
Contact: Fr. Albert Holtz, OSB
(973) 792-5751
Mission Area: Newark
Type of Service: teaching, tutoring, sports, clerical, community outreach
Term of Service: September - June; summer 5 weeks: month of August
Basic Benefits: room/board; stipend; medical insurance; possible deferment of student loans
Affiliation: Benedictine Monks, Newark Abbey
Email: aholtz@sbp.org
Web: www.newarkabbey.org

NOTRE DAME MISSION VOLUNTEER PROGRAM (L186)

403 Markland Ave.
Baltimore, MD 21212
Contact: Sr. Katherine Corr, SND
(410) 532-6864, ext. 12
Mission Area: rural, urban US; Non-AmeriCorps International opportunities are available in Kenya and Peru
Type of Service: tutoring, literacy education, GED, ESL
Term of Service: 1 year (renewable)
Basic Benefits: community housing; monthly stipend; medical insurance; AmeriCorps ed award
Basic Requirements: M/F; single/married w/o dependents; 21 and up; work experience and/or college education
Affiliation: Sisters of Notre Dame de Namur
Email: natloffice@ndmva.org
Web: www.ndmva.org

OFFICE OF LAY VOLUNTEERS (L188)
(Referral Agency), 144 W. Wood St.
Youngstown, OH 44503
Diocese of Youngstown
Contact: Thomas Aquinas Dolan, O.P., Director
(330) 744-8451, ext. 277
Affiliation: Diocese of Youngstown
Email: tadolan@dioceseof youngstown.org

OPERATION TEACH (L189)
(Teachers Enlisted to Advance Catholic Heritage)
4701 N. Charles St.
Baltimore, MD 21210-2476
Contact: Sr. Karen Kelly, Director, (410) 532-5326
Mission Areas: Catholic schools of the Baltimore area
Type of Service: elementary/secondary teaching
Term of Service: 2 years beginning July
Basic Benefits: stipend from diocesan schools sufficient for living/personal expenses; medical benefits; community living, spiritual and professional development; Master of Arts in Teaching from the College of Notre Dame of Maryland; loan deferment
Basic Requirements: M/F; single w/o dependents; recent bachelor's degree
Affiliation: College of Notre Dame of Maryland
Email: mkkelly@ndm.edu
Web: www.ndm.edu/academics/nd_abt_opteach.cfm

OUR LADY OF MERCY COMMUNITY OUTREACH (L190)

Volunteers in Ministry, PO Box 607, 1684 Brownswood Rd.
Johns Island, SC 29455
Contact: Sister Carol Wentworth, OLM, (843) 559-4109
Mission Areas: rural communities, Sea Islands, Charleston County, SC
Type of Service: education, ESL tutors, after school homework program, outreach to poor, soup kitchen, tutoring
Term of Service: long-term: 9 months; short-term: 1 week to 6 months, summer program in July
Basic Benefits: room/board; living allowance; medical insurance where necessary
Basic Requirements: M/F; 21 year and older; singe/married w/o dependents
Affiliation: Sisters of Charity of Our Lady of Mercy
Email: olmoutreach@aol.com
Web: www.olmoutreach.org

PACIFIC ALLIANCE FOR CATHOLIC EDUCATION (PACE) (L191)

University of Portland, School of Education, Portland, OR 97203
Contact: Mary P. Gallagher
(503) 943-7417
Mission Areas: Oregon, Washington, Utah
Type of Service: full-time teacher in Catholic school
Term of Service: 2 years
Basic Benefits: reduced salary of approximately $1000 monthly; health insurance; full scholarship for Master's degree; on site support, etc.
Basic Requirements: M/F; single; college graduate
Affiliation: University of Portland
Email: gallaghm@up.edu
Web: www.up.edu

B-145

PASSIONIST VOLUNTEERS (L193)
526 Monastery Place
Union City, NJ 07087
Contact: Jill Wallace, Jennifer Wiley
(347) 217-3619
Mission Areas: Appalachian
Mountains (WV); Brooklyn;
international: Jamaica and Honduras
(pending)
Type of Service: recreation,
community outreach with youth and
elderly, home repair, literacy,
mentoring, tutoring, youth ministry
Term of Service: 2 to 10 weeks;
summer; year long: Aug. - Aug.
Basic Benefits: room/board (in
community with other volunteers);
year long: room/board, stipend,
health insurance
Basic Requirements: M/F; single/
married/families with children/
retirees; 21 and up (summer: 18 and
up, out of high school for at least one
year, unless accompanied by older
family member)
Affiliation: Passionist Priests &
Brothers (Province of St. Paul of the
Cross)
Email: passionistvol@cpprov.org
Web: www.passionistvolunteers.org

PIARIST VOLUNTEERS (L194)
Highway 80, Box 870
Martin, KY 41649-0870
Contact: Fr. Thomas Carroll, Sch.P.
(606) 285-3950
Mission Areas: Appalachian region of
Eastern Kentucky
Type of Service: education, outreach
work
Term of Service: 1 year, renewable
Basic Benefits: room/board; stipend;
medical insurance; transportation
to/from mission site
Basic Requirements: M/F; single;
college education
Affiliation: Piarist Fathers and
Brothers

PIME VOLUNTEERS (L195)
17330 Quincy St., Detroit, MI 48221
Contact: Fr. Ken Mazur
(313) 342-4066
Mission Areas: Asia, Africa, Latin
America, Papua New Guinea
Type of Service: medical, physical
therapy, agriculture, teachers
Term of Service: short and long term
Basic Requirements: M/F; Catholic;
college graduate; useful skills
Email: volunteers@pimeusa.org
Web: www.pimeusa.org

PLACE CORPS (L196)
1 LMU Dr., University Hall, Suite
2400, Los Angeles, CA 90045

Contact: Diana Murphy
(310) 338-3774
Mission Area: Los Angeles
Type of Service: elementary/
secondary school teachers in under-
served schools in the Los Angeles
Archdiocese
Term of Service: 2 years
Basic Benefits: partial salary;
housing; health insurance;
AmeriCorps ed grant; possible
deferment and/or cancellation of
undergraduate student loans
Basic Requirements: M/F; bachelor's
degree; some Catholic education
background ideal; competency in
Spanish asset; willingness to live in
community while teaching full-time
and earning a master's degree
Affiliation: Loyola Marymount
University, Archdiocese of Los
Angeles, and the UCCE (University
Consortium for Catholic Education)
Email: place@lmu.edu
Web: www.lmu.edu/education/PLACE

PRESENTATION MINISTRIES (L197)
(OUR LADY OF)
3230 McHenry Ave.
Cincinnati, OH 45211
Contact: Marianne Lander
(513) 662-5378
Mission Areas: worldwide
Type of Service: Bible teaching,
retreats, publishing, developing
small Christian communities
Term of Service: one year
(renewable), non-paid volunteers
Basic Benefits: growth in holiness,
building God's kingdom
Basic Requirements: strongly
committed Catholic, love for Jesus in
the sacraments
Email: pubsandtapes@presentation
ministries.com
Web: www.presentationministries.com

PRO-LIFE VOLUNTEER CORPS (L198)
2900 Sunset Place #109
Los Angeles, CA 90005
Contacts: Sister Paula Vandegaer,
Joan Mount, Kathleen Hochderffer
(213) 382-2702 or 2156
Mission Areas: Los Angeles and
surrounding area
Type of Service: direct service or
assist in administration or
programming in pro-life agencies,
Respect Life offices, parishes,
maternity homes, day care centers,
hospices, settlement houses
Term of Service: 1 year, renewable
Basic Benefits: room/board; stipend;
medical insurance; transportation
to/from place of work
Basic Requirements: F; 21+; college
education or work experience; US

citizen or resident with employment
permit
Affiliation: Sisters of Social Service
Email: Vforlife@aol.com or
lifeservices@juno.com
Web: www.volunteersforlife.org

PROVIDENCE ALLIANCE (L199)
FOR CATHOLIC TEACHERS (PACT)
Providence College
Providence, RI 02918
Contact: Brother Patrick Carey, cfc,
(401) 865-2657
Mission Areas: dioceses listed below
Type of Service: teaching in Catholic
inner-city schools
Term of Service: 2 years
Basic Benefits: room/board;
maximum stipend of $14,500 per
year; health insurance; tuition-free
master's degree in education
Basic Requirements: M/F; bachelor's
degree; some Catholic education
background ideal, willingness to live
in community while teaching full-time
and earning a master's degree
Affiliation: Providence College,
University of Notre Dame, Dioceses
of Boston, Fall River, Providence,
Worcester, and Springfield
Email: pact@providence.edu
Web: www.providence.edu/pact

PROVIDENCE HOSPITALITY HOUSE (L200)
PO Box 22382, Seattle, WA 98122
Contact: Megan McArthur
(206) 322-2107
Mission Area: Seattle
Type of Service: provide nutritious
meals, creative activities for children,
weekly goals with mothers in
temporary emergency housing for
homeless women with children in
crisis
Term of Service: Sept.-July
Basic Benefits: room/board; stipend;
health/dental insurance
Basic Requirements: F; 21-40: good
mental/physical health; able to work
with a team
Affiliation: Sisters of Providence
Email: PHHTeam@aol.com

PROVIDENCE HOUSE, INC. (L203)
703 Lexington Ave.
Brooklyn, NY 11221
Administrative Office Contact:
Monzura Rhue, Director of
Administration
(718) 455-0197, ext. 13
fax: (718) 455-0692
Mission Areas: New York (Brooklyn,
Queens, Westchester County)
Type of Service: Long Term-Short/
Short-Term Volunteers. Active
volunteers in shelter for homeless

women and children. Providence House has eight residential shelters
Term of Service: 1 week to 1 year
Basic Benefits: room/board/stipend
Basic Requirements: F; 21 or older
Affiliation: Diocese of Brooklyn
Email: rhuem@providencehouse.org
Web: www.providencehouse.org

(L206)
PROVIDENCE VOLUNTEER MINISTRY (Saint Mary-of-the-Woods, IN)
Sisters of Providence, St. Mary-of-the-Woods, IN 47876-1095
Contact: Julie Szolek-Van Valkenburgh, (317) 695-4634
Mission Areas: CA, IN, IL, Taiwan
Type of Service: eco-justice and organic farming hospitality, education, health care, peace and justice, social service
Term of Service: long term (1 year)
Basic Benefits: room/board; stipend; medical insurance; spiritual direction and retreats; Americorps Education Award
Basic Requirements: M/F; single; 21 and up
Affiliation: Sisters of Providence of Saint Mary-of-the-Woods
Email: pvm@spsmw.org
Web: www.p-v-m.org

(L207)
QUEST - VOLUNTEERS FOR HAITI
4602 Clemson Rd.
College Park, MD 20740
Contact: Sr. Rita Ricker, RJM
(301) 927-7118
Mission Areas: Gros Morne, Jean Rabel (Haiti)
Type of Service: education, community work, nurses, agriculture
Term of Service: 5 weeks (summer); 1 year (renewable; Sept. to Aug.)
Basic Benefits: room/board; stipend/ medical insurance (year long)
Basic Requirements: M/F; single/ married/religious; 21 and older
Affiliation: Religious of Jesus and Mary
Email: collegeparkrjm@aol.com
Web: www.rjm-us.org

RdC MISSION VOLUNTEER PROGRAM (L208)
PO Box 920433
Needham, MA 02492
Rostro de Cristo (Face of Christ) Mission Volunteer Program
Contact: Jessie Hallerman, Assistant Director, 617-552-2281
Mission Area: Duran, Ecuador
Type of Service: education (primary, secondary, teacher, teacher's aide), child care, religious education, tutoring, soup kitchens, retreat groups, parish activities, hospital for

Hansen's disease, visiting orphanages, nursing homes, other social services, and more
Term of Service: long-term: 1 year starting with July 15 orientation; short-term: group retreat - 10 days to 2 weeks
Basic Benefits: room/board; health insurance; stipend
Basic Requirements: long-term: M/F; single; 21+; college degree or significant life/work experience; competence in Spanish; short-term: student at a high school or college participating in program
Affiliation: St. James Society; Archdiocese of Boston
Email: faceofchrist@gmail.com
Web: www.rostrodecristo.org

RED CLOUD VOLUNTEERS (L209)
Red Cloud Indian School
Pine Ridge, SD 57770
Contact: Patrick Gilger, SJ (605) 867-5888, ext. 236
Mission Area: Pine Ridge Indian Reservation, SD
Type of Service: elementary and secondary education
Term of Service: 1 school year (renewable; 2-3 years preferred)
Basic Benefits: room/board; monthly stipend; medical insurance; travel allowance; personal spiritual development
Basic Requirements: M/F; single/married; college degree; Christian
Affiliation: Jesuits (Wisconsin Province)
Email: redcloudvolunteers@gmail.com
Web: www.redcloudschool.org

REDEEMER MINISTRY CORPS (L210)
521 Moredon Rd.
Huntingdon Valley, PA 19006
Contact: Eileen Zebrowski
(215) 914-4116
Mission Areas: Philadelphia and suburbs
Type of Service: health care (nursing, therapies, pastoral care, hospice) social work, child care, elder care, homeless men/women/children, education
Term of Service: 1 year (renewable)
Basic Benefits: room/board; monthly stipend; medical insurance
Basic Requirements: M/F; single; 21 and over; Christian
Affiliation: Sisters of the Holy Redeemer
Email: rmcorps@aol.com
Web: www.sistersholyredeemer.org

RESPONSE-ABILITY (L212)
460 Shadeland Ave.
Drexel HIll, PA 19026
Contact: Liz Eager
(610) 626-1400, ext. 314
Mission Areas: Philadelphia, Los Angeles, Washington (DC), Dominican Republic; Santiago, Chile
Type of Service: education; health care
Term of Service: 1 or 2 year programs
Basic Benefits: room/board; stipend/medical insurance: long term
Basic Requirements: M/F; single; bachelor's degree
Affiliation: Society of the Holy Child Jesus
Email: teach@ravolunteers.org
Web: www.ravolunteers.org

SACRED HEART MONASTERY VOLUNTEER PROGRAM (L213)
Sacred Heart Monastery
Richardton, ND 58652
(701) 974-2121
Mission Area: Richardton, ND
Type of Service: Working with the elderly sisters, clerical work, computer work, working in Spirituality Center as hostess or secretary, garden/lawn work, dietary aide, baker, assisting with llamas, liturgy assistant/organist, telephone operator, housekeeping
Term of Service: Summer (1-3 months); long-term (3-6 months)
Basic Benefits: Room/board; stipend (long-term)
Basic Requirements: F; single
Email: richardtonsisters@sacredheartmonastery.com
Web: www.sacredheartmonastery.com

(L214)
ST. ANN'S CATHOLIC SCHOOL
PO Box 2000, Belcourt, ND 58316
Contact: Rev. Scott Brossart, SOLT
(701) 477-2667
Mission Area: Turtle Mt. Indian Reservation (ND)
Type of Service: certified elementary teachers, teachers' aides, administrative staff, religious education (school); staff/mentors for camp; maintenance; custodial; youth ministry; catechesis
Term of Service: August - May (school); June-July (camp)
Basic Benefits: room/board; monthly stipend; health insurance (negotiable); student loan deferment and possible student loan repayment
Basic Requirements: M/F; 19 and up; single/married/families; loyal to Catholic Church
Affiliation: Society of Our Lady of the Most Holy Trinity (Priests, Sisters)

Email: serveatstanns@yahoo.com
Web: www.soltnative.com

(L215)
SAINT ANTHONY INDIAN SCHOOL
PO Box 486, Zuni, NM 87327-0486
Contact: (Ms.) Nenita Mosqueda,
(505) 782-4596
Mission Areas: Zuni (reservation area)
Type of Service: teacher
Term of Service: 1-3 years
Basic Benefits: room; breakfast/
lunch-school days; health insurance;
licensed teacher, $13,000/year,
$11,000 if not; 3% cost of living
allowance
Basic Requirements: M/F; BSE or
BA degree
Email: nlmosqueda@yahoo.com

(L216)
ST. CHARLES LWANGA CENTER
4746 Carter Ave., Ste. 100
St. Louis, MO 63115-2238
Contact: Jane Wexler Brown,
Executive Director, (314) 367-7929
Mission Area: St. Louis
Type of Service: promote Christian
spiritual formation and leadership
development within the African-
American Catholic community and
all who collaborate with them
through youth ministry,
evangelization workshops, weekly
mass, pastoral care, marriage
maintenance, marriage preparation,
the ministry of consolation, and legal
education ministry.
Affiliation: Archdiocese of Saint Louis
Email: info@lwangacenter.org
Web: www.lwangacenter.org

(L217)
SAINT CHARLES LWANGA HOUSE
2204 Jolly Pond Rd.
Williamsburg, VA 23188
Contact: Sister Agnes Narocho,
Director, (757) 564-7371
Mission Area: Williamsburg
Type of Service: residence/day
support for people with disabilities,
working with children with special
needs, 24-hour children's respite care
Term of Service: 1-2 years
Basic Benefits: room/board;
transportation; stipend
Basic Requirements: M/F; college
degree; Catholic; High School/GED;
CNA; Computer Literate
Affiliation: Little Sisters of St. Francis
Email: lwangahouse@cox.net

(L218)
**ST. FRANCIS CATHOLIC
MISSION SCHOOL**
215 West Wilson Ave.
Gallup, NM 87301

Contact: Don Frank, Principal
(505) 863-3145
Mission Area: northern New Mexico
Type of Service: teachers: P-6
Term of Service: school year, Aug. -
June
Basic Benefits: housing; $300
monthly stipend; health insurance
Basic Requirements: M/F; single; 21
and up; college degree, Catholic
Affiliation: Diocese of Gallup

ST. JOSEPH WORKERS (L219)
1884 Randolph Ave.
St. Paul, MN 55105
Contacts: Suzanne Herder, CSJ,
(651) 696-2762; Bridgette Kelly,
(651) 690-7049
Mission Areas: Minneapolis/St. Paul
and surrounding area
Type of Service: teaching
English/other skills to immigrant
communities; community organizing;
assisting in providing free health
care to people in poverty; reaching
out to homeless people/families;
assistance to the elderly; justice
education/action with high
school/college students; working
directly with kids; advocating for
quality childcare for low income
families; legislative advocacy/
education, etc
Term of Service: 11 months (Aug.
through June)
Basic Benefits: room/board;
insurance, transportation to/from
work placement; living allowance;
AmeriCorps ed awards; loan
deferment; 2 graduate/
undergraduate courses through the
College of St. Catherine in St. Paul
Basic Requirements: F; 21-35
Affiliation: Sisters of Saint Joseph of
Carondelet (Saint Paul Province)
Email: sjw@csjstpaul.org
Web: www.stjosephworkers.org or
www.csjstpaul.org

ST. JOSEPH'S CATHOLIC (L220)
WORKER HOUSE
402 South Ave., PO Box 31049
Rochester, NY 14603
Contact: George McVey, Volunteer
Coordinator, (585) 232-3262
Mission Area: Rochester
Type of Service: work with poor and
homeless of Rochester, NY in soup
kitchen, shelter and outreach
Term of Service: 1 year or longer
Basic Benefits: housing with other
volunteers; stipend; medical insurance
Basic Requirements: M/F; ability to
get along with others in a diverse
Catholic worker community setting
Affiliation: Catholic Worker
Email: cathworker@frontiernet.net

(L221)
SAINT JOSEPH'S INDIAN SCHOOL
PO Box 89, Chamberlain, SD 57325
Contact: Melissa Hall, Human
Resources Associate
(605) 234-3311 or 800-568-4434
Mission Areas: Chamberlain, SD
Type of Service: 1 year, minimum
Basic Benefits: salary; health/dental/
vision/life/disability insurance
Basic Requirements: M/F;
single/married; Experience working
with children is helpful; degree not
required, but preferred
Affiliation: Congregation of the
Priests of the Sacred Heart (SCJs)
Email: hrdept@stjo.org
Web: www.stjo.org

(L223)
SAINT MICHAEL INDIAN SCHOOL
PO Box 650, St. Michael's, AZ 86511
Contact: Executive Director
(928) 871-4667
Type of Service: teachers, counselors,
coaches, maintenance personnel
Term of Service: academic year
(early August - early June)
Basic Benefits: Salary, housing and
utilities, medical insurance
Basic Requirements: M/F; teachers:
college degree, (preferably ed major)
Affiliation: Sisters of the Blessed
Sacrament
Web: www.smis1902.org

(L224)
**ST. VINCENT PALLOTTI CENTER
FOR APOSTOLIC DEVELOPMENT**
415 Michigan Ave. NE, Terrace
Level, Washington, DC 20017
(Clearinghouse/long-term/short-term
volunteer - Referral Agency)
NATIONAL OFFICE: 877-VOL-LINK
(877-865-5465) or 202-529-3330
Contact: Mike Goggin, National
Director
Email: pallotti@pallotticenter.org
Web: www.pallotticenter.org

SALESIAN LAY MISSIONERS (L225)
2 LeFevre Lane
New Rochelle, NY 10801
Contact: Adam Rudin, (914) 633-8344
Mission Areas: Bolivia, China, Sierra
Leone, India, Ecuador, Dominican
Republic, Sudan
Type of Service: youth minister,
religious education, staff for
recreation/camp services, rural life
ministry, counselor, pastoral/parish
minister, building tradesman,
Hispanic ministry, teaching in schools
Term of Service: 1-2 years
Basic Benefits: room/board; medical
insurance; transportation to/from

mission site
Basic Requirements: M/F; single/married w/o dependents; 20 minimum; college education or work experience; Christian commitment; US citizen
Affiliation: Salesians of Don Bosco (Priests, Brothers and Sisters)
Email: slm@salesianmissions.org
Web: www.SalesianLayMissioners.org

SALESIAN SISTERS VIDES (L226) VOLUNTEER PROGRAM
St. Joseph Center, 655 Belmont Ave., Haledon, NJ 07508
Contact: Sr. Denise Sickinger, FMA, (914) 937-4405 cell: (973) 851-7422
Mission Area: Newton/Paterson, NJ
Type of Service: summer camps: group counselor, recreational activities, arts/crafts, mission work
Term of Service: 3-7 weeks (summer)
Basic Benefits: room/board
Basic Requirements: 18-30 years; good health; desire to work with youth
Affiliation: Salesian Sisters of St. John Bosco (Eastern Province)
Email: east.director@vides.us
Web: www.salesiansisterseast.org

SAN MIGUEL SCHOOL (L227)
Back of the Yards Campus, 1949 W. 48th St., Chicago, IL 60609-4145
Contact: Karin McClelland
(773) 890-0233
Mission Area: inner city Chicago
Type of Service: education (grades 5-8, all subjects) for low-income, at-risk youth
Term of Service: 1 year minimum (2 years preferred)
Basic Benefits: room/board; stipend; medical insurance; AmeriCorps ed award; travel to and from site
Basic Requirements: M/F; teaching skills (preferred); experience with/love for early adolescents
Affiliation: DeLaSalle Christian Brothers (Midwest Province)
Web: www.sanmiguelchicago.org

SARNELLI SERVICE CORPS (L227-1)
Sarnelli House, PO Box 29303
Philadelphia, PA 19125
Contact: Father Kevin Murray, C.Ss.R.
(215) 356-7551
Mission Areas: inner city Philadelphia
Type of Service: ministries to abandoned poor
Term of Service: long-term: 6-12 months; short-term: 1-4 weeks
Basic Benefits: long-term: room/board, medical insurance; stipend; short-term: room/board
Basic Requirements: M/F; 20-26; openness to persons who are poor/abandoned; desire to live in faith-based community.

Affiliation: Blessed Sarnelli Community
Email: CSSRvols@aol.com

SCALABRINIAN VOLUNTEER (L228) PROGRAM
PO Box 77, El Paso, TX 79941-0077
Contact: Fr. Francisco Pellizzari, c.s., 011-52-16-870676
Mission Areas: urban parishes in Chicago, Los Angeles; border shelters: Tijuana, Tapachula, Ciudad Juarez, Nuevo Laredo - Tam (Mexico); Tecun-Uman (Guatemala)
Type of Service: migrant worker ministry, immigration/refugee services
Term of Service: one year, renewable
Basic Benefits: room/board; health insurance; monthly allowance
Basic Requirements: M/F; single/married w/o dependents; 21-35
Email: progvoluntariado@hotmail.com
Web: www.migrante.com.mx

SCHOOL SISTERS OF NOTRE (L229) DAME VOLUNTEER OPPORTUNITIES
170 Good Counsel Dr.
Mankato, MN 56001-3138
Contact: Ruth Jackson
(507) 389-4109, 4200
Mission Areas: St. Paul/Minneapolis, Cambridge, Mankato (MN); Standing Rock Reservation, Fort Yates (ND)
Type of Service: immigrants/refugees, women/children in crisis, Native American children, the elderly
Term of Service: short term/long term - varies
Basic Benefits: determined by specific site coordinator
Basic Requirements: M/F; high school juniors or seniors and older; single no dependents; good health
Affiliation: The School Sisters of Notre Dame
Email: rjackson@ssndmankato.org
Web: www.ssndmankato.org

SCN LAY MISSION (L230) VOLUNTEER PROGRAM
PO Box 9, Nazareth, KY 40048-0009
Contact: Sr. Luke Boiarski
(740) 859-2946
Mission Area: Belize, Central America; throughout United States
Type of Service: social outreach programs, cross-cultural programs, education, health care
Term of Service: one-week to three-week mission immersion experiences
Basic Requirements: Male/female; single/married; all religions; application/screening process; good health
Affiliation: Sisters of Charity of Nazareth

Email: lukescn@bardstown.com
Web: www.scnfamily.org

SIDE BY SIDE LAY (L232) VOLUNTEER PROGRAM
5625 Isleta Blvd., SW
Albuquerque, NM 87105
Contact: Sr. Kay Taylor, FdCC
(505) 873-2059; cell: (505) 400-4329
Mission Areas: Albuquerque (Overseas: see Canossian International Voluntary Service - VOICA) on the Internet)
Type of Service: pastoral ministry, health care, education, social work, community work
Term of Service: 1 year (renewable)
Basic Benefits: room/board; stipend; medical insurance
Basic Requirements: M/F; 20-35 (flexible); single; Catholic
Affiliation: Canossian Daughters of Charity
Email: sbsvolunteers@aol.com

SISTERS OF THE BLESSED (L233) SACRAMENT LAY VOLUNTEERS
1663 Bristol Pike
Bensalem, PA 19020-5796
Contact: Sr. Mary John Souliard, SBS, (215) 244-9900, ext. 383
Mission Area: St. Michaels on Navajo Reservation, AZ
Type of Service: education, house staff, nurse or nurse's aide
Term of Service: 10 months to 1 year (renewable)
Basic Benefits: room/board; stipend; medical insurance; transportation to/from mission site
Basic Requirements: M/F; single/married w/o dependents/widowed/religious; 21 and over; Catholic
Email: souliardm@aol.com or sbs@libertynet.org

SISTERS OF THE DIVINE (L235) SAVIOR SALVATORIAN COME AND SEE PROGRAMS
4311 North 100 St.
Milwaukee, WI 53222-1393
(414) 466-0810
Contact: Sr. Carol Jean Zais
Mission Area: Wisconsin
Type of Service: poverty relief services, elderly outreach, parish/pastoral ministries, homeless shelters
Term of Service: summer: extended weekend; 1 week (flexible)
Basic Requirements: F; single; Catholic; interested in religious life; 18 and up
Email: czais@salvatoriansisters.org
Web: www.sistersofthedivine savior.org

SISTERS OF ST. JOSEPH - COMPANIONS IN MISSION (L236)
975 E. Gardenia
Madison Heights, MI 48071-3431
Contact: Bernadette Dean, SSJ
Clearly title written mail:
Companions in Mission 2009
Mission Area: Kalamazoo (MI)
Type of Service: Service to the poor (soup kitchen), Meals on Wheels, Habitat for Humanity, youth and elderly programs
Term of Service: 1 week: June 28, 2009 to July 3, 2009
Basic Requirements: F; single/ married; 18 - 40
Email: bdean@csjoseph.org
Web: www.csjoseph.org

SISTERS OF SAINT JOSEPH VOLUNTEER CORPS (L238)
314 Gregory Street
Rochester, NY 14620
Contact: Sr. Donna Del Santo, SSJ, Coordinator, (585) 529-5689
Type of Service: Long-term: Only in Rochester, NY. St. Joseph's Neighborhood Center, an inner-city health and outreach center, serving the working poor and their families who are without health insurance. They are in need of nurses, doctors, social and outreach workers, fund raisers, clerical staff and GED tutors. Bethany House, a Catholic Worker House of Hospitality serving homeless women and children is in need of a full-time, female staff person. Short-term: In Rochester, NY: An inner-city Catholic, multicultural preschool through 5th grade elementary school; a nondenominational alternative school for children grades 3 to 9 who learn differently; a school for mentally challenged children and adults - All schools are in need of teachers, teacher aides, child care workers; Inner-city soup kitchens serving families and individuals; Inner-city health and outreach center serving the uninsured working poor is in need of nurses, doctors, social and outreach workers, clerical staff and GED tutors; A foster home for special needs children from birth to 21 years old; A daycare for special needs newborns to toddlers needing nurses as well as volunteers who could help with household chores, yard work, whatever is needed. All programs can use generalists to work in a variety of ways. Short Term in Pineapple, AL: Rural children's learning center, medical and dental clinic, elderly nutrition center, clothing room, transportation and outreach services. Program needs nurses, social and outreach workers, teachers, teacher aides, child care workers, as well as generalists.
Affiliation: Sisters of St. Joseph of Rochester
Email: volunteercorps@ ssjrochester.org
Web: www.ssjrochester.org

S.M.A. LAY MISSIONARIES (L239)
256 North Manor Circle
Takoma Park, MD 20912-4551
Contact: Theresa Hicks, Steve Price, Fr. Daniel Lynch, S.M.A.
(301) 891-2037
Mission Areas: Liberia, Ghana, Tanzania and ministries in US
Type of Service: education, health, development, agriculture, pastoral ministries, AIDS ministry, catechetics, social work, etc.
Term of Service: Formation: Sept.- Dec. in Takoma Park (MD); 3-4 months language and culture training in country of assignment, followed by 2 years service
Basic Benefits: room/board; stipend; medical insurance; transportation to/from mission site
Basic Requirements: M/F; single or married w/o dependents; college degree (or qualifications in area of expertise); 23-50 years (negotiable); Catholic (open to lay, priests, sisters, brothers)
Affiliation: Society of African Missions
Email: SMAAssociation@ comcast.net
Web: http://sma.cua.edu or www.smafathers.org

SOCIETY OF OUR LADY OF THE MOST HOLY TRINITY (L240)
PO Box 417, Bosque, NM 87006
Contacts: Rev. Dale A. Craig , SOLT
(505) 864-1800; Fax: (505) 864-1801
Mission Areas: Native America, Hispanic & Afro Americans throughout the US; Belize; Guatemala; Thailand; the Philippines; Mexico, Haiti, New Guinea, Africa (lay volunteers not in all areas)
Type of Service: education, catechetics, health care, evangelization, addictions, orphanage, pastoral ministries, community work, education, construction, mechanic, crafts, housekeeper, cook
Term of Service: orientation, 1 year minimum; society members: 3 year commitment
Basic Benefits: room/board
Basic Requirements: M/F; single/married/widowed with or w/o dependents; 18 and over; college degree needed for some; Catholic

Affiliation: Society of Our Lady of the Most Holy Trinity (Priests, Sisters)
Email: soltlaity@gmail.com
Web: www.societyofourlady.net

SOCIETY OF OUR MOTHER OF PEACE (L241)
Mary the Font Solitude, 6150 Antire Rd., High Ridge, MO 63049-2135
Contact: Sr. Mary Perpetua
(636) 677-3235
Mission Areas: St. Louis (MO), Springfield (MO), the Philippines, Nigeria
Type of Service: person-to-person evangelization especially within the poor Black community; manual and domestic work at the monastery: cooking, maintenance, carpentry, plumbing, etc.
Term of Service: Negotiable/but at least 2 years for manual and domestic service/long term preferred for evangelization service
Basic Benefits: room/board; stipend; prayer with the religious community
Basic Requirements: M/F; single/ married/divorced/separated (w/o dependents); Catholic
Affiliation: Society of Our Mother of Peace (Priests, Brothers, Sisters)
Email: marythefont@yahoo.com
Web: www.ourmotherofpeace.org

SOJOURNERS AND CALL TO RENEWAL (L242)
3333 14th Street, NW, Suite 200
Washington, DC 20010
Contact: Robin Fillmore
(202) 328-8842
Mission Area: Washington, DC
Type of Service: administrative, Internet support, development, marketing, editorial assignments, public policy research
Term of Service: 1 month to 1 year
Basic Requirements: commitment to social justice
Email: rfillmore@sojo.net
Web: www.sojo.net

SPIRITAN ASSOCIATES (L243-2)
Spiritan Hall, Houston, TX 77006
West of the Mississippi: Fr. Huy Q. Dinh, CSSp, (713) 529-0405
Mission Areas: Haiti, Tanzania, Ghana, US
Type of Service: education, administration, crafts, tradesman, agriculture, mechanic, pilot, administrator
Term of Service: 3 years
Basic Benefits: room/board; stipend; medical insurance; transportation to/from mission site; relocation allowance

Basic Requirements: 22 or older; college education plus a few years of professional experience
Email: joinusw@spiritans.org
Web: www.spiritans.org

(L245)
SU CASA CATHOLIC WORKER
Central American Martyrs Center
5045 S. Laflin St., Chicago, IL 60609
Contact: Volunteer Coordinator, (773) 376-9263
Mission Area: inner-city Chicago
Type of Service: work among homeless Latino families: community activities, neighborhood gardens, soup kitchen, etc.
Term of Service: 1 year minimum (summer, college break also)
Basic Benefits: room/board; stipend; medical insurance; AmeriCorps ed award
Basic Requirements: M/F; single/married/religious; 10 and older; Spanish helpful
Affiliation: Catholic Worker
Email: sucasacw@juno.com
Web: www.catholicworker.org/communities/commlistall.cfm

THE SUMMIT INSTITUTE (L246)
10915 E. 84th St., Tulsa , OK 74133
Contact: Mark Mann, Director
Mission Areas: long term: Tulsa, OK; short term: Mexico
Type of Service: long term: youth/campus ministry, recreation, camp counseling/coaching, short term: computer programming, website development, Internet religious education
Term of Service: long term: mostly 1 year, in some cases 2 years; short term: 1-3 months
Basic Benefits: room/board; access to transportation; AmeriCorps ed award
Basic Requirements: M/F; seniors, college student or graduate; skills in at least one service area
Email: mmann@summit.edu
Web: www.summit.edu

URBAN CATHOLIC (L247)
TEACHER CORPS
194 Beacon St.
Chestnut Hill, MA 02467
Boston College, Center for Catholic Education
Contact: Karen Kennedy
(617) 552-0602
Mission Area: Boston area inner-city schools
Type of Service: teaching
Term of Service: 2 years
Basic Benefits: room/board; stipend; medical/dental benefits; loan

forgiveness/deferment; tuition remission
Basic Requirements: M/F; 21 and older; college grads with student teaching experience
Affiliation: Archdiocese of Boston, Boston College
Email: uctc@bc.edu
Web: www.bc.edu/uctc

VIDES+USA (L249)
5630 West Commerce St.
San Antonio, TX 78237-1313
(Volunteers International for Development, Education and Service)
Contact: Sister Mary Gloria Mar, FMA
(210) 435-1919 cell: (210) 373-9532
Mission Areas: TX, LA, AZ, CA, NY, NJ, FL, and CO; over 90 nations worldwide in Africa, Asia, America, Europe and Australia
Type of Service: community outreach benefiting at-risk women and children; youth ministry; education; social services and healthcare in mission regions.
Term of Service: 2 months - 2 years
Basic Benefits: room/board; basic medical insurance
Basic Requirements: M/F; 18-35; single/married; US citizen/resident
Affiliation: Daughters of Mary Help of Christians (Salesian Sisters)
Email: director@vides.us
Web: www.vides.us or
www.cgfmanet.org or
www.vides.org

VIDES EAST USA (L249-1)
112 North 23rd Street
Kenilworth, NJ 07033-1256
(Satellite office of VIDES+USA)
Contact: Sister Denise Sickinger, FMA
(908) 276-4681 cell: (973) 851-7422
Mission Areas: TX, LA, AZ, CA, NY, NJ, FL, and CO; over 90 nations worldwide in Africa, Asia, America, Europe
Type of Service: community outreach benefiting at-risk women and children; youth ministry; education; social services and healthcare in mission regions.
Term of Service: 2 months - 2 years
Basic Benefits: room/board; basic medical insurance
Basic Requirements: M/F; 18-35; single/married; US citizen/resident
Affiliation: Daughters of Mary Help of Christians (Salesian Sisters)
Email: east.director@vides.us
Web: www.vides.us or
www.vides.org

VINCENTIAN SERVICE (L253-1)
CORPS (VSC)
4330 Olive St., St. Louis, MO 63108
VSC CENTRALContact: Sister Teresa Daly, (314) 533-4770, ext. 103
Mission Areas: Urban and rural areas throughout central and western US
Type of Service: Adult literacy teachers, advocacy workers, case workers for shelters and/or mentally ill, child care workers, community organizers, computer programmers, volunteer coordinators, crisis counselors, day care workers, fund raisers, health care professionals (RN, LPN, CNA, therapists), immigration/refugee counselors, legal aides, maintenance workers, nursing home assistants, outreach workers to the homebound elderly, parish ministers, pastoral care ministers, skilled laborers, social workers, teachers and teachers' aides (grade and middle schools), youth ministers.
Term of Service: 1 to 2 years (renewable).
Basic Benefits: room/board; monthly stipend; medical insurance; loan deferment; AmeriCorps ed award when available
Basic Requirements: M/F; single, married/widowed; 20 years and up; college degree or significant life/work experience; persons with disabilities possible; Christian; desire for challenge and ability to be flexible
Affiliation: Vincentian Priests & Brothers; Daughters of Charity
Web: www.vincentianservicecorps.org

VINCENTIAN SERVICE (L253-2)
CORPS (VSC)
25 San Fernando Way, Suite B
Daly City, CA 94015-2065
VSC WEST
Contact: Sister Camille Cuadra, DC
(650) 991-6465
Mission Areas: Urban areas in San Francisco Bay area and Los Angeles area
Type of Service: Adult literacy teachers, advocacy workers, case workers for shelters and/or mentally ill, child care workers, community organizers, computer programmers, volunteer coordinators, crisis counselors, day care workers, fund raisers, health care professionals (RN, LPN, CNA, therapists), immigration/refugee counselors, legal aides, maintenance workers, nursing home assistants, outreach workers to the homebound elderly, parish ministers, pastoral care ministers, skilled laborers, social workers, teachers and teachers'

aides (grade and middle schools), youth ministers.
Term of Service: 1 to 2 years (renewable).
Basic Benefits: room/board; monthly stipend; medical insurance; loan deferment; AmeriCorps ed award when available
Basic Requirements: M/F; single, married/widowed; 20 years and up; college degree or significant life/work experience; persons with disabilities possible; Christian; desire for challenge and ability to be flexible
Affiliation: Vincentian Priests & Brothers; Daughters of Charity
Email: vscwest@dochs.org
Web: www.vscorps.org

VOLUNTEER MISSIONARY MOVEMENT (L255)
5980 W. Loomis Rd.
Greendale, WI 53129
Contact: Julia Pagenkopf
(414) 423-8660
Mission Areas: Africa, Central America, central cities in US
Type of Service: health care, agriculture, community work, education, labor, pastoral ministry, social work, engineering, administrative
Term of Service: 2 years
Basic Benefits: vary according to project
Basic Requirements: M/F; single/married/widowed; 23 and over; Christian commitment
Affiliation: Lay, ecumenical, Catholic social justice tradition, non-profit
Email: jpagenkopf@vmmusa.org
Web: www.vmmusa.org

VOLUNTEERS FOR LIFE (L256)
2900 Sunset Place #109
Los Angeles, CA 90005
Contact: Sister Paula Vandegaer, SSS
(213) 382-2702
Mission Area: greater Los Angeles area
Type of Service: direct service/administration in pro-life agencies, Respect Life offices, maternity homes, day care centers, etc.

Term of Service: 1-2 years
Basic Benefits: room/board; stipend; medical insurance; transportation to and from place of work
Basic Requirements: F; 21 years and older; single/married w/o dependents; college education or work experience
Affiliation: Sisters of Social Service
Email: Vforlife@aol.com
Web: www.volunteersforlife.org

WOMEN IN SERVICE TO APPALACHIAN SUMMER PROGRAM (L260)
139 Highland Avenue
Watertown, MA 02472
Contact: (781) 933-1367
Mission Area: Rural Eastern Kentucky
Type of Service: home repair, parish visiting, recreation with school-age children, visiting elderly
Term of Service: 1 week
Basic Benefits: training in Appalachian culture; $150 fee covers room/board, insurance, transportation to/from Cincinnati
Basic Requirements: F; 18 and up: good health
Affiliation: Glenmary Home Missioners
Email: admissions@womenin service.org
Web: www.womeninservice.org

XAVERIAN VOLUNTEER CORPS (L261)
Xaverian Brothers Generalate,
Baltimore, MD 21229
Contact: Bro. Jim Connolly, CFX
(410) 644-0034
Mission Area: Haiti
Type of Service: sharing of one's self and gifts. Possibilities include tutoring, athletics, community formation, religious education, English as a second language, and working with youth, elderly, the sick, the poor and marginalized
Term of Service: 1 year (late June to late May)
Basic Benefits: strong community/spiritual life with live-in Xaverian Brothers; room/board; stipend; health insurance; travel to/from mission area
Basic Requirements: Men/Women; Catholic; 21 and up; college or work

experience; flexibility; desire for community and service; sense of humor; desire to deepen spiritual life.
Affiliation: Xaverian Brothers
Email: jconnlly@xaverian brothers.org
Web: www.xaverianbrothers.org

YOUNG DISCIPLES TEAMS (L262)
5201 Bishops Blvd., Ste. A
Fargo, ND 58104
Contact: (701) 356-7900
Mission Areas: rural parishes/reservations in North Dakota
Type of Service: summer camps; family nights; teen nights; proclaim the Gospel through catechesis, small group activities, music, drama, puppets, games
Term of Service: 10 weeks (summer)
Basic Requirements: M/F; 18-30; single
Affiliation: Diocese of Fargo
Email: youngdisciples@fargo diocese.org
Web: www.fargodiocese.org/youngdisciples

YOUTH SERVICE OPPORTUNITIES PROJECT (YSOP) (L263)
15 Rutherford Place
New York, NY 10003-3705
Contact: In New York: Lisa Gesson, (212) 598-0973; In Washington, DC: Dimitry Beauchamp, 1317 G Street NW, 20005, (202) 347-2525
Mission Area: throughout New York City, Washington, DC
Type of Service: ongoing programs at service agencies helping homeless and hungry people, typically: soup kitchens, drop-in centers, clothing and food banks and recreational programs for children living in family shelters.
Term of Service: single day, overnight, weeklong workcamps; internships in YSOP office - minimum of 6 weeks
Basic Requirements: M/F; hs/college students; nondenominational
Email: ysopnyc@ysop.org, ysopdc@ysop.org
Web: www.ysop.org

Associates, Oblates, Secular Institutes and Other Communities

APOSTOLIC OBLATES (A001)
(Secular Institute for Women)
For information contact: Teresa
Monaghen, AO, (402) 289-2670
205 S. Pine Dr., Fullerton, CA 92833
739 E. 87th St., Brooklyn, NY 11236
11002 N. 204th St., Elkhorn, NE
68022
Email: psm@prosanctity.org
Web: www.secularinstitutes.org/
www.prosanctity.org

APOSTOLIC SODALES (A002)
(Secular Institute for Diocesan
Priests), For information contact:
Rev. Thomas Weisbecker,
(402) 564-7151, 1565 18th St.,
Columbus, NE 68601
Email: frtom@esu7.org
Web: www.secularinstitutes.org/
as.htm

BLESSED TRINITY (A003)
MISSIONARY INSTITUTE
(An Association of the Faithful for
Women), Contact: Rosa Tirado (718)
359-5910, 154-14 Ash Avenue,
Flushing, NY 11355
Email: roniltirado@earthlink.net
Web: www.mcenacle.org/
branches.htm

CARITAS CHRISTI (A004)
(Secular Institute for Women)
Contact: Dolores M. Fischer,
(585) 342-8094, PO Box 9604,
Cincinnati, OH 45209-0604
Email: joannbear@fuse.net
Web: www.ccinfo.org

CATECHISTS OF SACRED (A005)
HEART OF JESUS [Ukrainian]
(Secular Institute for Women)
Contact: Cecilia Daciuk
(203) 327-6374, 161 Glenbrook Rd.,
Stamford, CT 06902

COMPANY OF ST. PAUL (A006)
(Secular Institute for Lay People and
Priests)Contact: Rev. Stuart
Sandberg, (914) 946-1019
52 Davis Ave., White Plains, NY
10605
Email: fssandberg@optonline.net
Web: www.secularinstitutes.org

CRUSADERS OF ST. MARY (A007)
(Secular Institute for Men)
Contact: Antonio Pérez-Alcalá
(703) 536-3546, (2001 Great Falls
St., McLean, VA 22101

Email: aperezalca@cox.net
Web: www.secularinstitutes.org/
csm.htm

DIOCESAN LABORER (A008)
PRIESTS, (Priestly Association)
Contact: Rev. Juan Puigbo, (202)
832-421, 3706 15th St. NE,
Washington, DC 20017
solcenter@hotmail.com
Web: www.solinstitutedc.com or
www.sacerdotesoperarios.org

DON BOSCO VOLUNTEERS (A010)
(Secular Institute for Women)
Contact: Carol McAvoy
(914) 723-0239, PO Box 300H,
Scarsdale, NY 10583
Email: seculardbvs@aol.com
Web: www.secularinstitutes.org/
dbv.htm

FR. KOLBE MISSIONARIES (A011)
OF THE IMMACULATA
Secular Institute for Women
For information contact:
Ada Locatelli, (626) 917-0040
531 E. Merced Ave., West Covina,
CA 91790-5025
Email: fkmincal@aol.com
Web: www.kolbemission.org,
www.secularinstitutes.org

FRANCISCAN MISSIONARIES (A012)
OF JESUS CRUCIFIED, (Association
of the Faithful for Men and Women.
Persons with disabilities most
welcome.)
For information contact: Bonnie J.
Fagan, FMJC, (518) 452-1696,
11 Dahlem Blvd., Niskayuna, NY
12309
Email: bjffmjc@aol.com
Web: www.secularinstitutes.org/
a-fmjc.htm

HANDMAIDS OF DIVINE (A013)
MERCY, (Secular Institute for Women)
Contact: (718) 295-3770, 2410
Hughes Ave., Bronx, NY 10458
Web: www.secularinstitutes.org

INSTITUTE OF THE HEART (A014)
OF JESUS, (Secular Institute for
Diocesan Priests and Lay Women;
Association of the Faithful for Lay
Men) Priests: Rev. Fred O'Brien, 60
William O'Connell Way, Boston, MA
02114
Men: David Bland, PO Box 631,
Marysville, CA 95901-0631

Women: Diana Bland, PO Box 487,
Muenster, TX 76252
Web: www.secularinstitutes.org

LAY MISSIONARIES OF THE (A015)
PASSION, (Secular Institute)
Contact: Constance Leist
(718) 387-3619, 311 Leonard St.,
Brooklyn, NY 11211-2307
Email: Leo311c@aol.com
Web: www.secularinstitutes.org

MISSION OF OUR LADY OF (A016)
BETHANY, (Secular Institute for
Women), Contact: Estelle Nichols
109 Rollins Rd., Nottingham, NH
03290
Web: www.secularinstitutes.org/
mlb.htm

MISSIONARIES OF THE (A020)
KINGSHIP OF CHRIST, (Based on
Franciscan spirituality: one Institute
for Women, one for Men)
Contact: Charleen Dahlin, Formation
Director, (508) 386-1417, PO Box
34513, Bethesda, MD 20827
Email: cdahlin@aol.com
Web: www.simkc.org,
www.secularinstitutes.org/mkcm.htm

OBLATE MISSIONARIES OF (A021)
MARY IMMACULATE
(Secular Institute for Women)
Contact: Pauline Labbe, 9 Bayberry
Drive, Atkinson, NH 03811
Email: pjlabbe1@juno.com
Web: www.ommi-is.org

OPUS SPIRITUS SANCTI (A022)
(Apostolic Life Community for
Sisters; Secular Institute for
Diocesan Priests; Secular Institute
for Single Women; Community of
Apostolic Christians; Apostolic Life
Community for Priests)
For information contact: Rev. James
McCormick, Midwest Coordinator,
phone and fax: (712) 688-2253,
301 East 4th St., Auburn, IA 51433
Email: frjim@iowatelecom.net
Web: www.secularinstitutes.org

PIUS X (A023)
(Secular Institute for Men) For
information contact: (603) 622-4849,
27 Cove St., Manchester, NH 03104
Email: info@ispx.org
Web: www.ispx.org,
www.secularinstitutes.org

B-153

REGNUM CHRISTI MOVEMENT (A024)
(Association for the promotion of the Christian vocation. For lay men/women, deacons and priests.)
Email: info@legionaries.org
Web: www.RegnumChristi.org

SECULAR INSTITUTE OF (A025)
ST. FRANCIS DE SALES
(Secular Institute composed of two groups: professed women; associates-men and women, married and single)
For information contact:
(GA area): Joan Liles, 412 Mill Pond Rd., Roswell, GA 30076
PA area): Dana Elzi, 104 West Main St., Middletown, PA 17057, (717) 948-5009
(VA area): Nancy Prizio, 3503 Jean St., Fairfax, VA 22030, (703) 591-5196, ncprizio@cox.net
Web: www.secularinstitutes.org/sfs.htm

SECULAR INSTITUTE OF THE (A026)
SCHOENSTATT SISTERS OF MARY
(Secular Institute for Women)
(262) 522-4200, W284 N 404 Cherry Ln., Waukesha, WI 53188-9416
Email: vocation@schsrsmary.org
Web: www.schsrsmary.org or
www.schoenstaetter
mariensch western.org

SERVITIUM CHRISTI (A027)
(Secular Institute for Women)
Contact: Olympia Panagatos, (212) 734-9748, 1550 York Ave., Apt. 17A, New York, NY 10028
Web: www.secularinstitutes.org/sc.htm

SOCIETY OF OUR LADY OF (A028)
THE WAY, (Secular Institute for Women) 2339 N. Catalina St., Los Angeles, CA 90027; 584 Capitol Ave., Bridgeport, CT 06606; 1064 Oxford Rd., Cleveland Heights, OH 44121; and 80 Manhattan Ave., Jersey City, NJ 07307
2339 N. Catalina St., Los Angeles, CA 90027-1128
Email: jllaca27@msn.com or matslow@aol.com
Web: www.saecimds.com

VOLUNTAS DEI INSTITUTE (A029)
(Secular Institute of Pontifical Right for priests, celibate laymen and married couples)
For information contact:
Rev. George Hazler, 2104 Eagle Pointe, Bloomfield Hills, MI 48304
Web: www.voluntasdeiusa.org,
www.secularinstitutes.org

VOLUNTEERS WITH (A029-1)
DON BOSCO, (Association of the Faithful for Celibate Men)
Contact: Fr. John Puntino, SDB, Salesian Center, (614) 440-0202 3356 Leighton Rd., Columbus, OH 43221
Email: puntinosdb@juno.com
Web: www.secularinstitutes.org

MISCELLANEOUS

ANAWIM COMMUNITY (A030)
(For Priests, Single Lay People and Married Couples)
Contacts: Fr. Daniel Healy, Director; Barbara Brennan, Co-Director
(908) 453-3886, fax: (908) 453-3786 85 Academy St., PO Box 207, Oxford, NJ 7863
Email: oxford@anawim.com
Web: www.anawim.com

ANAWIM COMMUNITY (A031)
(Frenchville, PA), (For Priests, Single Lay People and Married Couples. Also, long-term live-in volunteer program.)
Contact: Sister Therese Dush, (814) 263-4855, 1031 Germania Rd., PO Box 129, Frenchville, PA 16836
Email: anawimco@pennswoods.net
Web: www.anawimcommunity.com

APOSTLES OF THE INTERIOR (A032)
LIFE, Purpose: Consecrated to evangelization and to offering a service of spiritual assistance.
Contacts: Apostles of the Interior Life, c/o St. Mary's Catholic Center, 603 Church Ave., College Station, TX 77840 (979) 219-8025
Apostles of the Interior Life, c/o St. Lawrence Center at Kansas University, Fiat House, 1401 Engel Rd., Lawrence, KS 66044, (785) 856-7717
Email: usa@apostlesofll.org
Web: www.apostlesofil.org

APOSTOLATE FOR FAMILY (A033)
CONSECRATION
Consecrating families to the Holy Family and in the truths of our Faith, in the Spirit of Pope John Paul II through: Consecration in Truth Multimedia Library for families, parishes and schools; Familyland Television Network; International Familyland Centers; and Lay Ecclesial Teams
(740) 765-5500 or 800-77-FAMILY, fax: (740) 765-5561, 3375 County Rd. 36, Bloomingdale, OH 43910-7903
Email: usa@familyland.org
Web: www.familyland.org

BROTHERS OF ST. DISMAS (A035)
(BSD), Lay association for men (see Sisters of Mary Magdalen - lay association for women)
Contact: The Dismas/Magdalene Project, Inc., Deacon R.R. Leicht, Jr., (281) 489-8720, cell (832) 419-7493, fax: (281) 489-8727
Spiritual ministry to incarcerated Catholics: prison retreats; fraternity follow-up; reentry/post release assistance - Bishop approved)
Chapters in: TX, PA, FL, LA, & OK
Sacred Heart of Jesus, 6502 County Rd. 48, Manvel, TX 77578
Email: deaconbob1@hotmail.com
Web: www.dismag.org

CATHOLIC COMMUNITY (A035-1)
OF THE BEATITUDES
The "Friends of the Lamb" take annual commitments and receive a mission in the name of the Community. The "Beatitudes of the Holy Family" can work their way toward lifetime commitments as non-residential members. The "Priestly Fraternity of the Holy Family" are diocesan priests formed by the Community who take commitments to prayer and common life in a household of priests that is associated with one of the Beatitudes houses.
Rev. Sebastien Pelletier, Superior of the Denver House, (720) 855-9412 2924 W. 43rd Ave., Denver, CO 80211-1635
Email: beatitudes.denver@gmail.com
Web: www.beatitudes.us

COMMUNITY OF THE NEW (A036)
COVENANT, (Private Association of the Faithful, working together in parishes to carry out the new evangelization)
For Priests, Sisters, Lay Men and Women
Contact: Sister Brigid Meierotto, S.N.C., (303) 451-8677, fax: (303) 438-9556
Affiliation: Sisters of the New Covenant, 16440 Grays Way, Broomfield, CO 80023
Email: cetc@sncweb.org
Web: www.sncweb.org and www.vocations-snc.org

CONSECRATED WIDOWS (A042)
Purpose: Prayer and service of the Church, through a vow of perpetual chastity as a sign of the kingdom of God. (Pope John Paul II, Post-Synodal Apostolic Exhortation Vita Consecrata, No. 7)
Contact: Fr. Jean F. Hart, General Procurator, (361) 289-0807
Affiliation: The Society of Our Lady

B-154

of the Most Holy Trinity (Priests, Brothers, Sisters, Laity), PO Box 9299, Corpus Christi, TX 78469
Email: frjeanhart@hotmail.com
Web: www.solt3.org/widows.htm

MAGNIFICAT (A043)
A Ministry to Catholic Women
Purpose: To evangelize and to encourage Catholic women to grow in holiness through opening more fully to the gifts of the Holy Spirit
For: Catholic womenContact: Magnificat Chapter Information, (504) 828-6279, fax: (504) 828-1060
1629 Metairie Rd., Ste. 3, Metairie, LA 70005-3926
Email: magnificatcst@aol.com
Web: www.magnificat-ministry.org

MILES JESU (A044)
(Ecclesial Family of Consecrated Life) For: Lay and Consecrated Women/Men, Priests
Contacts: 800-654-7944, 7945
(Lay vocations, vocation discernment/retreats, feeding of the poor/homeless, support for the Pro-Life movement)
PO Box 267989, Chicago, IL 60626
Email: info@milesjesu.com
Web: www.milesjesu.com

PRESENTATION MINISTRIES (A045)
(Our Lady of), (An Association of the Faithful) Contact: Marianne Lander, (513) 662-5378
Affiliation: Archdiocese of Cincinnati
Small Christian Communities in the Presentation Ministries Network in Ft. Thomas and Paducah (KY); Greenfield and Indianapolis (IN); Grand Rapids and Northern Michigan (MI); Batavia (NY); Cincinnati, Cleveland, Dayton, NW Ohio, SW Ohio; Knoxville (TN): El Paso (TX)
3230 McHenry Ave., Cincinnati, OH 45211
Email: pubsandtapes@presentation ministries.com
Web: www.presentationministries .com

SERRA INTERNATIONAL (A046)
Purpose: To foster and promote vocations to the ministerial priesthood in the Catholic Church as a particular vocation to service, and to support priests in their sacred ministry; to encourage and affirm vocations to consecrated life in the Catholic Church; and to assist its members to recognize and respond in their own lives to God's call to holiness in Jesus Christ and through the Holy Spirit.
For: M/F, all ages, lay persons and permanent deacons
800-488-4008 or (312) 419-7411,

fax: 800-377-7877 or (312) 419-8077
70 East Lake St, Ste.1210, Chicago, IL 60601
Email: serra@serra.org
Web: www.serra.org

SISTERS OF ST. MARY MAGDALENE (SMM) (A047)
Lay association for women (see Brothers of St. Dismas - lay association for men)
Contact: The Dismas/Magdalene Project, Inc., Deacon R.R. Leicht, Jr., (281) 489-8720, cell: 832-419-7493, fax: (281) 489-8727
(Spiritual ministry to incarcerated Catholics: prison retreats; sorority follow-up; reentry/post release assistance - Bishop approved)
Chapters in Texas & Louisiana
Sacred Heart of Jesus , 6502 County Rd. 48, Manvel, TX 77578
Email: deaconbob1@hotmail.com
Web: www.dismag.org

US ASSOCIATION OF CONSECRATED VIRGINS (A048)
(An association of women in the United States who have been consecrated according to the Rite for the Consecration to a Life of Virginity for Women Living in the World, also described in Canon 604 of the Code of Canon Law)
For: Women
Contact: Judith M. Stegman, (517) 231-4366, fax: (253) 270-5507
USACV, 300 W. Ottawa St., Lansing, MI 48933-1577
Email: info@consecratedvirgins.org, jstegman@voyager.net
Web: www.consecratedvirgins.org

ASSOCIATES, THIRD ORDERS, OBLATES

ACJ ASSOCIATES (A050)
Contact: Evelyn Quinones Affiliation: Handmaids of the Sacred Heart of Jesus (acj) 2796 Galahad Dr. NE, Atlanta, GA 30345, (404) 636-5970
8141 NW 11 Court, Pembroke Pines, FL 33024
Email: qe212@bellsouth.net
Web: www.acjusa.org

AFFILIATES - SISTERS OF THE HOLY SPIRIT (S.H.S.) (A052)
Contact: Sister Marita Juras, (412) 683-2044
Affiliation: Sisters of the Holy Spirit (S.H.S.)
5246 Clarwin Ave., Pittsburgh, PA 15229
Email: mjuras2003@libcom.com
Web: www.sistersoftheholyspirit.com

APOSTLES OF THE RESURRECTION (A054)
(Chicago Western Province)
Contact: Sr. Christine Maria, C.R., Director of Associates, (773) 792-6363
Affiliation: Sisters of the Resurrection (C.R.)
7432 W. Talcott Ave., Chicago, IL 60631

APOSTLES OF THE RESURRECTION (A055)
(New York Eastern Province)
Contact: Sister Dolores Marie, C.R., (518) 732-2226
Affiliation: Sisters of the Resurrection (C.R.)
35 Boltwood Ave., Castleton-on-Hudson, NY 12033
Email: vocation@ resurrectionsisters.org
Web: www.resurrectionsisters.org

ASSOCIATE COMMUNITY OF DIVINE PROVIDENCE (A060)
Contact: Donna M. Esposito, ACDP, (859) 441-0700, ext. 308
Affiliation: Sisters of Divine Providence (Melbourne, KY)
St. Anne Convent, 1000 St. Anne Dr., Melbourne, KY 41059
Email: donnaeacdp@aol.com
Web: www.cdpkentucky.org

ASSOCIATE MEMBERS OF THE SOCIETY OF OUR MOTHER OF PEACE (SMP) (A061)
Mary the Font Solitude
Contact: Rev. Peter Sirangelo, (646) 275-6315
Affiliation: Society of Our Mother of Peace (SMP); Third Order
6150 Antire Rd., High Ridge, MO 63049
Email: marythefont@yahoo.com
Web: www.ourmotherofpeace.org

ASSOCIATE PROGRAM (A062)
Sisters of Charity of Leavenworth)
Contact: Sister Sharon Smith, SCL, (913) 758-6522
Affiliation: Sisters of Charity of Leavenworth
4200 S. 4th St., Leavenworth, KS 66048-5054
Email: ssmith@scls.org
Web: www.scls.org

ASSOCIATE PROGRAM OF THE DAUGHTERS OF THE HOLY SPIRIT (A063)
Contacts: Sr. Linda Babineau, DHS, Director, (860) 928-0891
Sr. Imelda Michaud DHS, Assistant Director, 503 M St., Patterson, CA 95363, (209) 892-3410
Affiliation: Daughters of the Holy Spirit
72 Church St. , Putnam, CT 06260-1810

B-155

Email: lindabdhs@sbcglobal.net or imeldadhs@evansinet.com
Web: www.d-hs.org

ASSOCIATE PROGRAM (A064)
(Congregation of St. Joseph - CSJ)
Contact: Kathy Sherman, CSJ, (708) 354-9200
Affiliation: The Congregation of St. Joseph in LaGrange, IL (CSJ)
1515 W. Ogden Ave., LaGrange Park, IL 60526
Email: Ksherman@csjlagrange.org
Web: www.csjlagrange.org

ASSOCIATE PROGRAM OF (A065)
THE VISITATION NUNS
Contact: Sr. Aimee Franklin, V.H.M., (718) 745-5151, fax: (718) 745-3680
Affiliation: Visitation Nuns (Brooklyn, NY)
Visitation Monastery
8902 Ridge Blvd., Brooklyn, NY 11209-5716
Email: vamonastery@aol.com
Web: www.visitationsisters.org/mona/bro_main.asp

ASSOCIATE PROGRAM TO (A066)
THE F.C.S.C.J.
Affiliation: Daughters of the Charity of the Sacred Heart of Jesus (F.C.S.C.J.)
Mount Sacred Heart, 226 Grove St., Littleton, NH 03561-4210, (603) 444-5346
Email: mocou@earthlink.net
Web: www.daughters-fcscj-charity-sacredheart.org or www.fcscj.org

ASSOCIATE RELATIONSHIP (A067)
PROGRAM (Sisters of St. Francis of Assisi, Milwaukee, WI)
St. Francis Convent
Contact: Sister Valerie Sepenski, OSF, (414) 744-1160
Affiliation: Sisters of St. Francis of Assisi
3221 South Lake Dr., Milwaukee, WI 53235-3799
Email: oarel@lakeosfs.org
Web: www.lakeosfs.org

ASSOCIATES - (A068)
CONGREGATION OF THE HUMILITY OF MARY, Contact: Pat Knopick, (563) 529-6140
Affiliation: Congregation of the Humility of Mary (C.H.M.)
820 W. Central Park Ave., Davenport, IA 52804-1900
Email: pkredsci@revealed.net
Web: www.chmiowa.org

ASSOCIATES IN MISSION (A069)
(Sisters of Charity of Cincinnati)
Contact: Mary Jo Mersmann, (513) 347-5473, fax: (513) 347-5467
Affiliation: Sisters of Charity of Cincinnati

5900 Delhi Rd., Mt. St. Joseph, OH 45051
Email: associates@srcharitycinti.org
Web: www.srcharitycinti.org/assoc.htm

ASSOCIATES OF ASSUMPTION (A070)
ABBEY, Assumption Abbey
Contact: Br. Francis or Mary Runde
Affiliation: Trappists
Rte. 5, Box 1056, Ava, MO 65608
Email: avavocations@hughes.net
Web: www.assumptionabbey.org

ASSOCIATES OF BLESSED (A071)
EDMUND RICE
Christian Brothers
Contact: Br. J. J. McCarthy, CFC, (914) 636-6194, ext. 25
Affiliation: Edmund Rice Christian Brothers North American Province
33 Pryer Terrace, New Rochelle, NY 10804
Email: jjm@cbinstitute.org
Web: www.iona.edu/about/CFC/Associates.htm

ASSOCIATES OF THE HOLY (A072)
FAMILY (Des Plaines, IL)
Affiliation: Sisters of the Holy Family of Nazareth
310 N. River Rd., Des Plaines, IL 60016-1211, (847) 298-6760
Email: sdol216@aol.com
Web: www.csfn.org

ASSOCIATES OF THE HOLY (A073)
FAMILY (Grand Prairie, TX)
Contact: Sister M. Beata, (972) 641-4496
Affiliation: Sisters of the Holy Family of Nazareth
1814 Egyptian Way, PO Box 530959,
Grand Prairie, TX 75053-0959
Email: sbeatac@yahoo.com
Web: www.tx-csfn.org/associates/associates.htm

ASSOCIATES OF THE HOLY (A075)
FAMILY (Philadelphia, PA)
Contact: Sr. M. Rita Partyka, CSFN, (215) 268-1053 Affiliation:
Sisters of the Holy Family of Nazareth (C.S.F.N.)
4001 Grant Ave., Philadelphia, PA 19114-2999
Email: partykar@msn.com
Web: csfn.org then phila-csfn.org

ASSOCIATES (Sisters of (A076)
the Assumption of the B.V.)
Contact: Sr. Nancy Sheridan, S.A.S.V.,
Affiliation: Sisters of the Assumption of the B.V.
316 Lincoln St., Worchester, MA 01605
Email: sherrysasv@att.net

ASSOCIATES OF THE (A078)
INCARNATE WORD
(Parma Heights, OH)
Contact: Sister Mary Rose Kocab, SIW, (440) 886-6440, ext. 1102
Affiliation: Sisters of the Incarnate Word and Blessed Sacrament (S.I.W.)
6618 Pearl Rd., Parma Heights, OH 44130-3808
Email: smrksiw@yahoo.com
Web: www.incarnatewordorder.org

ASSOCIATES OF THE (A079)
INCARNATE WORD (Victoria, TX)
Contact: Sister Emiliana Grafe, IWBS, (361) 575-7111
Affiliation: Congregation of the Incarnate Word and Blessed Sacrament (IWBS)
1101 N.E. Water St., Victoria, TX 77901
Email: srmemiliana@yahoo.com
Web: http://www.rsbp.org/iwbs.html or http://www.iwbsvictoria.org

ASSOCIATES OF NOTRE (A080)
DAME
Contact: Janice Rooney
Affiliation: Sisters of Notre Dame de Namur (SNDdeN)
(Note: Associates of Notre Dame are found wherever the Sisters minister. See their listing in the "Religious Communities for Women" section.)
3 Silver Lake Dr., Apt. 21, Nashua, NH 03060
Email: julienne.sullivan@SNDdeN.org
Web: www.SNDdeN.org

ASSOCIATES OF THE POOR (A081)
SERVANTS OF THE MOTHER OF GOD
Contact: Sr. Teresa Twomey, S.M.G., (732) 442-7783
Affiliation: Poor Servants of the Mother of God
Emmaus House, 101 Center St., Perth Amboy, NJ 8861
Email: sistertsmg@aol.com
Web: www.poorservants.com

ASSOCIATES OF THE SISTERS (A082)
OF CHARITY OF ST. HYACINTHE
US Regional Administration, (207) 797-8607
Affiliation: Sisters of Charity of St. Hyacinthe (S.C.S.H.) (Grey Nuns)
98 Campus Ave, Lewiston, ME 04240

ASSOCIATES OF THE SISTERS (A084)
OF THE LIVING WORD
Contact: Sr. Lynda Rink, SLW, (847) 577-5972
Affiliation: Sisters of the Living Word
800 N. Fernandez Ave.-B, Arlington Heights, IL 60004
Email: lrink@slw.org
Web: www.slw.org

ASSOCIATES OF THE SISTERS (A085)
OF ST. JOSEPH OF BUFFALO
Audrey Mang, Associate and Susan
Puleo, Associate, (716) 759-6454
Affiliation: Sisters of St. Joseph of
Buffalo
10324 Main St., Clarence, NY 14031
Email: membership@ssjbuffalo.org
Web: www.ssjbuffalo.org

ASSOCIATES OF THE SISTERS (A090)
OF ST. JOSEPH OF ERIE
Contact: Sr. Ann Marie Cappello,
SSJ, (814) 836-4199
Affiliation: Sisters of St. Joseph of
Northwestern Pennsylvania (SSJ)
5031 West Ridge Rd., Erie, PA
16506-1249
Email: s.amcappello@ssjerie.org
Web: www.sssjerie.org

ASSOCIATES OF THE SISTERS (A091)
OF ST. JOSEPH (Holyoke, MA)
Contact: Susan Lavoie,
(413) 536-0853, ext. 249
Affiliation: Sisters of St. Joseph of
Springfield (S.S.J.)
34 Lower Westfield Rd., Ste.1,
Holyoke, MA 01040-2739
Email: slavoie@ssjspringfield.com
Web: ssjspringfield.org

AUXILIARY OBLATES (A094)
Contact: Mother Gloria Castro,
(845) 226-5671
Affiliation: Sisters Oblates to the
Blessed Trinity
St. Aloysius Novitiate, Beekman Rd.,
PO Box 98, Hopewell Junction, NY
12533
Email: JStab35097@aol.com
Web: www.Staloysius-NY.org

BASILIAN ASSOCIATES (A095)
(Fox Chase Manor, PA)
Contact: Sister Rita Stremba,
OSBM, (215) 379-3998 est. 503
Affiliation: Basilian - Sisters of the
Order of St. Basil the Great
(Ukrainian Byzantine Rite)
710 Fox Chase Rd., Fox Chase
Manor, PA 19046-4198
Web: www.stbasils.com/
associate.html

BASILIAN ASSOCIATES (A096)
(Uniontown, PA)
Contact: Sr. Barbara Jean
Mihalchick, OSBM, (724) 438-8644
Affiliation: Basilians - Sisters of St.
Basil the Great (Byzantine Catholic
Church
500 W. Main St., Box 878,
Uniontown, PA 15401
Email: basilian-a@verizon.net
Web: www.sistersofstbasil.org

BENEDICTINE OBLATES (A097)
(Covington, KY)
St. Walburg Monastery
Contact: Sr. Mary Tewes, O.S.B.,
(859) 331-6324
Affiliation: Benedictine Sisters
(Covington, KY)
2500 Amsterdam Rd., Covington, KY
41017
Email: tewes_m@olvisitation.net
Web: www.stwalburg.org

BENEDICTINE ASSOCIATES (A098)
(Lacey, WA), St. Placid Priory
Contact: Sister Monika Ellis, OSB,
(360) 438-2595 Affiliation:
Benedictine Sisters (Lacey, WA)
500 College St., NE, Lacey, WA
98516
Email: mellis@stplacid.org
Web: www.stplacid.org

BENEDICTINE OBLATES (A099)
(Atchison, KS), Mount St. Scholastica
(913) 360-6200
Affiliation: Benedictine Sisters
(Atchison, KS)
Mount St. Scholastica, 801 S. 8th
St., Atchison, KS 66002
Web: www.mountosb.org

BENEDICTINE OBLATES (A100)
(Aurora, IL)
Contact: Director, Oblates
(630) 897-7215 ext. 312,
fax: (630) 897-0393
Affiliation: Benedictine Monks
(Marmion Abbey)
Marmion Abbey, 850 Butterfield Rd.,
Aurora, IL 60502
Email: jrippinger@marmion.org
Web: www.marmion.org/abbey/
abbey.html

BENEDICTINE OBLATES (A110)
(Beech Grove, IN)
Our Lady of Grace Monastery
Contact: Sr. Antoinette Purcell, OSB,
(317) 787-3287, fax: (317) 780-2368
Affiliation: Sisters of St. Benedict
(Beech Grove, IN)
1402 Southern Ave., Beech Grove,
IN 46107-1160
Email: antoinette@benedictine.com
Web: www.benedictine.com

BENEDICTINE OBLATES (A111)
(Bismarck, ND), Annunciation
Monastery, (701) 255-1520Affiliation:
Benedictine Sisters (Bismarck, ND)
7520 University Dr., Bismarck, ND
58504
Web: www.annunciation
monastery .org

BENEDICTINE OBLATES (A112)
(Byzantine)
Contact: Sister Agnes Knapik, OSB,
(330) 856-1813

Affiliation: Benedictine Sisters
(Byzantine)
8640 Squires Lane NE, Warren, OH
44484-1646
Email: agnes@netdotcom.com
Web: www.benedictinebyzantine.org

BENEDICTINE OBLATES (A113)
(Canyon, TX), St. Benedict Monastery
Contact: Sister Marcella Schmalz,
OSB, (806) 655-9317
Affiliation: Benedictine Sisters
(Canyon, TX)
17825 South Western St., Canyon,
TX 79015
Email: smary@amaonline.com
Web: www.osbcanyontx.org

BENEDICTINE OBLATES (A114)
(Chicago, IL)
St. Scholastica Monastery
Contact: Benita Coffey, OSB,
(773) 764-2413, ext. 327
Affiliation: Benedictine Sisters
(Chicago, IL)
7430 N. Ridge Blvd., Chicago, IL
60645
Email: bcoffey@osbchicago.org
Web: www.osbchicago.org

BENEDICTINE OBLATES (A115)
(Cleveland, OH)
St. Andrew Svorad Abbey
Contact: Rev. Michael Brunovsky,
OSB, (216) 721-5300, ext. 268
Affiliation: Benedictine Monks
10510 Buckeye Rd.,
Cleveland, OH 44104
Email: mpb1993@msn.com
Web: www.bocohio.org

BENEDICTINE OBLATES (A116)
(Clyde, MO)
Benedictine Monastery
Contact: Oblate Director,
(660) 944-2221
Affiliation: Benedictine Sisters of
Perpetual Adoration
Benedictine Monastery, 31970 State
Highway P, Clyde, MO 64432-8100
Email: jeanfr@bspa.us
Web: www.benedictinesisters.org

BENEDICTINE OBLATES (A117)
(Colorado Springs, CO)
Benet Hill Monastery
Contact: Sister Joseph Marie
Jacobsen, O.S.B., (719) 633-0655
Affiliation: Benedictine Sisters
Benet Hill Monastery,
2555 N. Chelton Rd.,
Colorado Springs, CO 80909
Email: benet@qwest.net
Web: www.benethillmonastery.org/
monastic-life/oblate.html

BENEDICTINE OBLATES (A118)
(Columbia, MO)
Our Lady of Peace Monastery
Contact: Sister Barbara Bock,
(573) 446-2300 Affiliation:
Benedictine Sisters (Columbia, MO)
3710 W. Broadway, Columbia, MO
65203-0116
Email: barbbock1@juno.com
Web: www.benedictinesister.org/
oblates.htm

BENEDICTINE OBLATES (A119)
(Conception, MO), Conception Abbey
Contact: Fr. Kenneth Reichert,
O.S.B., (660) 944-3165
Affiliation: Benedictine Monks
(Conception, MO)
Conception Abbey, 37174 State
Hwy. V V, Conception, MO 64433
Email: oblates@conception.edu
Web: www.ConceptionAbbey.org

BENEDICTINE OBLATES (A120)
(Cottonwood, ID)
Monastery of St. Gertrude
Contact: Sr. Teresa Jackson, O.S.B.
or Jeannette Kelley, O.bl.S.B.
Affiliation: Benedictine Sisters
465 Keuterville Rd., Cottonwood, ID
83522-9408
Email: oblates@stgertrudes.org
Web: www.StGertrudes.org

BENEDICTINE OBLATES (A121)
(Cullman, AL)
Contact: Fr. Thomas O'Connor,
OSB, (256) 734-8291, ext. 233
Affiliation: Benedictine Monk
Saint Bernard Abbey, Cullman, AL
35055
Web: www.stbernardabbey.com

BENEDICTINE OBLATES (A122)
(Elkhorn, NE), Mount Michael Abbey
Contact: Father Louis Sojka, (402)
289-2541Affiliation: Benedictine
Monks (Elkhorn, NE)
22520 Mount Michael Rd., Elkhorn,
NE 68022-3400
Email: lsojka@mountmike.creighton
.edu
Web: www.mountmichael.org/
vocation.htm

BENEDICTINE OBLATES (A123)
(Emmaus, PA)
Transfiguration Monastery
Contact: Sister Martina Revak,
O.S.B., (610) 965-6818
Affiliation: Benedictine Sisters
(Emmaus, PA)
526 Fairview St., Emmaus, PA
18049-3837
Email: smartina@entermail.net

BENEDICTINE OBLATES (A124)
(Ferdinand, IN)
Monastery Immaculate Conception

Contacts: Sister Barbara Ann, O.S.B.,
Sister Mary Victor Kercher, O.S.B.,
Oblate Team
(812) 367-1411, ext. 3130
Affiliation: Benedictine Sisters
(Ferdinand, IN)
Monastery Immaculate Conception,
802 E. 10th St., Ferdinand, IN
47532-9239
Email: sylviag@thedome.org or
mvictor@thedome.org

BENEDICTINE OBLATES (A125)
(Fort Smith, AR)
Contact: Sr. Magdalen Stanton,
O.S.B., (479) 783-4147
Affiliation: Benedictine Sisters
St. Scholastica Monastery, PO Box
3489, 1301 S. Albert Pike, Fort
Smith, AR 72913-3489
Email: magdalen@scholasticafort
smith.org
Web: www.scholasticafortsmith.org

BENEDICTINE OBLATES (A126)
(Grand Terrace, CA)
Holy Spirit Monastery
Contact: Sr. Mary Ann Schepers,
OSB, (909) 783-3811, 4446,
fax: (909) 783-3525
Affiliation: Benedictine Sisters
22791 Pico St., Grand Terrace, CA
92313-5725
Email: hsmonastery@prodigy.net
Web: www.holyspiritmonastery.org

BENEDICTINE OBLATES (A127)
(Hingham, MA)
Contacts: Abbot Nicholas, OSB,
Father Andrew, OSB,
(781) 749-2155
Affiliation: Benedictine Monks
(Glastonbury Abbey)
16 Hull St., Hingham, MA 02043
Web: www.glastonburyabbey.org/
oblates.htm

BENEDICTINE OBLATES (A128)
(Jonesboro, AR)
Holy Angels Convent, Olivetan
Benedictines
Contact: Sister Mary John Seyler,
OSB, (870) 243-2440
Affiliation: Benedictine Sisters
(Jonesboro, AR)
Holy Angels Convent, Olivetan
Benedictines,
1699 CR766/PO Drawer 130,
Jonesboro, AR 72403-0130
Email: srseyler@olivben.org
Web: www.olivben.org

BENEDICTINE OBLATES (A129)
(Lacey, WA)
Saint Martin’s Abbey
Contact: Br. Edmund Ebbers,
O.S.B., (360) 491-4700,
fax: (360) 438-4441
Affiliation: Benedictine Monks

Saint Martin's Abbey, 5300 Pacific
Ave. SE, Lacey, WA 98503-1297
Email: oblates@stmartin.edu
Web: www.stmartin.edu/abbey/
newsletter.htm

BENEDICTINE OBLATES (A130)
(Elizabeth, NJ)
Saint Walburga Monastery
(908) 352-4278
Contact: Sr. Mariette Therese
Bernier, OSB
Affiliation: Benedictine Sisters
(Elizabeth, NJ)
851 N. Broad St., Elizabeth, NJ
07208
Email: srmariette@aol.com
Web: www.catholic-forum.com/
bensisnj

BENEDICTINE OBLATES (A135)
(Lacey, WA), St. Placid Priory
Contact: Sister Lucy Wynkoop,
OSB, (360) 438-1771
Affiliation: Benedictine Sisters
(Lacey, WA)
St. Placid Priory, 500 College St.
NE, Lacey, WA 98516
Email: lwynkoop@stplacid.org
Web: www.stplacid.org

OBLATES OF ST. BENEDICT (A136)
(Latrobe, PA), Saint Vincent Archabbey
Contact: Fr. Donald Raila, O.S.B. or
Br. Jeremiah Lange, O.S.B.,
(724) 805-2201
Affiliation: Benedictine Monks
(Latrobe, PA)
Saint Vincent Archabbey,
300 Fraser Purchase Rd.,
Latrobe, PA 15650-2690
Email: jeremiah.lange@
email.stvincent.edu
Web: www.benedictine.stvincent
.edu/archabbey

BENEDICTINE OBLATES (A136-1)
(Lisle, IL)
Contact: Rev. David Turner, OSB,
Director of Oblates
Affiliation: St. Procopius Abbey
(American-Cassinese Congregation)
St. Procopius Abbey, 5601 College
Rd., Lisle, IL 60532
Email: st_procopius_oblates@
yahoo.com
Web: www.procopius.org

BENEDICTINE OBLATES (A137)
(Martin, KY)
The Dwelling Place Monastery
Contact: Sister Judy Yanker, OSB,
(606) 886-9624
Affiliation: Benedictine Sisters
The Dwelling Place Monastery, 150
Mount Tabor Rd., Martin, KY 41649
Email: mtabor@hotmail.com
Web: www.geocities.com/athens/
9871

B-158

BENEDICTINE ASSOCIATES (A138)
(Marvin, SD), Blue Cloud Abbey
Contact: Fr. Denis Quinkert, O.S.B.,
(605) 398-9200, ext. 302
Affiliation: Benedictine Monks
(Marvin, SD)
Blue Cloud Abbey, PO Box 98,
Marvin, SD 57251
Email: vocation@bluecloud.org
Web: www.bluecloud.org/
assoc-cand.html

BENEDICTINE OBLATES (A139)
(Morristown, NJ)
St. Mary's Abbey, (973) 538-3231
Affiliation: Benedictine Monks
St. Mary's Abbey, 230 Mendham
Rd., Morristown, NJ 7960
Email: osbmonks@delbarton.org
Web: www.osbmonks.org

BENEDICTINE OBLATES (A141)
(Richardton, ND)
Sacred Heart Monastery,
(701) 974-2121
Affiliation: Benedictine Sisters
(Richardton, ND)
8969 Highway 10, PO Box 364,
Richardton, ND 58652
Email: vocations@sacredheart
monastery.com
Web: www.sacredheart
monastery .com

BENEDICTINE OBLATES (A142)
(Rock Island, IL), St. Mary Monastery
(309) 283-2106
Affiliation: Benedictine Sisters (Rock
Island, IL)
St. Mary Monastery, 2200 88th Ave.
W., Rock Island, IL 61201-7649
Email: oblates@smmsisters.org
Web: www.smmsisters.org

BENEDICTINE OBLATES (A143)
(Newark Abbey Oblates)
Newark Abbey
Contact: Rev. Albert T. Holtz, OSB,
(973) 792-5751
Affiliation: Benedictine Monks
(Newark Abbey)
520 Dr. Martin Luther King Jr. Blvd.,
Newark, NJ 07102-1314
Email: aholtz@sbp.org
Web: www.newarkabbeyoblates.org

BENEDICTINE OBLATES (A144)
(Petersham, MA)
Contact: Sr. Mary Angela Kloss,
O.S.B., 978-724-3213
Affiliation: Benedictine Nuns
St. Scholastica Priory, Box 606,
271 N. Main St.,
Petersham, MA 01366-0606
Email: smangkloss333@aol.com
Web: www.stscholasticapriory.org

BENEDICTINE OBLATES (A145)
(Pittsburgh, PA)
Oblates Program:Sister Raphael
Frank, OSB, (412) 931-2844, ext.129

Affiliation: Benedictine Sisters of
Pittsburgh
4530 Perrysville Ave., Pittsburgh, PA
15229-2296
Email: raphfrank@yahoo.com
Web: www.osbpgh.org

BENEDICTINE OBLATES (A150)
(Rapid City, SD), St. Martin Monastery
(605) 343-8011
Affiliation: Benedictine Sisters (Rapid
City, SD)
St. Martin Monastery, 2110-C St.
Martin's Dr., Rapid City, SD 57702
Email: info@blackhillsbenedictine
.com or srmarmion@aol.com
Web: www.blackhills
benedictine .com

BENEDICTINE OBLATES (A151)
(St. Benedict, LA: St. Joseph Abbey)
Contact: Fr. Dominic Braud, OSB,
(985) 892-1800
Affiliation: Benedictine Monks
St Joseph Abbey,
St. Benedict, LA 70457

BENEDICTINE OBLATES (A152)
(St. Benedict, OR)
Contact: Rev. Pius X Harding, OSB,
(503) 845-3113 Affiliation:
Benedictine Monks
Mount Angel Abbey, One Abbey Dr.,
St. Benedict, OR 97373
Email: oblatedirector@mtangel.edu
Web: www.mountangelabbey.org

BENEDICTINE OBLATES (A153)
(St. David, AZ)
Holy Trinity Monastery Contact:
Guest Coordinator, (520) 720-4642,
ext. 17, fax: (520) 720-4202
Affiliation: Benedictine Monks and
Nuns (Olivetan Benedictines)
Holy Trinity Monastery, PO Box 298,
St. David, AZ 85630-0298
Email: guestmaster@theriver.com
Web: http://personal.riverusers.com
/~trinitylib/associates.htm

BENEDICTINE OBLATES (St. (A154)
Joseph, MN)
Saint Benedict's Monastery
Contact: S. Helene Mercier, OSB,
(320) 363-7144 Affiliation:
Benedictine Sisters (St. Joseph, MN)
Saint Benedict's Monastery, 104
Chapel Lane, St. Joseph, MN
56374-0220
Email: hmercier@csbsju.edu
Web: www.sbm.osb.org

BENEDICTINE OBLATES (A155)
(St. Leo, FL), Holy Name Monastery
Contact: S. Mary David Hydro, OSB,
(352) 588-8320
Affiliation: Benedictine Sisters (St. Leo)
Holy Name Monastery, PO Box

2450, St. Leo, FL 33574-2450
Email: mary.david.hydro@saintleo
.edu
Web: www.floridabenedictines.com

BENEDICTINE OBLATES (A156)
(Saint Leo, FL)
Contact: Rev. Isaac Camacho, OSB,
Director and/or Natalie T. Sitek,
Oblate Coordinator, (352) 588-8180
Affiliation: Benedictine Monks
Saint Leo Abbey, Saint Leo, FL
33574-2350
Email: natalieoblstleo@aol.com
Web: www.saintleoabbey.org

BENEDICTINE OBLATES (A157)
(St. Meinrad, IN)
Contact: Fr. Meinrad Brune, OSB,
Director of Benedictine Oblates,
(812) 357-6817, fax: (812) 357-6325
Affiliation: Benedictine Monks (Saint
Meinrad Archabbey, IN)
Saint Meinrad Archabbey, 200 Hill
Dr., St. Meinrad, IN 47577
Email: oblates@saintmeinrad.edu
Web: www.saintmeinrad.edu/
monastery_oblates.aspx

BENEDICTINE OBLATES (A158)
(St. Paul, MN), St. Paul's Monastery
Contact: Director of Oblates,
(651) 777-8181
Affiliation: Benedictine Sisters
2675 Larpenteur Ave. E., St. Paul,
MN 55109-5097
Web: www.osb.org/spm

BENEDICTINE OBLATES (A159)
(Schuyler, NE)
Contact: Fr. Volker Futter, OSB,
(402) 352-2177
Affiliation: Benedictine Monks (O.S.B.)
(Congregation of St. Ottilien for
Foreign Missions)
Christ the King Priory-Benedictine
Mission House, PO Box 528,
Schuyler, NE 68661-0528
Email: frvolker@benedictinemission
house.com
Web: www.benedictine
missionhouse.com

BENEDICTINE OBLATES (A160)
(Valyermo, CA), St. Andrew's Abbey
Contact: Rev. Aelred Niespolo, OSB,
(661) 944-2178, fax: (661) 944-1076
Affiliation: Benedictine Monks
St. Andrew's Abbey, PO Box 40,
Valyermo, CA 93563-0040
Web: www.valyermo.com

BENEDICTINE OBLATES (A162)
(Washington, DC), St. Anselm's Abbey
Contact: (202) 269-2300
Affiliation: Benedictine Monks (St.
Anselm's Abbey, Washington, DC)
4501 S. Dakota Ave. NE,
Washington, DC 20017

Email: dcabbey@erols.com
Web: www.stanselms.com

BENEDICTINE OBLATES (A163)
(Watertown, SD)
Mother of God Monastery
Contact: S. Jeanne Giese, OSB,
(605) 882-6650
Affiliation: Benedictine Sisters
(Watertown, SD)
Mother of God Monastery, 110 28th
Ave. SE, # 201, Watertown, SD
57201
Email: monastery@dailypost.com
Web: www.watertown
benedictines.org

BENEDICTINE OBLATES (A164)
(Westfield, VT), Monastery of the
Immaculate Heart of Mary
Contact: tba (802) 744-6525
Affiliation: Benedictine Nuns of the
Congregation of Solesmes
Benedictine Monastery, Immaculate
Heart of Mary, 4103 VT Rte. 100,
Westfield, VT 05874
Email: monastery@
ihmwestfield .com
Web: www.ihmwestfield.com or
www.solesmes.com

BENEDICTINE OBLATES (A170)
(Yankton, SD), Sacred Heart Monastery
Contact: S. Joelle Bauer,
(605) 668-6000
Affiliation: Benedictine Sisters
(Yankton, SD)
1005 West 8th,
Yankton, SD 57078-3389
Email: jbauer@mtmc.edu
Web: www.yanktonbenedictines.org

BENEDICTINE OBLATES (A171)
Contact: Oblate Director,
(760) 967-4200, ext. 200
Affiliation: Benedictine Monks
650 Benet Hill Rd., Oceanside, CA
92058-1253
Email: princeabby@aol.com
Web: www.princeofpeaceabbey.org

BENEDICTINES OF JESUS (A172)
CRUCIFIED
Monastery of the Glorious Cross
Contact: Director of Oblates, (203)
315-9964, (203) 315-0106 fax: (203)
483-5829, 61 Burban Dr., Branford,
CT 06405-4003
Email: rabecwes@comcast.net
Web: www.benedictinesjc.org

BERNARDINE FRANCISCAN (A173)
ASSOCIATES
Contact: Sr. Jean Jacobchik, OSF,
(610) 796-8971
Affiliation: Bernardine Franciscan
Sisters
460 Saint Bernardine St., Reading,
PA 19607
Email: jjacobchik@aol.com
Web: www.bfranciscan.org

BON SECOURS ASSOCIATES (A174)
Contact: Amy Kulesa,
(410) 442-3131
Affiliation: Sisters of Bon Secours
1525 Marriottsville Rd.,
Marriottsville, MD 21104
Email: amy_kulesa@bshsi.org

CAMALDOLESE OBLATES (A175)
Contact: Rev. Robert Hale, OSB
Cam., (831) 667-0635
Affiliation: Camaldolese Hermits
New Camaldoli Hermitage, 62475
Coast Hwy. 1, Big Sur, CA 93920
Email: camoblates@
contemplation.com
Web: www.contemplation.com

CCVI ASSOCIATES (A176)
Contact: Catherine Wolfer, (713)
580-6563, fax: (713) 580-6586
Affiliation: Sisters of Charity of the
Incarnate Word - Houston
Villa de Matel, PO Box 230969,
Houston, TX 77223-0969
Email: cwolfer@ccvi-vdm.org
Web: www.sistersofcharity.org

CDP ASSOCIATE (A177)
**COMMITMENT (Congregation
of Divine Providence (CDP)
San Antonio, TX)**
Our Lady of the Lake Convent
Contact: Sr. Lucille Ann Fritsch,
(210) 434-1866, ext. 1105,
fax: (210) 431-9965
Affiliation: Congregation of Divine
Providence (CDP) San Antonio, TX
515 S.W. 24th St., San Antonio, TX
78207-4619
Email: lfritsch@cdptexas.org
Web: www.cdptexas.org/
associates.htm

CENACLE (A178)
**AFFILIATES/COMPANIONS &
AUXILIARIES**
Contact: Sr. Janice Bernowski, r.c.,
(773) 528-6300, fax: (773) 549-0554
Affiliation: Cenacle Sisters
Cenacle Sisters, 513 W. Fullerton
Parkway, Chicago, IL 60614
Email:
vocations@cenaclesisters.org
auxiliaries@cenaclesisters.org

COJOURNER (A179)
Contact: Ann Redig osf, Central
Minister, Rochester Franciscan Life
Teams
(507) 282-7441/1-888-277-4741
Affiliation: Franciscan Sisters of
Rochester, MN
1001 14th St. NW, Ste.100,
Rochester, MN 55901-2525
Email: ann.redig@myclearwave.net
Web: www.rochesterfranciscan.org

COJOURNERS (A180)
Presentation Heights
Contact: Sister Marilyn Dunn, PBVM,
(605) 964-4071
Affiliation: Presentation Sisters of
Aberdeen, SD
PO Box 476, Eagle Butte, SD 57625
Email: srmarilyn.dunn@
presentation.edu
Web: www.presentationsisters.org

COMMUNITY OF PASSIONIST (A181)
PARTNERS, Passionist Community
Tim O'Brien, (773) 631-1686
Affiliation: Passionists
5700 N Harlem Ave.,
Chicago, IL 60631
Email: Tim0707@aol.com
Web: www.passionist.org/partners

CSA ASSOCIATE (A184)
RELATIONSHIP, St. Agnes Convent
Contact: Ellen Swan, (920) 907-2318
Affiliation: Congregation of St. Agnes
(C.S.A.)
320 County Rd. K,
Fond du Lac, WI 54935
Email: eswan@csasisters.org
Web: www.csasisters.org

CSA ASSOCIATES (A185)
Mt. Augustine
(330) 659-5100
Affiliation: Sisters of Charity of St.
Augustine
Mt. Augustine, 5232 Broadview Rd.,
Richfield, OH 44286
Email: srs@srsofcharity.org
Web: www.srsofcharity.org

CSJ ASSOCIATES (A186)
(Sisters of St. Joseph of Brentwood)
St. Joseph Convent Contact: CSJ
Associates Co-Directors,
(631) 273-4531
Affiliation: Sisters of St. Joseph of
Brentwood
1725 Brentwood Rd,
Brentwood, NY 11717
Email: csjassociates@aol.com
Web: www.csjbrentwoodny.org

CSJ ASSOCIATES (A187)
(Congregation of St. Joseph)
Contact: Sr. Catherine Lee or Carol
Hughes, (216) 252-0440, Ext. 422
Affiliation: Congregation of St.
Joseph
3430 Rocky River Dr., Cleveland,
OH 44111
Email: clevelandassociates@
csjoseph.org
Web: www.csjoseph.org

CSJ ASSOCIATES (A189)
(Sisters of St. Joseph of Wichita)
Contact: Sister Josephine O'Gorman,
CSJ, (316) 686-7171
Affiliation: Sisters of St. Joseph of

Wichita (CSJ)
3700 E. Lincoln, Wichita, KS 67218
Email: sistersofstjoseph@
csjwichita.org
Web: www.csjwichita.org

CSJP ASSOCIATES (A190)
**(Sisters of St. Joseph of Peace
(C.S.J.P.) (Bellevue, WA)**
Contact: Kathy Allard, CSJP-A,
(425) 451-1770
Affiliation: Congregation of the
Sisters of St. Joseph of Peace
(C.S.J.P.)
1663 Killarney Way, PO Box 248,
Bellevue, WA 98009
Email: kallard@csjp-olp.org
Web: www.csjp.org/olp

CSJP ASSOCIATES (A191)
**(Sisters of St. Joseph of Peace
(C.S.J.P.) (Englewood Cliffs, NJ)**
Shalom Center
Contacts: Kate Chambers, CSJP
Associate; Sr. Maureen D'Auria,
CSJP, (201) 568-6348, ext. 23
Affiliation: Sisters of St. Joseph of
Peace (C.S.J.P.)
399 Hudson Terr.,
Englewood Cliffs, NJ 07632
Email: katechambers@yahoo.com
Web: www.csjp.org/sjp

DMJ ASSOCIATES (A192)
Contact: Sister Enda Creegan, DMJ,
(310) 377-4867
Affiliation: Daughters of Mary and
Joseph
5300 Crest Rd., Rancho Palos
Verdes, CA 90275-5004
Email: dmjca@earthlink.net
Web: www.dmjca.org

DOMINICAN ASSOCIATES (A193)
(Adrian, MI)
Contact: Patricia Magee,
(517) 266-3531
Affiliation: Dominican Sisters of
Adrian
1257 E. Siena Heights Dr., Adrian,
MI 49221-1793
Email: pmagee@adrian
dominicans.org
Web: www.adriandominicans.org

DOMINICAN ASSOCIATES (A194)
(Blauvelt, NY)
Contact: Sister Barbara Ann Sgro
Affiliation: Dominican Sisters of
Blauvelt (NY)
20 Greenville Ave.,
Jersey City, NJ 07305
Email: barbaraanns@renewintl.org

DOMINICAN ASSOCIATES (A195)
(Caldwell, NJ)
Contacts: Ann Murtha, O.P.,
(973) 226-1577, ext. 12;
Carol Van Billiard, O.P.,
(973) 729-1682 \

Affiliation: Dominican Sisters of
Caldwell, NJ
1 Ryerson Ave., Caldwell, NJ 07006
Email: annvm@hicom.net or
ols9395@aol.com
Web: www.caldwellop.org

LAY ASSOCIATES OF THE (A197)
**DOMINICAN SISTERS OF THE
PRESENTATION (Dighton, MA)**
Contact: Sr. Carole Mello, OP,
(508) 674-5600, ext. 2061
Affiliation: Dominican Sisters of
Charity of the Presentation of the
Blessed Virgin
3012 Elm St., Dighton, MA 02715
Email: crlmello@netscape.net
Web: www.DominicanSistersofthe
presentation.org

DOMINICAN ASSOCIATES (A198)
(Elkins Park, PA)
Contact: Sr. Barbara Ebner, OP,
(518) 393-4169
Affiliation: Dominican Sisters of St.
Catherine de Ricci
1945 Union St.,
Niskayuna, NY 12309
Email: bebnerop@nycap.rr.com

DOMINICAN ASSOCIATES (A199)
(Grand Rapids, MI), Marywood
Contact: Jean Williams, OP,
800-253-7343, (616) 459-2910, ext.
144, fax: (616) 454-6105
Affiliation: Dominican Sisters (Grand
Rapids, MI)
2025 E. Fulton St., Grand Rapids, MI
49503-3895
Email: jawilliams@grdominicans.org
Web: www.GRDominicans.org

DOMINICAN ASSOCIATES (A230)
(Great Bend, KS)
Contact: Kathy Goetz, OP, (620)
792-1232, fax: (620) 792-1746
Affiliation: Dominican Sisters of
Great Bend
3600 Broadway,
Great Bend, KS 67530
Email: kathy@ksdom.org
Web: www.ksdom.org

DOMINICAN LAITY (A231)
(Lancaster, PA)
Monastery of the Immaculate Heart
of MaryContact: Genevieve Liebl,
(717) 569-2104
Affiliation: Dominican Nuns of the
Perpetual Rosary
1834 Lititz Pike, Lancaster, PA
17601-6585
Email: mon1hm@juno.com

DOMINICAN ASSOCIATES (A233)
(Mission San Jose)
Mission San Jose Contact: Sr.
Cecilia Canales, OP, (510) 657-2468
Affiliation: Dominican Sisters of

Mission San Jose
43326 Mission Blvd.,
Fremont, CA 94539
Email: cecilia@msjdominicans.org
Web: www.msjdominicans.org

DOMINICAN ASSOCIATES (A234)
(Racine, WI), Siena Center
Contact: Ruthanne Reed, OP, and
Karen Vollmer, OP, Co-Directors
Affiliation: Dominican Sisters of
Racine
5635 Erie St.,
Racine, WI 53402-1900
Email:
associates@racinedominicans.org
Web: www.racinedominicans.org/
associate_pages/associates.html

DOMINICAN ASSOCIATES (A235)
(St. Catharine, KY)
4830 Walnut Grove Rd., Memphis,
TN 38117
Email: bpate@saa-sds.org
Web: www.opkentucky.org

DOMINICAN ASSOCIATES (A236)
(Sinsinawa, WI)
Contact : Erica Jordan, OP,
(608) 748-4411, ext. 822
Affiliation: Dominican Sisters of
Sinsinawa
585 County Rd. Z, Sinsinawa, WI
53824-9701
Email: dkieler@sinsinawa.org
Web: www.sinsinawa.org

DOMINICAN ASSOCIATES (A237)
(Springfield, IL), Sacred Heart Convent
Contact: Associate Director,
(217) 787-0481
Affiliation: Dominican Sisters of
Springfield (IL)
1237 W. Monroe St.,
Springfield, IL 62704
Email: spmary@spdom.org
Web: www.springfieldop.org

DOMINICAN LAITY (A238)
Monastery of Our Lady of the
Rosary, (908) 273-1228
President: Maureen Brennan, TOP
Affiliation: Dominican Nuns (Summit,
NJ)
543 Springfield Ave., Summit, NJ
07901-4498

DOMINICAN ASSOCIATES (A239)
(Tacoma, WA)
Tacoma Dominican Center
Contact: Dolores Hutson, OP, and
Pattie Bastian, OPA, (253) 272-9688
Affiliation: Dominican Sisters of
Tacoma
935 Fawcett Ave. So., Tacoma, WA
98402-5605
Email: doloresh@tacoma-op.org or
pmbastian@comcast.net
Web: www.tacoma-op.org

DOMINICAN LAITY (A240)
(Menlo Park, CA)
215 Oak Grove Ave., Menlo Park,
CA 94025
Web: www.op.org/nunsmenlo

LAY DOMINICANS (A251)
(Central Province), St. Dominic Priory
Contact: Fr. James R. Motl, O.P.
Affiliation: Dominicans Friars,
Province of St. Albert the Great
3601 Lindell Blvd., St. Louis, MO
63108-3393
Email: motljr@slu.edu
Web: www.domcentral.org/oplaity/
default.htm

DOMINICAN LAITY (A252)
(Eastern Province)
(see Third Order of Saint Dominic -
Saint Joseph Province)

DOMINICAN LAITY (A253)
(Southern Province)
Contact: Bruce Trigo, Provincial
Moderator, (985) 764-3099
Affiliation: Dominicans Sisters &
Friars
73 Melrose Drive,
Destrehan, LA 70047
Email: btrigo@cox.net
Web: www.op.org/oplaity/
laycat.htm#south

LAY DOMINICANS (A254)
(Western Province)
Contact: Tony Galati, O.P.L.,
(503) 299-8439
Affiliation: Dominican Order
9375 SW Aspen St., Beaverton, OR
97005
Email: tonyg@teleport.com
Web: http://laydominicanswest.org

DONNÉS OF REPARATION (A255)
Contact: Sister Mary Immaculate,
SR, (503) 236-4207
fax: (503) 236-3400
Affiliation: Sisters of Reparation of
the Sacred Wounds of Jesus (S.R.)
2120 S.E. 24th Ave., Portland, OR
97214-5504
Email: repsrs@comcast.net
Web: www.ReparationSisters.org

EMD ASSOCIATES (A256)
Contact: Associates Coordinator
(859) 336-9303, ext. 383
fax: (859) 336-9306
Affiliation: Eucharistic Missionaries
of St. Dominic
2645 Bardstown Rd., St. Catharine,
KY 40061-9435
Email: info@emdsisters.org
Web: www.emdsisters.org/
associates.html

FAUSTINUM ASSOCIATION OF (A257)
APOSTLES OF THE DIVINE MERCY
Contact: Sr. M. Caterina Esselen,
O.L.M., (617) 288-1202
fax: (617) 288-1177
Affiliation: The Congregation of the
Sisters of Our Lady of Mercy
241 Neponset Ave., Dorchester, MA
02122
Email: faustinum@sisterfaustina.org
Web: www.faustinum.pl

FELICIAN ASSOCIATES (A258)
(Buffalo, NY)
Contact: Sister Suzanne Marie
Kush, CSSF,
Affiliation: Felician Sisters (Buffalo,
NY)
Villa Maria, 600 Doat St., Buffalo, NY
14211-2602
Email: smkush@yahoo.com
Web: www.feliciansisters.org

FELICIAN ASSOCIATES (A259)
(Chicago, IL)
Mother of Good Counsel Province
(773) 463-3020
Affiliation: Felician Sisters
3800 W. Peterson Ave., Chicago, IL
60659-3116
Email: scarole@felicianschicago.org
Web: www.felicianschicago.org

FELICIAN ASSOCIATES (A270)
(Coraopolis, PA)
Contact: Sister Mary Faith
Balawejder, CSSF, (412) 264-2890,
fax: (412) 264-7047
Affiliation: Felician Sisters
1500 Woodcrest Ave., Coraopolis,
PA 15108-3099
Email: faithbala@yahoo.com
Web: www.felicianspa.org

FELICIAN ASSOCIATES (A271)
(Livonia, MI)
Presentation of the B.V.M. Convent
Contact: Sister Mary De Sales
Herman, CSSF, (734) 591-1730
Affiliation: Felician Sisters
(Presentation of the Blessed Virgin
Mary Province)
36800 Schoolcraft Rd.,
Livonia, MI 48150
Email: cssf@felicianslivonia.org
Web: www.felicianslivonia.org

FRANCISCAN AFFILIATION (A273)
(Franciscan Sisters of Perpetual
Adoration, La Crosse, WI)
Contact: Marci Madary, Affiliation
Co-Minister, (608) 791-5610
Affiliation: Franciscan Sisters of
Perpetual Adoration, (FSPA) (La
Crosse, WI)
912 Market St., La Crosse, WI
54601-8800
Email: mmadary@fspa.org
Web: www.fspa.org

FRANCISCAN ASSOCIATES (A274)
(Franciscan Sisters of Allegany)
Contact: Sr. Joyce Ramage, OSF,
(716) 933-0634
Affiliation: Franciscan Sisters of
Allegany
PO Box 698, Portville, NY 14770
Email: FSAAssoc@yahoo.com
Web: www.AlleganyFranciscans.org

FRANCISCAN ASSOCIATES (A276)
(Dubuque, IA)
Contacts: Helen Nelson, osf,
Michelle Watters, Co-Directors,
(563) 583-9786
Affiliation: Sisters of St. Francis of
the Holy Family
Mount St. Francis,
Dubuque, IA 52001
Email: hnelson@osfdbq.org
Web: www.osfdbq.org

FRANCISCAN ASSOCIATES (A277)
(Frankfort, IL)
Contact: Sr. Ella Binz, OSF,
(815) 469-4895, ext. 0
Affiliation: Franciscan Sisters of the
Sacred Heart (Frankfort, IL)
St. Francis Woods, 9201 W. St.
Francis Rd., Frankfort, IL 60423-
8335
Email: ellabinz@aol.com
Web: www.fssh.com

FRANCISCAN ASSOCIATES (A278)
(Green Bay, WI)
Contact: Sr. Francis Bangert,
Affiliation: Sisters of St. Francis of
the Holy Cross
3110 Nicolet Drive, Green Bay, WI
54311-7212
Email: Sr.Fran@gbfranciscans.org
Web: www.gbfranciscans.org

FRANCISCAN ASSOCIATES (A280)
(Little Falls, MN), St. Francis Convent
Contact: Geri Dietz, (320) 632-0698
Affiliation: Franciscan Sisters of Little
Falls, MN
116 8th Ave. SE, Little Falls, MN
56345-3597
Email: associates@fslf.org
Web: www.fslf.org

FRANCISCAN ASSOCIATES (A290)
(Franciscan Sisters of Oldenburg)
Contacts: Judy Hillman,
(812) 933-6457
Sr. Joan Laughlin, OSF,
(812) 933-6439Affiliation: Franciscan
Sisters of Oldenburg, IN
PO Box 100, Oldenburg, IN 47036-
0100
Email: jlaughlin@oldenburgosf.com
or
jhillman@oldenburgosf.com
Web: oldenburgfranciscans.org

B-162

FRANCISCAN ASSOCIATES (A291)
(Sylvania, OH)
Contacts: Sr. Maria Goretti Sodd,
Vincenz Marie Meyer, Associate
Co-Directors, (419) 824-3635
Affiliation: Sisters of St. Francis
(Sylvania, OH) (Congregation of Our
Lady of Lourdes)
6832 Convent Blvd., Sylvania, OH
43560
Email: mgoretti@sistersosf.org
Web: www.sistersosf.org

FRANCISCAN ASSOCIATES (A292)
(Syracuse, NY)
Contact: Sr. Helen Hofmann, OSF,
(315) 634-7018
Affiliation: Sisters of St. Francis of
the Neumann Communities
2500 Grant Blvd., Syracuse, NY
13208
Email: hhofmann@osfsyr.org
Web: www.sosf.org

FRANCISCAN ASSOCIATES (A293)
(Tiffin, OH)
Contact 1: Sister Roberta Doneth,
1230 21st Street, NW, Canton,OH
44709, bdoneth@tiffinfranciscans.org
Contact 2: Miss Sue Nowak, Miss
Kay Shrewsbery, 4130 Rose Garden
Dr., Toledo, OH 43623
susan.nowak@utoledo.edu,
kshrewsbery@tiffinfranciscans.org
St. Francis Convent, 200 St. Francis
Ave., Tiffin, OH 44883
Email: osftiffin@tiffinfranciscans.org
Web: www.tiffinfranciscans.org

FRANCISCAN ASSOCIATES (A295)
(Wheaton, IL)
Contact: Jeanne Connolly,
(630) 462-7422
Affiliation: Franciscan Sisters,
Daughter of the Sacred Hearts of
Jesus and Mary (Wheaton
Franciscans) (O.S.F.)
PO Box 667, Wheaton, IL 60189-
0667
Email: jconnolly@wheaton
franciscan.org
Web: www.wheatonfranciscan.org

FRANCISCAN ASSOCIATES (A296)
(Williamsville, NY)
(716) 632-2155
Affiliation: Sisters of St. Francis of
the Neumann Communities
St. Mary of the Angels, 201 Reist St.,
PO Box 275, Williamsville, NY 14231
Email: hhofmann@sosf.org
Web: www.sosf.org

FRANCISCAN ASSOCIATES (A297)
**(School Sisters of the Third Order of
St. Francis) (Bethlehem)**
Contact: Sr. Marguerite Stewart,
OSF, (610) 866-2597
Affiliation: School Sisters of the Third
Order of St. Francis (Bethlehem)

395 Bridle Path Rd., Bethlehem, PA
18017
Email: peace@enter.net
Web: www.franciscansisters-pa.org

FRANCISCAN ASSOCIATES (A298)
**(School Sisters of the Third Order of
St. Francis) (Pittsburgh)**
Contact: Sister M. Francesca
Parana, OSF, (412) 761-6004
Affiliation: School Sisters of the Third
Order of St. Francis (Pittsburgh)
Mount Assisi Convent, 934 Forest
Ave., Pittsburgh, PA 15202
Email: mtassisi@verizon.net
Web: www.franciscansisters-pa.org

FRANCISCAN ASSOCIATES (A299)
**(Sisters of St. Francis of Penance
and Christian Charity)**
Contacts: Sister Ann McDermott,
OSF, (305) 762-1182
Zoila Diaz, 2415 Hayes St.,
Hollywood, FL 33020
Affiliation: Sisters of St. Francis of
Penance and Christian Charity
(Stella Niagara, NY)
2615 Roosevelt St., Hollywood, FL
33020
Email: annmcd@miamiarch.org or
zoilaldiaz@prodigy.net
Web: www.franciscans-stella-
niagara.org/assoc.htm

FRANCISCAN ASSOCIATES (A310)
**(Sisters of St. Francis of Penance
and Christian Charity)**
Contact: Margie Will, OSF, (650)
369-1725
Affiliation: Sisters of St. Francis of
Penance and Christian Charity
PO Box 1028, Redwood City, CA
94064

FRANCISCAN ASSOCIATES (A311)
**(Sisters of St. Francis of the
Providence of God) (Pittsburgh)**
Contact: Vocation Office,
(412) 882-9911
Affiliation: (Sisters of St. Francis of
the Providence of God) (Pittsburgh)
3603 McRoberts Rd.,
Pittsburgh, PA 15234
Web: www.osfprov.org

FSSJ ASSOCIATE PROGRAM (A312)
Contact: Sr. Paula Zelazo,
(716) 649-1205
Affiliation: Franciscan Sisters of St.
Joseph (FSSJ)
5286 S. Park Ave.,
Hamburg, NY 14075
Email: Genadmin@fssj.org
Web: www.franciscansister
shamburg .org

GENESEE LAY (A313)
CONTEMPLATIVES
Contact: Margaret Mary Weider,
(585) 538-9254 Affiliation: Trappists

Abbey of the Genesee,
Piffard, NY 14533
Email: margaretmary31@
hotmail.com
Web: www.geneseeabbey.org/lay

GOOD SHEPHERD (A314)
AFFILIATION
Contact: Sister Joanne Roy, s.c.i.m.,
(207) 283-0323 Affiliation: Servants
of the Immaculate Heart of Mary
(S.C.I.M.) (also known as Good
Shepherd Sisters of Quebec)
27 Thornton Ave., Saco, ME 04072
Email: joanneroy@gwi.net

GREY NUN ASSOCIATES (A315)
Contact: Sr. Joan Daly, GNSH,
(215) 968-4236
Affiliation: Grey Nuns of the Sacred
Heart
1750 Quarry Rd.,
Yardley, PA 19067-3998
Web: www.greynun.org

HM ASSOCIATE PROGRAM (A316)
Contact: Sr. Carla Rutter, HM and
Kris Wasilewski, Co-Directors
(724) 964-8920, ext. 3075
Affiliation: Sisters of the Humility of
Mary (H.M.)
PO Box 706, Villa Maria, PA 16155-
0706
Email: associates20@humilityof
mary.org
Web: www.humilityofmary.org

HOLY CROSS ASSOCIATES (A317)
(Manchester, NH)
Contact: Shirley H. Brien, Director,
(603) 627-2079 Affiliation: Sisters of
Holy Cross
60 Riverbank Rd.,
Manchester, NH 03103
Email: rondalla@comcast.net
Web: www.sistersofholycross.org

HOLY CROSS ASSOCIATES (A318)
(Merrill, WI)
Contact: Carol Mancl,
(715) 539-1471
Affiliation: Holy Cross Sisters
1400 O'Day St., Merrill, WI 54452
Email: cmancl@belltower
residence.org
Web: www.holycrosssisters.org

HOLY FAMILY ASSOCIATES (A330)
Contact: (510) 624-4500
Affiliation: Sisters of the Holy Family
PO Box 3248,
Fremont, CA 94539-0324
Email: shfmem@aol.com
Web: www.holyfamilysisters.com

HOLY UNION ASSOCIATES (A331)
Contact: Sister Patricia Heath,
Director, (757) 484-2015 or

Eileen McIntyre, Co-Director, 15
Parker Ave., Brockton, MA 02302
(508) 586-9757
Affiliation: Holy Union Sisters
(SUSC) (US Province)
3910 Breezeport Way, #101, Suffolk,
VA 23435-1089
Email: patricia.heath@husmilton.org
Web: www.holyunionsisters.org

(A332)
IBVM ASSOCIATE RELATIONSHIP
Contact: Mary Howard Moriarty,
IBVM
(773) 734-2420
Affiliation: Institute of the Blessed
Virgin Mary (IBVM)
3215 E. 91st St., Chicago, IL 60617
Email: mwcmaryhoward@aol.com
Web: www.ibvm.us

IDENTE FAMILY (A333)
Contact: Dolores Sanchez, M.Id.,
(718) 526-3595, fax: (718) 526-9632
Affiliation: Idente Missionaries of
Christ the Redeemer
143-48 84th Dr., Briarwood, NY
11435-2232
Email: dolores.sanchez4@
        verizon.net

IGNATIAN ASSOCIATES (A334)
Contact: Joan Shrout,
(414) 389-9540 Affiliation: Jesuits
(Wisconsin Province)
3195 S. Superior St., Room 101,
Milwaukee, WI 53207
Email: jshrout@jesuitswisprov.org
Web: www.ignatianassociates.org

IHM ASSOCIATES (A335)
Contact: Associate Coordinator,
(734) 240-9821
Affiliation: Sisters, Servants of the
Immaculate Heart of Mary (IHM)
610 W. Elm, Monroe, MI 48162
Email: mstuhlreyer@ihmsisters.org
Web: www.ihmsisters.org

INCARNATE WORD (A336)
ASSOCIATES
Contact: (361) 882-5413
Affiliation: Congregation of the
Incarnate Word and Blessed
Sacrament (I.W.B.S.)
2930 S. Alameda St., Corpus Christi,
TX 78404-2798
Email: sawagner@iwbscc.org
Web: www.iwbscc.org

INCARNATE WORD (A337)
ASSOCIATES (C.V.I.)
Contact: (713) 668-0423
Affiliation: Congregation of the
Incarnate Word and Blessed
Sacrament (C.V.I.)
3400 Bradford Pl., Houston, TX
77025-1398
Web: falcon.incarnateword.org/cvi

LAY ASSOCIATES (SISTERS (A338)
OF ST. JOHN THE BAPTIST (C.S.JB.)
Contact: Sr. Michele, C.S.JB.,
(718) 931-3000, ext. 3116
Affiliation: Sisters of St. John the
Baptist (C.S. JB.)
3304 Waterbury Ave., Bronx, NY
10465
Email: smichele50@aol.com
Web: http://baptistines.home.att.net/

LAY CANOSSIANS (A339)
Contact: Helena Anderson,
(209) 223-3553
Affiliation: Canossian Daughters of
Charity, 5625 Isleta Blvd., SW,
Albuquerque, NM 87105,
505-873-2854
PO Box 173, Pine Grove, CA 95665
Email: helena@volcano.net
Web: www.fdcc.org/in/
missionariesec/ missiona.htm

LAY CARMELITES (A350)
THIRD ORDER SECULAR (Darien, IL)
Contact: Sr. Mary Martin, O.Carm.,
(630) 969-5050
Affiliation: Carmelites (Darien, IL)
8501 Bailey Rd., Darien, IL 60561-
8418
Email: laycarmelites@carmelnet.org
Web: www.carmelnet.org/toc/
toc.htm

LAY CARMELITES - (A351)
**THIRD ORDER SECULAR (St. Elias
Province, NY)**
Contact: Provincial Director, Office of
Lay Carmelites, (845) 344-2474
Affiliation: Carmelite Friars
(Middletown, NY)
PO Box 3079, Middletown, NY
10940
Email: jsoreth@frontiernet.net
Web: www.carmelites.com

LAY CLARETIANS (A352)
Lay Claretians are a group of
dedicated lay people who share the
zeal of St. Anthony Claret, a restless
apostle who was impelled by the
love of Christ to make a difference
among the poor and needy. Lay
Claretians are moved by the same
spirit that directed Anthony Claret, to
live Christian faith by serving others.
There are currently more than
twenty Lay Claretians in the United
States, who carry on the mission of
Claret in their own busy lives.
Contact: Father Steve
Keusenkothen, C.M.F.,
(312) 236-7846 Affiliation: The
Claretian Missionaries (Priests and
Brothers)
205 W. Monroe St., Chicago, IL
60606
Email: frsteve@claretians.org
Web: www.claretianvocations.org

LAY MISSIONARIES OF THE (A353)
SACRED HEART (LAY M.S.C.)
Sacred Heart Villa
Contact: Sr. Theresa Molchanow,
MSC, (610) 929-5751, ext. 218
Affiliation: Missionary Sisters of the
Most Sacred Heart of Jesus (M.S.C.)
51 Seminary Avenue, Reading, PA
19605
Email: theresamsc@yahoo.com
Web: www.mscreading.org

LAY SALVATORIANS (A354)
Contact: Ms. Judy Davis, SDS,
National Director of Lay
Salvatorians, (931) 474-8186
Affiliation: The Salvatorians (Priests,
Brothers, Sisters)
128 Clearview Dr., McMinnville, TN
37110-1615
Email: jgdavis@blomand.net
Web: www.laysalvatorians.com

LITTLE COMPANY OF MARY (A355)
ASSOCIATES
Contact: Sister Jean Stickney,
L.C.M., (708) 229-5797
Affiliation: Little Company of Mary
Sisters
9350 So. California Ave., Evergreen
Pk., IL 60805
Email: vocations@lcmh.org
Web: www.lcmh.org

LORETTO CO-MEMBERS (A356)
Contact: 877-LORETTO or
(314) 962-8112
Affiliation: Sisters of Loretto (S.L.)
590 E. Lockwood Ave., St. Louis,
MO 63119
Email: malderson@loretto
        community.org
Web: www.lorettocommunity.org

MARIANIST LAY NETWORK (A357)
OF NORTH AMERICA
Affiliation: Marianists, Society of Mary
1341 N. Delaware Ave., #406,
Philadelphia, PA 19125-4300
Email: mlnna@aol.com
Web: www.mlnna.com

MARIE RIVIER ASSOCIATION (A358)
Contact: Sr. Estelle Leveillee,
(603) 669-1080, ext. 309
Affiliation: Sisters of the Presentation
of Mary (p.m.)
495 Mammoth Rd.,
Manchester, NH 03014
Email: srestelle@juno.com
Web: www.presentationofmary.com

MARYKNOLL AFFILIATES (A359)
Contacts: Fred Goddard,
877-897-2386 (tel., fax)
Affiliation: Maryknoll Fathers,
Brothers, Sisters and Lay Missioners
PO Box 311, Maryknoll, NY 10545-
0311

B-164

Email: inquiries@maryknoll
affiliates.org
Web: www.maryknollaffiliates.org

MERCEDARIAN THIRD ORDER (A360)
Contact: Rev. James W. Mayer, O.
de M., (215) 879-0594
Affiliation: The Order of Mercy
6398 Drexel Rd., Philadelphia, PA
19151-2596
Email: vocations@orderofmercy.org
Web: www.orderofmercy.org

MERCY ASSOCIATES (A370)
(South Central Community)
Contact: (410) 467-1079 (As of
November 10) Affiliation: Sisters of
Mercy - former regional communities
of Baltimore, Cincinnati, St. Louis
and North Carolina
4103-B Roland Ave., Baltimore, MD
21211-2035
Email: jmcloughlin@mercysc.org
Web: www.mercysc.org

MERCY ASSOCIATES (A372)
(West Midwest Community)
Contact: 877-50-MERCY or
(650) 340-7458
 Affiliation: Sisters of Mercy of the
Americas (R.S.M.) (West Midwest
Community)
2300 Adeline Dr., Burlingame, CA
94010
Web: www.mercyburl.org

MERCY ASSOCIATES (A373)
(West Midwest Community)
Contact: (319) 364-5196 or
(319) 364-3617 (Wilma)
 Affiliation: Sisters of Mercy of the
Americas (R.S.M.) (West Midwest
Community)
1125 Prairie Dr. NE, Cedar Rapids,
IA 52404
Email: wilmamc@imonmail.com
Web: www.sistersofmercy.org

MERCY ASSOCIATES (A374)
(South Central Community)
Contact: John McLaughlin, Director,
Sr. Marilyn Gottemoeller, RSM,
Assistant Director, (513) 221-1800
Affiliation: Sisters of Mercy of the
Americas (R.S.M.) (South Central
Community)
2335 Grandview Ave., Cincinnati,
OH 45206
Email: mgottemoeller@mercysc.org
or jmcloughlin@mercysc.org
Web: www.mercycincinnati.org

MERCY ASSOCIATES (A375)
(West Midwest Community)
Contact: (248) 476-8000
Affiliation: Sisters of Mercy of the
Americas (R.S.M.) (West Midwest
Community)
29000 Eleven Mile Rd., Farmington

Hills, MI 48336-1405
Email: associates@mercydetroit.org
Web: www.sistersofmercy.org

MERCY ASSOCIATES (A376)
(South Central Community)
Contact: (410) 467-1079 (As of
November 10)
Affiliation: Sisters of Mercy - former
regional communities of Baltimore,
Cincinnati, St. Louis and North
Carolina, Belmont, NC
Email: jmcloughlin@mercysc.org
Web: www.mercysc.org

MERCY ASSOCIATES (A378)
(Northeast Community)
Contact: Nancy Burke,
(401) 434-0486
Affiliation: Sisters of Mercy of the
Americas (R.S.M.) (Northeast
Community)
3070 Pawtucket Avenue,
Riverside, RI 02915
Email: associate@mercyri.org
Web: www.mercyri.org/
associates.htm

MERCY ASSOCIATES (A379)
**(New York, Pennsylvania, Pacific
West Community)**
Contact: Sister Nancy Whitley, RSM
and Mary Austin, Co-Diectors
(716) 288-2710, ext. 252
Affiliation: Sisters of Mercy of the
Americas (R.S.M.)
1437 Blossom Rd.,
Rochester, NY 14610
Email: nwhitley@mercynyppaw.org

MISSIONARY BENEDICTINE (A380)
OBLATES
Contact: Sr. Celine Shock, (402)
371-3438
Affiliation: Missionary Benedictine
Sisters
Immaculata Monastery, 300 N. 18th
St., Norfolk, NE 68701-3687
Email: srcelineosb@yahoo.com
Web: www.norfolkmbs.org

(A390)
**MISSIONARY CENACLE
APOSTOLATE (MCA)**
Apostolado de Cen´culo
Misioners (ACM)
Contact: Mrs. Alma Robles, General
Custodian, (787) 752-9327
Affiliation: Missionary Servants of the
Most Blessed Trinity (MSBT)
Missionary Servants of the Most
Holy Trinity (ST)
 Blessed Trinity Missionary Institute
(BTMI)
All four branches form the
Missionary Cenacle Family (MCF)
Calle Robles 516, Los Colobos Park,
Carolina, PR 985
Email: mcaalma@yahoo.com

Web: http://mcenacle.org/mca/
mca.htm

MISSIONARY SISTERS (A391)
ASSOCIATES
Contact: Sr. Joanne Riggs, smic,
(973) 279-3790Affiliation: Missionary
Sisters of the Immaculate
Conception of the Mother of God
(S.M.I.C.)
PO Box 3026, 779 Broadway,
Paterson, NJ 7509
Email: newmembership@
smic-missionarysisters.com

MSC LAY ASSOCIATES (A392)
Contact: (630) 892-2371Affiliation:
Missionaries of the Sacred Heart
(MSC)
PO Box 270, Aurora, IL 60507-0270
Email: info@misacor-usa.org
Web: www.misacor-usa.org

NORBERTINES (A393)
ASSOCIATES/OBLATES
Contact: Rev. Andrew Ciferni, O.
Praem., (610) 647-2530, ext. 122,
fax: (610) 651-0219
Affiliation: Norbertine Fathers and
Brothers
Daylesford Abbey, 220 S. Valley Rd.,
Paoli, PA 19301-1999
Email: wkelly@daylesford.org
Web: www.Daylesford.org

(A394)
**NORTH AMERICAN CONFERENCE
OF ASSOCIATES AND RELIGIOUS
(NACAR)**
Contact: Sr. Catherine Schwemer,
PHJC, (219) 397-5298, fax: (219)
397-5307
Clearinghouse for all US and
Canadian Associates. Research,
networking, workshops, international
convention
4321 Elm Street,
East Chicago, IN 46312
Email: nacar96@juno.com
Web: www.nacar96.org

NOTRE DAME ASSOCIATES (A395)
Contact: Sr. Margaret Hickey, N.D.,
(402) 455-2994
Affiliation: Notre Dame Sisters (N.D.)
3501 State St., Omaha, NE 68112
Email: margareth@notreda
mesisters.org
Web: www.notredamesisters.org

OBLATE ASSOCIATE (A396)
PROGRAM
Associate Program is for young men,
college age or older, considering
Religious in the future
Contact: Fr. Martin Lukas, OSFS,
(419) 724-9851
Affliation: Oblates of St. Francis de
Sales (Toledo/Detroit Province)

B-165

2043 Parkside Blvd., Toledo, OH
43607
Email: mlosfs@aol.com
Web: www.oblates.us

OBLATE ASSOCIATE (A397)
PROGRAM
Contact: Fr. Kevin Nadolski, OSFS,
(302) 656-8529, fax: (302) 658-8052
Affliation: Oblates of St. Francis de
Sales
2200 Kentmere Parkway,
Wilmlinton, DE 19806
Email: knadolski@oblates.org
Web: www.oblates.org/vocations

OBLATES OF ST. PAUL (A398)
Contact: (716) 754-7489
Affiliation: Barnabite Fathers and
Brothers
1023 Swann Rd., PO Box 167,
Youngstown, NY 14174-0167
Email: barnabitesusa@
fatimashrine.com

O.C.D.S. (A399)
Contact: O.C.D.S. President, (219)
838-7111 Affiliation: Discaled
Carmelite Fathers
Our Lady of Mt. Carmel Monastery,
1628 Ridge Rd., Munster, IN 46321

PASSIONIST SISTERS LAY (A400)
ASSOCIATE PROGRAM
Contact: Sister Aideen Langan, CP,
(401) 294-3554
Affiliation: Passionist Sisters (Sisters
of the Cross and Passion)
One Wright Lane,
North Kingstown, CT 02852
Email: aideencp@sbcglobal.net
Web: www.passionistsisters.org

PHJC ASSOCIATE (A401)
COMMUNITY
Contact: Gayle Fiwek,
(574) 936-9936
Affiliation: Poor Handmaids of Jesus
Christ (PHJC)
PHJC Ministry Center, PO Box 1,
Donaldson, IN 46513
Email: gfiwek@poorhandmaids.org
Web: www.poorhandmaids.org

PFM ASSOCIATES (A402)
Contact: Sr. Irma Gendreau, p.f.m.,
(508) 756-0978
Affiliation: Little Franciscans of Mary
(P.F.M.)
2 Dupont St., Worcester, MA 01604
Email: migpfm@verizon.net

PRECIOUS BLOOD (A403)
COMPANIONS
Contacts: Marie Trout,
(816) 781-4344
Affiliation: Missionaries of the
Precious Blood (C.PP.S.)

2130 Saint Gaspar Way, Liberty, MO
64068-7941
Email: companionshc@yahoo.com
Web: www.catholic-forum.com/
cpps-kc

PRESENTATION (A404)
ASSOCIATES (Dubuque, IA)
Contacts: Lynn Mary Wagner,
PBVM, Karla Berns, (563) 588-2008,
fax: (563) 588-4463
Affiliation: Presentation Sisters of
Dubuque
2360 Carter Rd., Dubuque, IA
52001-2997
Email: pbvmassoc@yahoo.com
Web: www.dubuquepresentations
.org/ New_Site/Associate_
Membership.html

PRESENTATION ASSOCIATES (A405)
(San Francisco, CA)
Contact: Associate Committee
Member, (415) 422-5019
Affiliation: Sisters of the Presentation
of the Blessed Virgin Mary (San
Francisco)
281 Masonic Ave., San Francisco,
CA 94118
Web: www.presentationsisterssf.org

PRESENTATION ASSOCIATES (A406)
(South Fargo, ND)
Presentation Ministries
Contact: Sr. Francine Janousek,
BVM, (701) 235-8246
Affiliation: Sisters of the Presentation
of the Blessed Virgin Mary (Fargo)
(PBVM)
3001 11th Street , South Fargo, ND
58103
Email: fjanousek@juno.com
Web: www.presentationsisters
fargo.com

PROVIDENCE ASSOCIATES (A407)
(Western US)
Contacts: Katherine Smith, SP, (503)
235-8215; Marie Ilch, PA,
(509) 466-4124
Affiliation: Sisters of Providence
(S.P.) (Western US)
9 E. Ninth Ave., Spokane, WA
99202-1209
Email: k8smithsp@aol.com;
ilchmm@msn.com
Web: www.sistersofprovidence.net

REDEEMER ASSOCIATES (A408)
Redeemer Associates Office,
(215) 914-4015, fax: (215) 914-4111
Affiliation: Sisters of the Holy
Redeemer
521 Moredon Rd., Huntingdon
Valley, PA 19006
Email: RAssociates@holyredeemer
.com
Web: www.sistersholyredeemer.org/
associates

REDEMPTORISTINE (A409)
ASSOCIATE PROGRAM
Contact: (845) 384-6533
Affiliation: Redemptoristine Nuns
(O.Ss.R.)
Mother of Perpetual Help Monastery,
PO Box 220, Esopus, NY 12429-
0220
Email: rednuns@juno.com
Web: http://macc.catholic.org/
redemp/Index.html

ROSSELLIAN FAMILY (A410)
OUTREACH
Contact: Sister Mary Grace
DeJoseph, DM, (856) 697-2983
Affiliation: Daughters of Our Lady of
Mercy
(For families)
Villa Rossello, 1009 Main Rd.,
Newfield, NJ 08344-5203
Email: dmnewfield@yahoo.com

SACRED HEARTS SECULAR (A415)
BRANCH
Contact: Fr. Patrick Killilea, SS.CC.,
(508) 992-7300
Affiliation: Sacred Hearts
Community, Priests and Brothers-
Eastern Province
41 Harding Rd.,
Fairhaven, MA 02719
Web: www.sscc.org

ST. JOSEPH CHRISTIAN (A416)
COMMUNITY
Contacts: Bernadette Dean, SSJ,
Marie Hogan, SSJ, (248) 582-
9163Affiliation: Sisters of St. Joseph
of Nazareth (S.S.J.)
975 E. Gardenia, Madison Heights,
MI 48071-3431
Email: membership@ssjnazareth
.org
Web: www.SSJNazareth.org

ST. LEONARD'S HOUSE (A417)
Contact: Fr. Giampietro Gasparin,
C.S.J., (440) 934-6270 Affiliation:
Congregation of St. Joseph
4076 Case Rd., Avon, OH 44011
Email: FrGiampietro@road
runner.com
Web: www.stleonardrc.com

SECULAR FRANCISCAN (A419)
**ORDER (Formerly Third Order of St.
Francis)**
Contact: 800-FRANCIS Affiliation:
Franciscan Friars, Brothers and
Sisters
1615 Vine St., Cincinnati, OH 45202
Web: www.nafra-sfo.org/regions
.html
(regional fraternities listed)

SECULAR OBLATES OF (A420)
HOLY TRINITY ABBEY
Contact: Fr. Leander Dosch, ocso,
(801) 745-3784
Affiliation: Trappists
Holy Trinity Abbey, 1250 South 9500
East, Huntsville, UT 84317
Email: ldosch@xmission.com
Web: www.holytrinityabbey.org

SECULAR ORDER OF (A422)
DISCALCED CARMELITES
(O.C.D.S.) (Salt Lake City)
Contact: O.C.D.S. Director,
(801) 277-6075
Affiliation: Carmelite Nuns, Discalced
Carmel of the Immaculate Heart of
Mary, 5714 Holladay Blvd., Salt Lake
City, UT 84121
Email: smjcarm@xmission.com
Web: www.carmelslc.org

SECULAR ORDER OF (A423)
DISCALCED CARMELITES
(O.C.D.S.) (San Diego, CA)
Contact: Janie Hoffner, OCDS,
(858) 453-0721
Affiliation: Carmelite Nuns,
Discalced, Carmelite Monastery of
the Trinity, 5158 Hawley Blvd., San
Diego, CA 92116-1934
2430 Soderblom Ave., San Diego,
CA 92122
Email: choffne1@san.rr.com
Web: www.carmelife.org

SECULAR SERVITES (A425)
Contact: Rev. Vidal Martinez,
O.S.M., (773) 354-9561;
(773) 638-5800. ext. 48
Affiliation: Servite Friars
3121 W. Jackson Blvd., Chicago, IL
60612-2729
Email: osmsecular@aol.com
Web: www.servite.org

SETON FAMILY (A426)
Contact: Gertrude Foley, SC, (724)
853-7948, ext. 194
Affiliation: Sisters of Charity of Seton
Hill
Caritas Christi, Mt. Thor Rd.,
Greensburg, PA 15601-3429
Email: gfoley@scsh.org
Web: www.scsh.org

SFP ASSOCIATE PROGRAM (A427)
Contact: Sr. Marilyn Fischer,
SFPAffiliation: Franciscan Sisters of
the Poor (SFP)
222 East 19th St., Apt. 1C, New
York, NY 10003
Email: fischersrm@msn.com
Web: www.franciscansisters.org

SHCJ ASSOCIATES (A427-1)
Contact: Ms. Catherine Duffy,
(610) 626-1400
Affiliation: Society of the Holy Child
Jesus (SHCJ)
460 Shadeland Ave., Drexel, PA
19026-2312
Email: associates-usa@shcj.org
Web: www.shcj.org

SISTERS HOME VISITORS (A428)
OF MARY
Contact: Sr. Rosemarie Abate, HVM,
(313) 869-2160
Affiliation: Home Visitors of Mary
(H.V.M.)
121 E. Boston Blvd., Detroit, MI
48202-1318
Email: homevisitors@att.net

SISTERS OF CHARITY OF (A429)
THE INCARNATE WORD
ASSOCIATES (San Antonio, TX)
Contact: Coordinator of U.S.
Associates, 800-497-4363
Affiliation: Sisters of Charity of the
Incarnate Word (CCVI) (San
Antonio, TX)
PO Box 15378, San Antonio, TX
78212-8578
Email: usassociates@
amormeus.org
Web: www.incarnatewordsisters.org

SISTERS OF THE DIVINE (A431)
COMPASSION ASSOCIATE
MEMBERSHIP
Contact: Ellen Baker,
(914) 631-1182
Affiliation: Sisters of the Divine
Compassion, 72 Benedict Ave.,
Tarrytown, NY 10591
Email: ellenbaker@verizon.net
Web: www.divinecompassion.org

SISTERS OF THE HOLY (A432)
NAMES ASSOCIATES U.S.
ONTARIO PROVINCE
Contact: Sr. Shirley Roberg, SNJM,
(503) 675-7100
Association with Sisters of the Holy
Names of Jesus and Mary in
spirituality and ministry
PO Box 398, Marylhurst, OR 97036
Email: sroberg@earthlink.net
Web: www.snjmusontario.org

SISTERS OF THE HOLY (A433)
NAMES ASSOCIATES
(Spokane, WA)
Contact: Sister Betty McLellan, (509)
328-7470, fax: (509) 328-9824
Affiliation: Sisters of the Holy Names
of Jesus and Mary (SNJM)
(Spokane, WA)
2911 West Fort Wright Dr., Spokane,
WA 99224
Email: bmclellan@snjmwa.org
Web: www.snjm.org

SISTERS OF SAINTS CYRIL (A434)
AND METHODIUS ASSOCIATES
(570) 275-3581Affiliation: Sisters of
Saints Cyril and Methodius
Villa Sacred Heart , Danville, PA
17821-1698
Web: www.sscm.org

SISTERS OF ST. FRANCIS (A434-1)
ASSOCIATES (Clinton, IA)
Contact: (563) 242-7611,
fax: (563) 243-0007
Affiliation: Sisters of St. Francis
(Clinton, Iowa)
588 N. Bluff Blvd., Clinton, IA 52732-
3953
Email: sisters@
clintonfranciscans.com
Web: www.clintonfranciscans.com

SISTERS OF ST. FRANCIS OF (A435)
MARY IMMACULATE ASSOCIATE
RELATIONSHIP
Contact: Sister Sharon Frederick,
OSF, (815) 740-5030
Affiliation:Sisters of St. Francis of
Mary Immaculate
1433 Essington Rd., Joliet, IL 60435
Email: sfrederick@stfrancis.edu

SISTERS OF ST. MARY (A436)
ASSOCIATES
Contact: Sister Patricia Ste. Marie,
(940) 692-9770
Affiliation: Sisters of St. Mary of
Namur (S.S.M.N.)
3000 Lansing Blvd., Wichita Falls,
TX 76309
Email: mercycom@sbcglobal.net
Web: web2.airmail.net/ssmn

SISTERS OF SOCIAL (A437)
SERVICE ASSOCIATES
Contact: (818) 285-3355
Affiliation: Sisters of Social Service
4316 Lanai Road, Encino, CA 91436
Email: j.felion@sbcglobal.net
Web: http://sistersofsocialservice
.com/ home.html

SODALITIUM CHRISTIANAE (A438)
VITAE, (For consecrated lay men
and priests)
For information contact: Jorge Luna,
(303) 747-0201, fax: (303) 747-2892
Camp Saint Malo, 10758 Hwy. 7,
Allenspark, CO 80510
Email: jorgeluna@saintmalo.org
Web: www.sodalitium.us,
www.saintmalo.org/scv.htm,
www.sodalitium.com

SPIRITAN ASSOCIATES (A439)
Contact: (412) 831-0302
Affiliation: Holy Spirit Fathers and
Brothers (Spiritans)
6230 Brush Run Rd., Bethel Park,
PA 15102
Email: joinus@spiritans.org
Web: www.spiritans.org

SSJ AGREGES (A440)
Contacts: Sister Carole Proia, Sister Elaine Englert, (585) 641-8118
Affiliation: Sisters of St. Joseph of Rochester
150 French Rd., Rochester, NY 14618-3798
Email: cproia@ssjrochester.org, eenglert@ssjrochester.org
Web: www.ssjvolunteers.org/assocmem.htm

SSM ASSOCIATES (A441)
Contact: Sister M. Raphael Narcisi, (414) 357-8940
Affiliation: Sisters of the Sorrowful Mother (Third Order Regular of St. Francis of Assisi) (SSM)
9056 North Deerbrook Trail, Brown Deer, WI 53223-2454
Email: ssmassoc@aol.com
Web: www.ssmfranciscans.org

SSMO ASSOCIATES (A442)
Contact: Sister Catherine Hertel, SSMO, (503) 644-9181
Affiliation: Sisters of St. Mary of Oregon (S.S.M.O.)
4440 SW 148th Ave., Beaverton, OR 97007
Email: srcatherineh@ssmo.org
Web: www.ssmo.org

SSND ASSOCIATES (A443)
(Milwaukee Province)
Contact: Rosemary Bonk, SSND or Marni Geissler, Associate, (262) 782-9850, ext. 1017
fax: (262) 207-0051
Notre Dame Hall, 13105 Watertown Plank Rd., Elm Grove, WI 53122-2291
Email: rbonk@ssnd-milw.org or mgeissler@ssnd-milw.org

STIGMATINE LAY (A444)
ASSOCIATES
554 Lexington St., Waltham, MA 02452
Email: admin@espousal.org
Web: www.espousal.org

(A445)
THIRD ORDER OF THE INSTITUTE OF THE INCARNATE WORD
Contact: (212) 534-4422 Affiliation: Institute of the Incarnate Word (Priests)
Saint Paul the Apostle Church, 113 E. 117th St., New York, NY 10035-5257
Email: prov.immaculate.conception@ ive.org
Web: www.iveamerica.org

THIRD ORDER OF MARY (A446)
Northeast US (6 New England states, NY, MI, WI): Fr. Albert Dianni, S.M., (617) 262-2271
Affiliation: Marist Fathers and Brothers (Boston Province)
698 Beacon St., Boston, MA 02115
Email: smvocations@aol.com

THIRD ORDER OF MARY (A447)
Southern, Western US
Contact: Fr. Edwin Keel, SM, (304) 242-0406, fax: (304) 243-0837
Affiliation: Marist Fathers and Brothers (Atlanta Province)
Marist Laity Center, 2244 Marshall Ave., Wheeling, WV 26003
Email: maristelk@comcast.net
Web: www.maristlaity.org

THIRD ORDER OF (A448)
ST. DOMINIC (Province of St. Joseph)
Contact: Fr. James M. Sullivan, O.P., (212) 744-2080
Affiliation: Dominicans Friars
141 East 65th St., New York, NY 10065
Email: jmsullivan@op.org
Web: www.3op.org

URSULINE ASSOCIATES (A449)
(Mount Saint Joseph)
Contacts: Marian Bennett, (270) 229-2006, mbennett@maplemount.org
Sr. Marietta Wethington, OSU, (270) 229-2009
Affiliation: Ursuline Sisters of Mount Saint Joseph
8001 Cummings Rd., Maple Mount, KY 42356
Email: associates@maplemount.org
Web: www.ursulinesmsj.org/associates

URSULINE ASSOCIATES (A451)
(St. Martin, OH)
Contact: Sr. Patricia Homan, OSU, (513) 875-2020, ext. 27
Affiliation: Ursuline Sisters
20860 S. R. 251, St. Martin, OH 45118
Email: phoman@tds.net
Web: www.ursulinesofbc.org

URSULINE ASSOCIATES (A452)
(Ursuline Sisters of Tildonk)
Contact: Linda A. Siani
Sr. Sheila Molloy, St. John the Baptist Parish, 1488 No. Country Rd., Wading River, NY 11792
Affiliation: Ursuline Sisters of Tildonk, 81-15 Utopia Pkwy., Jamaica, NY 11432, (718) 591-0681
399 Miller Ave., Freeport, NY 11520-6112
Email: srmolloy@optonline.net
Web: http://tressy.tripod.com

URSULINE ASSOCIATES (A453)
(Toledo, OH)
Contact: Sr. Sandy Sherman. OSU, (419) 536-9587 Affiliation: Ursuline Sisters (Toledo, OH)
4045 Indian Rd., Toledo, OH 43606
Email: sanjea_43606@yahoo.com
Web: toledoursulines.org

(A454)
URSULINE SISTERS ASSOCIATES (Cleveland, OH)
Contact: Sister Mary Ellen Brinovec, OSU, (440) 449-1200, ext. 114
Affiliation: Ursuline Sisters (Cleveland, OH)
2600 Lander Rd., Pepper Pike (Cleveland), OH 44124
Email: mebrinovec@ ursulinesisters .org
Web: http://ursulinesisters.org/

VEDRUNA FRIENDS (A455)
Contact: (202) 832-2114
Affiliation: Carmelite Sisters of Charity
1222 Monroe St. NE, Washington, DC 20017-2507

VENERINI ASSOCIATES (A456)
Contact: Sr. Joanne Eneguess,
Affiliation: Religious Venerini Sisters (M.P.V.)
23 Edward St., Worcester, MA 01605
Email: jeneguess@aol.com
Web: www.venerinisisters.com

VINCENTIAN ASSOCIATES (A457)
For more information, please contact: Director, (412) 364-3000
Affiliation: Vincentian Sisters of Charity (V.S.C.)
8200 McKnight Rd., Pittsburgh, PA 15237
Email: mabehary@ vincentiansrspgh .org
Web: www.vincentiansrspgh.org

B-168

Prayer to Know My Vocation

My Lord and my God, you are Love itself, the source of all love and goodness. Out of love you created me to know you, to love you, and to serve you in a unique way, as no one else can. I believe that you have a plan for my life, that you have a mission in your Kingdom reserved for me alone. Your plan and your mission are far better than any other I might choose: they will glorify you, fulfill the desires of my heart, and bring salvation to those souls who are depending on my generous response.

Lord grant me the light of grace I need to see the next step in Your plan; grant me the generosity necessary to follow your call; and grant me the courage required to take up my cross and to follow you.

Show me your will, O gentle and eternal God, and help me to say with Mary, "I am the servant of the Lord; let it be done to me according to your word." Let me say with Jesus, "Let not my will be done, but yours." Amen.

*Reprinted with permission from
the Diocese of Rapid City, SD
www.Gods-call.org*